SPACE MANUFACTURING FACILITIES
(Space Colonies)

Proceedings of the Princeton/AIAA/NASA Conference
May 7-9, 1975

(Including the Proceedings of the May, 1974
Princeton Conference on Space Colonization)

Edited by
Jerry Grey

March 1, 1977

Published by
American Institute of Aeronautics and Astronautics, Inc.
1290 Avenue of the Americas
New York, N. Y. 10019

PREFACE

The American Institute of Aeronautics and Astronautics, the professional society which represents 25,000 aerospace engineers, scientists, and students, was a cosponsor of the May 1975 Princeton/AIAA/NASA Conference on Space Manufacturing Facilities (Space Colonies) and has edited and published this Proceedings. The Institute took this action so that these early steps toward the widespread utilization of space for the Earth's peoples can be disseminated to the widest possible audience, particularly to responsible members of the aerospace profession. Arthur Kantrowitz, in his opening statement at this Conference, expressed the viewpoint of many of the AIAA's members:

"This is a time in which it is desperately necessary that we be able to see a reasonable future....This Conference might, in the future, be recognized as one of the more important things that was happening in 1975."

Jerry Grey, Editor
February 1977

ABSTRACT

The Princeton/AIAA/NASA Conference on Space Manufacturing Facilities (Space Colonies), held May 7-9, 1975, explored construction methods, productivity, and payoff to the Earth of permanent industrial habitats near the L5 Earth-Moon Lagrange libration point. Discussions were based on 1970's technology, and on the use of lunar surface raw materials and solar energy as the sources for a rapidly expanding industrial economy. Satellite solar power stations built at L5, for use in geosynchronous orbit to supply energy to the Earth, were studied as possible industrial products for the 1990-2000 time period.

The Conference was organized and operated by the Princeton University Conference, and was co-sponsored by the American Institute of Aeronautics and Astronautics (AIAA) and the National Aeronautics and Space Administration (NASA). Authors were drawn from universities, government organizations, and private industry.

TABLE OF CONTENTS

(continued)

INTRODUCTION

Gerard K. O'Neill
Princeton University

During 1969-72, calculations were made at Princeton relating to long-term development for our necessarily technology-based society. They were focused on energy and materials resources, and on the physical conditions for achieving high productivity and an expanding economy without damage to the environment.

Briefly, these calculations suggested the possibility of establishing a permanent beachead in space, in the form of a manufacturing facility at L5, a gravitationally stable location in free space in the lunar orbit. At that location, where sunlight would be available 24 hours per day, the facility could use solar power for all its energy needs: (1) after concentration by mirrors, for all industrial process heating; (2) directly for the growing of crops under high-yield conditions; and (3) as a heat source for electric turbogenerators for all electrical needs.

Its location was also chosen to allow obtaining nearly all the material for the construction of the facility itself, and all the raw material for its manufacturing operations, from the lunar surface. Because the energy required to move materials from the lunar surface to L5 would be about a factor of twenty lower than for moving materials from the Earth, and because the Moon has a vacuum environment, it appeared possible to obtain materials at a cost about 1/100 of that which would be required for transport from the Earth.

A facility of this kind was assumed to be a living and working habitat of large dimensions, Earthlike in environment and capable of supporting a population of the order of 10,000 people. The existence of this facility would then constitute the first step in a bootstrap process, in which habitat numbers could grow without the need to draw energy or materials from the Earth. It was not intended that these facilities would return material products to the planetary surface, but that they could, more economically than the Earth, build products whose end use would be at or near escape distance.

In these studies the condition was set that only 1970's technology was to be used. No rocket motor more advanced than the space shuttle main engine was to be required, and no nuclear-powered vehicle was to be considered. The transport of raw materials from the Moon to the habitat site was to be made by an electromagnetic accelerating device (mass-driver) running on solar power. it would accelerate compacted lunar payloads of a few kilograms each to the lunar escape velocity, provide precise guidance, and then release them to climb out of the lunar gravitational field; they would arrive at escape distance moving at near-zero speed. Such a device has never been built, but its performance is calculable and its construction would require only the technology of the present day; it could be constructed and tested on Earth.

With good direction and high priority, but not under "crash program" conditions, I estimate that the first space manufacturing facility could be in place with its productive capacity working by about 1988. Although the first habitat would accommodate a thousand times as many people as have now been to the Moon, the cost-saving techniques just described should permit its construction for a total cost comparable to that of Project Apollo. Even the highest estimate which I have so far heard, an estimate generated independently by a team within NASA and intended to be on the high side, is only a small fraction of the presently estimated cost of Project Independence.

Early Work. We have grown used to the fact that new technological developments, often heralded as beneficial, almost as often turn out to be absurd or counter-productive when all their implications are considered or when their natural growth is projected a moderate interval into the future. The first three years of the Princeton work were therefore devoted not only to finding solutions to the basic physics questions connected with the new development, but to establishing how large space habitats could eventually become within the limitations of presently available materials, and especially to examining how soon materials limits would be encountered. The conclusions were favorable: habitat sizes up to several hundred square miles in land area appeared possible, and asteroidal materials (not adding the resources of the Earth or of the Moon) appeared adequate for the eventual construction of total land areas many thousands of times as large as that of the Earth, should that ever prove to be desirable.

Beginning in late 1972 private lectures on this subject were given, and study of the economics was begun. In May 1974 a small, informal conference was held on the topic at Princeton. The Proceedings of that Conference are included as an Appendix to this document. As a result of a front-page article in the New York Times, reporting the 1974 Conference in favorable terms, a considerable wave of publicity was generated and is still growing.

The intensity of the public response seems to have three causes: the possibility of direct personal participation in a frontier activity; the sense, expressed by many correspondents, that this approach may be the most beneficial long-term solution to a number of problems of current urgency; and the realization that no new breakthroughs would be required for its attainment. In terms of mail, letters from individuals and organizations have been in favor of the new development by a factor of about 100 to 1. Many individuals with considerable technical qualifications have written to offer their services on an unpaid volunteer basis, and are now doing useful work to further these ideas. Environmentalist groups which have so far expressed an opinion have been uniformly in favor.

Recent Developments. The first technical publications on this topic were a letter to Nature and an article in Physics Today (September 1974). A significant consequence of the Physics Today article has been the acceptance of the basic physics calculations; the article has been widely read and reprint requests for it are still arriving from many parts of the world; yet in spite of intensive review and exposure to a large technically trained readership, no significant disagreement with any of the numbers or calculations has so far appeared

The reaction from NASA has been favorable. Although these ideas were unknown to the agency until May 1974, by January of 1975 NASA headquarters and one of its research laboratories had jointly given to Princeton a small grant for further research; I consider this to the credit of some far-sighted individuals within the agency. Interest, particularly among the younger people of the NASA laboratories, is also strong.

Energy Needs at the Earth's Surface. Until the autumn of 1974 I had considered the development of space habitats or colonies as a desirable long-term goal, but did not see any possibility for immediate payback to the Earth. I still regard it as impractical to think of the habitats sending back manufactured products to the Earth, except for very small, specialized high-value items. Clearly, though, even the earliest such habitat would be in a favorable location for producing (from lunar material) and assembling (at its zero-gravity industrial site) large objects whose end use would be at or near escape distance from the Earth.

One such product could be satellite solar power stations, for relocation in geosynchronous orbit to supply electric power to the Earth's surface by a low-intensity microwave link. The satellite power station concept has been under discussion since 1968, and research on it is supported at a modest level. It appears to have considerable advantages from an environmental viewpoint over liquid-metal fast-breeder reactors or other fission power sources. It has not been taken very seriously so far, though, mainly because its achievement of economic feasibility appeared to depend on reducing by large factors (10 to 20) solar cell mass and cost and lift costs to geosynchronous orbit.

It appears that a more conventional kind of satellite solar power station, using turbogenerators rather than solar cells, could be built at L5 for about one tenth the price required for construction and launch from the Earth. Relocation from L5 to geosynchronous orbit, included in the estimates, would be a small fraction of the total cost. If these numbers are correct, once a space manufacturing facility is established satellite solar power could become competitive even without any technology beyond that of the 1970's. Maintenance costs of such a system should be low, so after amortization the power costs of satellite solar energy should decrease. An article on this subject was written and published by *Science* (December 1975).

Interaction with NASA. The agency supported the Princeton work initially on a temporary basis at a low level: $25,000 per year. That support continues, and has been expanded somewhat. NASA has also conducted a year-long study of its own on the question of its role during the years 1980-2000: the "Outlook for Space" report, published in January 1976. The report included some discussion of the space manufacturing facilities concept. Major events related to this work are NASA Ames Laboratory/Stanford University Summer Studies, one scheduled for June 16-August 22, 1975, with a probable follow-on in 1976 and subsequent years. Twenty full-time participants for the 1975 study have been selected from about 100 applicants.

The Future. Up to the present time the technical work has developed on a rapid time scale, and every indication is that public interest is growing at a similar rate; in addition several more popular articles based on interviews are already scheduled for publication.

If the potential payoff from the new development is in fact as great and as near as many of us now estimate, a loss of time now, in the early research phase, would be as serious as a corresponding loss occurring later on. Much time could be saved if a substantial effort were put into each of the following points: small-scale closed-environment agricultural growth tests; minimum-cost atmospheric mixes based mainly on chemical sources identical to lunar materials; detailed design of the mass-driver; design of a simplified lift-vehicle and a simple space-tug, both to be derived from existing hardware and to require a minimum of new development effort; thorough and responsible cost estimation with participation from a number of independent sources of expertise both inside and outside the government; and detailed time estimates with alternate routes explored.

Altogether, if carried out in parallel, these studies would probably cost from $600 to $900 thousand, about 1/3,000 of NASA's annual budget. With such an input, for example, it should be possible in about a year to answer positively any remaining questions about basic feasibility, to block out a minimum-cost, minimum-time program leading to a first space manufacturing facility, and to design and cost out a satellite solar power station in considerable detail. If the necessary money were available and I had some degree of control over how it were to be spent, I would put most of it into studies within existing governmental, university and industrial laboratories, reserving very little for Princeton; most of the necessary expertise is located in other places.

SECTION I: CONSTRUCTION

1. The Space Manufacturing Facility Concept

Gerard K. O'Neill
Princeton University

We define a space manufacturing facility as a permanent or very long-term human community, in an orbit so high above the Earth or any other planetary body that it can use solar power continuously without frequent eclipsing. Such a community, once established, must be entirely self-sustaining rather than continuously resupplied from the Earth. It should be constructed almost entirely from materials available in space, such as those of the lunar surface or the asteroids. The space manufacturing facility uses its free solar energy and its easy access to the materials of space to produce manufactured products whose end use is in a very high orbit or at escape distance.

The economic rationale of a space manufacturing facility is based on three elements. The first is energy: in free space, in a high orbit, not only is solar energy available continuously without interruption, but the total amount received in a year is about ten times as much as arrives on an equal area on the Earth's surface, even in the most cloud-free portions of the American southwest.

The second element is materials. The energy cost of lifting materials from the lunar surface to escape distance is about one twentieth as much as for lifting materials from the surface of the Earth. In addition, the Moon has no atmosphere, so a stationary launching device on the lunar surface can operate without atmospheric drag, and can be optimized for the most efficient payload size. Our estimates indicate that these two advantages would permit the lifting of lunar material to escape distance for the order of one percent of the overall

cost that launch from the Earth would require. We call the device that does that job a mass-driver.

The third element in the economic rationale for space manufacturing facilities is that in free space, one has the availability of zero gravity, in which very large objects could be assembled free of all constraints of payload size. At the same time, perhaps only a few meters away, a comfortable habitat for living could exist, providing Earth-normal gravity by slow rotation.

The "bootstrap" principle is central to the idea of a space manufacturing facility; that is, we would begin by establishing a relatively small mining and mass-driver base on the Moon and a construction base near the eventual site of the first space manufacturing facility at L5. Once the material sent out by the mass-driver has been processed and used to build the first habitat, the industrial productivity of the habitat itself is used, in part, to build additional mass-drivers and their solar powerplants, to be sent to the moon to increase the mass throughput. In the third step, reducing costs still further, the mass drivers could be built on the Moon itself.

The fourth step, well in the future, would bypass the materials transport question completely; the production and processing equipment would be taken to the asteroid belt and used directly for the local construction of a new habitat. The essential advantage of that approach would be that the new habitat could be built and brought into production, and so begin to amortize its construction cost in advance of the time that its mass would need to be transported. On completion of a habitat near the asteroid belt, about one generation – thirty years – would be required for the habitat to be relocated near the Earth-orbiting community of other habitats, or in some other orbit entirely. Though I mention this as an ultimate logical development, in this Conference we will be concerned for the most part only with the first step: the establishment and productivity of the first space community.

One measure of the newness of the concept of space manufacturing facilities is that we are still searching for a satisfactory name to describe it. The words "Community", "Habitat", "Facility", or "Frontier" fail to describe the economic rationale. "Colonization" suggests drive and purpose, but in the past has often meant the exploitation of one group by another. Yet in space colonization there need be no such exploitation, because the materials and energy of space are now unused.

Though I describe this concept as new, I would like to recognize the contributions of others who came before us, above all Konstantin Tsiolkowsky, who, in my opinion, saw even further than others who came years laters than his own time. I cannot neglect to mention these others, among the most prominent of whom were J.D. Bernal, Dandridge Cole, and John Stroud.

It is beyond the scope of this conference to define optimized geometries or make detailed estimates of time or cost. In that regard, I am very grateful for the excellent cooperation of NASA, particularly the Office of Space Flight and the Marshall Space Flight Center. A preliminary guess, based on our discussions so far, would put the earliest technically possible date for the first space community at somewhere between 1988 and the year 2000. Cost estimates are from somewhat above Project Apollo to a maximum of one or two tenths of the cost of Project Independence.

Some goals which are suitable to be addressed at this Conference are as follows:

- First, and perhaps most important, the identification of any problems so fundamental as to invalidate the entire concept.

- Identification of steps which have the largest elements of uncertainty about them and which will require the greatest effort in further study.

- Identification of elements which are uncertain,

but which could be brought to a much higher level of certainty by a relatively modest additional effort. These may be candidates for the earliest attack by an additional but still modest research effort.

- Assembly of vital pieces of information from fields which up to now have been isolated from each other.

- Identification of methods not yet explored by which savings in time or cost of habitat construction or manufacturing processes could be made.

- Identification of methods for realizing, in spite of our imperfect human institutions, the construction of the first space community.

- Identification of intermediate steps in engineering development which could lead toward a space manufacturing facility while also serving other purposes.

Two suggestions were made to the authors of papers presented at this conference, in the spirit of working hypotheses, to provide focus and coherence:

(1) To restrict the discussion to existing technology; that is, to processes and materials which already exist or which can be proven feasible on the basis of straightforward engineering practice.

(2) To think in terms of an early time-scale which, given adequate priority soon enough, could see the first manufacturing facility in space before the end of the 1980's. Such a schedule is realizable, and the facility will be built only if it offers an important payoff within a time scale of human decisions. Fifteen years is, in my opinion, such a horizon.

When we consider possible geometries, we must realize that the final actuality may look very different. To start the ball rolling, I have suggested the configuration shown in Figure 1. This is a side view of a possible first community; I'll call it "Island One" until someone suggests a better name. Its length is about 1000 meters, its diameter about 200 meters. The rotation rate is once every twenty seconds, so gravity is Earth-normal inside. The axis is always pointed toward the Sun. Two such cylinders are linked by a light framework through bearings. Though the total mass is about half a million tons, which is the same as the total mass of a modern supertanker, the bearing forces are only sixty pounds; about the same as on a child's bicycle wheel. Surprisingly, the excavation left on the surface of the Moon after removal of the half million tons of material needed to build this structure would be only about five meters deep and about 200 meters long and wide, not even enough to keep one small bulldozer fully occupied over a five or six year period.

In this design, a population of about ten thousand people is located in four villages of 2500 each, located in the four endcaps. These four villages have independent control of their day-night cycles and seasons. One efficient possibility is their operation on three different time-zones, eight hours apart. In that way the heavy industry, which is located just outside the habitat in zero gravity, can operate 24 hours a day, but with none of the workers on a night shift. One possible location for the community would be in orbit about the L5 Lagrange libration point of the Earth-Moon system. The stable orbit about that point has a length of about half a million miles, so there would be room for many thousands of communities in it.

We assume cosmic ray protection in the amount of about 130 grams per square centimeter for the endcap villages, to guard against heavy primary cosmic rays and solar flares. The cylinder areas in

that design are left for agriculture and are protected against flares only.

To illustrate the possibilities for architecture, Figure 2 shows a possible design for a village. The shielding goes all the way around. It would all be terraced and planted. Sunshine comes in through the solars, and the apartments in which people would be living are located at the lower right. The apartments could provide around two hundred square meters of floor space for a family of five, which is equal to rather affluent suburban American living conditions. In addition, each family could have a garden, where good weather could be counted on, and where, presumably, there needn't be any mosquitoes. Birds and animals, though, ought to flourish in this environment.

There could even be a river for swimming and boating, and beaches for sunbathing. Near the axis there are possibilities for low-gravity swimming and diving and human-powered flight. In summary, though Island One would be of modest size, it would be more attractive than nearly all of the industrial towns with which it could be compared on Earth.

During the past year, since the 1974 Conference reported in the Appendix, four studies were performed at Princeton. These are summarized as follows:

(1) The use of the "mass driver" (the Transport Linear Accelerator) as a space reaction engine has been explored. Table 1 shows the range of applications and performance figures for the mass driver used in this context. For the

Figure 1 Early Version of a "Model 1" Space Manufacturing Facility

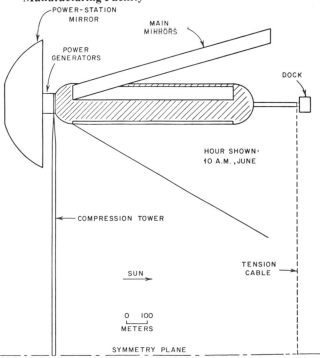

Figure 2 One Proposal for the Interior Configuration of Living Quarters in Space

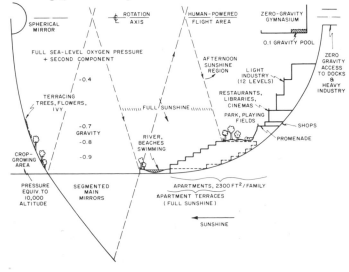

Table 1 Mass-Driver as Reaction Engine

Max. Field (Gauss)	Length (km)	Impulse Payload (kg)	Velocity Change (m/sec)	Exhaust Velocity (m/sec)	Specific Impulse (sec)
10,000	13	9	2,100	2,400	245
10,000	50	3	13,600	7,100	725
30,000	50	3	13,600	12,300	1,255

maximum magnetic field of ten thousand gauss, proposed for the mass driver to be built on the surface of the Moon, the reaction-engine thrust would be about two tons and the exhaust velocity twenty-four hundred meters per second. That corresponds to a specific impulse of about two hundred forty seconds, which is just about right to move a large payload over the velocity interval of about twenty-one hundred meters per second which represents the difference between L5 and a geosynchronous orbit about the Earth. The growth potential of the mass driver appears sufficient for later tasks requiring specific impulses in the range from seven hundred to twelve hundred, as indicated by the parameters shown in Table 1.

(2) The habitat size has been studied as a function of structure mass and internal atmospheric pressure. Three facts push toward use of a low pressure atmosphere enriched in oxygen: (a) habitat structural mass is almost exactly proportional to pressure, though almost independent of the artificial gravity provided; (b) nitrogen is not used directly in human, animal or plant respiration, although it makes up 79% of our atmospheric pressure; and (c) the Moon is probably rather poor in nitrogen, but its surface is about 40% oxygen by weight.

It turns out that for a structure mass of about fifteen tons per person, one could reach a cylinder diameter of about seven hundred meters. A habitat of that size, with an internal pressure of two to three pounds per square inch of oxygen, could easily support one hundred thousand people. Before considering that possibility further, we will have to find out whether or not there are long-term physiological effects from a nearly pure oxygen atmosphere, and we're also going to have to learn more about fire protection in large volumes, at low oxygen pressure, in the presence of an abundant supply of water. None of the NASA studies performed to date covers that situation.

(3) A comparative estimate was made for construction of a large radio-telescope array at L5; equivalent, for example, to Project Cyclops. This would be a single paraboloidal dish five thousand meters in diameter, plus an occulting disc ten kilometers in diameter to block radio interference from the Earth. The total mass of aluminum would be eleven thousand tons. Estimates indicate that the array could probably be constructed at L5 for around one twentieth to one tenth the cost of an equivalent structure on Earth, which would need smaller paraboloids braced against winds and gravity.

(4) The prospects have been examined for providing energy to Earth from powerplants manufactured and located in space. Satellite solar power stations have been considered since the mid-1960's. In concept, these would be large arrays of solar cells or large turbo-generator sets, located in geosynchronous orbit, transmitting power by a microwave link for conversion to power grid frequencies at the surface of the Earth. The principal difficulty is the cost of transporting such power stations from the Earth's surface. Reducing that cost requires very advanced lift vehicles of enormous size. However, using materials brought from the lunar surface to a space manufacturing facility by the same mass driver that brings up the original construction materials, the powerplant mass-to-power ratio no longer matters much, and economic feasibility appears to be achievable even with existing or near-term figures for powerplant mass.

The general range of parameters is shown in Table 2 for a satellite solar power station delivering five thousand megawatts to Earth. The estimated market for new powerplants in the year 1990 in the United States alone is about seventy-five billion dollars per year, using the installed cost of $1200/kWe quoted by the National Geographic (April 1975 issue) for the most recent large hydroelectric project.

Because some of us think of the space

Table 2   Cost Estimate for a Space Solar Power Station Manufactured at L5

Item	Total Needed	Unit Factor	Cost (Billions)
Power Plant	8,000 MW	$450/kW	$ 3.6
Lunar Materials to L5	160,000 tons	$3/pound	1.06
Amplitron Magnets (from Earth)	330 tons	$500 pound	.31
Materials Processing	160,000 tons	$5/pound	1.76
Microwave Tubes	8,000 MW	$25/kW	.20
Assembly at L5	80,000 tons	$5/pound	.88
Reaction Mass to L5	109,000 tons	$3/pound	.72
Processing Reaction Mass	109,000 tons	$1/pound	.24
1/4 Cost of Mass-Driver	(1/4) × 1,600 tons	$200/pound	.18
Receiver Station (on Earth)	5,600 MW	$75/kW	.42
Total			$ 9.37

manufacturing facility concept as real and immediate, we tend to be deep in engineering details, but we should not lose sight of the fact that such discussions are not the reason why this concept has aroused such an extraordinary amount of popular interest. The vistas offered by the flexibility of the living conditions in space habitats, which have appeared as artists' conceptions in a number of publications, constitutes a major incentive to "get on with the job." I do wish to remind you, however, that the authors whose papers follow have attempted to provide us with some of their knowledge, and that the presence of their papers here does not necessarily constitute their endorsement of a concept which is still, for many people, very rich in future shock.

DISCUSSION

Q. *Why L5 and not also L4?*

A. I have been placed in the position rather often recently of having to get up in front of a television camera and in thirty seconds give the entire concept of space manufacturing facilities. There just isn't time to say L4 as well as L5, but of course, you are absolutely right. The stable orbit around L4 is presumably just as big as that around L5.

Q. *It is surprising that in establishing a habitat in space you seek to recreate as closely as possible conditions on the Earth. It seems much more imaginative to consider the many new opportunities that one would hope would be developed by the high-orbit habitat.*

A. You are quite right. However, to turn this into a reality, it has to receive a tremendous amount of popular acceptance. If we were to say that it was necessary, or even advisable, to adopt very unearthlike surroundings, that would turn off a great many people. But I certainly believe that after you have built one of these facilities, particularly when another generation has grown up on it, there will be many possibilities which are much more attractive.

Anyone who takes the trouble to read Konstantin Tsiolkowsky's book "Beyond the Planet Earth" will find that he anticipated an enormous number of these possibilities, in numerical detail.

Q. *It seems to be a common assumption that these facilities have to be located at the same distance from the Sun that the Earth is, in order that their temperatures be about right. Yet by controlling the color of the surface and the opening of the panels, it should be possible to put them either much closer to the Sun or fairly far away. Do you have an idea of what range of distances from the Sun would be practical?*

A. Yes, I went through that calculation a few months ago. My talk did mention that it is practical to take production machinery out to the asteroid belt and build a habitat right there. It is easy, just by putting up bigger mirrors, to provide the Earth-normal solar constant. With reasonable limits on the amount of mass which is put into mirrors as opposed to the rest of the habitat, I calculated that it was possible to go out roughly a fraction of one percent of the distance to the nearest star; that is, far beyond the limits of our solar system.

Q. *Your tables are in terms of dollar cost. In the space facility, what do dollars mean?*

A. We tend to think of dollars as wealth, but they are not the real wealth. The real wealth, presumably, is productivity: energy, materials, and information. In the space facility, therefore, wealth is being generated.

2. Transport of Lunar Material to The Sites of The Colonies*

T. A. Heppenheimer
California Institute of Technology

Abstract. The problem of lunar mass transport to the libration-point colony is treated as a problem in conceptual systems design. The mass is accelerated to lunar escape by a tracked magnetically-levitated mass driver. The aim sensitivity is of the order of one kilometer in miss distance (at L5) per 10^{-3} meter/sec velocity error at the Moon.

A system is described which may achieve velocity dispersions $\leq 10^{-5}$ meter/sec. This system measures time of passage between two checkpoints; the event of checkpoint passage is defined as the event of the first photons from a laser falling on a photodetector. By successively uncaging more and more sensitive accelerometers onboard the mass driver vehicle, and by using measured velocities and accelerations to control cutoff times for successive stages of acceleration, high launch velocity accuracy is attainable. Control of the other five degrees of vehicle motion may be achieved through the magnetic suspension system. (From trajectory considerations, it is shown that the mass driver must be located on the lunar farside. Possible sites include Mare Moscoviense and the basins Korolev and Mendeleev.)

The catcher vehicle, or L5 construction station, accepts the incoming mass packages with velocities of several hundred meters/sec. The interception is performed by chambers operating in a "Venus-Fly-Trap" mode. When a chamber is struck by a mass package, it closes and gas is admitted, entraining the mass; the resultant slurry then is piped to the

processing plant. Station keeping is performed by mass drivers using rotary pellet launchers.

The resultant system can process a throughput of some 10^5 tons per year and is expandable to handle larger rates.

Introduction. Work to date on problems of space colonization has emphasized the importance of lunar resources in construction of the colony. The tracked magnetically levitated mass driver, with linear synchronous motor drive, has been identified as a conceptual means for launching lunar material toward the site of the colony. But the mass driver is to operate simply as a catapult or cannon, with its projectiles not subject to midcourse or terminal guidance. Thus, it is clear that a dominant consideration in mass driver design is the achievement of unprecedentedly precise aim.

This paper is concerned with establishment of aim requirements, and with identification of conceptual means for their achievement. Solution of this problem leads immediately to a conceptual design for the mass-driver. To improve the aim achievable, it is desirable to obtain the highest practical impact velocity at the colony consistent with strength-of-materials considerations. Thus, the target or L5 construction station must be capable of capturing the lunar material, which will ordinarily arrive with masses and velocities typical of 19th-century naval cannonballs. To counteract the momentum gain from such impacts, the catcher vehicle requires a stationkeeping system which may involve a mass expulsion system operating with a

*Supported by NASA Grant NGL 05-002-003.

portion of the captured mass. The paper is thus also concerned with conceptual design of certain of the L5 construction station subsystems.

The emphasis here is on qualitative or conceptional considerations. This reflects the belief that in view of the unprecedented nature of the lunar mass transport problem, the first concern must be with identifying systems which will work, so as to provide a framework for quantitative preliminary design. The conceptual designs given here are not intended to be definitive. They represent principally the opinions of the author, and it is entirely possible that other workers may devise alternate means for solution of specific problems. This paper should be considered as providing an "existence proof" of a practical solution to the problem of lunar mass transport.

Trajectory Considerations. As a zeroth approximation, the Moon-L5 trajectory may be treated as a hyperbolic orbit initially tangent to the lunar surface (Figure 3). Let r =radial distance from lunar center, e =hyperbola eccentricity, θ =orbit true anomaly, μ =lunar gravitational mass; the orbit is initially at perilune with $r=r_{\min}$, $\theta=0$. Then,

$$r = \frac{r_{\min}(1+e)}{1+e\cos\theta}$$

$$\dot{r} = \sqrt{\frac{\mu}{r_{\min}(1+e)}}\, e\sin\theta \qquad (1)$$

$$r\dot{\theta} = \sqrt{\frac{\mu}{r_{\min}(1+e)}}\,(1+e\cos\theta)$$

Now let $v=v_{\max}$ when $r=r_{\min}$; $v\to v_\infty$ as $r\to\infty$. Here $v_{\max}$ is launch velocity and v_∞ is hyperbolic excess velocity. Also, let θ_∞ be the angle of the outbound asymptote; $\theta=1+e\cos\theta_\infty$. Due to errors in launch conditions, θ_∞ is subject to change. At the distance to L5, $r_{\rm L5}=4\times10^5$ km, so an error $d\theta_\infty=1°$ is equivalent to a miss distance of 6700 km.

There are three components of velocity error. ΔV is parallel to the launch velocity vector. $\dot{r}$ is parallel to r and leads to launch not tangent to the lunar surface. $\dot{z}$ is out-of-plane, i.e., to the left or right of the orbit track along the lunar surface. The associated errors $d\theta_\infty$ and miss distances at L5 then are derivable from Eqs. (1) and are given:

$$\Delta V{:}\, d\theta_\infty = \frac{2\Delta V}{v_\infty e}$$

Miss = 8000 km/m/sec per 100 m/sec of v_∞

$$\dot{r}{:}\, d\theta_\infty = \frac{\sqrt{e+1}}{v_c e}\,\dot{r}, \quad \text{Miss} = 400\ \text{km/m/sec} \qquad (2)$$

$$\dot{z}{:}\, d\theta_\infty = \dot{z}/v_{\max}, \quad \text{Miss} = 160\ \text{km/m/sec}$$

In Eqs. (2), miss distances are given per m/sec of velocity component error. In the first of (2), $d\theta_\infty$ is reduced for higher values of v_∞. For $v_\infty=100$ m/sec, Miss = 8000 km/m/sec; for $v_\infty=200$ m/sec, Miss = 400 km/m/sec; for $v_\infty=500$ m/sec, Miss = 160 km/m/sec; etc. In the second of (2), v_c = circular orbit velocity at the lunar surface ~ 1500 m/sec. Also, in deriving miss distances, we have taken $e=1$, since near-parabolic orbits are to be anticipated. (For $v_\infty=500$ m/sec and $v_{\max}=2400$ m/sec, $e=1.091$.)

Thus, even for relatively high values of v_∞ (e.g. 500 m/sec), it is concluded that dispersions of ~ 1000 km/m/sec are to be expected. Since a practical L5 construction station can hardly exceed a kilometer or so in dimensions, it is clear that launch velocity must be controlled to $\sim 10^{-3}$ m/sec, or $v_{\min}$ must be accurate to a fraction 4×10^{-7}.

To achieve further insight into the nature of Moon-L5 trajectories, let us advance from the zeroth (hyperbolic) approximation to a first approximation: the restricted three-body problem. Using a double-precision program written by Roger Broucke of Jet Propulsion Laboratory, David R. Bender (also of JPL) has integrated a series of

Figure 3　Hyperbolic-orbit Approximation to a Moon-L5 Transfer

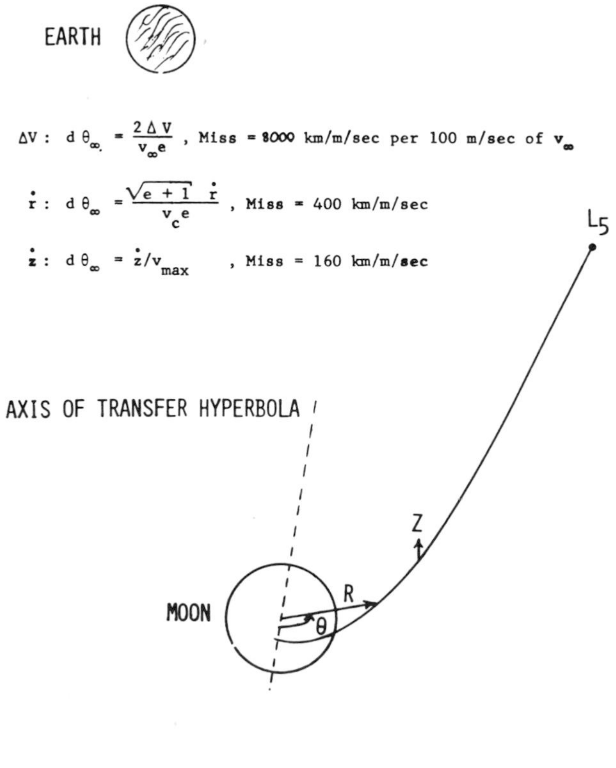

EARTH

$\Delta V:\ d\,\theta_\infty = \dfrac{2\,\Delta V}{v_\infty e}$, Miss = 8000 km/m/sec per 100 m/sec of v_∞

$\dot{r}:\ d\,\theta_\infty = \dfrac{\sqrt{e+1}}{v_c e}\,\dot{r}$, Miss = 400 km/m/sec

$\dot{z}:\ d\,\theta_\infty = \dot{z}/v_{\max}$, Miss = 160 km/m/sec

L5

AXIS OF TRANSFER HYPERBOLA

MOON

14

orbits and has identified several as lying close to candidate Moon-L5 trajectories. The integrations were initiated at L5 for specified values of Jacobi constant C, and consisted of orbits with initial velocity magnitude fixed by the given C. Initial velocity direction was varied in steps of 1° for successive integrations. Those trajectories which passed with one lunar radius of the lunar mass center were accepted as candidates for lunar material transport.

Bender found that below a minimum velocity at L5, approximately 80m/sec, no Moon-intercepting trajectories could be found. This is consistent with consideration of L5 as lying within a shallow potential well, so that some energy is required to reach the Moon. For higher velocities, two families of solutions were found, merging into the cited single solution at C = −1.491. This solution had transfer time 3.51 time units, or 15.29 days. The two-solution families were designated the "slow" and "fast" solutions, since their transfer times, for given C, were respectively greater or less than the nominal value, 15.29 days.

Bender's data, for several values of C, are given in Table 3. The following are given: Jacobi constant C, velocity magnitude at L5, velocity direction at L5, and transfer time, respectively, for the fast and slow solutions.

Bender also computed several cases of orbit sensitivity. This was done by first establishing a nominal orbit which passes from L5 to a point close to the surface of the Moon. The reverse orbit − from the Moon to L5 − then was regarded as following from initial conditions at the Moon. The initial velocity was then perturbed so as to establish the cases of perturbations in ΔV and in $\dot r$, and the resulting miss at L5 found by integrating the resultant trajectories. The sensitivity data from this work is given in Table 4. Also given are error estimates from Eqs. (2), with v_∞ taken as (distance to L5)/(transfer time).

It is seen that the errors in θ_∞ due to $\dot r$ are comparable to, but somewhat greater than, the errors predicted by Eq. (2). All computed miss sensitivities are ~ 1000 km/m/sec or less. For the case of ΔV errors, a fortuitous situation is observed: for fast trajectories, the sensitivity may be considerably less than is predicted by Eq. (2). For slow transfers, the sensitivity is considerably greater. Thus, only fast transfers are of interest for actual operations.

These results, while preliminary, give the conclusion that for arrival velocities at L5 of a few hundred meters per second, miss sensitivities are of the order 1 km/m/sec, in both ΔV and $\dot r$. Out-of-plane motion was not studied due to the computer program treating only the planar case of motion; however, Eq. (2) suggests that the sensitivity is least for the $\dot z$ component of launch velocity error.

Consider now Figure 4, which shows several cases of computed trajectories between the Moon and L5. It is seen that change in C, or transition from a slow to fast transfer, strongly influences the trajectory in the vicinity of L5, but has little influence on the trajectory in the vicinity of the Moon. In particular, the near-Moon portion lies very nearly in the direction of Earth. This may be regarded as representative of the direction of the hyperbola outbound asymptote. But since the hyperbolic portion of the trajectory turns through some 70° or more, it follows immediately that the lunar mass-driver must be located on the far side of the Moon.

Table 3   Reference Transfer Trajectories, Moon - L5

C, Jacobi Integral	Velocity at L5, m/sec	Fast Transfers		Slow Transfers	
		Transfer Time, Days	Arrival Angle, Deg.	Transfer Time, Days	Arrival Angle, Deg.
−1.40	442	7.54	118.5	22.66	280.6
−1.41	419	7.76	119.7	22.62	280.9
−1.42	394	8.06	121	22.53	281.2
−1.43	366	8.37	122.6	22.41	281.3
−1.44	336	8.71	124.4	22.15	281.3
−1.45	304	9.15	126.6	22.00	281.0
−1.46	266	9.68	129.8	21.72	280.3
−1.47	224	10.36	134.4	21.08	278.1
−1.48	171	11.40	142.8	19.88	272.6
−1.488	112.2	13.05	162.0	17.54	246.0
−1.49	91.5	13.87	178.5	16.64	239.5
−1.491	79.2	15.29	208.5	15.29	208.5
−1.492	64.7	No trajectories found			

Table 4 Aim Sensitivities at Launch

C, Jacobi Integral	Velocity at L5, m/sec	Type of Transfer	$\dot{r}$ Error, Eqs. (2)	$\dot{r}$ Error, Computed	ΔV Error, Eqs. (2)	ΔV Error, Computed
−1.491	79.2	Fast/Slow	400	119	2800	5000
−1.488	112.2	Fast	400	643	2400	2000
−1.488	112.2	Slow	400	596	3420	12,000
−1.45	304.0	Fast	400	715	1790	200
−1.45	304.0	Slow	400	1190	4060	16,000

NOTE: All quoted errors are in km/m/sec.

This point is sufficiently important to deserve close attention. A mass-driver located on the eastern or western extremity of the nearside, launching into the Earth-facing direction, produces a trajectory with asymptote 70° from the Earth-Moon line of centers. But to reach L5 or L4, the asymptote must be at an angle of ~10° from the line of centers.

Accordingly, we must consider suitable sites on the farside. A body launched tangent to the lunar surface with escape velocity appears to accelerate away from the surface with the local acceleration due to gravity. That is, if h is altitude then $\ddot{h} \sim 1.6$ m/sec². To be sure of clearing lunar peaks, it is desirable to have h ~ 5000 m when passing over them; with velocity 2400 m/sec, this implies a distance from launch of 190 km. Thus, a suitable

launch site must be in one of the great impact basins, with some 200 km of terrain which is no more than moderately rough.

There do exist farside basins which meet these criteria and in addition are suitably located. One is Korolev Basin; like most farside basins, it has not been subject to the large-scale lava flooding which on the nearside has created the great smooth maria. Its surface is moderately cratered, though not to a degree which would ease the large-scale basin structure. The basin is 450 km in diameter, and just inside the eastern periphery there are lightly-cratered regions which may be suitable mass-driver sites.

Similar remarks apply to the basin Mendeleev. This basin has a diameter of 330 km and over much of its surface it is less heavily cratered than is Korolev. Again there are numerous lightly-cratered regions suitable for mass-driver sites.

The Korolev and Mendeleev basins are described topographically as "nectarian", i.e., similar to the terrain of Mare Nectaris. The Lunar Orbiter photography had a resolution of <1 km, and it is known that nectarian terrains may be topographically rough on smaller scales. In particular, even in the smooth-appearing regions, there may be secondary craters of ~100 m diameter.

The major lava-flooded farside basin is Mare Moscoviense. Its dark basin floor renders difficult the observation of fine terrain detail; nevertheless, it is clear that Moscoviense is cratered to a degree comparable to Korolev or Mendeleev. Numerous small craters are evident and the presence of secondary craters may be inferred. Although Moscoviense's lava flooding makes it a promising site, the available Lunar Orbiter photography is insufficient to identify topographically smooth regions.

It thus is far from clear that the mass driver can be sited on terrain as smooth as the best Apollo sites. There may be a requirement for bulldozers

Figure 4 Computed Reference Trajectories, Moon-L5, in the Restricted Three-body Problem

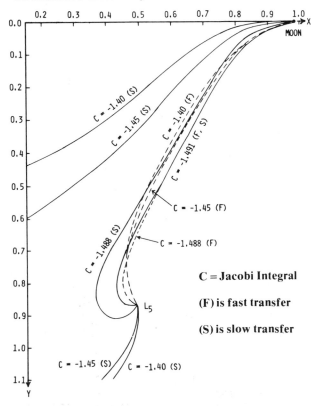

and other earth-moving equipment capable of operating in the lunar environment. While the task of construction will not be akin to road-building in the mountains, it probably will not be as easy as road-building on the plains. It may be like road-building on heavily gullied and eroded badlands.

Lunar farside communications will not be a problem, since one can place a communications satellite in a "halo orbit" at the translunar libration point (Ref. 1).

Thus, from this preliminary study of trajectory considerations, one derives two major conclusions:

- The aim sensitivity is $\sim 10^3$ km/m/sec

- Lunar farside basins are the required sites for the mass driver

Mass Driver Design. The basic principles of the linear synchronous motor, conceived as the electromagnetic drive for the mass driver, are well known (Ref. 2). The fundamental principle is that of force on a current-carrying wire in a magnetic field.

For preliminary sizing, the most important parameters are the length and power required. For accelerations of the order of 100 m/sec^2, the length is of the order of several tens of kilometers. Average power is the product (throughput) (kinetic energy per kilogram), or 3.1 MW per kg/sec of mean throughput.

The launch energy per kilogram is approximately one kilowatt-hour, an easily-handled quantity. Thus, it should be entirely feasible to install a solar-electric powerplant sized to deliver the averaged power load. During launch operations there are high peaking loads, which can be met using a flywheel energy storage system. Such a system involves flywheels coupled to motor-generators in such a manner that energy may be stored by spinning up the flywheel; when the energy is to be released, the flywheel is engaged to turn the generator. A single ten-tonW flywheel spinning at 3000 rpm stores over 100 kW-hr. of energy.

Further energy savings are permitted through use of regenerative braking. In acceleration, the electromagnetic fields of the linear synchronous stator, in the mass-driver track, do work on the accelerating vehicle; in braking, the vehicle does work against the fields, acting as a linear generator. The currents induced in the windings of the stator, through passage of the magnet-carrying vehicle, are fed to the power source, conditioned, and used to drive the motor-flywheel system. Use of regenerative braking offers the prospect that the required energy for a launch is input with high efficiency into the accelerated lunar mass, with relatively little being wasted in the acceleration/braking cycle of the "bucket", or mass-carrying vehicle.

The major problem, then, is to achieve the requisite launch tolerance of $\sim 10^{-3}$ m/sec, with a launch velocity of ~ 2.4 km/sec. This small a velocity shift can be measured using Mossbauer spectroscopy, since Mossbauer spectral lines are of width corresponding to $\sim 10^{-3}$ m/sec in doppler shift.

Thus, one could conceive a collimated Mossbauer gamma-ray beam received by a Mossbauer detector on the mass-carrying vehicle. When the vehicle velocity is at the desired limit, resonant absorption would cause a falloff in the detected signal, and this could be made to generate a cutoff command to the stator.

Unfortunately, however, such a requirement can only be met by the presently not-yet-existing gamma-ray laser (Ref. 3). Moreover, the laser would have to generate a spectral line offset in wavelength from the detector resonant wavelength. The offset would be 8 parts in 10^6, corresponding to a Doppler-induced shift of 2400 m/sec. It is far from clear whether such an offset can be introduced. In laboratory experiments involving small offsets, velocity shifts of a few centimeters per second are introduced by mounting the detector on an acoustically-driven vibrating plate, but this method is clearly unsuited to the present problem. It is concluded that the Mossbauer-spectroscopy method is beyond the current state of the art.

Alternately, one might seek to use microwave doppler velocity determination. In the tracking of spacecraft, velocity determinations accurate to $\sim 10^{-3}$ m/sec are routinely achieved. However, this is possible only after several hours of tracking. In the case of the mass-driver, the time for tracking is typically of the order of 0.1 second, since a sequence of several velocity determinations may be required, together with velocity corrections, in order to achieve convergence to the desired launch velocity.

Suppose, for example, that we use a phase-stable transponder on the vehicle and measure the phase of the returned signal to an accuracy of 0.1λ. For a doppler velocity measurement error of 10^{-3} m/sec and 0.1 sec measurement time, the signal wavelength is no greater than 10^{-3} m. Thus, RF doppler velocity determination is a problem in millimeter-wave technology. Since existing millimeter-wave technology may be applied down to approximately λ = 0.5 millimeter, it follows that this technology is in principle adequate to the task. However, the price for its use is acceptance of an L5 catcher system of the order of a kilometer in extent.

Consider now a third alternative: the "checkpoint" method, wherein one times the vehicle in its passage between two successive checkpoints. Depending on the accuracy of the measured intercheckpoint distance and on the accuracy of the measured passage time, the velocity may be determined to great precision.

What is measured, of course, is not the instantaneous velocity but the mean velocity during the passage. This velocity may be changing due to drag from the vehicle magnetic suspension, as well as from gravity. In a subsequent discussion, we consider a suspension which minimizes these problems.

For specificity, let the checkpoints be 250 m apart, so the passage time is 0.1 second. The spacing can be measured with interferometry. Changes in the spacing may occur through lunar tides and lunar seismicity. However, an optical interferometer can easily detect a change in spacing of 0.01 λ ~ 5×10^{-9} m, so the spacing at any time may be known accurate to 2 parts in 10^{11}.

The passage time may be measured to an accuracy of 10^{-9} sec through an adaptation of the means used to measure photon time-of-flight in lunar ranging experiments. The event of checkpoint passage by the vehicle is defined as the event of receiving at a photodetector the first photons from a checkpoint-mounted laser, scattered or reflected from a vehicle-mounted panel. Then, velocity measurements are achievable with accuracy of a few microns per second. The associated dispersion at L5 is of the order of a few meters.

It is now necessary to describe fully how such a measurement accuracy may indeed be achieved as well as how it may be used to guarantee a comparable accuracy in the achieved launch conditions.

Figure 5 illustrates observation of the event of checkpoint passage. The laser is conceived as

Figure 5 Event of Checkpoint Passage

having aperture ~ 1 cm and diffraction-limited performance. Laser power is not critical, since even a 1-watt-device emits ~ 10^{11} photons per nanosecond. But the laser must be aligned perpendicular to the track, with an accuracy of at least 10^{-4} radian.

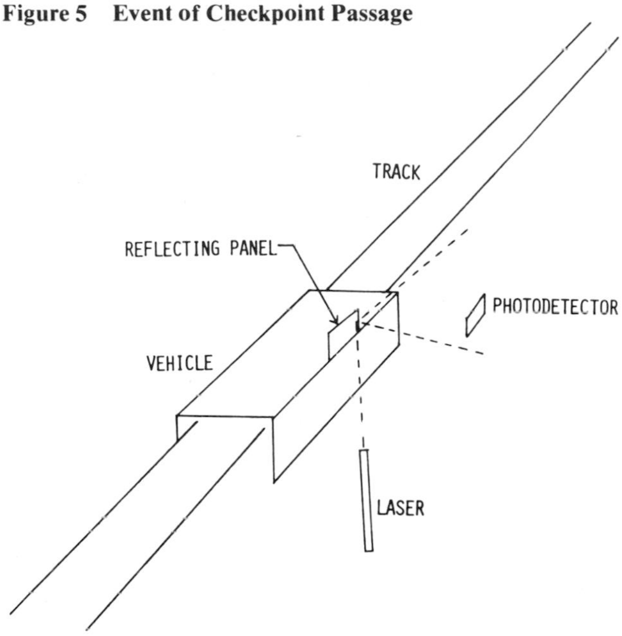

The reflecting panel is the side of a knife-edge, diffusely reflecting and of least moderately high albedo. The panel passes ~ 1 cm from the laser and its front edge coincides as closely as possible (< 1 cm) with the axis of the vehicle center of gravity; it is mounted atop the vehicle in such a manner that the laser beam is not first reflected from any other part of the vehicle.

In a nanosecond the vehicle moves 2.5 microns; the accuracies cited insure that the observed event of checkpoint passage implies a vehicle position known to rather better than this value. The vehicle may experience roll or pitch in its motion; the panel is made diffuse rather than specular, so that when it cuts the laser beam it will nonetheless act as though there were no roll or pitch. The panel front edge coincides with the center-of-gravity axis so that vehicle yaw of up to 0.01 radian still will not produce a cosine-type shift $> 10^{-6}$ m in the apparent front-edge position. Similarly, the vehicle may be up to a centimeter to the left or right of its proper position on the track; but then it will still clear the laser, and the laser, being accurately aligned, will produce a within-tolerance cosine-type shift in the detected vehicle position.

The photodetector is mounted in such a manner

Figure 6 Mass Driver Launch Sequence

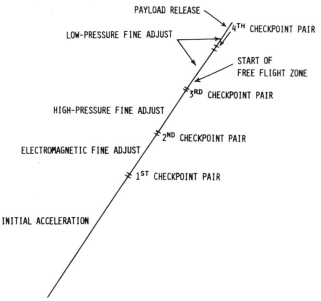

as to never see the laser beam directly, and the beam can be directed so as not to reflect from local topography or checkpoint structure. The detector also can be made not to see any illuminated surface save the vehicle reflector. Signal-to-noise ratio can be improved by equipping the detector with a narrowband inteference filter and by switching it on only during a brief time-gate, activated by vehicle approach. While single-photon detection is practicable it is not required, since it can easily be arranged that in the first nanosecond of passage, $> 10^6$ photons strike the detector.

The event of passing the first checkpoint starts an atomic clock; the passage of the second checkpoint generates a cutoff signal to a CW laser which continually illuminates a photoreceiver on the first checkpoint. Cutoff of the received signal stops the clock. By maintaining a constant electronic system temperature one prevents the introduction of unknown signal-processing delays which would lead to an erroneous measurement.

How can the velocity be controlled to the desired accuracy? This is shown in Figure 6. The vehicle carries an onboard integrating accelerometer; when this instrument signals achievement of velocity, the vehicle signals the trackside linear synchronous motor phase control to shut off the accelerating drive. If the instrument is comparable in capability to present-day inertial velocity cutoff instrumentation for missiles, the initial cutoff has accuracy ~ 1 m/sec. Then the vehicle passes the first checkpoint pair; its velocity is measured and telemetered to the onboard guidance, and a more

sensitive accelerometer is uncaged. The vehicle then enters the first velocity correction zone; an acceleration of ~ 1 m/sec^2 is applied and cut off by the onboard-generated signal. This zone is ~ 2.5 km in length and corrects vehicle velocity to $\sim 10^{-2}$ m/sec.

Again the vehicle passes a checkpoint pair and receives a velocity update. But for subsequent fine adjustment it appears preferable to use onboard cold-gas ejection systems. If vehicle mass (with payload) is ~ 100 kg, a velocity correction of 10^{-2} m/sec (accuracy: 10^{-4} m/sec) is achievable with a high-pressure system of 10^3 m/sec exhaust velocity ejecting 10^{-3} kg of gas (100 cm^3 at 10 atmospheres pressure); a final stage of velocity adjustment may involve a low-pressure cold-gas system and achieve 10^{-6} m/sec accuracy.

But it is necessary to achieve comparable control of motion in five other degrees of freedom. This is the responsibility of the track and the vehicle suspension system.

The principal requirements on the track are a simple close-tolerance design which can be turned out in long lengths like steel rail and which can be laid in a highly uniform straigth line along a prepared roadbed. Indeed, it may be desirable to lay the track as a continuous extrusion from a mobile continuous-casting furnace. The vehicle suspension must provide low magnetic drag, high restoring forces (so as to center the vehicle over the track), and capability for damping (energy absorption) so as to inhibit oscillations. These requirements are met by the design concept of Figure 7.

The track is entirely of aluminum or magnesium, metals available in great quantity from lunar rocks. It can be readily fabricated as an extrusion and hot-rolled to achieve surface finish.

The suspension involves fore-and-aft pairs of superconducting current-carrying coils straddling the track rails. This is a "null-flux" type of suspension (Powell and Danby, 1966). Such a suspension is inherently low in magnetic drag and provides high restoring forces. Indeed, the restoring forces are such as to produce a very stiff suspension, so that accurate track alignment is essential. To provide damping, the superconducting coils may be supported by a beam which attaches to the vehicle structure by a ball-and-socket joint. The joint is recessed within a rigid tube filled with hard rubber or a similar substance capable of rapid damping of small oscillations. The configuration of Fig. 7 is inherently stable once the vehicle exceeds lunar escape velocity, since it then tends to lift from the track.

The track is to be laid in a straight line, as may be readily verified by laser measurements during construction. But it also must not change its tilt or deviate from its nominal curvature as (for example) an arc of the lunoid (lunar geoid). It is clear that even a slight dip or rise in the track, or tilt away from the level, could impose unacceptable transient roll or pitch motions. It is not required that all such motions be entirely removed, but it is required that if they occur, they be sufficiently reproducible from launch to launch as to prevent random velocity errors which are out of tolerance.

During the main acceleration phase, one may tolerate a moderately jerky ride; errors in leveling of up to a centimeter per hundred meters of track lead to transient accelerations in pitch or heave not exceeding 10 m/sec^2, and errors in track leveling of up to 5 degrees per kilometer give transient roll accelerations under 1 radian/sec^2. A simple way to test for such errors is to run the vehicle along the track at successively higher speeds, with onboard accelerometers. Data from these instruments show what corrections must be made in track alignment. This method may also be used to achieve a suitably smooth ride within the more sensitive velocity-adjustment sections of the track.

It is a simple matter to provide several kilometers of track for terminal velocity adjustment which accurately follows a free flight trajectory in three dimensions, as can be verified by laser. A 10 km length of such track, elevated over much of its length, is 12 m above the ground at the end. And in all track construction, the high visibility in the lunar vacuum is a distinct asset. For example, one may place a number of reticles upon the track, up to several hundred meters apart, and sight along them with a theodolite. This technique shows local misalignment to better than centimeter accuracy per kilometer of track.

We come now to the release of the payload. Hopefully, the payload can be ordinarily regolithic material loaded into the lunar equivalent of a burlap bag (for example, a bag of light aluminum wire weave). The release mechanism then must avoid perturbing the motion of the payload; this can be done by a two-step release.

An iron disc may be attached to the payload and

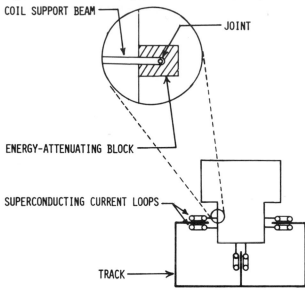

Figure 7 Track and Suspension in Cross Section

COIL SUPPORT BEAM

JOINT

ENERGY-ATTENUATING BLOCK

SUPERCONDUCTING CURRENT LOOPS

TRACK

the vehicle may carry an electromagnet on a retractable boom which is in contact with the disc. The payload is secured by retractable plates during acceleration and initial velocity adjustment. Then the plates retract, and during the fine velocity adjustment the payload is held only by the boom magnet. Then this magnet is switched off and the boom retracted. From that point on the payload is in free flight.

In systems tests, payloads may be launched with velocity just under escape. They will execute highly eccentric elliptical orbits and it can be arranged that they spend tens of hours in flight before again impacting the lunar surface. The dispersion of the impact points can be observed and the system modified to achieve a desired dispersion. Then the initial payload is launched to L5. It carries a transponder or beacon so that its approach can be observed, for terminal maneuvering by the L5 station. Thereafter, a steady stream of lunar material may be received at L5.

The L5 Station. While an overall description of the L5 station is beyond the scope of this paper, certain of its subsystems fall within this scope. These are the subsystems relating to payload capture and to control of station motion by mass expulsion.

The mass-catcher system should have diameter ~ 30 m or less. The launch velocity dispersion is of the order of a few microns/sec; this leads to a miss dispersion at L5 of the order of 10 meters. A conceptual overall layout for the mass-catcher and

Figure 8   Mass Collection Module

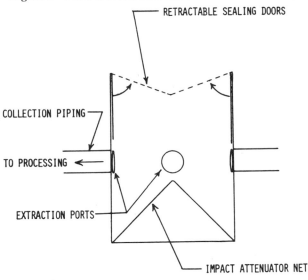

detail of a catcher module are shown in Figure 8.

The catcher module may operate in a "Venus-Fly-Trap" mode. An incoming payload impacts the conical target net, which is of Kevlar, wire netting, or other construction capable of withstanding the impact. The module itself is sufficiently thick-walled to withstand a glancing impact, or to withstand the impact of the payload rebounding from the target net. The impact stimulates the closing of the chamber with gas-tight doors. Then oxygen is admitted to the chamber, pressurizing it to the pressure of the collection piping. The wire-weave "burlap bag" containing the payload splits open at impact, and following pressurization the chamber contains a mass of lunar material dispersed in entraining gas. Then the chamber is purged, and the collection piping carries off the entrained material.

A stationkeeping system is required to compensate for the impulses received from the arriving payloads. This system ejects a fraction of the received mass; to keep the mass loss fraction at a modest level, the ejection velocity must be several times the arrival velocity. This immediately suggests the mass-driver.

But a linear mass-driver would be a lengthy and unwieldy structure which would whip around like the flagella of a spermatozoon. Thus it is desirable for the mass-driver to involve a circular track, in analogy with a cyclotron. Such a device, however, involves other problems, notably the high centripetal accelerations (thousands of g's) for systems of a few hundred seconds of specific impulse and

Figure 9   Pellet Injection for Rotary Launcher

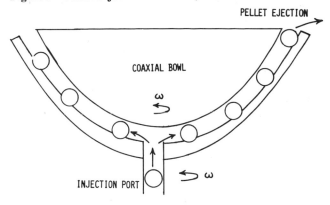

with diameters ~1 km. Such accelerations lead to severe difficulties in vehicle suspension and in provision for release of mass.

An attractive alternative then is the rotary pellet launcher, proposed by O'Neill as a possible mode of lunar transport (Ref. 4). This involves a set of rapidly rotating tubes, resembling helicopter blades. It is hopeless to seek launch accuracies suitable for lunar mass transport with this system. But for efficient thrust, the release of mass pellets need be controlled only to an accuracy of ~60° in launch direction. This may be achievable using uniform spherical sintered pellets which are fed under control into the axis end of the rotating tubes. A possible injection mechanism is illustrated in Fig. 9, following Ref. 5.

If the mass of a pellet is m, its ejection velocity V_e and the rate of pellet ejection n per second, the thrust (in newtons) is $m\,n\,V_e$. The injection mechanism is essentially a rapidly spinning parabolic bowl with a helical groove running around the inner surface. This begins at the bottom of the bowl, on the spin axis where the pellet is injected, and ends at the lip of the bowl where the pellet has a speed of ~100 m/sec and is ejected into a rotating tube. Many pellets are in the bowl at the same time; they are kept separated by a series of craters in the helical groove. The spin axis of the bowl is deflected every $1/n$ seconds to "stutter" its operation. It is this stuttering which moves a pellet from one crater to the next in its journey along the groove and which actually ejects it into the rotating tube. The bowl cannot be left "open." A second bowl is located coaxially with the first; the separation between them is just larger than the pellet diameter, and the helical groove along which the pellet moves is a helical tunnel.

In designing the L5 station, one must consider its

21

capability for self-growth. Thus, a stripped-down station may be initially emplaced, with few catcher modules and limited production capacity. The station intercepts only a fraction of the payloads launched from the Moon, but with them it undertakes to grow. In a short time it becomes capable of capturing and processing virtually all the lunar-launched mass, and then is ready to begin building the colony proper.

Summary and Conclusion. The problem of lunar mass transport is seen to yield in principle to a conceptually simple solution. This is a magnetically-levitated linear-synchronous drive mass launcher, with velocity controlled through onboard accelerometers operating together with precision measurements of passage time between checkpoints.

The foregoing discussion has emphasized novel features such as the velocity measurement system. System considerations involving straightforward engineering design have received little attention. But further work must move beyond descriptive identification of requirements and into the realm of detailed design studies and tradeoff analyses, leading to evolution of preliminary designs.

Accordingly, the following list of potential research studies is proposed:

• Precision trajectory integrations in the perturbed elliptic restricted three-body problem, to confirm aim sensitivities and to establish bounds on lunar regions suitable for siting.

• Optimal sizing of L5 mass collector: tradeoff between smaller, stronger collector (due to higher impact velocity) and larger, lighter system.

• Linear synchronous motor studies: available current in windings, phase control for synchroneity at high velocities,

• Drag characteristics of suspension: probable associated variation in velocity during passage between checkpoints and after final correction to velocity.

• Manufacturing and construction processes for track and electromagnetic drive.

• Feasibility of regenerative braking.

• Sources of error in velocity measurement (e.g.,

variable delays due to electronic circuitry).

• Lunar earth-moving and mining equipment.

• Minimization of vehicle mass in view of its subsystems: accelerometer, onboard computer, gas jets, suspension, superconducting magnetic coils.

• Minimization of mass to be transported from Earth.

• System maintenance, duty cycle, and downtime.

It may be possible to address some or all of these issues, as well as others which may be defined, during the 1975 NASA summer study. But the points cited deal with *how* some things are to be done, not whether they can be done. It appears that the feasibility and practicality of lunar mass transport is established and that the major problems are of an engineering nature.

DISCUSSION

Q. You raised the question that there is a possibility of exploring the L4 as well as the L5 site. Would that permit you to leave from the nearside of the Moon, instead of the farside?

A. No. The trajectories are only about 10° off the Earth-Moon line of centers, so switching L5 to L4 would only flip them about 20°, not enough to move the launch point around to the nearside.

Q. Your assumption on being able to measure distances accurately and track a line properly depends on the fact that the Moon is a rigid, unmoving object. Is it? Also, since the plane of librations of the Moon varies, and since your track is fixed, somehow you would have to steer your pellet in a lateral direction in order to arrive at the same location at L5.

A. With regard to the nonrigidity of the Moon, we could anchor the checkpoints in lunar bedrock and measure their spacing by interferometry or by means of a device known to geologists as the beaming off-strain gauge, which gets comparable accuracy. So while it *is* true that lunar seismic effects might cause small shifts in checkpoint alignment or in the distance between checkpoints, we could measure them quite accurately.

With regard to the Moon's libration, it *does* wobble, not only *in* the plane of its orbit, but also *out* of the plane of its orbit. Thus the catcher station will have to be able to range over a fairly wide area of space so as to catch the stream of material. The analogy is therefore not that of a cannonball, but rather a stream of water from a garden hose. If you shoot that stream of water and I try to catch it in a bucket, I can run with the bucket and continue to catch it, as long as you don't wobble the hose too much.

Q. *How far do you have to run? What's the maximum libration, and over what period of time?*

A. I would anticipate a few tens of thousands of kilometers, well within the range of the type of orbit that we are considering, over a period of about a month.

Q. *You show a number of orbits, some of which appear to intersect the L5 position coming from the oppostie direction. Did you intentionally pick the mass/velocity components so that some of the material would come from opposite directions, reducing the necessity for a velocity adjustment in the catcher at L5?*

A. That's an interesting question; it's a possibility I haven't considered. Those trajectories are associated with different values of the energy — the Jacobi constant. Those trajectories which curve around and come in from the back typically have far greater sensitivity in aim, so you would have to launch perhaps ten times as much material in order to achieve the same flux at the station. This makes your suggestion less desirable, although it *is* interesting, and we may find a way to make use of it.

Q. *One part in 10^7 in electronics is a rather tiny time interval. You might be able to achieve a continuous velocity adjustment on the track by means of a much simpler system, using doppler measurements reflecting a patch on your vehicle.*

A. I considered the possibility of using doppler. It turns out that if you are going to use a traditional type of doppler in which radiation falls on the vehicle and you look for a shift in the line, that shift will have to be measured to about one part in 10^{-11}. That is because we are concerned with the ratio of one millimeter per second to the speed of light. This would require a very high frequency electromagnetic region where it is rather difficult to work. We might be able to make use of the gamma ray laser, but that hasn't been invented yet.

Q. *But it's only ten thousand cycles that you have to measure: one part in 10^{11}. That's no problem at all with a visible laser.*

A. But can we define a laser spectral line and measure it in real time to six decimal places? I know we see laser wavelengths quoted typically to four, five or even six significant figures. We would need it to about eleven or twelve significant figures, and would need to measure that continuously in real time.

Q. *Laser techniques are used for measuring velocities with immense precision in all kinds of techniques now. The laser velocimeter has been very well developed for doing just that job, and it is an extremely precise instrument. I think it will answer these problems.*

A. In that case, then, we have other possibilities for this application. Thanks for that suggestion.

Q. *What is the vertical configuration of the track? At what angle is it aligned to the surface of the Moon? Is it the horizontal plane?*

A. Yes. I see no reason why we shouldn't want to use the horizontal plane and then let the payloads go into free flight, so that they begin to rise gently up above the lunar surface.

3.   Lunar Materials

David R. Criswell
Lunar Science Institute

The mass requirements for O'Neill's Model 1 are half a million metric tons of soil to be launched from the Moon and about ten thousand metric tons of materials and people to be launched from Earth. Five thousand four hundred metric tons from the Earth would be hydrogen to combine with the lunar oxygen to make water at L5. The complete breakdown is illustrated in Table 5.

One of the first questions to be asked is whether we can get that hydrogen from the Moon. Unfortunately, however, there's no spot on Earth as anhydrous as the lunar surface.

No lunar water has been reported; only sample contamination by terrestrial water. There are not even minerals present which required water for their formation, and these minerals date over a four-billion-year period. The Moon is the most unlikely source that one could imagine for extracting hydrogen or water. Dust is the principal characteristic of the lunar surface. The dust is easy to work with. It contains material from virtually everywhere on the Moon. Particles less than one millimeter in size compose from eighty percent to, in some cases, ninety eight percent of the visible surface and the bulk of the regolith down to depths of many meters.

Figure 10 shows histograms of the mass distribution of various lunar soils from the Apollo 17 site. The horizontal scales are millimeters, microns, and the logrithmic ϕ-units used in sedimentology. These diagrams clearly show that the soil is extremely fine-grained, with average sizes which peak around sixty microns. There is a significant percentage of mass of soil in these samples less than four microns in size. There are soils returned from the Moon that are even finer-grained, with the order of ten percent of the material less than ten microns in size. This particle size distribution is the key to providing the hydrogen for the first space manufacturing facility, because this soil contain hydrogen implanted from the solar wind.

This unique property of the surface geology of the Moon is illustrated by the old poem:

Big fleas have little fleas
Which upon their backs do bite'em
But little fleas have smaller fleas
And so ad infinitum.

This is really what the lunar surface is like. Figure 11 shows a tip of a grain that's one hundred microns across. it is an agglutinate composed of grains that are stuck to one another by a glass matrix. The smallest grains that you can see in this picture are less than a micron in size. They go on down to tenths of a micron and smaller.

In that one-hundred-micron volume is a microcosm of the entire Moon, a somewhat representative sample of material from every place on the Moon that has been exposed to the solar wind. Each grain in this picture, down to the smallest size, has gas of solar origin distributed through it in two ways: in volume-correlated form - that is, distributed on a per-unit-mass basis through

Table 5 Model I Mass Requirements; Transportation; Salaries
(Non-recurring Terrestrial Expenses)

Mass and Costs of Transportation to L5 from:

Item	Earth Mass (KMT)[1]	Earth Cost ($ × 10⁹)[2]	Item	Moon Mass (KMT)	Moon Cost ($ × 10⁹)[4]
Generator Plants	1.	.94	Aluminum	20.	0.4
Initial Structures	1.	94.	Glass	10.	0.2
Specially Fabri-cated Equipment	1.	.94	Soil, Rock & Construction Materials	420.	8.48
Machines & Tools	0.8	75	Oxygen for Water	44.8	0.91
2000 People & Equipment	0.2	.44[3]			
Dehydrated Food	0.6	.56			
*Liquid Hydrogen	5.6	5.24			
Totals	10.0KMT	9.81 × 10⁹		494.8KMT	10 × 10⁹

*If one can obtain hydrogen from the Moon then

	−5.6	−5.24	Lunar Hydrogen	+ 5.6	0.11
New Totals	4.4KMT	4.57 × 10⁹		≃ 500KMT	10.11 × 10⁹
New Transportation Total					15 × 10⁹[5]

(1) Thousand Metric Tons
(2) $935/kg
(3) $4,410/kg
(4) $10 × 10⁹ for lunar base to supply ≃ 500MT to L5 (or 4) for average cost of $20/kg.
(5) Revised project total (O'Neill 1974) would be approximately $25 × 10^{+9} with major expenditure being 8.4 × 10^{+9} for L5 and terrestrial salaries

each grain; and in surface-correlated form − evenly distributed on the surface of the grain. It's this last point that is important. Surface correlation is, I think, the key to obtaining hydrogen and other elements from the Moon for the early lunar operations, where a minimum of complexity is desired on the Moon and in space.

Figure 12 is a plot of concentration of an arbitrary species; e.g., in number of atoms per unit mass or per unit volume on the vertical (ordinate) scale; the horizontal (abscissa) scale is the radius of the grain size. For spherical grains, the surface area of the material goes up in inverse proportion to the average radius of the grains. For example, if a one-centimeter-diameter spherical grain were crushed into tenth-micron particles, its surface area would increase by a factor of 10^5.

Hydrogen, helium, the inert gases, and many

Figure 10 Particle Size Distributions of Various Lunar Soil Samples

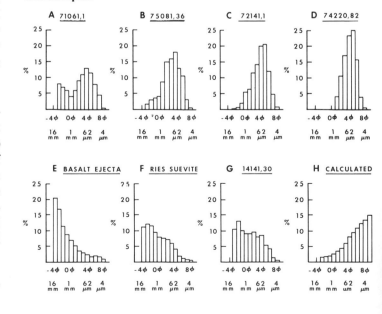

Figure 11 Micron Grain of Lunar Soil (1000 Magnification), Showing Agglutinate Composition

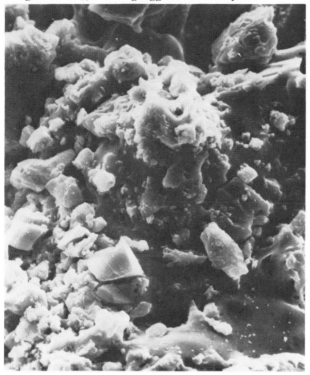

Figure 13 Photomicrograph of Lunar Material Showing 2%-5% Iron

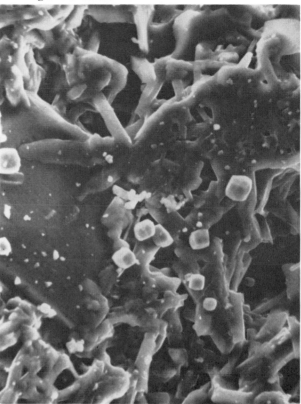

reactive materials such as carbon and nitrogen are distributed in surface-correlated form in the lunar soil. Hydrogen is the least surface-correlated of those examples. Sufficient surface correlation exists in many of the Apollo samples such that the bulk of the implanted material is actually contained in the grains under ten microns, which are a small fraction

Figure 12 Species Contribution vs Particle Grain Size

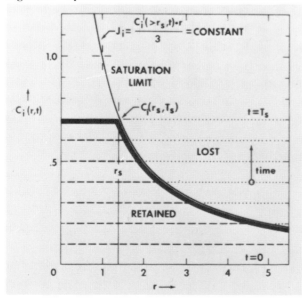

of the total volume of the soil. It appears possible to extract those grains either mechanically (sieving), electrostatically, or possibly by magnetic separation. The agglutinates are quite often separated from lunar samples simply by pulling them out with a bar magnet.

The problem we face is a massive one, however: five thousand four hundred metric tons of hydrogen consists of 3×10^{33} hydrogen atoms. The typical bulk concentration of hydrogen in the lunar soil is the order of 2×10^{19} hydrogen atoms per gram, ranging in the Apollo 17 soil (not the best example) up to 9×10^{19}. The half-million tons of soil necessary for the construction of Model 1 would produce 4.5×10^{31} hydrogen atoms, or one and a half percent of what is needed. Further, we need in some way to sieve the smallest grains out of a volume which is sixty-six times larger to separate out the hydrogen-rich or volatile-rich component.

The half million tons of soil corresponds to a ditch five meters deep and 0.1 kilometer in radius. To obtain the necessary 5400 tons of hydrogen, we'd need to process material from a ditch 0.4 kilometer in radius and, again, five meters deep.

27

This seems like an enormous amount, but actually it is very much like digging in face-powder: if you undercut it, it collapses under the tool. As long as you don't hit large rocks, which you can navigate around, you can expend very little energy and still process this material. The mechanical energy required simply to lift the material up to a separating machine and then redeposit the residue would only require 1.8 horsepower operating continuously over the six year period. Even allowing a factor of ten or a hundred for the power actually required to extract the finest grains, this is not a particularly unwieldy number.

The task can probably be made much easier by careful selection of site, locating the very finest-grain material, going to special mineralogies, higher agglutinate contents, and high ilmenite contents, which are also iron-rich. It should be possible to get a rough idea of the location of these optimal low-latitude sites by orbital inspection on the basis of the Apollo data in hand. A polar orbiter will be required to survey the entire Moon, and in-situ testing will be required to determine the actual ideal sites.

Figure 13 indicates some of the possibilities raised by considering other special characteristics of the lunar material. This photo is about two or three hundred microns across, and shows crystal grains from vugs, inside grains of the lunar surface. They are pure iron blebs, of sub-micron size, distributed across the surface. Most free iron is associated with agglutinates. If you go to the very finest fraction of the lunar material, the quantity of pure iron can sometimes approach two to five percent by volume. It can be separated by straightforward magnetic separation techniques. It is also possible that surface-correlated carbon and nitrogen can be produced in quantities somewhat lower than that of the hydrogen for the same sample, possibly a factor of five. Again though, you can optimize this by careful selection of where you do your sieving.

4.   Deep Space Material Sources

K. Eric Drexler

Massachusetts Institute of Technology

There are three opportunities for the use of materials available in the asteroid belt.

The asteroids lie mostly in a broad belt between Mars and Jupiter. There are many thousands of them; they range in size from a thousand kilometers down to fine dust, and have variable composition. Most are in the main belt, but there exists a limited selection of mostly smaller asteroids in near-Earth space that are more accessible. Also, recent observations from spacecraft cameras indicate the possible presence of clouds of material, probably of asteroidal composition, at L4 and L5.

The first opportunity for the use of deep-space material is for the local support of colonies. The asteroids have available the energy, metals, and organic materials necessary to support colonies in comfort and provide for their expansion for many centuries. In virtually all respects the asteroids are a resource base equivalent in quality to the resources found on the Earth.

The second opportunity relates to the question of hydrogen and organic materials. The Moon is probably not a good source for hydrogen, but the asteroids do represent a practical supply because carbonaceous chondrite material is widely distributed throughout the belt. This material contains some 10% water, which is extractable at temperatures of about 200°C, and about one half the organic materials content of terrestrial oil shale.

Because of the ease of processing this material, the supply for a fair-sized colony at L5 could probably be provided by a very small station in the asteroids, and return of this material could be accomplished relatively easily by using atmospheric braking on arrival at the Earth.. With such braking one can deliver material from the inner edge of the belt for a velocity increment difference of about 3.9 kilometers per second. Using a current-technology liquid hydrogen/liquid oxygen rocket, one only needs a mass ratio of about four, and, of course, the propellant might be obtained from the 10% water which has been observed in the asteroid belt.

This will become a practical undertaking when the technology becomes available and when the demand at L5 grows sufficiently. A major problem is that the work crew that is sent to the asteroids would be approximately a year's travel time from Earth, and therefore would have to be relatively self-sufficient. Thus a certain minimum demand is needed before such an operation becomes practical.

The third opportunity is that of supplying the Earth with steel from the asteroid belt. The asteroids contain steel in chunks ranging from about 100 kilometers in diameter down to dust. It is, in its native form, a strong, tough, ductile, and corrosion-resistant material and, for engineering purposes, is superior to most of the steel produced on the surface of the Earth. This is largely because it contains approximately 5% nickel.

It has been proposed to use nuclear pulse propulsion to transport about a cubic kilometer of this steel to any Earth orbit, to process it there, and then to deliver it to the surface of the Earth.

Because transportation costs are estimated to be less than 5% of the value of the steel that is returned, a substantial profit is possible.

The processing in orbit is relatively simple: chunks of steel are melted in solar furnaces, the molten steel is then centrifuged to draw off about 10% impurities, mostly silicate and sulfide slags, and it is then cast into forms which can be assembled into re-entry bodies for delivery to the surface of the Earth.

The present value of steel on the world market is approximately $100 per ton, and the world demand is about $70 billion per year. At these rates, a cubic kilometer represents a ten-year supply and is worth $700 billion. The schedule would be defined by the construction times needed to produce the processing facilities at L5, the maneuvering times imposed by celestial mechanics for sending "prospector" probes out to the asteroid belt, the time needed to equip and send out a work crew equipped with about a thousand one-hundred-megaton hydrogen bombs, etc., and appears to indicate a time for initial deliveries from about 1989 to the year 2000.

The capital costs are estimated at $20 billion for the transportation phase, plus the order of $30 billion for processing equipment at L5. This equipment could be constructed on site by boot-strap methods from lunar materials; it consists mostly of mirror surface area and solar furnace cavities plus some centrifuges.

One essential requirement for the implementation of this proposal is public and international acceptance of the detonation of hydrogen bombs in deep space. From physical grounds this is an entirely safe thing to do, because the solar wind would disperse outward, away from the Sun and the Earth, any materials of a radioactive nature or other debris from the explosions. If this proposal turns out to be technically feasible, its economic benefits should overcome the financial and political barriers that stand in its way.

DISCUSSION

Q. *Where did the basic idea for your proposal originate?*

A. The information that I used was largely derived from a Project Icarus study done at MIT some years ago, I believe in 1968. The question then was: if Icarus is going to strike the Earth, how would you divert it?

Q. *Looking a little further into space, do you consider the resource value of the satellites of say, Jupiter?*

A. Yes. The problem with the satellites of Jupiter, aside from their size and distance, is that they're quite possibly not differentiated in the way that asteroidal materials are, into nickel/iron, silicates, and carbonaceous chondrites. This indication is based on spectroscopic evidence of their surfaces.

Q. *Could they have undifferentiated surfaces and differentiated cores?*

A. Quite possibly, but then you have to mine rather deeply. The asteroids have the advantage of already having been fractured by impacts, so all the materials that you need are exposed on the surface, sometimes in usable-sized chunks.

Q. *What amount of material would you expect to find at L4 and L5, based on an analogy from the amount of material seen at the Lagrangian points of the orbit of Jupiter?*

A. I don't know that you can draw a valid comparison. The Lagrangian points of Jupiter contain a number of bodies in the 100-kilometer size range, but the gravitational stability questions are entirely different.

Q. *Have you done any work on the possibility of contamination of the asteroid steel by the thermonuclear explosions?*

A. Presumably you would detonate all your devices on the same face of the object. Each explosion removes a certain amount of surface material, probably much of the contaminated material from the previous blast. In any case, the contaminated material would be a very small fraction of a cubic kilometer.

Q. *You have based your arguments on an analogy between the asteroids and the meteorites that we see in museums. Isn't that relationship poorly understood?*

A. My estimates are not based on meteorite analysis, but on Michael Gaffee's work on reflection spectroscopy of the asteroids. These data indicated not only that the observed asteroids were made out of steel, but they provided estimates of the ratio of iron to nickel in that steel.

Q. *How solid is the evidence for nitrogen in the asteroids?*

A. The nitrogen content of carbonaceous chondrite material is about one third of a percent.

Q. *Deimos and Phobos, the moons of Mars, are theorized to be of the same composition as most of the asteroidal material. Do we have any additional information from the observation of these objects as to what the composition of asteroidal material is?*

A. Not really. We still don't know whether Deimos and Phobos are made out of basaltic material, which is ordinary rock, or carbonaceous chondrite material, which more resembles silt or dirt. They are definitely not nickel-iron.

5. Baseline L5 Construction Station

Gerald W. Driggers
Southern Research Institute

Introduction

Construction of the first habitat will require several years and a substantial construction crew (Ref. 4). For purposes of this study a construction crew of approximately 2000 men and women was assumed to require comfortable and safe accommodations for several years. The period of time is relatively inconsequential in defining the basic station or its operation except in trading off the methodology of environmental maintenance and food/water provision. Because of uncertainty in the true lifetime requirement, ten years was assumed where it was important, such as trading off farming vs. Earth supply for food.

The study was divided into six parts, with the first two parts occurring simultaneously:

(1) Requirements Definition
(2) Literature Review
(3) Configuration Tradeoffs/Selection
(4) Design Refinement
(5) Weight Estimates
(6) Cost/Schedule Estimates

Previous work was used (Refs. 6, 7) to the maximum extent practical without inhibiting creativity. In specific instances where new elements were designed, the major masses were estimated and a compensating factor used to allow for unknown details. These factors ranged from 1.05 to 1.3, based on level of complexity and knowledge (i.e., available data) on the individual elements.

The resulting station design is not the result of extensive study and optimization, but is indicative of the general requirements that result from a 2000-person assumption. Additionally, the commonality of this design with the space station/space base studies of 1969-1970 should lend an increased level of confidence in the feasibility of constructing such a station.

Basic Requirements/Assumptions

Requirements. The purpose of the L5 personnel/construction station (P/CS) is the support of 2000 people in a safe, reasonably comfortable environment for individual periods of six to twelve months over a total time span of approximately ten years. The ten-year time span allows pre- and post-habitat construction periods, assuming Model 1 assembly requires about six years. In addition to accommodations, the requirement for working volume was defined as a sphere 100 meters in diameter, to provide a "shirt-sleeve" environment.

Assumptions.

(1) The solar power system to be used by the Model 1 habitat would be constructed during the initial assembly of the P/CS and be available for use as demanded by P/CS startup (an alternative to this will be mentioned later).

(2) Crew rotation would be based on twelve-month tours at L5, necessitating extended periods of artifical gravity conditioning for the crew

members. A period of six months was considered but offered no obvious advantages. Some mass savings might be realized in the P/CS by careful design (making use of the zero-g condition) but the added transportation, operations, training/retraining, and similar costs do not appear to support such a potential advantage. The effects of living in zero-g, even with periodic enforced exercise/negative-pressure treatments, must be considered uncertain today. On the other hand, twelve-month isolated tours for men and women on construction projects and in military service have been relatively common. If good morale is maintained and the incentives are sufficient (i.e., money, prestige, adventure, etc), a twelve-month tour at L5 should present no stumbling block to obtaining good personnel who will work at Earth-average or better efficiency.

Implicit to this assumption are two others. One is that normal construction materials and geometrical arrangements will be sufficient to hold radiation dosage for twelve months to an acceptable level exclusive of severe solar flares. The second assumption is that a solar flare shelter is required.

(3) Specific dimensions and maximum masses for payload capability to L5 have not been established. It was assumed that modular payloads of fifteen meters diameter and 150 metric tons were not unreasonable. Early tradeoffs in configurations showed a distinct advantage for the fifteen-meter diameter over ten meters.

(4) The minimum food requirement assuming Earth supply would be a diet of 2800-3000 k-cal/day with 17-19 percent protein (Refs. 8, 9). This translates to some 0.63 kg/day/person of dried food of the type used on Apollo missions. These foods might not prove appropriate for maintaining morale over a one-year period, and the average food requirement would surely be higher. For tradeoffs conducted between a closed ecological system (farm) and regular resupply a minimum of 0.80 kg/day/person was assumed.

(5) Living and work areas will have multiple egress and large air volume access. Multiple egress decreases the possibility that accident or meteor encounter will block off a particular area and also allows much more rapid evacuation. It also allows a much better "traffic pattern", especially during shift changes. Access to a substantial air volume is required to assure sufficiently long evacuation times in case a compartment is exposed to vacuum. Repair operations could also be assisted.

(6) The atmosphere will be oxygen and nitrogen at eight psi with 30 percent O_2 (2.4 psi partial pressure), for both the station and the construction spheres. The effect of this assumption was primarily in the mass of the spheres, and should yield conservative mass estimates, since lower pressures (say five psi) may be acceptable. If the living volume required one-atmosphere pressure (14.7 psi), the spheres would have to be operated at about eight psi to avoid problems with the bends (which occur at about seven psi) during shift changes. It is obviously preferable to operate both the living and work volumes at the same pressure.

Another factor favoring the eight psi pressure is the advantage of using a space suit operating near that pressure. A crewman transferring from the high pressure of a one-atmosphere station to a five-psi pressure suit would be required to prebreath pure oxygen for approximately two hours prior to depressurizing below eight psi.

Configuration and Geometry Tradeoffs

Configuration Selection. The variety of configurations and geometrical arrangements one can postulate which provide the basic requirements of artifical gravity and a 100-meter-diameter construction sphere are quite large. The station configurations considered in this study were grouped into two categories: monolithic and modular, as illustrated in Figure 14. The monolithic concepts are representative of stations which would be constructed in space from building materials and subsystems shipped from Earth. The modular concepts would be assembled in space from modules and systems constructed on Earth. Previous tradeoffs between these concepts have generally selected the modular approach (Ref. 10); it was assumed in the present study that significant differences do not exist in mass, cost or schedule among the choices. The validity of this assumption (based on some definition of "significant differences") has not been determined.

Ten parameters were selected for configuration comparisons (Table 6). Each concept was rated on a relative scale within each category, so that the highest total score represented the preferred option. Concepts H and J rank equally well, with H having a slight edge. One other factor which favored the Double-Spoked Parallel Cluster Station (DSPCS) was postulated: a high level of protection solar flare shelter could be incorporated with relative ease using the volume between the spokes. With the axis of rotation oriented properly, Concept H would

Figure 14 Personnel Station Configuration Options

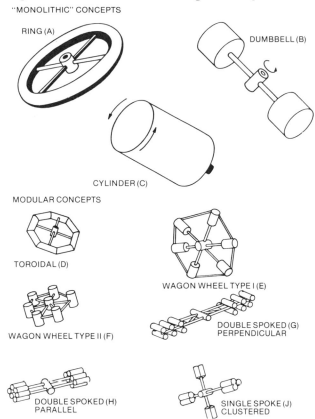

"MONOLITHIC" CONCEPTS

RING (A)

DUMBBELL (B)

CYLINDER (C)

MODULAR CONCEPTS

TOROIDAL (D)

WAGON WHEEL TYPE I (E)

WAGON WHEEL TYPE II (F)

DOUBLE SPOKED (G)
PERPENDICULAR

DOUBLE SPOKED (H)
PARALLEL

SINGLE SPOKE (J)
CLUSTERED

Table 6   Configuration Trade-Off Factors

1. Earth Construction
2. Launch Load Compatibility
3. Space Assembly Simplicity
4. Evolutionary Capability
5. Personnel Traffic Capability and Control
6. Multiple Egress Ease (Construction and Design)
7. Living Area Gravity Variation
8. Coriolis Effects
9. Sphere Attachment Compatibility
10. Central Life Support/Control Compatibility

provide more natural protection features than possible with J. Thus the DSPCS modular station was selected for detailed study.

Major Element Geometry. Geometrical arrangements for the major elements (i.e., station, construction sphere, and power station) range from all free-flying and separate, with some orientation constraints, to fully connected and integrated. The selection of a preferred arrangement was also complicated by uncertainty over whether one or two personnel stations would be preferable from an evolution, safety and management standpoint. Some considerations of several representative options are presented in Table 7. Other combinations can of course be postulated.

It was decided for the sake of conservatism (lowest probability of full complement loss) and flexibility to assume a dual station capability with either personnel station capable of supporting the full complement of personnel for a limited time in emergencies. To avoid thru-space transport on a routine large scale (shift change), construction spheres were assumed attached to each DSPCS. The flexibility of this configuration for assembling large components of the habitat simultaneously is obvious. Additionally, it might prove desirable to

house the material production facilities in one sphere and the assembly operations in the second. Specific volume requirements for these operations were not defined at the time of this study, necessitating an assumption.

The question of power station location is particularly challenging, since it will be quite large and certainly necessary for the processing of thousands of tons of lunar raw materials. Since the power station must be continually pointed sunward, it would be ill-advised to attach it to the DSPCS/CS combination. Even if a counter-rotating net zero angular momentum personnel station were built, maneuvering motions for the CS and its contents would probably be unacceptable. Relatively simple alternate solutions are available, namely large power cables from PS to CS through universal systems or a direct microwave link.

The microwave link is attractive from a system simplicity standpoint, the only substantial drawback being the DC conversion efficiency. The dynamic coupling of stations and a set of large power cables could dictate a control system for the cables alone. Personnel station power requirements should not exceed 1.10 megawatts (based on extrapolating studies which included experiment support; Ref. 7). At fifty percent total transmission and conversion efficiency, assuming a 100-megawatt habitat power system, some 48.9 megawatts would be available for construction station use. This would produce, for example, about 24,000 tons of aluminum over a two year period (Ref. 5). Some additional power (about two megawatts) could be gained by covering each CS with solar cells. This is based on 50 percent sphere illumination and solar electric propulsion stage area requirements of 9.30 m²/kW (ref. 11).

Transmitting over a relatively short distance and through space, we can assume the difference in

Table 7   Considerations in Geometrical Arrangement Selection

	Option	Comments
I.	Single DSPCS $^+$, Separate CS*, Separate PS**	Minimum Dynamic Interaction Maximizes Power Conversion Inefficiency Requires Personnel Thru-Space Transportation High DSPCS Damage Impact
II.	Single DSPCS, Attached CS, Separate PS	Increased Dynamic Interaction Power Conversion Inefficiency Some Personnel Thru-Space Transport Required High DSPCS Damage Impact CS Air Volume Available to DSPCS Continuous Rotating Joints Required
III.	Single DSPCS, Attached CS and PS	Maximizes Dynamic Interactions Minimum Power Conversion Inefficiency No Personnel Thru-Space Transport Required High DSPCS Damage Impact Maximum Air Volume Interchange Potential
IV.	Dual DSPCS, Separate CS and PS	Greater On-Orbit Total Mass Maximizes Power Conversion Inefficiency Requires Personnel Thru-Space Transportation Lower DSPCS Damage Impact Better Personnel Traffic Control
V.	Dual DSPCS, with CS attached to each, Separate PS	Greater On-Orbit Total Mass Power Conversion Inefficiency Some Personnel Thru-Space Transport Required Lower DSPCS Damage Impact Best Personnel Traffic Control Good Construction Station Flexibility

+ DSPCS - Double-Spoked, Parallel-Cluster station
*CS - Construction Station
**PS - Power Station

reception density and broadcast density to be small. At 0.40 kW/m^2, some 2500 m^2 would be required to receive 100 megawatts of broadcast power. Assuming one CS required eight percent of this at any given time, the reception area on the sphere would be only fifty meters in diameter. Safety features would of course be necessary to avoid having shuttles, tugs, and personnel entering the transmission beam. Good indoctrination and traffic control should make that problem quite manageable, and maneuvering near a set of free flying cables could present an even greater danger. A feedback loop should be incorporated into the system such that obscuration of, say, five percent of the receiving area would cause transmission termination. A smaller or larger percentage might be required to fit within closely defined safety requirements and limit-cycle pointing accuracies. A transmitter-off option would naturally necessitate a backup capability on each personnel/construction station (P/CS) to insure continued life support and orderly production shut-down or idle. It thus seems advisable to provide a power generation capability autonomous to each station. It was assumed that

each DSPCS/CS combination would be equipped with either solar or nuclear power systems as a secondary mode. A tertiary mode of backup batteries for each module family (three units, as defined later) was also considered necessary in case of an extreme emergency such as loss of part of a sphere and for routine use during an Earth eclipse.

The geometrical arrangement resulting from these considerations is shown in Figure 15. The axis of rotation of each station is perpendicular to the Earth orbital plane, and the stations are offset such that one never shadows the other. The power station maintains position "north" of each P/CS. If solar cells were chosen as the secondary power source and the spheres were completely covered, no maneuvers would be required during a one year cycle other than PS rotation and nominal formation "flying."

General Module and Station Design

To arrive at a desirable modular arrangement and size it was necessary to define the floor space and

Figure 15 Geometric Arrangement of Personnel/Construction Stations (P/CS) and Power Station (PS)

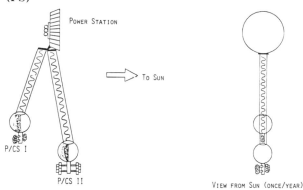

POWER STATION

To Sun

P/CS I

P/CS II

VIEW FROM SUN (ONCE/YEAR)

Table 8   Module Area Requirements

Personnel (51 People)

Quarters	256 m²
Wardroom, Gym	18
Galley	8
Personal Hygiene Facilities	12
Medical	8
Laundry Facilities	3
Storage Area	14
Dining Area	20
	339 m²

For 3 Modules

Control Stations (Prime and Backup)	42
Maintenance	14
Subsystems	47
Expendable Storage	112
Tunnels, Aisles, Hatches	93
	308 m²

volume requirements for various elements of the system. This included quarters, recreation, galley, dining, control stations, environmental subsystems, etc. Guidelines developed in space station/space base studies were used extensively with adjustments made for scale (Refs. 6,7). It was assumed that three adjoining modules would comprise an autonomous unit. This is an obvious choice, since two passive modules can easily be tied directly to an active one on the selected P/CS design. Autonomy of each module was considered unnecessary in this type design. The desired areas by function are presented in Table 8.

Module Size. Diameters of 10, 15, and 20 meters were considered. A ten-meter diameter with four floors yields approximately 314 m²/module; fifteen meters with three floors is 531 m²/module; and twenty meters with two levels offers 628 m²/module. Twenty meters is attractive, since it offers twice the area at less than twice the mass because floor mass doubles but shell mass remains constant (radius doubles, length halves). The attractiveness increases as one realizes that some sixty-eight ten-meter modules would be required to house the construction crew plus operations people (about 2340 people total) as opposed to only thirty at twenty meters: less than half due to efficiencies gained in using floor space and fewer operations people.

Launch considerations are also significant in considering these options. It is reasonable to assume dual launch of the ten-meter modules at under fifty tons each if the total height of approximately thirty meters presented no launch dynamics problems. Launch of the twenty-meter elements would have to be one at a time due to overall mass. A near-term capability to lift twenty-meter payloads might also be considered somewhat

optimistic. These considerations led to further study of the fifteen-meter diameter.

As a conservative judgment two decks out of each nine (three 15-meter modules) were allocated to controls, maintenance, etc., leaving seven for personnel. Using 338 m² for 51 people, we find that crew distribution is 186 personnel per three modules. An operation crew of some 232 (116 per P/CS) looks quite reasonable based on extrapolation of space base requirements, yielding a total of thirty-six modules or eighteen per P/CS. Using space station masses and adjusting for crew habitation only (with no power supply, for example) the 10-m module is estimated to weigh 48 tons. A transfer coefficient of 1.38 was derived to estimate the masses for a 15-m module. A safety factor of 1.1 was used as the "uncertainty factor", yielding an overall coefficient of 1.52. Thus a personnel module (PM) fifteen meters in diameter was estimated to weigh 73 tons. The Central Resources Module (CRM) of each triplet was estimated at 57 tons and 86 tons for 10 m and 15 m, respectively. The PM and CRM mass estimates were verified using nomographs developed for manned space system planning. Agreement was within ten percent.

Assuming a low Earth orbit capability of 150 tons/launch and a constraint on payload length of approximately 30-40 meters, the complement of 10-m modules would require thirty-four flights. The 15-m PM's would require twelve launches and the

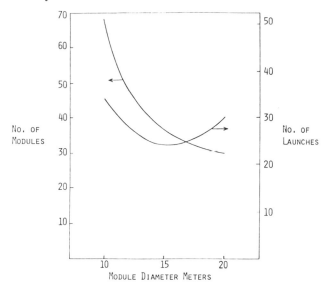

Figure 16 Requirements for Numbers of Modules and Number of Launches as a Function of Module Diameter Only

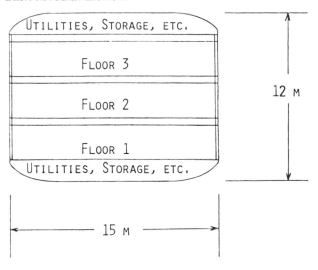

Figure 17 Structural Arrangement and Dimensions for Basic Modular Element

CRM's would require twelve (one per flight) for a total of twenty-four. Figure 16 illustrates that the tradeoff in module diameter and number of launches optimizes at 15 meters due to the vehicle capabilities assumed. The optimum will shift left or right as a function of variation in those assumptions. Some relatively large changes would be required to shift the preferred diameter more than ±2 meters, however.

Based on the above considerations, the basic modular building block shown in Figure 17 was adopted. A central tunnel and toroidal end caps may be preferable to a continuous elliptical shape, but this study was not able to address that level of detail. Each floor level was assumed to be connected by sealable doors to at least one other PM or CRM on all levels, with multiple interconnects where feasible. Each would also have at least one direct access to a "spoke."

Parallel Cluster Geometry. The arrangement of the clustered elements selected as the baseline configuration is presented in Figure 18. A number of arrangements are possible, but no detailed tradeoffs in terms of heat rejection, structural preference, system dynamics, or personnel traffic were performed. Since no significant effects on overall mass estimates were obvious, there appeared to be no need at present for such a study. Careful attention should be paid to required stiffness about the axis of rotation and the axis of symmetry between the spokes in a detailed design. Transfer of centrifugal loads into the spokes and load path

sensitivity to shifting personnel and equipment must also be considered in a final geometry selection. The scheme presented in Figure 18 meets the baseline established for this study.

Overall P/CS Dimensions. The establishment of the overall dimensions for the P/CS combination was basically driven by the pseudo-gravity requirement. Figure 19 shows the relationship between revolutions per minute (RPM) and radius for an Earth gravity (1.0g) equivalent and also g-variation at constant RPM. The generally accepted maximum of four RPM (e.g., Refs. 7 and 13) is indicated by a dashed line. A mean sixty-meter radius was selected and the cluster situated to give ±9 meters from "highest" to "lowest" floor level. The maximum-g level (on the bottom floor) is 1.15 and the minimum-g level (on the top floor) is 0.85. The acceptability of this variation is presently a matter of conjecture. It might be advisable to rotate quarters during a one-year tour to facilitate readaptation on return to Earth; no data exist on which to base such a decision, however.

The general configuration and dimensions for the station are shown in Figures 20 and 21. A rotating hub of 15 meters diameter is assumed, with a despin system located at either end: one for the construction sphere and one for a regular docking port and airlock. Resistojets, using biowaste gases (CO_2 and CH_4) and water as propellant, could be used to maintain the spin-despin interface. Resistojets, hydrazine thrusters, or a combination of the two would be mounted on despin segments for stationkeeping and stabilization as required. Properly implemented control-moment gyros could be advantageous in this respect, considering the

38

Figure 18 Module Cluster Geometry Selected for Baseline Study

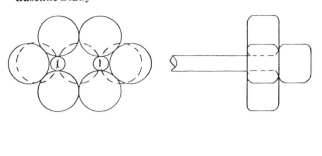

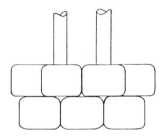

Figure 19 RPM at Constant G and Pseudo-Gravity at Constant RPM as a Function of Radius

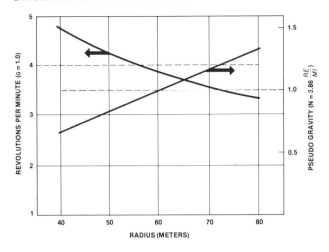

Figure 20 Overall Layout and Dimensions for the Personnel/Construction Station

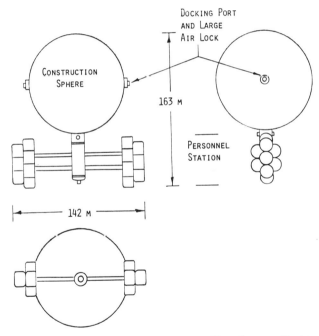

lifetime requirement for the station. Detailed study of the mass distribution, disturbing torques, physical location, and similar factors would be required to establish this.

Construction Sphere Design. The 100-meter diameter processing and construction sphere, although simple in concept, represents a formidable design challenge. The forcing functions on the design are basically:

(1) Internal pressurization.
(2) Large ingress/egress area.
(3) Crew radiation protection.
(4) Zero-g shop provision.

The approach taken in this study was to estimate the mass of the sphere within an order of magnitude and explore the sensitivities of the estimate. Data on some areas (for example, required radiation protection) were not immediately available in the course of the study, necessitating certain assumptions.

The mass of the shell was estimated initially by assuming a homogeneous membrane and applying basic elasticity theory. Aluminum was assumed as the construction material, using a rather conservative 30,000 psi working stress. At one-atmosphere working pressure the mass calculated was 1034 tons. The result using this approach is a direct function of material density and pressure and an inverse function of working stress. The influence of varying density and pressure at constant working

stress is shown in Figure 22. The lower limit assumed for internal pressure is compatible with avoiding the bends if an Earth-normal type atmosphere is used in the personnel station.

The effect of reducing the density of the construction material is quite apparent. This advantage is realizable in two ways. One is to use a composite material such as graphite/epoxy, which is presently undergoing extensive research on applications to long-duration space missions. The working stress assumed here is well within the capability of this material and a host of other composites. Densities of 1.40 to 2.0 are easily achieved. The second approach is to use structural concepts (such as

Figure 21 Details of Personnel/Construction Station

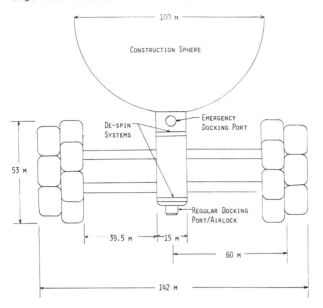

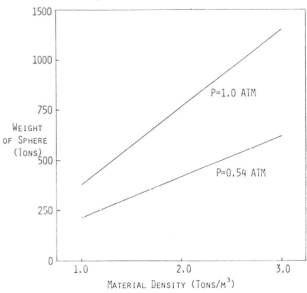

isogrid) made from one or more materials to cause an effective density decrease.

The need for large areas of the sphere surface to be open periodically is a complicating factor in initial mass estimation. The sphere is no longer continuous, and the stress fields during pressurization become complicated. The optimum design will depend heavily on the final material and structural concepts adopted. For example, a removable triangular section would be best adapted to an isogrid type construction, whereas a circular or elliptical segment would be logical with isotropic composites or aluminum. The mass impact was accounted for by use of a higher uncertainty factor as defined earlier.

The question of what constitutes sufficient crew radiation protection is particularly difficult. If complete protection against heavy primaries and their secondaries were required, the sphere mass would become unreasonable. Using a criterion of 130 gm/cm² , the shell, if aluminum, would be 48 cm thick. Use of a carbon liner (about 1.20 times more efficient than aluminum at 100-200 Mev energy levels) would reduce the thickness to about 32 cm, still unreasonable. The magnitude of these numbers can be appreciated when they are compared to the 1.22 cm used to calculate the 1034 tons given earlier. An alternative solution to radiation protection has been suggested which might afford this same level of protection at substantial mass savings: enclose the station in a properly constructed magnetic field. Time and data did not

allow consideration of this option in this study, however.

Fortunately, it does not appear necessary to install such a high level of protection on a full station basis. The highest anticipated dose rates (rem/hr) and accumulated doses (rem) are associated with intense solar flare activities. Protection during these periods is incorporated in this design in the form of solar flare shelters located amid the module clusters. Each of these would be capable of supporting 30 percent of the construction and operations crew for several hours. It is basically a module ten meters in diameter and fifteen meters long with four decks (see subsequent paragraphs for design details). Each would be equipped with 300 comfortable reclining seats, reading material, movies, and some food and drink, and would be connected with full redundancy to two CRMs.

The normal environment afforded in the P/CS for life support has been assumed adequate to keep cosmic radiation doses within acceptable levels for a one year tour. Careful internal arrangement in the CS, CRMS, and PMs will contribute to achieving this. It may be necessary, however, to trade off additional station mass for shorter crew cycles if further data indicate this assumption to be fallacious.

The general design of the zero-g processing facilities, shops, and construction areas was beyond the scope of this study. A flat assumption of 300 tons per sphere (two flights each) was made to cover outfitting the interior.

Construction Sphere Mass. The mass of the sphere structure, attachments, and miscellaneous appointments was calculated based on a working pressure of 0.54 atmospheres and a construction material effective density of 2.0 tons/m^3. To cover uncertainty in items mentioned above an "ignorance factor" of 1.30 was applied. Total estimated mass is then 542 tons.

Solar Flare Shelter. The flare shelter mentioned in the previous section was designed to provide maximum crew protection during extraordinarily high solar activity. By assuming completely redundant support module interfaces, stay times could be made practically indefinite with brief excursions for food and water. The confinement would, of course, make this most undesirable. The infrequent use of the shelter will probably be for stays of three to eight hours. One m^2 has been allocated per man, with individual reclining seats provided, each equipped with a fold-away desk. Entertainment would consist of reading matter, movies, and various low-area-requirement games. The shelter would naturally double as the primary recreation area for off-duty crew members.

The design of the shield is based on stopping 400 Mev protons and gamma flux resulting from hard electron radiation. Criterion used was a dose rate of 15 mrem/day (0.63 mrem/hr) with the assumption that this is consistent with the average rate in other station areas. If dose rates were lower on the average, this could be increased with a commensurate decrease in shield size and mass. Also, if a one-year continuous exposure rate of greater than 15 mrem/day is acceptable, the shield mass could also be reduced. The mass estimated using the above assumptions is probably quite conservative with respect to proton energy and gamma radiation protection.

The required size for a 300-person capacity was determined to be ten meters diameter and fifteen meters length. For strength purposes the outer shell was assumed to be aluminum (0.5 cm thick) with a 25-cm carbon liner and an inner 0.25-cm shell of lead. Hydrogen has been shown to be superior to carbon in arresting heavy primaries but the volumetric requirements make it impractical in this application (Ref. 14). Aluminum is also effective, but only about 80 percent as good as carbon on a

g/cm^2 basis. The lead inner liner is included as a gamma absorber in the event of need for hard electron radiation protection.

The structure of the station surrounding the shelter was assumed to be the equivalent of eight cm of aluminum. The total shelter mass was developed as follows:

Aluminum Shell	8.5 tons
Carbonaceous Liner (Crystallite carbon "or silicon carbide")	505.5 tons
Lead Shell	17.8 tons
Floors and Structure	8.5 tons
Chairs and Furnishings	3.0 tons
	543.3 tons

Using an uncertainty factor of 1.05, the total mass becomes 570 tons/shelter.

The massiveness of the shelter is obviously driven by the carbon liner. An option worthy of consideration would be substitution of lunar raw material in the liner of an empty shell shipped from Earth. This might require some non-optimum phasing of the lunar base and L5 station systems, since the shelter would be desirable some months before the construction spheres were ready to begin processing materials. The tradeoff would basically involve added costs for lunar base operations versus the cost of 500 tons of carbon and, say, three launch operations.

Spoke Function, Construction, and Mass. The dual spokes to each cluster are arranged to provide ready access from any module. The use of dual spokes allows programming of traffic in a fashion compatible with system dynamics (angular rate, disturbance, torques, etc.). Each spoke is compatible with an elevator system which adapts to either personnel or cargo transfer. In order to facilitate shift changes and related personnel transfer, an elevator four meters in diameter and six meters long with three floors was assumed. An allowance of 2/3 m^2 per person yields a 56-person capacity. This allows only three trips per shift change. To offset the shifting force vector caused by Coriolis effect during elevator motion, it would be desirable to provide each individual with a stabilizing device such as a post or slab. Near the core, the lateral forces acting on a person due to Coriolis effect would be greater than the lengthwise forces, necessitating such a device.

Core and Docking Ports. The core is assumed to be

basically a shell with elevator shafts running through as primary load paths between spokes. The need to move objects past the elevator shafts makes the 15-meter diameter attractive. This also allows elevators from both spokes to occupy the core simultaneously in case of emergy. The mass estimated (including three docking ports) was 55.3 tons.

Total Mass Estimate. The masses calculated in the previous sections are as follows:

24 PMs	= 24 (73)	= 1752	tons
12 CRMs	= 12 (86)	= 1032	tons
2 Spheres	= 2 (542)	= 1084	tons
8 Spokes	= 8 (10.5)	= 84	tons
2 Cores	= 2 (55)	= 110	tons
	Total Station	4062	tons
	Sphere Outfitting	600	tons
	Total All	4662	tons

Mass per P/CS (No Flare Shelters)	2331 tons
Solar Flare Shelters, 2 (570) =	1140 tons
Total mass per P/CS	3471 tons

The philosophy followed in arriving at these estimates was one of careful conservatism. It is unlikely that a reasonable design explored in detail would arrive at a higher total mass requirement, but a lower total mass may be achievable if less stringent requirements were imposed on radiation protection, for example. The uncertainty factors used were based on experience and personal philosophy and probably tend to be conservative. Some alternate configurations and geometrical arrangements which are probably feasible within this mass estimate are presented in a later section. It is interesting to note that a 2000-man station considered by Ehricke was estimated to weigh about 6000 tons (Ref. 10).

A cylinder 100 meters in diameter with hemispherical ends was assumed as the structural unit. The cylindrical length was 127 meters. One transparent end cap and an axisymmetric spherical reflector were arranged as indicated in Figure 23. A working stress of 30,000 psi was assumed for the cylinder material at a density of 2.0 tons/m³. An uncertainty factor of 1.30 was used to account for all internal processing and cycle management functions as well as the reflector, air locks, docking ports, ACS system, etc. A parametric analysis of the influence of acceleration levels and internal pressure was conducted to analyze the tradeoffs. The mass of the atmosphere required initially to

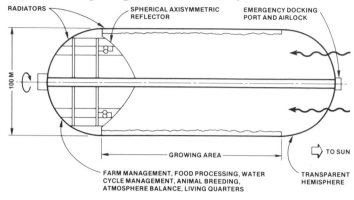

Figure 23 Large Integral Farm Unit Concept

pressurize the cylinder volume was calculated separately and was found to be about 1000 tons at 8 psi. The design was modified to a hollow cylinder with toroidal ends. Net savings were about 500 tons on the total mass (atmosphere mass saved minus additional structure).

Environmental System Tradeoffs

The mass estimates presented in the previous sections are based on use of specific types of subsystems for environmental control. The numbers have their basis in Space Base and Planetary Mission Module (PMM) studies. The types of systems assumed are delineated below. It is interesting to note that the mass of the atmosphere on board the baseline station design is some 747 tons (using dry air densities) if the entire P/CS is operated at 0.54 atm. (8 psi). If the personnel station were operated at one atmosphere and the CS at 0.54 atm., the total is 804 tons, 680 tons of which is in the spheres. If the sphere pressure were reduced to about 5 psi, the atmosphere mass would reduce by about 30 percent. Initial pressurization gases to operate the personnel station at one atm. were inherent in the mass estimates (using Space Base data) so that part of the P/CS can be assumed to operate at 8 psi or 14.7 psi.

A leak rate for the station was estimated using PMM calculations and assuming surface area relations. Total losses (two P/CSs) were calculated to be 236 kg/day for nitrogen and 127 kg/day for oxygen. Electrolysis of surplus metabolic water should yield about 223 kg/day of O_2, more than sufficient for makeup. It is assumed that the remainder would go to support of O_2 consumptive processes on board. Makeup of the lost N_2 would require a lift mass to the station of about 111 tons/year, including 3000-psi tanks for transport.

The installation and maintenance of an ammonia decomposition plant to process waste would appear to be more than justified. The mass of such a system is encompassed by the uncertainty factor adjustment used.

Oxygen Recovery. Membrane diffusion and decomposition by the Sabatier process are assumed for CO_2 removal and primary oxygen replenishment. With a yield of 0.73 kg O_2/man-day from 1.02 kg CO_2/man/day and assuming an average consumption of 0.91 kg O_2/man-day yields a net requirement of 406 kg/day of which 96 kg/day comes from surplus metabolic water. This translates to a requirement for 113 tons per year of additional oxygen, or a launch mass requirement of 158 tons/year with 3000-psi tanks.

Closed Ecosystem vs. Farm. In trading off food provision methodology a farm designed to be capable of supporting the crew was compared to obtaining 0.80 kg/man/day of food from Earth.

The assumptions in the farm design and calculations were as follows:

Growing Area: 40,000 m^2 (Ref. 8)

Soil Depth: 0.30 meters

Soil Density: 0.33 tons/m^3

The estimated total mass (including 4000 tons of soil) is presented in Figure 24 as functions of acceleration (at constant pressure) and pressure (at constant acceleration). Comparison of the two curves for constant acceleration shows the significant influence of pressure relative to the insignificance of pseudo-gravity level. As long as material and soil density remain low, the shell mass can be estimated accurately as a function of pressure only. Another mass function of pressure is leak losses per day. At a pressure of 10 psi, the leak rate (based on PMM data) was estimated at 207 kg/day N_2 and 112 kg/day O_2. This would have to be supplied by processing of lunar materials and/or Earth supply.

The total mass requirement of food brought from Earth at 0.80 kg/man-day, as a function of years of operation, is shown in Figure 25. Also shown are mass requirements for a minimum farm operating at low pressure and pseudo-gravity. Note that no water other than that contained in the 0.33 g/cm^3 soil mass is included in any internal or structural mass estimates. Any required biomass has also not

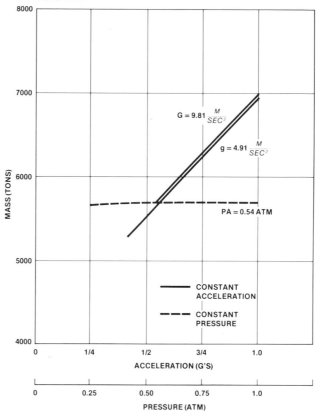

Figure 24 Farm Mass as a Function of Pressure and Acceleration

been considered. Obviously, if the soil must be brought from Earth the farm offers no advantage in food production. It also appears to offer no advantage in atmosphere and waste processing, since a period of one to two years of support would be necessary on the station prior to farm integration. Such a period of time justifies a closed environmental system regardless of eventual farm availability.

If the low-density soil assumed here can be manufactured from lunar material some potential advantage may exist with the farm, as shown by the lower line in Figure 25. The assumptions are significant, however, and increases in soil mass or atmospheric pressure percentage will increase the shell mass.

The discussion thus far has centered on mass-to-L5 tradeoffs on the ecosystem. Another item of significance would be the development cost for such a farm. It would represent a huge station unit in itself, even if attached to the P/CS. If closed-loop systems were required for the early P/CS operations time, as seems likely, almost all farm development costs would be additive to the basic transportation cost tradeoff. On the other hand,

Figure 25   Comparison of Food Supply Techniques as a Function of Years of Station Operation on the Basis of Total Mass Required

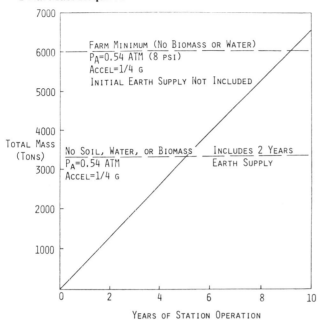

FARM MINIMUM (NO BIOMASS OR WATER)
P_A=0.54 ATM (8 PSI)
ACCEL=1/4 G
INITIAL EARTH SUPPLY NOT INCLUDED

NO SOIL, WATER, OR BIOMASS
P_A=0.54 ATM
ACCEL=1/4 G
INCLUDES 2 YEARS EARTH SUPPLY

TOTAL MASS (TONS)

YEARS OF STATION OPERATION

Figure 26   Conceptual 15-Meter-Diameter Farm Module

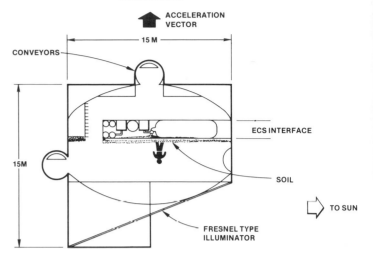

MODULAR FARM

ACCELERATION VECTOR

15 M

CONVEYORS

ECS INTERFACE

15M

SOIL

TO SUN

FRESNEL TYPE ILLUMINATOR

farming operations at L5 will have to be developed for eventual use in the habitat. A logical course of action would be development of a somewhat smaller farm constructed primarily of lunar materials during the years of habitat construction and tied into the P/CS for experimental purposes. Such a farm could provide a percentage of the food required the last few years of P/CS operation. This possibility was not assumed in the defined support requirements for the P/CS, however. A conceptual design for a modular experimental farm made up of 15-m-diameter units arranged on a pseudo-gravity wheel is shown in Figures 26 and 27.

Water Management. A combination of two processes would be used in water reclamation. Waste waters would first be recovered by reverse osmosis and filtration. Wash water can be supplied at this point. Potable water would be obtained by vapor diffusion with compression of the reverse osmosis brine. Urine would be recovered completely by the diffusion and compression process.

Other Systems. Other requirements in environmental systems include particulate control, contaminant control, heat rejection, waste management, and humidity control. Another area is life support in terms of meteoroid protection, system safety, and hygiene. All have been considered with the assumption that those defined for Space Base would be fully adequate and/or representative of the needs of the L5 station.

Launch Requirements. The number of launch operations required to establish the P/CS was determined using assumptions on payload capability noted earlier. On a pure mass per payload basis only 23 flights would be required to place sufficient mass for one P/CS in orbit. The use of the modular systems increases the number to 31, however, of which eight are required for flare shelters. The breakdown of launches is shown and illustrated in Figure 28. *No personnel launches are included.*

Although no launch operations study was

Figure 27   Possible Arrangement of 15-Meter Experimental Farm Modules

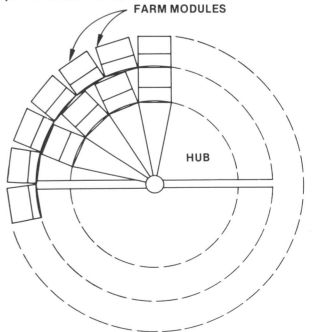

FARM MODULES

HUB

44

Figure 28 Buildup and Launch Sequence for One Personnel/Construction Station

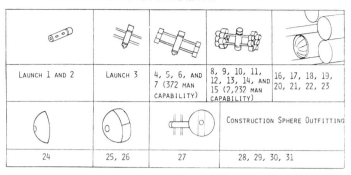

Launch 1 and 2	Launch 3	4, 5, 6, and 7 (372 man capability)	8, 9, 10, 11, 12, 13, 14, and 15 (2,232 man capability)	16, 17, 18, 19, 20, 21, 22, 23
			Construction Sphere Outfitting	
24	25, 26	27	28, 29, 30, 31	

Figure 29 Management Organization and Personnel Distribution

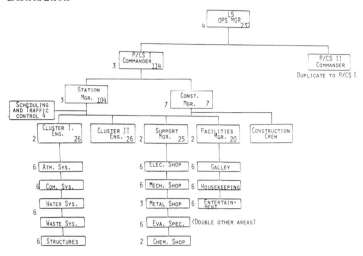

conducted, it appears that a three-pad operation with twenty-day turnaround capability (three launches per month) is a minimum requirement. At that the complete double P/CS assembly period would require 21 months. A lesser time may be impractical from an orbital operations standpoint. A set of detailed time lines would have to be developed to establish a set of optimum one, two and three-shift assembly operations. Assembly, checkout and startup of a facility of this type could probably be done within a year with optimum crew buildup and two-shift operation.

Sixty-two launches are needed to establish both P/CS systems with outfitted spheres and pressurized personnel areas. Some 680 tons of pressurization gas are needed to operate the spheres at 0.54 atmosphere, which translates to 880 tons of transported mass. This would require no additional launches if the gas is flown along with the 24 individual CRMs using surplus capability (about 60 tons/flight). The remaining surplus is assumed to go to crew support during initial P/CS construction. That would provide about 540 tons for a two-year buildup. The adequacy of this number has not been rigorously verified.

At a three-per-month capability, twenty-one months would be necessary for transportation of materials only.

Operational support of the program will require periodic launches, primarily make-up gases and food. The oxygen requires 158 tons of launch mass per year, including 3000-psi tanks. The food need is approximately 652 tons/year. Coupled with 90 tons of ACS propellant, spares, etc. the launch rate is six/year. Launches in support of crew rotation requirements will depend on the specific personnel carrier capabilities available in the station operations time frame. A crew rotation cycle of 50 percent every six months is probably about right, so

that the system is never manned completely by a new crew.

Operations Personnel Distribution

The 232 operations and support personnel for the station (116 per P/CS) will be involved in management, scheduling, systems survey and maintenance, food provision, housekeeping, and crew entertainment. Some of these functions will require around-the-clock availability of personnel, while others may be one or two-shift operations with occasional overtime as required. A possible organization and manpower distribution by function is shown in Figure 29.

Cost Estimates

Total Program Cost. The costs associated with establishing and maintaining the P/CS are necessarily very rough at this level of study effort. Costing was broken down into three categories:

(1) Design, development, test and evaluation (DDT & E) of common systems, specifically personnel modules, central resources modules, cores, spokes, shelters, and spheres.

(2) Production costs

(3) Operations costs

The cost analysis was done at the assembly and system level based on mass and complexity factors. Charts and nomographs developed by the Air Force Systems Command were used. Judgment was employed to adjust the nomograph numbers to make them more applicable to a P/CS type system.

Table 9   Launch Breakdown for One Personnel/Construction Station (PCS)

Stages	Launch No.
Core, Despin, Airlocks	1-2
Spokes	3
4 PMs, 2 CRMs (372 Man Capability)	4-7
20 PMs, 10 CRMs	9-15
Flare Shelters (System Spin-up)	16-23
Lower Hemisphere Segments or Materials	24
Central Segment of Sphere with Ports, Airlocks	25-26
Upper Hemisphere Segments or Materials	27
Sphere Outfitting	28-31

Consideration of the basis for the nomographs and charts was the key factor in the adjustment. Considered in the costing were:

Environmental Control Systems

Communication Systems

Computer Processing/Interface Systems

Power Systems

ACS Systems

Navigation and Control Systems

Control Stations

Structures and Furnishings

Tooling and Special Test Equipment

Systems Integration

Manufacturing and Test Facilities

Ground Equipment

Ground Stations

First Unit Construction and Testing

Production

Acceptance Costs

Transportation

Sustaining Engineering

Ground Equipment Maintenance

Ground Station Maintenance

On-Orbit Salaries

A detailed breakdown by major system and individual cost element is given in Table 10. The program total is $17,734 million.

After completion of this exercise a separate crude cost estimate was made using costs developed as part of the space station/space base studies. The results of that analysis were:

Development	
Personnel Station	$5.24B
Sphere	2.24B
Production	8.60B
Operations	1.37B
	$17.45B

This number did not include launch vehicle support, experiments, or on-orbit crew salaries and training. The comparable number from Table 9 is $17.315B. The similarity of these estimates is more striking than was anticipated (difference of less than one percent). At the level of this study, however, neither number should be considered better than about ± 20 percent, say $14B to $20B.

Potential Cost Reduction. Areas of potential cost reduction were considered to see if design assumptions had a large influence on cost. The two areas with the most potential improvements are development and production, which represent $13,278M or 84 percent of the basic cost. In development, reducing the sophistication of such items as communications, computerized processing, and controls and systems integration could possibly save $350M. If a simple direct hard line between power station and P/CS is practical, about $50M in microwave system development drops out. No other areas show any immediately obvious potential for savings. This $400M represents 7 percent of the estimated development cost.

Table 10   Cost Summary in Millions of 1975 Dollars

Cost Element	PM and CRM	Core	Spokes	Sphere	Shelter	Totals
Development	2,408	285	22	2,265	371	5,351
First Unit	PM 243 CRM 288	62	5	821	87	1,506
Manufacturing, Test Facilities, AGE and Ground Station	600	15	6	300	15	936
Production, Spares, and Transportation	6,689	98	26	851 (second unit)	263	7,927
Totals	10,228	460	59	4,237	736	15,720

Operations (10 years)

Acceptance Costs	$ 20 M	(2 years)
Sustaining Engineering	1,337 M	
AGE Maintenance	90 M	
Ground Station Maintenance	150 M	
Total	$1,595 M	
On Orbit Salaries	419 M	
	$2,014 M	

Total Program Cost (Excluding Launches): $17,734 M

In production, use of one CRM per cluster instead of three (assuming the floor space were sufficient) could save about $150M. Two spokes instead of four might save $8M if stiffness requirements and design did not prove to be difficult problems. The total mass in the spokes would stay about the same, since rotational loads size them. Another $30M might be saved in going from microwave to cable power unless the cable requires a separate stability and control system, which is quite possible. Deletion of the solar cells on the sphere for secondary power would decrease production about $1M. Reduced sophistication (as mentioned above) would lower PM, CRM and sphere costs about $120M. Net production potential savings appears to be about $319M, or 4 percent of the basic production cost.

The potential savings identified amount to only 4 percent of the estimated total program cost. This is well within the "noise level" of a study such as this. Truly substantial savings would have to come from much more basic considerations such as management, quality control, and safety philosophy. A great deal of the money tied up in these estimates represents paperwork and exhaustive rechecking and testing. It is doubtful, however, that a minimum-cost "skunkworks" approach to a program of this type is viable. A

detailed exercise embodying "design to cost" philosphy might yield some interesting possibilities with regard to minimum crew support requirements and alternate construction facilities. As long as the basic assumptions of this study apply, it is not obvious that a monolithic arrangement for the personnel station would be cheaper, since on-orbit operations costs begin to mount, offsetting the decreased-mass advantage. An integral P/CS could potentially cost $50-100M more or less than the costs previously presented (depending on geometry), but again, no substantial savings are obvious. Until more details of the station and its development and operation philosophy are worked out, the $17.7B estimate appears reasonable.

Potential Launch Costs. Although no hard data are presently available on heavy-lift launch system costs, an estimate was made using the parameter dollars/ton on orbit. At a capability of 150 tons per launch and a cost of $220/kg ($100/lb) a launch would cost $33M. The 62 launches to establish the two-P/CS system would cost $2,046M. A six-per-year support launch rate would cost $198M on the same basis, or $1,980M over ten years.

Cost Comparison to Other Programs. Without dwelling on the details, the following estimated program costs are presented for general com-

Figure 30   Nominal L5 Construction Station Schedule

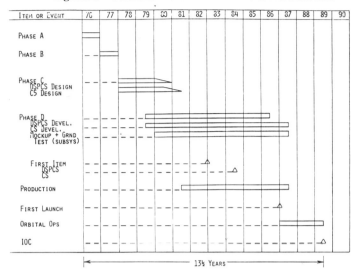

ITEM OR EVENT	76	77	78	79	80	81	82	83	84	85	86	87	88	89	90
PHASE A															
PHASE B															
PHASE C DSPCS DESIGN CS DESIGN															
PHASE D DSPCS DEVEL. CS DEVEL. MOCKUP + GRND TEST (SUBSYS)															
FIRST ITEM DSPCS CS															
PRODUCTION															
FIRST LAUNCH															
ORBITAL OPS															
IOC															

|←————————————————— 13½ YEARS —————————————————→|

parison:

12-Man Space Station (1970 estimate)	
McDonnell Douglas	$6,781M
North American Rockwell	$7,500M
60-Man Space Base (assumes Preceding Station Development and Operation)	$4,850M
Station + Base (1970 estimate; (no base experiments included)	$12,350M
2-Stage Fully Reusable Shuttle (1972 estimate)	$11,500M

Construction Station Schedule. A very rough schedule commensurate with the estimated costs of the last section is presented in Figure 30. The total time span until processing operations are under way at L5 is 13-1/2 years from initiation of Phase A. Of this total, 5-1/2 years are consumed in initial study and design and final on-orbit assembly. As points of comparison, the 12-man space station was projected to need about nine years (Phase A to IOC) and the 60-man space base thirteen years total (assuming space station concurrent).

Infusion of large sums of money and revitalization of the principles of "concurrency" could shorten this by five years. The risks would be greater, especially if careful program integration and extensive ground testing were sacrificed.

Alternate Integral Configurations. A number of alternate integral P/CS configurations were

Figure 31   Potential Integral Stations Using the Basic Building Blocks Developed

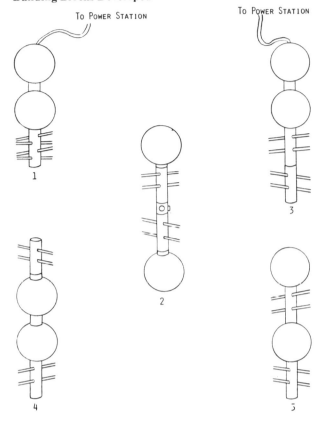

postulated near the completion of the study to assist in visualization of potential benefits for integration into one unit. The five possibilities considered are shown in Figure 31. The power cable was considered an option on each configuration, although it is only shown on two. All but Number 1 could have counter-rotating personnel stations if advantageous. Configuration 1 offered the greatest potential for cost reduction, not significantly relative to program totals, as discussed earlier.

Summary. A first-cut design for a construction station at L5 has been completed. Configuration and geometrical arrangement tradeoffs led to selection of two modular stations, each with a 100-meter-diameter construction volume. Total mass of each personnel/construction station (P/CS) is estimated to be 3471 metric tons, including 1140 tons for high-energy particle shelters. A trade-off between farming and food transportation favored importing food for the station lifetime on the basis of required mass to L5. It is proposed that an experimental farm leading to habitat outfitting be a part of the construction station program.

The estimated cost of the program is $17,734M based on a cursory review of cost parameters at the system and subsystem level. The potential for some cost reductions exists with changes in the assumptions used in the study. The total span of the program was crudely estimated to be 13-1/2 years from Phase A initiation to initial orbital capability (both stations). More detailed study would be required to refine the schedule estimate. Both cost and schedule estimates show reasonable agreement (when complexity is considered) with large programs studied to the Partial Phase A level (Space Station/Base and Fully Reusable Shuttle).

With an assumed capability of 150 metric tons per launch using a heavy-lift vehicle, sixty-two flights will be required (exclusive of personnel transport) to place the two P/CS systems in orbit. Support requirements are estimated to be six flights per year.

It must be emphasized that this was a preliminary study and all quantitative results are probably no better than ±20 percent. If the error in methodology is not that great, it is quite likely that the sensitivity to assumptions is. A more exhaustive study is needed to test the results.

DISCUSSION

Q. *The first problem seems to be how to convince anyone to put up this station in the first place; that is, how would you make a profit from it? Could you produce a satellite for making energy and then sell the energy to Earth? Has anybody figured out the order-of-magnitude cost of such a program?*

A. No, there's just been no time to do that, nor is there sufficient expertise among those of us who are in that business. We've gotten sophisticated enough to know that we have to use life-cycle costing, depreciated amortization, and so on, but there's not yet been an overall program costing to determine net yield, net payback, etc. It is certainly one of the most urgent tasks to be accomplsihed.

We do have some idea of overall cost on the basis of the cooperative studies that have been done, particularly by the NASA people from Huntsville. There appear to be limits between what Apollo cost and something like one or two tenths of Project Independence; that is, between fifty or sixty and maybe $200 billion.

The *timing* is the other half of that question, and it depends on the total market for power

stations in orbit. For the U.S. alone, in the year 1990, that's about $75 billion a year; worldwide it presumably could be a lot greater. So the entire program we're discussing is almost certainly less than about two years' powerplant investment.

Q. *What did you assume for the cost per pound to get to orbit?*

A. There are no launch costs presented in this study because they were not available as an input. Everything is in terms of number of launches; operations require about six launches a year at 150 metric tons each launch plus the initial 62 launches. If we assume a hundred dollars a pound capability, or thirty three million dollars a launch, the support requirement is about $2 billion for the initial 62 launches. If the cost is fifty dollars a pound, it gets cut in half (about $2 billion total), but if I use O'Neill's rather conservative $400/pound, the total launch cost goes to about $16 billion – almost the same as the station cost itself.

Q. *If it should turn out that for physiological and other reasons a weightless design might be possible, how would that change your estimates?*

A. It would have very little effect because of the modular approach. Modules are sized for the launch environment and by the fact that they're built on Earth. So when you put them into the rotational mode, as long as your spokes are stiff enough and you control the system dynamics properly, the rotation doesn't cost you anything. The big sphere, of course, is already at zero g.

Q. *Your figures do not include training?*

A. No, but we think training costs are small enough to be lost "in the noise."

Q. *How do mass and cost scale with linear dimension? Does this yield any particular range of optimum sizes, or can you build any size modules with about the same amount of effort?*

A. Scaling is not linear. For example, if you have the capability of launching two twenty-meter-diameter modules at a time, which would be a pretty massive system, you would come up with a different design and different masses, not in linear proportion. We haven't addressed the quantitative scaling question in this study, though.

Q. *Could you discuss the function and sizing of the construction sphere?*

A. We arbitrarily selected the 100-m diameter, principally because of constraints on the large segments of the end-cap. The leak rates, that is, the loss of O_2 and N_2, are also significant design constraints.

Q. *To calibrate your cost models, if you were to use them to cost out the Skylab program, how accurate would they be?*

A. I have no idea; we never costed out Skylab. If you cost out the L5 construction station using the NASA costing guidelines that went into a space station/space base, as I've said, you get the same numbers. I am not saying that that lends credibility to my model as being the only way to go; if you did a design-to-cost exercise, very much in vogue today, I really don't know how it would come out.

Q. *Would the energy needs of this project sub-stantially affect the U.S. energy needs of the next few years?*

A. The total mass of the things we are talking about here is in the "noise level" of what our material production is, so I would guess the energy cost would be quite small. More important, though, is the fact that by beginning to exploit those resources, we would have a dramatic effect on the energy picture, because we would stop worrying about running out of energy hundreds of years from now.

6. Earth-to-Orbit Transportation for Advanced Space Facilities

Hubert P. Davis
NASA/Johnson Space Center

In considering what may occur in the year 1990, it is useful to project ourselves back an equivalent time into the past. In 1958, the United States was involved in a tail-chase effort to put a very small satellite into low Earth orbit, using a derivative of an army artillery rocket. In only 10 short years, we were able to proceed from that achievement to flying the Apollo spacecraft using a launch vehicle, the Saturn V, which was capable of placing more than 100 metric tons into low orbit on a fairly routine basis: once every 3 months toward the latter part of the Apollo program. By 1969, we also had developed the ability to traverse cislunar space and to land on and take off from the lunar surface with manned vehicles. In the succeeding years, we have taken the first steps toward a truly economic transportation system with the space shuttle program. What the next 15 to 20 years can bring, I believe, is more dependent on the demand for launch services than it is upon the technology. It is therefore appropriate for me to review the present technology – the space shuttle – to show that we do indeed mean business in achieving this first step.

Figure 32 shows an overview of the shuttle program schedule. In 1977 we will begin flying the orbiter OV 101 airframe at Edwards Air Force Base, doing the approach and landing tests to prove its capability as an aircraft. The orbiter is both a spacecraft and an aircraft; its operational activity in space will begin with the first manned orbital flight in 1979, leading toward a truly operational capability, compared to our past history, in about 3 or 4 more years.

Figure 33 is a photograph of the vertical fin of the first flight vehicle, being manufactured in Farmingdale by the Fairchild Republic Corporation, in its final stages of being prepared for shipment to the assembly plant in Palmdale, California.

Figure 34 shows the aft section of the vehicle containing the thrust truss which will support the three main engines, under construction at the Rockwell International Downey plant. This structure is more reminiscent of a shipyard than what we are accustomed to seeing in past spacecraft manufacturing. It is indeed a massive structure.

Figure 35 provides a better feel for the size of the orbiter. This part of the orbiter vehicle, the mid-body, includes the payload bay. It was built by General Dynamics in San Diego.

The wings are being built by Grumman Aerospace at Bethpage, New York. Figure 36 shows one of the two wing sections of the vehicle; the orbiter is about the size of a moderately large commercial aircraft; e.g., the DC-9.

Figure 37 is the "business end" of the first space habitat – the crew cabin of the orbiter 101, the first flight vehicle. It is a pressure vessel of welded aluminum construction. It is at the Rockwell Downey plant, being prepared to have its systems installed prior to being slipped inside the structural shell which surrounds it that will, in turn, support the heat-shield material. This section is capable of housing a maximum complement of seven people.

We have a requirement for the orbiter to remain on orbit for seven days with the people resident in the cabin and in the companion Spacelab being fabricated by the European Space Agency.

The Spacelab will be housed in the payload bay. "Extension kits" of additional consumable sup-

Figure 32   Space Shuttle Program Activities

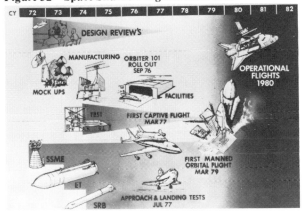

Figure 33   Orbiter Vertical Fin Under Construction

Figure 34   Aft Section of Orbiter Under Construction

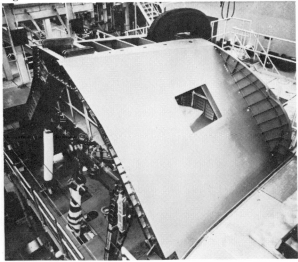

Figure 35   Midbody of the Orbiter Vehicle, Showing Payload Bay

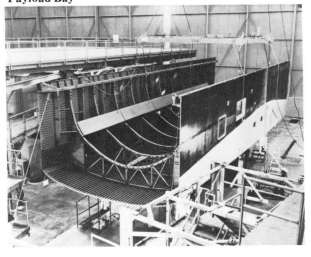

plies, such as fuel cell reactants and food, will be available as part of the baseline shuttle program to permit an orbital stay of up to 30 days. We see the potential within the next 10 years to extend that orbital stay to 3 or more months, using the basic shuttle orbiter spacecraft as the base.

These photographs of the shuttle flight article will, I hope, persuade you that we are engaged in a very serious endeavor indeed — we plan to fly this thing. These flights will actually begin the process of space industrialization, and we leave it up to the nation's and the world's creative people to devise, for us, many of the details of the specific useful tasks we can accomplish in the next succeeding steps.

Looking toward those next steps, Table 11 outlines a current study called "Future Space Transportation Systems Analysis," detailed in Table 12. The purpose of this study is to explore beyond the traffic model that the shuttle system is designed to support in order to identify what other, perhaps more speculative, space missions we might be called upon to accomplish between now and the year 2000, so that we can see what might be needed in the way of transportation system characteristics and requirements. Table 12 illustrates quite a broad range of programs being considered, including satellite energy systems as the last activity noted in the Table.

Some of the preliminary results of the first phase of this study can be illustrated. Figure 38 shows the lunar lander with orbital transfer vehicle (OTV) enroute to the Moon. Figure 39 shows the orbiting

Figure 36   Orbiter Wing Section Being Assembled

Table 11.   Future Space Transportation Sytems Analysis

OPTIONS:	Low Earth Orbit Space Station
	Geosynchronous Operations
	Lunar Surface Sortie
	Orbiting Lunar Station
	Lunar Surface Base
	Manned Planetary Exploration
	Automated Lunar Exploration
	Automated Planetary Exploration
	Nuclear Waste Disposal
	Satellite Energy Systems

lunar station (OLS) with the lunar lander. Figure 40 shows the lunar lander on the lunar surface.

Figure 41 indicates some of the near-term possibilities in Earth launch vehicles. All are based upon essentially the same level of technology that we are now bringing to bear in the present shuttle program. The illustration on the right of Figure 41 is a "Low-Cost Heavy-Lift Launch Vehicle," which Boeing has identified as being necessary to very large-scale programs such as the space power satellite or construction of O'Neill's Model 1 station. There are others who are considerably more optimistic about the sophistication of the large launch vehicle than this chart indicates. Such optimistic views are, of course, all to the good in the economic projection. However, confining technology to what we have in hand today, it is my belief that if the demand presents itself, we can

indeed build and fly launch systems such as the one in Figure 41. This vehicle is quite adequate to put up the large 15-meter-diameter space station Driggers has discussed.

Figure 42 indicates one possible way to revise the Launch Complex 39 area at Kennedy Space Center for very heavy launch demands. On the left the figure shows the existing pads A and B, utilized for the Saturn launches of the Apollo and Skylab programs. Figure 42 shows how the facility could be reconfigured, with a fresh-water lake to be used by the vertical landing launch vehicle for a water landing without suffering the penalties of an open-sea landing: salt water corrosion and the necessity for the long tow-back operation. Surrounding the lagoon are the launch sites themselves – three or more of them – reached by barge. There is, therefore, no land handling of the launch vehicle necessary to prepare it for reflight. In the background is the industrial area, and in the far background the receiving antennae for the power produced by the space satellite. The electrical power

Figure 37   Cabin of the First Space Shuttle Orbiter

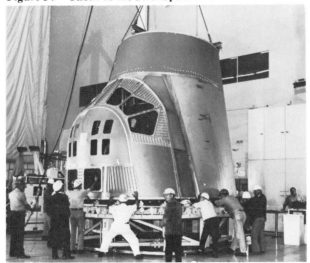

Figure 38 Lunar Lander (at right) with Orbital Transport Vehicle

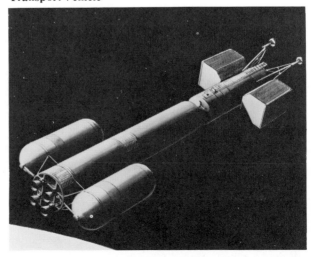

Table 12   Future Space Transportation System Program Options

Program	Missions	Objectives
1. Low Earth Orbit Space Stations	• 12-man modular or unitary station • 60-man space base	• Broad spectrum Earth observatory • Develop space manufacturing • Scientific investigations
2. Geosynchronous Operations	• 8-man modular or unitary station • Satellite maintenance sortie	• Earth observations • Communication/Navigation • Maintenance and repair of automated spacecraft
3. Independent Lunar Surface Sorties	• 4-man self supporting landing	• In-depth exploration of selected areas
4. Orbiting Lunar Station	• 8-man modular or unitary station with surface sortie	• Broad spectrum surface observation • 4-man, 28-day sorties
5. Lunar Surface Base	• 6-man, 6-month • 12-man, semipermanent	• Astronomical observations • Surface exploration • Indigenous material utilization

6. Manned Planetary Exploration	• Manned Mars landing
	   • Opposition
	   • Conjunction
	   • Venus swing by
		• 3-man, 30 day sortie
		 • Planetology
		 • Effects of modifying forces
		 • Search for life forms

7. Automated Lunar Exploration	• Orbital observatory • Backside lander • Relay satellite	• Broadband scientific observation • Long duration Rover with sample return
8. Automated Planetary Exploration	• Mars lander • Jupiter atmosphere probe • Ganymede lander	• Rover/sample return • Investigate upper cloud system • Orbital observation and surface sample analysis
9. Nuclear Waste Disposal	• Refined Waste • Total waste	• Permanent waste disposal
10. Satellite Energy Systems	• On-orbit power generation • On-orbit power reflectors	• Commercial electric power • Long range power transmission

is used, by electrolysis of seawater, to produce the hydrogen and oxygen propellant supplies for the launch vehicle and, in addition, to provide liquid hydrogen for payload.

Figure 43 shows a space shuttle orbiter docked to a low orbital assembly station at about 500 kilometers altitude (Florida can be seen in the lower left corner). The U-shaped portion of the illustration is the space station; the remainder of the picture illustrates a solar-thermal type of space power satellite under construction. This illustration gives some indication of the scale of the job that we might be called upon to do, using a combination of

the shuttle for personnel transport and a low-cost launch vehicle for the heavy-lift function.

Table 13 is a synopsis of the results of the Boeing Future Space Transportation System study, illustrating the demonstrable needs for space transportation that come from the potential future programs reviewed. "HLV" stands for "Heavy Lift Vehicle," shown in Figure 38, that Tischler describes in a subsequent paper. The "LTV" is a "Lunar Transport Vehicle," or lunar module (see Figures 39 & 40). The "LCHLV" is the "Low-Cost Heavy-Lift Vehicle" (the right-hand vehicle in Figure 41), and the "LCOTV" is the "Low-Cost

Figure 39   Orbiting Lunar Station (at left) with Lunar Lander

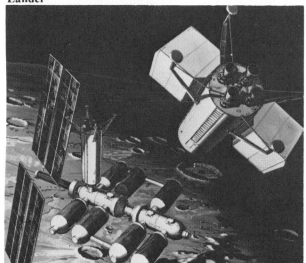

Figure 40   Lunar Lander on the Moon's Surface

Orbital Transport Vehicle,'' which may use an electric propulsion system to reduce the cost of transporting payloads from low Earth orbit to the high orbits. The majority of the programs reviewed in this study can be achieved by straightforward derivations of the shuttle vehicle. If, however, we engage in the power satellite program, we do indeed have the necessity of bringing into being a more capable launch system.

We turn now to an examination of the

capabilities we might project to fulfill the space transportation requirements. There are two activities underway which lend insight into these capabilities. One is an in-house NASA study called "Outlook for Space." Part of that study was the "Energy Systems" forecast of anticipated Earth-to-low-orbit transportation capability through the year 2000. This was done by simply querying some 25 people qualified to make forecasts in this arena.

The second activity, which is just beginning, is a

Table 13.   Future Space Transportation Systems: Transportation System Summary

	Shuttle or Shuttle + IUS or FCT	Signif Benefit from HLV	HLV	OTV	LTV	LCHLV and LCOTV
Modular Low Orbit Space Station	X					
Unitary Low Orbit Space Station & Space Base	X		X			
Geosynchronous Satellite Maintenance	X			X		
Geosynchronous Modular Station	X	X		X		
Geosynchronous Unitary Station	X		X	X		
Independent Lunar Surface Sorties	X	X			X	
Modular Orbiting Lunar Station	X	X		X	X	
Unitary Orbiting Lunar Station	X		X	X	X	
Lunar Surface Base	X	X		X	X	
Manned Planetary Landing	X		X	X		
Automated Lunar	X					
Mars Sample Return	X	X		X		
Jupiter Buoyant Probe	X	X		X		
Ganyeme Lander	X			X		
Nuclear Waste Disposal (Refined Waste)	X	X				
Power Satellites						X

Figure 41 Current-technology Earth Launch Vehicles

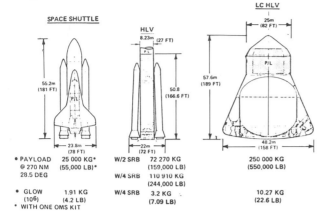

SPACE SHUTTLE

55.2m (181 FT)

P/L

23.8m (78 FT)

HLV

8.23m (27 FT)

P/L

50.8 (166.6 FT)

22m (72 FT)

LC HLV

25m (82 FT)

P/L

57.6m (189 FT)

48.2m (158 FT)

- PAYLOAD @ 270 NM 28.5 DEG   25 000 KG* (55,000 LB)*
- GLOW (10⁶)   1.91 KG (4.2 LB)
- WITH ONE OMS KIT

W/2 SRB   72 270 KG (159,000 LB)
W/4 SRB   110 910 KG (244,000 LB)
W/4 SRB   3.2 KG (7.09 LB)

250 000 KG (550,000 LB)

10.27 KG (22.6 LB)

Figure 42 Kennedy Space Center Reconfigured to Launch and Recover a Low-Cost Heavy-Lift Launch Vehicle

contracted heavy-lift launch vehicle study. This will be a 10-month study of heavy-lift launch vehicles which can be derived from the technology base provided by the shuttle.

The approach used in the "Outlook for Space" vehicle forecasts is illustrated by Table 14. In order to identify a broad range of potential demand projections that the launch vehicle design and fabrication community might be called upon to support, we defined three parameters for the conceptual definition of the various vehicle concepts.

The first of these parameters is the required flux of mass from the surface of the Earth to low Earth orbit (payload delivered per year). The second parameter was the flux of mass from the low orbit back to the surface of the Earth (payload returned per year). The reason for differentiating between them was that the two transportation legs pose profoundly different requirements upon the vehicle

Figure 43 Solar-Thermal Power Satellite Under Construction Showing Shuttle and Space Station

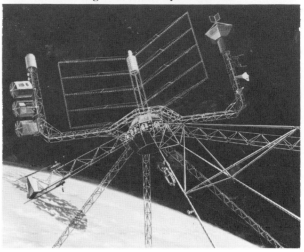

design. The third parameter was the minimum mass of payload required of each launch vehicle flight. The study asked several key questions of the forecasters:

- What do you think it is going to cost (both recurring and nonrecurring) to achieve a capability at Level 1, Level 2, Level 3, and finally, the very ambitious Level 4?

- Tell us the types of launch vehicle concepts you have in mind to satisfy each level of launch service.

- What are the critical areas that are not directly economic in the conventional sense, but may be equal in importance; e.g., what is the utilization of resources that are critical to the Earth? Do we, at Level 4, for example, require a larger quantity of an alloy material for building the launch vehicle than the Earth can spare for this purpose? What effect may each level launch activity have upon the Earth environment (the upper atmosphere in particular)? What do you foresee in terms of safety considerations that might either inhibit us from going all the way to Level 4 or that might have to be carefully considered in the design of these vehicles?

A brief overview of the results appears in Figures 44 (Level 2), 45 (Level 3), and 46 (Level 4). It is interesting to note that no one was able to come up with a truly revolutionary launch vehicle development. Significant reductions in launch cost did, however, appear within our grasp with chemical rocketry, by employing some minor extrapolations of technology, by achieving the

Table 14. Approach Used in "Outlook for Space" Launch Vehicle Forecast

- Request assistance from "forecasters" in government and industry
- Divide launch activity into four levels

	Payload/Year (Pounds)		
	Up	Down	Payload/Launch
- Level I	.5 M	0	30 k
- Level II	4 M	1 M	60 k
- Level III	20 M	2 M	400 k
- Level IV	100 M	2 M	2 M

- Request cost estimation at each level from each forecaster
- Vehicle concepts definition requested to support cost estimates
- Forecasters asked to address related areas:
    - Use of critical resources
    - Effect on Earth environment
    - Safety considerations

benefits of reuse and, at the high flux rates, significant benefits of scale. Another consensus was that we can achieve the first two levels of launch service by modest upgrading of the shuttle system. There seemed to be a consensus that we will need to develop a liquid booster for the shuttle when the mission frequency increases beyond the current projections. There was some interest expressed in airbreathing first stages, but no one was able to come up with a concept which didn't have the very large nonrecurring costs required to bring an air-breathing booster into operation. The forecasters expressed a near-term need for a new high-propellant-density booster engine to support the reusable liquid booster work for either shuttle derivatives or the heavy-lift class of launch vehicle. There was a considerable divergence of opinion among the forecasters as to whether we should attempt to have a single-stage launch vehicle or a two-stage design. Several people made the point that this choice is almost entirely dependent upon the technology level which the materials and structures people can bring to bear upon the problem.

We found from this survey that the current space shuttle program is expected to be a very beneficial long-term investment for the United States (see Figure 47). This hybrid spacecraft/aircraft will be with us, with improvements in the propulsion scheme, for a number of years. The present shuttle system has a significant amount of inherent growth potential to accommodate the larger space delivery and operations tasks as they come on line. The heavy lift vehicle will or will not come along, almost

entirely dependent upon the demand for launch services. Should we have very heavy demands for launch services, it may be that a vehicle in the 100 to 200 metric ton class per launch will prove to be more advantageous than attempting to build an even larger vehicle. The benefits of scale appear to disappear as we reach that payload mass. As a consequence of the very high flux rates, it may become necessary for us to launch daily, or perhaps even more often than once per day, from the lakeside launch pads at Kennedy Space Center (shown in Figure 42). In any event, we may have to arrange our thinking and provide the logistics and staffing so that we can launch these large launch vehicles on a daily or more frequent basis if we are going to achieve the construction, in a reasonable period of time, of the very large space systems such as those discussed by Driggers and O'Neill. That launch rate does not, however, appear to be a task outside our grasp.

One of the most important items in the consensus of the study forecasters is shown on the bottom lines of Table 15: the order of $50 per kilogram appears to be the minimum attainable cost of launching mass from the surface of the Earth to low Earth orbit.

Table 16 shows the matrix of requirements selected for this study. We have called for launch to a sufficiently high orbit to avoid drag pulling the payload back into the atmosphere, and the mass level indicated is commensurate with the characteristics of the station described by Driggers.

57

Figure 44   Level 2 Launch Vehicle Concepts

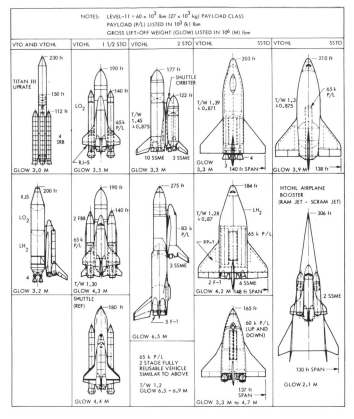

Figure 45   Level 3 Launch Vehicle Concepts

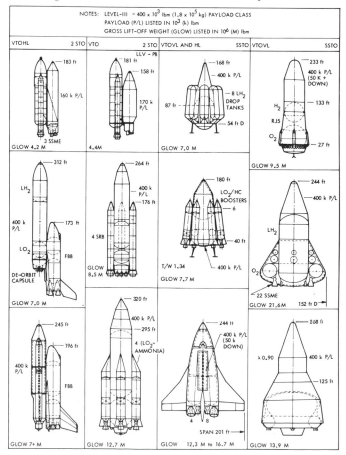

Figure 46   Level 4 Launch Vehicle Concepts

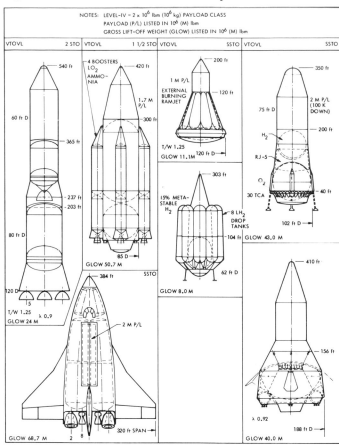

Figure 47   Level 3 Launch Vehicle Nonrecurring Cost Estimates

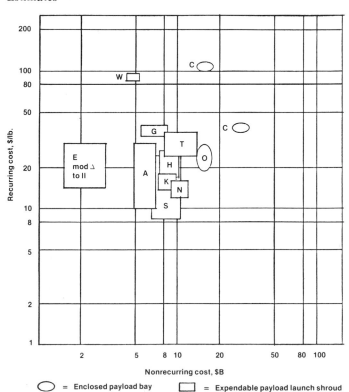

Table 15. Summary of Consensus of Launch-Vehicle Forecasters

● Space shuttle can accommodate Levels 1 and 11 traffic
● Significant incentive to uprate shuttle booster when operationally mature
  - Reduce payload costs to $80/lb by year 2000
  - Nonrecurring costs from $0.6 to $1.5B
● Fully reusable shuttle can reduce payload costs to $50/lb, for NRC of $1.5 to $4B
● Winged SSTO may replace shuttle if technology permits
  - Mid to late 1990's
  - Reduce payload costs to $20 to 40/lb
  - NRC $5 to $10B
● Heavy-Lift VTOVL attractive at high flight rate
  - Nonrecurring/investment of $8 to $10B less expensive than winged HL vehicle
  - Reduce payload costs to about $25/lb
● By year 2000, overall reduction of payload to LEO costs to the $20 to $30/lb range can be achieved provided:
  - Large technology movement caused by shuttle continues to be supported
  - Program requirements generate the need to launch numerous large payloads

In summary, if the requirement can be generated, it is my belief that the launch vehicle community can fill the need. Technology advances would be highly advantageous to launch vehicle design and operations, but we are not dependent upon advances beyond the shuttle technology to do even the large scale space programs discussed in these Proceedings.

DISCUSSION

Q. Did I understand correctly that in the first shuttle flight test, the shuttle will lift off from the top of a jumbo jet and fly down?

A. Yes. It is an approach and landing test, whose primary purpose is to demonstrate that we do indeed know how to execute an unpowered (gliding) landing of the craft.

Q. What is the Phase A implication of the Heavy-Lift Launch Vechicle (HLLV) study?

A. Like most Phase A studies, it is a feasibility study. It establishes estimated costs, resource needs, requirements, level of technology, etc. After perhaps one to five years evaluation, a Phase B study goes into detailed definition.

Not one of three of these studies materializes into a program; perhaps one in five. We completed Phases A and B on space stations as far back as 1969, but there is as yet no program.

Q. Are there any estimates yet of development costs for Level III and Level IV launch vehicles?

A. No, not yet.

Table 16. Study Requirements for Annual Launch Rate

Payload Class Metric Tons (k lbs)	Activity Level Metric Tons/Year* (lbs/year)				
	500 (1.1 M)	2500 (5.5 M)	5000 (11 M)	25000 (55 M)	125000 (275 M)
1. 60-90 (132-198)	7	34	67	334	1667
2. 90-135 (198-298)	5	23	45	223	1111
3. 135-200 (298-441)	3	15	30	150	747
4. 200-300 (441-661)	-	7	20	100	500
5. 300-450 (661-992)	-	-	14	67	333

*To a 500 km (270 × 270 n.mi.), 28.5° inclined orbit

Q. *One of the clear consequences of a space manufacturing facility is a large transfer of personnel up and back. For two thousand people, you'll need a much bigger launch vehicle capability for people than I've heard discussed.*

A. Although the space shuttle has a capability of only seven people in its crew compartment, we have the equivalent of very nearly a wide-bodied jet aircraft volume available to use in the payload bay, some 4.5 by 18 meters. Once the system has sufficient operational maturity for commitment to such a mission, similar to that of a commercial wide-bodied jet, it's easy to draw up a configuration that might handle several hundred people per launch, well within its payload mass capability. That's highly speculative, of course, because there is no demand today for such a mission.

7.   Advanced Earth-to-Orbit Transportation For Large Space Facilities, 1980-2000

Robert Salkeld
System Development Corporation

Abstract

This paper considers prospects for advanced Earth-to-orbit transportation in support of large scale space operations for the period 1980-2000. The analysis is based on a hypothetical traffic model associated with the current space colonization concept, and space transport design and cost data drawn from inputs to the 1975 NASA study, "Outlook for Space." A specific evolutionary family of Earth-to-orbit vehicles is identified which can economically meet the transportation needs of the space colonies project. This evolution proceeds from the current space shuttle through improved shuttle derivatives to fully reusable single-stage-to-orbit vehicles. Such a family of vehicles can be based on current and near-term structural and propulsion technology, a key requirement being development of a liquid rocket boost engine using dense propellants. Alternative concepts for orbit-to-orbit tugs, both chemical and nuclear, are also compared in terms of their impact on total transportation costs. The overall results indicate that the transportation requirements for large space facilities can be met in a straightforward manner, and that transportation costs could turn out to be lower than some current estimates by a factor of two or more.

Nomenclature

C = cost, 1975 dollars
D = drag, lb
F = thrust, lb
g = acceleration of gravity, ft/sec^2
I = specific impulse, sec
m = vehicle mass remaining, slugs

$\bar{u}$ = effective exhaust velocity for both modes operating concurrently, ft/sec
V = volume of propellant burned, ft^3
W = total cumulative weight to 200 NM/28.5° orbit, lb
w = weight, lb
v = vehicle velocity, ft/sec
β = flight path angle from local vertical, deg
ρ = propellant bulk density, lb/ft^3
$\bar{\rho}$ = effective ρ for both modes operating concurrently, lb/ft^3

Subscripts
$0, 1, 2, bo$ = initial, mode 1, mode 2, burnout
i = inert
n = non-recurring
p = payload
r = recurring

Introduction

As a first-generation step in the direction of lower-cost Earth-to-orbit transportation, the space shuttle is an important building block in any plan to develop colonies, manufacturing facilities, or other large installations in space. The purpose of this paper is to explore how first-generation shuttle technologies and their derivatives can lead to fully reusable single-stage-to-orbit shuttles which show promise of becoming the truly practical, economical space transports of the future.

Analysis

The reasoning of this paper begins from two points of departure: (1) a hypothetical space traffic projection for the construction of space colonies during 1981-1998; and (2) an evolutionary sequence of Earth-to-near-orbit vehicles, starting with the current space shuttle, which are likely to become available in this time period.

Figure 48 Hypothetical Earth-to-Space Traffic Model for Space Colonies (Ref. 4)

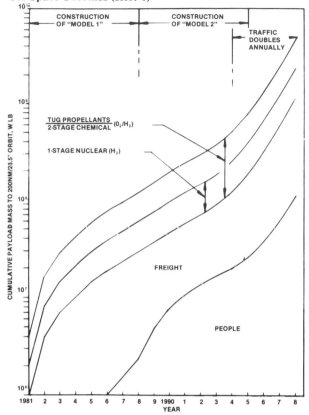

The traffic projection shown in Figure 48 assumes the completion of a "Model 1" colony in 1988, a "Model 2" colony in 1995, and an annual doubling of traffic after 1994 as colony replication/multiplication begins (Ref. 4). Note that unless some type of high-energy orbit-to-orbit transport (or tug) is used to relay payloads from 200 NM orbit to L5 or the Moon, or lunar propellants are used, then at least half the total mass lifted to near orbit must be tug propellants (chemical and nuclear tugs are defined and described later). It is believed that although the schedule of Figure 48 may be quite optimistic, so also may be the assumed mass requirements, with the results that the projected cumulative mass vs time may not be unreasonable.

A possible evolutionary sequence of transport vehicles is shown in Table 17 (Ref. 15). The sizes and costs of shuttle derivatives are substantially set by the characteristics of the shuttle itself, but the second generation single-stage-to-orbit vehicles are not so constrained, and their optimal sizes must be determined by analysis. This analysis starts from the curves of non-recurring and recurring cost vs vehicle payload capability, shown in Figure 49.* Since the estimates of Ref. 15 fall reasonable close together, the trends of Figure 49 fit the input

estimates well, and also are consistent with the results of other studies for both vertical-takeoff-horizontal-landing (VTOHL) and vertical-takeoff-vertical-landing (VTOVL) vehicles (Refs. 16-18).

The curves of non-recurring and (recurring costs) x (W) are added together in Figures 50 and 51 to show minimum total cost as a function of payload capability for various values of W. These results show that the VTOHL vehicle considered in Ref. 16 (wp = 80,000 lb) is reasonably well-sized for $5 \times 10^7 < W < 5 \times 10^8$ lb, and that the VTOVL vehicles considered in Ref. 15 (wp = 4,000,000 lb) are reasonably well-sized for $3 \times 10^8 < W < 3 \times 10^9$ lb. Thus, it appears that the VTOVL size selected in Ref. 15, though perhaps somewhat small, is adequate for the present mission and will be retained for this analysis.

Further confirmation of the VTOHL result, as well as some indication of time-phased requirements for the vehicles in question, can be obtained by writing the equations for the costs from Table 17 and Figure 49;

$$(C_n + C_r W)_{\text{Shuttle}} = 0 + 160W \tag{1}$$

$$(C_n + C_r W)_{\substack{\text{Derivatives} \\ 1\&2}} = 1.7 \times 10^9 + 73W** \tag{2}$$

$$(C_n + C_r W)_{\text{VTOHL}} = 2.5 \times 10^9 + 1.14 \times 10^6 \text{wp}^{0.70}$$
$$+ \left(\frac{1.2 \times 10^6}{\text{wp}} + 20 \right) W \tag{3}$$

$$(C_n + C_r W)_{\text{VTOVL}} = 2.0 \times 10^9 + 2.30 \times 10^6 \text{wp}^{0.61}$$
$$+ \left(\frac{2.0 \times 10^6}{\text{wp}} + 10 \right) W \tag{4}$$

and then equating them to form breakeven conditions. In this approach, for example, the breakeven value of W between shuttle derivatives and VTOHL single-stage would be that obtained by setting Eq. (3) equal to Eq. (2), and adding the result to the breakeven W obtained by setting Eq. (2) equal to Eq. (1).

The results of this analysis are shown in Figure 52, which indicates that for the traffic model

---

*From this point forward, all considerations will refer to vehicles using mixed-mode propulsion, since it can be shown that for the single-stage-to-orbit mission (or stage-and-a-half), mixed-mode is preferable to single-mode propulsion for all propellant combinations of practical interest.

** Assumes shuttle derivatives 1 and 2 become available concurrently, that non-recurring costs are additive, and that recurring costs are weighted according to the freight/people ratio of Figure 48.

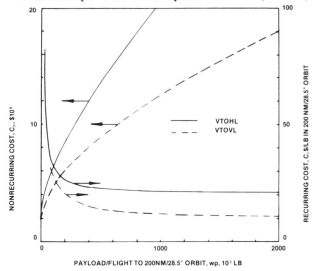

Figure 49 Single-stage-to-orbit Recurring and Nonrecurring Costs (Curves fitted to inputs for 1975 NASA study: "Outlook for Space 1980-2000"; Ref. 15)

assumed in Figure 48, shuttle derivatives would be desired in 1983, the VTOHL single-stage shuttle in 1988, and the VTOHL single-stage shuttle in 1992. Note that the VTOHL size (wp = 80,000 lb) considered in Ref. 16 is very close to the earliest breakeven for the present assumptions. That size is therefore selected for the present study.

A sequential family of Earth-to-near-orbit transport vehicles resulting from the foregoing analysis is shown in Figre 53. Note the continuous threads of technology leading from one to the next in a series of steps:(1) *development of a basic 800,000 lb (sea level) thrust high-pressure O_2/RJ-5 engine,* with modification of the external tank, eliminates the need for solid boosters and leads to an improved derivative retaining the standard orbiter; (2) adapting the basic O_2/RJ-5 engine to

dual fuel capability, retaining the modified external tank from step (1) but now without the orbiter, leads to a large lift derivative; (3) using the O_2/RJ-5 and dual-fuel engines already developed, and the vehicle technology developed and proven for the standard orbiter, leads to a fully reusable VTOHL single-stage shuttle and (4) again using the engines already developed, together with new vertical-landing knowhow (perhaps built up in a separate demonstration program), leads to a fully reusable VTOVL single-stage heavy freighter.

For emergency, rescue and other special missions requiring quick reaction end enhanced operational flexibility, a small manned shuttle capable of direct flight between Earth and geosynchronous, L5, or lunar orbits could be configured as shown in Figure 54. This vehicle consists of the reference VTOHL single-stage shuttle as first stage, and a small manned lifting body vehicle with drop tanks and oxygen/hydrogen propulsion as second stage. The second stage with its drop tanks is placed in 200NM/28.5° orbit by the single-stage-to-orbit transport (which can augment its boost capability by carrying additional oxygen/hydrogen propellants in the empty payload bay if necessary). The second stage then extends the flight to far orbit, executes its on-orbit mission, and de-orbits to direct reentry and horizontal landing on Earth. (Previous work has shown that aerodynamic braking and direct re-entry offer performance as well as operational advantages compared with return to near orbit, since the far-orbit shuttle is not burdened by the propulsion required for near-orbit injection, and the Earth-to-near-orbit shuttle does not have to wait for it in near-orbit; Ref. 19.)

In considering Earth-to-orbit transportation for

Table 17.   Possible Evolution of Earth-to-Orbit Transportation Vehicles
(Based on inputs for 1975 NASA study: "Outlook for Space 1980-2000"; Ref. 15)

Vehicle	Payload, lb in Low Orbit (200NM/28.5°)	Nonrecurring Cost, 10^9	Recurring Cost, $/lb in Low Orbit
Shuttle	60,000	5.5 (Funded)	160
Shuttle Derivatives			
1) Std. Orbiter, No Solids (Primarily for people)	60,000	0.7	100
2) Large-Lift Derivative (Primarily for freight)	170,000	1.0	70
Single-Stage-To-Orbit			
VTOHL	*	*	*
VTOVL	*	*	*

*Ranges of options available-optima to be determined

VTOHL = Vertical-Takeoff-Horizontal-Landing
VTOVL = Vertical-Takeoff-Vertical-Landing

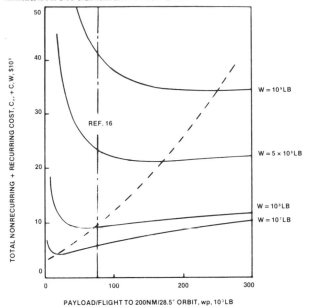

Figure 50 VTOHL Single-stage-to-orbit Sizing Optimization for Minimum Total Cost

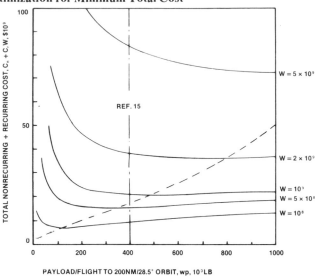

Figure 51 VTOVL Single-stage-to-orbit Sizing Optimization for Minimum Total Cost

deep space facilities, special attention must be focused on the means used to transport payloads from near orbit to deep space. Depending on the propulsive concept selected for orbit-to-orbit tugs, the Earth-to-near-orbit-shuttle may or may not be required to supply large masses of tug propellants to near orbit. As shown in Figure 55, a variety of concepts can be identified for orbit-to-orbit shuttles. High-thrust devices can be built on the basis of already available technology, while low-thrust devices in the size ranges of interest here will not be available for another one or two decades (Ref. 15). High-thrust shuttles will likely be required for passengers and certain electronic equipment to avoid undue time spent in the environment of the Van Allen high energy proton belts which encircle the Earth, but low-thrust devices may be suitable for other equipment, and beneficial because of their high exhaust velocities.

Therefore, the remainder of this analysis considers the above family of Earth-to-near-orbit transports in conjunction with three types of orbit-to-orbit shuttles: (1) fully reusable chemical oxygen/hydrogen tug using two identifcal stages, as specified in Table 18; (2) fully reusable single-stage solid core nuclear hydrogen tug, also specified in Table 18; and (3) some form of tug (undefined) which imposes little or no propellant transport requirement on the Earth-to-near-orbit shuttle. (This could include, for example, chemical tugs which pick up their hydrogen from Earth in near-orbit and their oxygen from the Moon in lunar orbit or L5; Ref. 22.)

Total Earth-to-near-orbit transportation costs for the assumed traffic model can be generated using the above data on Earth-to-near-orbit vehicle evolution and advanced orbit-to-orbit shuttles. The results are shown in Figures 56-58*. They are summarized in Figure 59 in terms of cost per pound in near (200NM/28.5°) orbit, compared to the cost estimates of Ref. 4, and in relation to the following questions: (1) What is the effect of the type of tug assumed? (2) How do different vehicle combinations compare? (3) What is the cost penalty if it is decided that all passenger flights must land horizontally? (4) What is the effect of making comparisons only through completion of "Model 1"? – of "Model 2"? – of five years' doubling?

Observations

(1) Current and near-term vehicle and chemical propulsion technology appear adequate to support Earth-to-near-orbit transportation requirements for large deep space facilities in the period 1980-2000, even on as ambitious a scale as projected in Ref. 4.

(2) Transportation cost per pound to L5 or lunar orbit may be reduced to $50-150 per pound, or less than 50 percent of the costs assumed in Ref. 4.

(3) Introduction of improved shuttle derivatives at an early date is clearly desirable, even for less ambitious traffic projections.

(4) Introduction of single-stage-to-orbit shuttles is

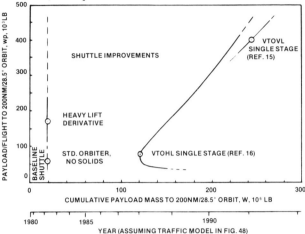

Figure 52 Regimes of Economic Preference for Earth-to-Orbit Trnasportation Vehicles

desirable in the late 1980's for the traffic projected in Ref. 4.

(5) An important technological key to both shuttle derivatives and single-stage-to-orbit is development of a high-pressure oxygen/hydrocarbon boost engine.

(6) The solid core nuclear tug could reduce total transportation costs by up to 50 percent, compared with a two-stage chemical tug.

(7) Horizontal landing capability is feasible for all passenger flights at a total cost penalty of less than 10 percent of transportation costs, and less than 5 percent of total program costs.

(8) Development of a very large vertical-landing freighter is justified only if operations expand beyond "Model 2".

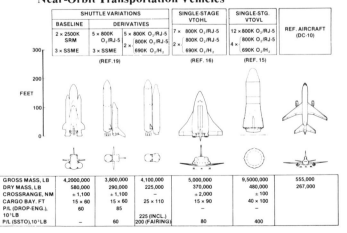

Figure 53 Possible Evolutionary Family of Earth-To-Near-Orbit Transportation Vehicles

SHUTTLE VARIATIONS			SINGLE-STAGE VTOHL	SINGLE-STG. VTOVL	REF. AIRCRAFT (DC-10)
BASELINE	DERIVATIVES				
2 × 2500K SRM 3 × SSME	5 × 800K O_2/RJ-5 3 × SSME	5 × 800K O_2/RJ-5 2 × {800K O_2/RJ-5, 690K O_2/H_2}	7 × 800K O_2/RJ-5 2 × {800K O_2/RJ-5, 690K O_2/H_2}	12 × 800K O_2/RJ-5 4 × {800K O_2/RJ-5, 690K O_2/H_2}	
(REF.19)			(REF. 16)	(REF. 15)	

GROSS MASS, LB	4,2000,000	3,800,000	4,100,000	5,000,000	9,5000,000	555,000
DRY MASS, LB	580,000	290,000	225,000	370,000	480,000	267,000
CROSSRANGE, NM	± 1,100	± 1,100	–	± 2,000	± 100	
CARGO BAY. FT	15 × 60	15 × 60	25 × 110	15 × 90	40 × 100	
P/L (DROP-ENG.), 10³LB	60	85		–	–	
P/L (SSTO),10³LB	–	60	225 (INCL.) 200 (FAIRING)	80	400	

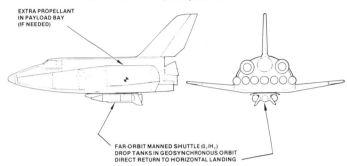

Figure 54 Direct-Flight Deep-Space Manned Shuttle (for emergency, rescue, etc.)

Crew of two plus following round-trip payloads:

100NM/Polar: 5000 lb ($R = 18{,}000$ ft/sec)

Geosynchronous: 5000 lb

L-5 (or lunar orbit): 10,000 lb

Figure 55 Concept Matrix for Orbit-to-Orbit Tugs (Estimated technology dates from Ref. 15)

PROPULSION \ ENERGY SOURCE		CHEMICAL	NUCLEAR	SOLAR
HIGH THRUST[a]	GASES	TECHNOLOGY AVAILABLE NOW		
	SOLIDS	"MASS DRIVERS" 1995 TECHNOLOGY?		
LOW THRUST[b]	PARTICLES (INTERNAL FORCE)	"LASER-HEATED" 1990?	"NUCLEAR ELECTRIC" 1990?	"SOLAR ELECTRIC" 1985?
	PARTICLES (EXTERNAL FORCE)			"SOLAR SAIL" 1980?

[a] SIGNIFICANT PROPELLANT MASS REQ'D (EARTH-TO-NEAR-ORBIT)
[b] LITTLE OR NO PROPELLANT MASS REQ'D (EARTH-TO-NEAR-ORBIT)

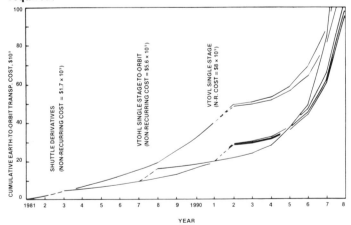

Figure 56 Cumulative Earth-to-Near-Orbit Transportation Costs vs Time, 1975 Dollars (Assumes O_2/H_2) must be placed in orbit for chemical rocket tug)

- **Non-recurring costs shown in IOC year for clarity.**
- **Beyond 1991 diverging curves show added cost if VL vehicles not acceptable for passengers, and HL is required.**

*Note that Figures 56-58 do not include non-recurring and operational costs associated with tug hardware. It is assumed, however, that tugs can be reused at least 10-20 times, so that effects of these cost items should be relatively small.

Figure 57 Cumulative Earth-to-Near-Orbit Transportation Costs vs Time, 1975 Dollars (Assumes H$_2$ must be placed in orbit for nuclear solid core rocket tug)
- Non-recurring costs shown in IOC year for clarity.
- Beyond 1991, diverging curves show added cost if VL vehicle not acceptable for passengers, and HL is required.

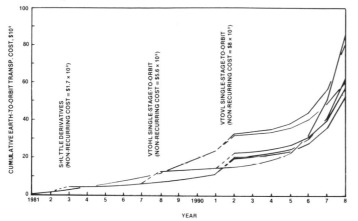

Figure 58 Cumulative Earth-to-Near-Orbit Transportation Costs vs Time, 1975 Dollars (Assumes no tug propellants need be lifted from Earth to low orbit)
- Non-recurring costs shown in IOC year for clarity.
- Beyond 1991, diverging curves show added cost if VL vehicles not acceptable for passengers, and HL is required.

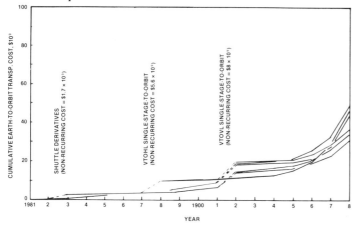

DISCUSSION

Q. What interest rate did you use in your discounted economics calculations?

A. I did not use discounting economics in this study.

Q. How did you generate your tradeoff curves between development costs and recurring costs?

A. They were simple present estimates of RDT&E costs (in $1975) on the one hand, and what

Figure 59 Comparison of Transportation Costs (Dollars per pound to L5 or lunar orbit including non-recurring and recurring costs for Earth-to-orbit vehicles, and propellant transportation costs for near-orbit-based tugs)

ASSUMPTIONS		COLONIZATION STAGE		THROUGH "MODEL 1"	THROUGH "MODEL 2"	THROUGH 1998 (DOUBLING AFTER "MODEL 2")
REF. (1): INCL. TUG OPN'L. COSTS AND TUG LUNAR PROP'S. FOR "MASS DRIVER"				601	333	–
TUG CLASS		HL VEHICLES REQ'D FOR PEOPLE?	VEHICLE COMBINATIONS[a]			
"MASS DRIVER" USING LUNAR PROPELLANTS, OR OTHER TUGS REQ'G. LITTLE OR NO PRO- PELLANTS LIFTED FROM EARTH		YES	S/VTOVL	161	157	42
			S/D/VTOVL	143	130	34
			S/D/VTOHL	342(143[b])	105	40
			S/D/VTOHL/ VTOVL	143	160	32
		NO	S/D/VTOVL	161	146	29
			S/D/VTOVL	143	123	27
CHEMICAL 2-STAGE (O$_2$/H$_2$)		YES	S/VTOVL	655	426	113
			S/D/VTOVL	380	261	90
			S/D/VTOHL	556(380[b])	230	139
			S/D/VTOHL/ VTOVL	380	258	84
		NO	S/VTOVL	655	415	100
			S/D/VTOVL	380	254	82
NUCLEAR 1-STAGE (H$_2$)		YES	S/VTOVL	407	281	70
			S/D/VTOVL	240	178	54
			S/D/VTOHL	431(240[b])	150	75
			S/D/VTOVL/ VTOHL	240	197	50
		NO	S/VTOVL	407	270	57
			S/D/VTOVL	240	172	46

[a] S – baseline shuttle
D = S derivatives (eliminate solids, heavy lift derivative)
[b] Excludes non-recurring cost of VTOHL, which does not participate in "Model 1"

could be achieved in dollars per pound in orbit with that kind of a vehicle.

Q. What considerations have been given to the impact of sending these large chemical rockets through the upper atmosphere? Is there an environmental impact?

A. That's one of the reasons that we're interested in liquid oxygen-kerosene, rather than some of the other propellants which may have received consideration, such as the amines or solid propellant rockets. All those combinations deliver oxides of nitrogen, hydrochloric acid, and so forth. What we get from oxygen-kerosene is just some unburned hydrocarbons. It's nothing like the problem of exhaust from high-flying SST's for example, because the trajectories are steep. The exhausts are thus not stratified, and a large fraction of them are expelled at extremely high altitudes, well above the ozone layer.

Q. What is the current status of high density, high pressure, liquid rocket engines and will they be ready in time for 1983 utilization?

A. If they were pursued at the right level of effort, they could be. One of the key jobs to be done is to show that the engine can be cooled with oxygen at these pressures. That has been demonstrated in Germany during the sixties at somewhat lower pressures. There is a funded NASA study, about to begin, on a spectrum of these kinds of rocket engines.

66

8. Laser Propulsion to Earth Orbit

Arthur Kantrowitz
AVCO Everett Research Laboratory

For many decades it was proposed that chemical rockets could be built to propel objects to Earth orbit and beyond. It was always admitted that such rockets would be very much larger than the payloads they propelled because of our inability to attain jet velocities close to orbital velocities. Nevertheless, the drive to expand man's horizons, which is at the heart of the space effort, was so compelling that this operation was undertaken in spite of its considerable costs. Indeed, several important applications for instrumented space vehicles have been found which clearly justify their cost even on very simple economic grounds. However, a great deal of uncertainty exists about the future of manned space flight and the colonization of space, primarily because of the enormous costs of these operations. This cost is closely related to the costs of boosters and the very large installations needed for their operations (the large costs of space vehicles themselves result mainly from the necessity to prevent failure at almost any cost and to minimize vehicle and payload mass).

There is another possibility for powering vehicles that go from Earth to orbit: beaming power from the ground to the vehicle, and using this power to accelerate an on-board propellant to velocities much higher than those attained with chemical rockets. This possibility is attractive for two reasons: almost all of the machinery is on the ground where repeated use offers a tremendous opportunity for cost saving; and it is possible, as in electrically propelled jets, to achieve specific im-

pulses virtually as high as desired. It has been proposed many times that transmission of radio waves or microwaves could some day implement an entirely different space program than that powered by rockets. However, radio waves and even microwaves spread by diffraction too much to be concentrated on a vehicle's antennae. Nevertheless, this is a very attractive idea; the kinetic energy of an object in low Earth orbit is about 4½ kilowatt-hours per pound, which amounts to only a few cents worth of electricity at current prices. Transmitting power to accelerate a vehicle into orbit offers a major opportunity to reduce the costs of space operations.

We can today begin to see a realistic way of accomplishing this dream. The high-power laser provides an energy source whose beam can be transmitted through the atmosphere without large loss either by diffraction or absorption. Furthermore, laser beams impinging on an object can easily evaporate material and produce jets with specific impulses ranging into the thousands of seconds.

Let us calculate the amount of power necessary to place a 1-ton payload in low Earth orbit. Assume that the propellant is heated enough so the latent heat of evaporation can be neglected and that all the vapor enthalpy is efficiently converted to a jet of velocity V. Then the laser power absorbed by the vapor is

$$P = \tfrac{1}{2}\dot{m}V^2$$

67

where $\dot{m}$ = vehicle mass loss rate (propellant vaporization rate). Neglecting atmospheric drag and gravity, the thrust is then

$$T = \dot{m}V = m\dot{v}$$

where $\dot{v}$ = vehicle acceleration. The specific impulse can be varied over the wide limits by suitable choice of propellant and by time variation of the laser power.

Another interesting and simple case to analyze is $V = v$: ejected mass just coming to rest in Earth coordinates. In this case the momentum of the vehicle stays constant, since no momentum remains in the wake. If P is constant, then the vehicle acceleration $\dot{v}$ will be constant during the laser propulsion trajectory:

$$P = \tfrac{1}{2}\dot{m}v^2 = \tfrac{1}{2}m\ v\ \dot{v}$$

For a final orbital velocity of 8×10^5 cm/sec, assuming that we accelerate at 10g (10^4 cm/sec^2):

$$P/m_0 = \tfrac{1}{2}8 \times 10^9 \ ergs/sec\ gm$$

$$= 400\ watts/gm = 400\ MW/ton$$

where m_0 is the mass reaching orbital velocity.

After making allowances (see below) for propagation losses, thruster losses, etc., it seems reasonable to suppose that the laser assembly required would have a power output of about 10^9 watts. In order to provide something like an "engine out" capability and also to reduce development costs, I would propose that we use 100 MW lasers.

It is worth noting that the diffraction spreading of beamed power which defeated the microwave propulsion system is completely tolerable for the laser wavelengths. For example, at a wave length $\lambda = 10.6$ microns the diffraction spreading of a laser beam $2.4\lambda/D$ can be held to 10^{-5} radians with a mirror diameter $D = 2.4$ meters. The scattering of the laser beam by atmospheric disturbances is of the order of 10^{-5} radians for very good seeing from high mountains. With vehicle receiver optics one or two meters in diameter the laser beam could be concentrated on the receiver optics at ranges of 100 km.

Problems in Laser Propulsion. Before a project of this sort could be undertaken, a number of problems must receive a much fuller exploration. In most cases only speculative answers can now be given.

(1) The first problem is undoubtedly the scaling of lasers from presently obtained powers to the order of 100 MW. The physical dimensions of a 100 MW laser can be estimated from the performance of existing CO_2 E-beam sustainer lasers which produce approximately 50 joules per liter-atmosphere of laser medium. Thus, for 100 MW, 2 million liters per second will be required, and if the gas flows at 10^5 cm per second at a pressure of 0.3 atm and room temperature, the flow area will be about 7 square meters. The power required for such a laser might be more like 500 MW, since the efficiency obtainable is of the order of 20%. Thus the power required to drive all ten lasers would be about 5 GW. I do not want to minimize the problem of scaling up lasers to this order of magnitude. However, I know of no physical limitations which will prevent us from doing so.

I would like to illustrate the difficulties by considering what I believe to be the toughest problem in scaling up to this order of magnitude: obtaining the medium homogeneity necessary to achieve the high optical quality postulated. If we select a laser optical path length of, say, 10 meters and we ask that the beam brightness be within 10% of the theoretical maximum, this requires that the medium be homogeneous in optical path length to about 0.3 of a wave length (λ). This requires that the density variation averaged along the optical path length be less than $\tfrac{1}{2}$%. The significance of this can be seen from the fact that in order to produce the laser energy (50 joules per liter) postulated, we must approximately double the temperature of the gas while it is flowing through the laser region. Thus, it is required that the heat disposition be controlled through the laser region to about $\tfrac{1}{2}$% and that density variations due to other causes be held similarly small or be optically compensated. This, of course, is an engineering problem of considerable proportions. It is reminiscent of the difficulties in making large high quality optical mirrors. One needs a technique of iterative testing and adjustment to achieve this kind of precision.

(2) The second problem is the problem of pointing the lasers at the proper part of the vehicle, which will require pointing accuracy similar to that which is obtained with astronomical telescopes (10^{-5} radians). There are two differences between the pointing of these lasers and the pointing of an astronomical telescope. First, the slewing rate is

much more rapid with accompanying rigidity requirements. On the other hand, closed loop operation can be utilized with the cooperative target vehicle, which can telemeter pointing errors back to the lasers.

(3) The problem of propagation through the atmosphere will also require attention. The propagation of intense laser beams through the atmosphere alters the translational temperature either positively or negatively, depending on the nature of the absorption. Thus, if the energy absorbed is quickly transferred to translational energy, it will produce an acoustic expansion, eventually lowering the density. On the other hand, absorption by CO_2 of 10.6 micron radiation results in the removal of CO_2 molecules from the 100 state which is then refilled from translational energy, resulting in decreased translational energy and enventually in increased density. The problems involved are well understood in principle, but the achievement of a system adequate to compensate for them in practice will require considerable research and development.

A second propagation problem that might present even larger difficulties is atmospheric breakdown. High-intensity laser beams produce local gas breakdowns when they impinge on atmospheric dust particles. While these phenomena are not understood quantitatively, it is possible to estimate a rough upper bound to the power that can be safely transmitted. In the continuous-wave (CW) 10.6μ laser the power limit seems to be above 1 MW/cm^2. For pulsed lasers about 10 joules/cm^2 can apparently be transmitted without serious gas breakdown. If we have a beam of one square meter cross section, the propagation of 10^9 watts calls for an average power of 10^5 watts per square cm. Thus, it seems that at least for propagation, breakdown limits will not prevent the laser propulsion envisaged here.

It is clear that more work is necessary on the propagation of high power laser beams. Very little information exists on their transmission through the upper atmosphere. These are problems that will require considerable research and development before laser propulsion can be realized.

(4) Perhaps the biggest uncertainty exists in the area of converting laser energy into thrust at the proper specific impulse (about 800 seconds) and with high efficiency. There is, of course, much evidence that high-velocity jets can be produced by evaporating metal with lasers, but in general this has not been done with high efficiency: generally less than 20%. One reason for the low efficiency is that with small laser spots gas flows into a solid angle of about 2π, so that only a small fraction of the momentum is directed. This can be overcome for laser pulses by making the pulse duration short enough; however, it must be remembered that atmospheric breakdown limits may be a constraint here. Another source of loss will be energy reradiated from material heated by an intense laser beam.

Concluding Remarks. I have suggested that the development of the high power laser will have an important impact on aeronautics and perhaps will revolutionize the technology of the propulsion of vehicles to orbit. The load capacity of a laser propulsion system promises to be orders of magnitude greater than that achievable practically with rocket propulsion systems. It could be the fundamental supply system for massive Earth orbit assembly projects. If developed it could provide the propulsion for modules from which large-scale manned orbital stations could be assembled.

Projects of this sort are distinctly unfashionable in these pessimistic times, and it may well be that years will elapse before the serious R&D efforts to realize an advance of this kind can be begun. In the meantime, the development of high power lasers for lesser objectives will hopefully continue. The study of propagation through the atmosphere is continuing, and if sufficient research can be done on thrustor development, perhaps laser propulsion can become a realistic option when enthusiasm for taking the next step into space is rekindled.

DISCUSSION

Q. *Could you give a very rough estimate of what the recurring costs per pound into low Earth orbit would be?*

A. About a factor of ten less than the shuttle cost, I would think: about $30.

Q. *Have you considered using large mirrors in space to reflect sunlight into a chamber? That way you wouldn't even need to use a laser. This means of propulsion might be used for moving material in low Earth orbit to the lunar orbit or L5.*

A. I would remind you that the diameter of the Sun is half an degree. That makes a very important difficulty. You need the ability to focus sharply, and sunlight cannot be focused that sharply.

69

Q. Can't they get solar furances to reach several thousand Kelvin?

A. Yes, but only when surrounded with mirrors.

Q. Could laser propulsion be used for upper stage requirements?

A. Yes. That's exactly what I would do.

9. Near-Term Chemically-Propelled Space Transport Systems

Adelbert O. Tischler

The task to be performed by near-term applications of chemical space propulsion systems has been defined by O'Neill as follows:

(a) 10,000 tons at L5 (1800 tons by 1982)

(b) 3,000 tons on the lunar surface.

This implies that 1800 tons would have to be launched by the shuttle launch vehicle, since that is presumably the only launch vehicle available in 1982. The hypothesis also requires 10,000 people at L5 and 200 people on the lunar surface. If we provide that these people must be accommodated by an equivalent of 200 pounds per person, we need to carry about 1,000 tons of human flesh and protective covering to L5 and 20 tons to the lunar surface. It is my purpose to show how this can be accomplished by means of chemical propulsion systems.

These requirements can be restated into a more specific problem: to translate these payloads into the equivalent mass requirements in low Earth orbit that would be necessary to deliver the specified tonnages to L5 and the Moon using a hydrogen-oxygen system. It would be presumptuous of me to design a future payload hauler that would do this, but I shall lay out the elements of a nearer term system, where each element can be transported to L5 by a device which can be lifted in turn by the shuttle. That, of course, will satisy the 1982 requirement. I will do the analysis in parametric form, so that if the assumed performance parameters hold, the example can serve to establish the mass ratios for all the space transport systems, and the design of a practical system for the 1989 period would be reduced merely to an engineering problem.

All of my calculations are based on the use of the hydrogen-oxygen propellant system because of its high specific impulse. I will also assume, for simplicity, that there is no long-term boil-off. Although that is a rather drastic assumption, we have postulated that power is available at both L5 and the lunar surface to refrigerate the liquid hydrogen which would otherwise escape. This would reduce propellant boil-off to that which would be lost during transport of the systems from one point to another in space; that kind of boil-off might be reduced to ½ percent of the hydrogen per day, with only a lightly insulated system to keep the mass down. Thus boiloff in space does not need to be a serious problem. However, because some of the operations will be conducted on the lunar surface where there is considerable reflection from the surface itself, storage of hydrogen there poses something more of a problem than storage of hydrogen or oxygen in space. This may make it useful to consider a combination such as liquid oxygen with amine fuels which, while it will cost 30% more in mass for the transport system, will reduce the boil-off problem very appreciably.

Table 19 lists the representative velocity increment (ΔV) requirements that have to be met for the mission of going from the low Earth orbit (LEO) to a lunar parking orbit (LPO). Low Earth orbit to the L5 position is actually slightly less, but

Table 19. Representative ΔV Requirements for Space Transport

Mission	ΔV, ft/sec
LEO → LPO	13,000
LEO → L-5	13,400
LPO → L-5	7,200
L 5 → LPO	6,100
LPO → L-5	2,250
L 5 → GSO	5,700

to first order these two missions are almost equivalent.

Going from the lunar parking orbit to the lunar surface (LS) requires a throttlable engine and a hovering maneuver before the final touchdown. Thus I have allowed 7,200 feet per second for that maneuver, whereas I have allowed only 6,100 feet per second for the ascent maneuver, which does not require hovering. Table 18 also lists the requirement for going from the lunar parking orbit to L5 and from L5 to the geosynchronous orbit (GSO). I have not examined ways of performing these missions, so there may be ways that those ΔV's can be reduced. However, such refinements will have little effect on gross propulsion system characteristics.

The hydrogen-oxygen system that I have assumed for the calculations provides an effective specific impulse of 462 pound-seconds per pound. Since there will be some losses (e.g., about 3%) in the system due to vector, attitude control and boil-off, we must have an engine whose capability is of the order of 477 seconds, which calls for an expansion ratio of the order of perhaps 450. I also assume a high mass fraction, 0.91, but since these stages are quite large, I believe this can be achieved. It has, in fact, been achieved in the second stage of the Saturn V, which also is a hydrogen-oxygen stage.

In all my calculations, I have assumed that we can't waste the equipment. That is, the hydrogen-oxygen stage has the function of delivering its payload and then returning to the starting point for reuse with a new propellant supply. For trips of the order of 13,400 feet per second, I choose to use two stages. Although it is technically feasible to do this mission in one stage, the mass fractions, and in particular the fact that there is a considerable amount of inert mass that has to be propelled both ways, penalize the payload capability rather severely. The inert mass must be given a total ΔV of the order of 27,000 feet per second.

It is not only possible, but relatively straight-

forward and easy, to use a two-stage system in such a way that both stages can be recovered, as shown in Figure 60. This is a "slingshot" operation. The first stage accelerates the vehicle from a circular low Earth orbit into an elliptical orbit with an indefinite apogee, coming back to the perigee point. It imparts a velocity change of about 6,200 feet per second. The second stage then takes over and produces 4,200 feet per second, enough to reach the lunar parking orbit or L5. The second stage then refires, imparting the order of 3,000 feet per second to circularize the maneuver. It delivers its payload and has enough velocity increment left to return again to low Earth orbit, again performing the 4,2000 foot-per-second maneuver to achieve the orbit for refueling and reuse. The scheme looks more complicated on Figure 60 than, in fact, it is to execute.

The deploy/retrieve capability of the two-stage hydrogen-oxygen system is shown in Figure 61. I will now put a further stipulation on the system, which is that the two stages be identical in size. The payloads that can be deployed are shown along the abscissa as a fraction of the initial mass. The payloads that could be retrieved, if you took those stages up empty, is shown along the ordinate. Any combination of deployment and retrieval is represented by a point along the line shown. The payload that can be taken, either to L5 or to the lunar parking orbit, is about one third of what is initially in low Earth orbit, and immediately we can estimate what is required in the lunar mass orbit for inserting 10,000 tons at L5. I will use, for the sake of simplicity, the figure of one third; thus the 10,000 tons translates immediately into 30,000 tons required in low Earth orbit to accomplish the injection of that payload.

Figure 60 Method for Utilizing Two Recoverable Stages for Transport from Low Earth Orbit to Lunar Parking Orbit or L5

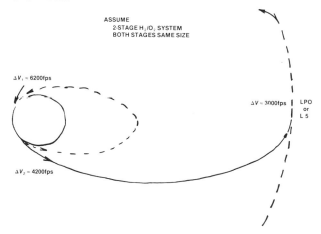

72

Figure 61 Deploy/Retrieve Capability for 2-Stage Hydrogen/Oxygen System

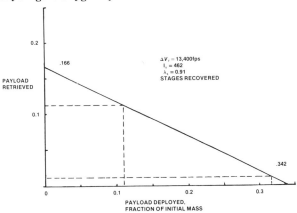

Now let's tackle the problem of 3,000 tons on the lunar surface. Here we have a more difficult situation in that we have to start from the lunar parking orbit, having gotten there by the same type of system just described, and bring whatever we have parked there down to the lunar surface. These maneuvers are to be conducted in a gravitational field, and even though this g-field is, at the surface of the Moon, only about one sixth what it is at the surface of the Earth, it prohibits the use of the loosely jointed assemblies which are possible in zero-g space.

Figure 38, cited earlier, shows both the transfer vehicle and the lunar lander in transit. Figure 40, also cited earlier, shows what the landing configuration ought to look like. The core is a propulsion stage, above which is a personnel module. Strapped to the sides are equipment modules; they are carried there to reduce the center of gravity as much as possible, and could presumably be left on the surface as the payload.

Figure 62 Deploy/Retrieve Capability for Single Stage Hydrogen/Oxygen System

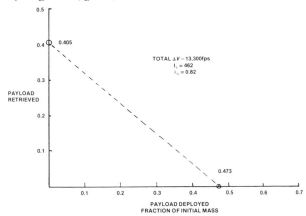

This system will leave the lunar parking orbit, land on the surface, deploy its payload, and then be lifted by the propulsion system through a ΔV of 6,200 feet per second back to the lunar parking orbit, there to be refueled. It is so configured that the propulsion module and the crew module can be carried in the shuttle, having a diameter of 4.4 meters. It has landing legs. It does need structural capability and strength and is an assembled unit. For the purpose of calculating what this system would require in terms of lunar parking orbit mass to land 3,000 tons on the lunar surface, I have used a stage propellant mass fraction for the entire device of .82, which might be a little on the high side. I have assumed the system total mass as it leaves the lunar parking orbit to be 180,000 pounds.

Using this system and the parameters that I have chosen, Figure 62 shows that we can land about 0.473 of the original lunar parking orbit mass on the surface of the Moon as useful payload and still get the propulsion stage back. I am going to make a rough approximation here and say that that is close to 0.5. The line is shown dotted because, with the ΔV's going and coming being different in this case, I am not sure whether it is a straight line or some sort of catenary curve. However, we are concerned only with the number .473, and if that is, in fact, close enough to one half, we can say that our 90-ton system will land 45 tons of payload. We then calculate very quickly that to put 3,000 tons of equipment on the lunar surface using this system (and also a transporter to bring the system, plus the payload, from low Earth orbit) will require 6,000 tons in the lunar parking orbit and 18,000 tons in the low Earth orbit.

Roughly, then, to accomplish the complete task of landing 3,000 tons on the Moon and bringing 10,000 tons to L5, the total mass required in low Earth orbit is about 50,000 tons.

There is an error in the way I have conducted these estimates, but that error is sufficiently small that I chose to neglect it: in calculating the masses required to be transported, I did not account for the masses that were being returned for reuse. In other words, I didn't, in making those mass estimates, fully account for the fact that I was reusing a system for the second, third, etc., time. For materials launched out of low Earth orbit to either L5 or the lunar parking orbit, this amounts to overestimating the mass requirement in low Earth orbit by about 5%, and for payloads from the lunar parking orbit to the lunar surface, the error is of the order of 10%. Because of attrition and replacement of stages and other equipment, I believe this error to be of the same order as might be expected of trips in which no payload was delivered. There are certainly going to be a number of executive, legislative, and management trips (non-productive in terms of mass transported) to account for this.

Thus, it will require 50,000 tons in low Earth orbit to do the job that we set out to do. There is nothing frightening about that number! This represents roughly 500 flights of a launch vehicle having Saturn V capability; that is, 250,000 pounds of payload capability in low Earth orbit. There is nothing about this that is remarkable. Stretched over ten years, this represents a flight a week. With a larger launch vehicle, the numbers would be shifted to require even fewer flights. I think that is well within the technological capability of this country to handle, so that in no way does it frighten me or even cause me concern.

Now let's turn to the first 1800 tons that must be delivered to L5. Because of the time frame, we will have to do this with the space shuttle. What follows is an engineering layout of a system to accomplish such a requirement.

Orbital assembly of bigger systems than can be carried in one shuttle flight certainly appears to be the right way to do the job. Although the ultimate mass of such an assembled system can be decided somewhat arbitrarily, I decided that one of the constraints would be that the modules, tanks, etc., fit the dimensions of the shuttle bay, which is 60 feet long and 15 feet in diameter and has a payload capacity of 63,000 pounds, as described by Davis in detail.

As shown in Table 20, it would take 11 flights of the shuttle to do the job, that is to transport to low Earth orbit 633,000 pounds of system, propellants and payload. Stage One carries with it all of the

Table 21. Modular Tank Sizing, O/F = 6.0

	Liquid Oxygen Tank	Liquid Hydrogen Tank
Ullage, %	6	14
Propellant mass, lb.	183K	30.5K
Volume, cu. ft.	2,700	7,800
Diameter, ft.	14	14
Length, ft.	21	54, or 2 at 29 each

liquid oxygen necessary for Stage One, and weighs 63,000 pounds; no strange coincidence. Stage Two is exactly the same kind of stage, because I elected to use the same size stage in both instances. Now, we need to take up liquid oxygen to put into each of these tanks, so the next four flights are engaged in carrying up sufficient oxygen to fill the two tanks already up there (I defer the liquid hydrogen to reduce boil-off). The 7th, 8th, and 9th shuttle flights each carry up 63,000 pounds of payload, for a total of 189,000 pounds. Finally, the liquid hydrogen is carried up in two flights. Because the liquid hydrogen is low in density, we only need to carry 33,000 pounds per stage, but in order to keep the stages symmetrical, I elected to carry the same quantity in two tanks for each stage.

Table 21 shows the volume of the tanks using an oxygen/hydrogen ratio of six. One tank to carry almost 31,000 pounds of liquid hydrogen has a length of about 54 feet, if the diameter is confined to 14 feet. For the sake of propulsion stage symmetry, and at the cost of stage mass fraction, I prefer to carry the same quantity of propellant in two tanks, each 29 feet in length. The oxygen tank has a length of 21 feet if its diameter is 14 feet, and this is readily accommodated in the shuttle. Allowing for the ullages shown, the total mass required for the oxygen is 183,000 pounds, and the toal mass required for the first stage of the hydrogen is 30,500 pounds.

Figure 63 shows the system when assembled. Only liquid oxygen is transferred from tanker to stage. The liquid hydrogen tanks are simply attached to the stage and become the stage system tanks. Stage One is on the right with two hydrogen tanks, which have been carried up separately and attached to the stage. The oxygen tank is carried up with the stage and is refueled by tanker operation. Stage Two is exactly the same. The payloads are on the left. The space transportation vehicle ignition mass, the mass in low Earth orbit, is 444,000 pounds. The payload mass is about 189,000 pounds at launch and 180,000 pounds when it reaches the lunar parking orbit or L5.

Table 20. Modular Delivery to Low-Earth Orbit (LEO)

Shuttle Flight No.	Mission	Mass in LEO (pounds)
1	Stage 1, L O_2	13K, 50K
2	Stage 2, L O_2	13K, 50K
3	L O_2 Tanker	63K
4	"	63K
5	"	63K
6	"	63K
7	Payload	63K
8	Payload	63K
9	Payload	63K
10	L H_2 Tank	33K
11	"	33K

Figure 63   Modular Space Transport Vehicle

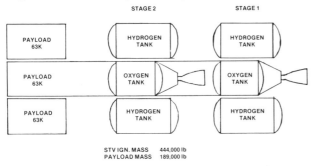

STV IGN. MASS   444,000 lb
PAYLOAD MASS   189,000 lb

Figure 39, cited previously, shows on the right the Modular Space Transport Vehicle just described. What is shown is the lunar landing system; one of the stages is shown, one is already gone. The payload is on the left.

Figure 64 is essentially the plot we discussed before, but reduced to practical mass terms. It shows what payloads the stages can take to L5 or the lunar parking orbit, using the masses that I used. It comes out to 203,000 pounds, but its real capability is better represented as 3 shuttle trips, or 189,000 pounds. The system capabilities then allow a return to low Earth orbit of 6,000 pounds for every flight to L5. These figures provide a mass at L5 of 30% of the low Earth orbit mass, somewhat less than the one-third I assumed in earlier calculations. The capability of bringing 6,000 pounds back with each flight just might turn out to be useful, so it seems to me that system makes pretty good sense.

This specific case illustrates that even cursory attention to the pragmatic engineering details of the capability per stage, matching with the launch vehicle, etc., will modify the academic solution, but not really terribly much. All of the answers in this

Figure 64 Payload Capability for Modular 2-Stage Hydrogen/Oxygen Space Transportation Vehicle

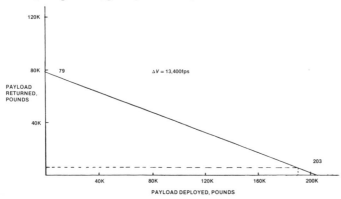

brief space propulsion analysis indicate solutions that are technologically reasonable, even in the optimistic time frames given for implementing the entire system of power generation in space.

One matter I haven't discussed, and I have avoided it rather deliberately, is the matter of costs for developing and producing this equipment. Such cost estimates can be made readily by anyone who is expert in the propulsion field.

DISCUSSION

Q. *It is a good thing to see people dreaming again. We used to do things like this all the time a few years back. Why not spend a million dollars to bring NERVA (Nuclear Engine for Rocket Vehicle Applications) to operational status and use it?*

A. That argument has to be examined. The assumptions that I was presumed to work on did not include it. Addressing the question, though, I think there are some problems that should not be overlooked in operating a nuclear system in space. One of them is what you need to do to shield the personnel involved in the operation from the radiation that you generate. I also would bring up the question, since I ended on the point of cost, of reminding you that this operation is just a matter of delivering a payload, and one has to look at the cost to see whether the chemical approach isn't, in fact, the cheaper way to do it rather than using a nuclear system.

There is also a psychological point: a lot of people, particularly younger people, have a hatred of nuclear power. One of the reasons for doing the job without invoking nuclear power is that you avoid raising all these emotional issues. Further, I have been told by NASA that anytime professional NASA cost estimators hear the word "nuclear rocket," the price of any piece of equipment, even if it's got nothing nuclear in it but is just labeled as part of that system, goes up by a factor of about six.

Q. *Aside from the development costs, could you give an estimate on the dollars per pound based only on the system payload?*

A. There are two factors involved in the cost. One is the development cost, the so-called non-recurring cost, and the other is the recurring cost. I am not sure which would dominate. The fact is, I don't think the systems or the operations in space begin to approach the operational costs of getting everything into Earth orbit, because the masses are reduced at every step of the process. You can translate the whole problem back into what it costs you to put the mass up into low Earth orbit, and I don't think you have to multiply it even by two to encompass all the rest of the systems.

Q. *If that's 50,000 tons, or roughly a hundred million pounds, and we use O'Neill's figure of four hundred dollars a pound, it's forty billion dollars.*

A. That's not an incredible number.

Q. *Would you say that the cost of putting mass in Earth orbit would be substantially less if they were started from the upper Earth atmosphere?*

For example, a lighter-than-air craft might be used as a launching platform.

A. That point comes up again and again. It is true that you can reduce the mass of the launch vehicle by some amount — I'm not sure how big it is, but I'm sure it's under five percent. I don't think that kind of operation would ever be justified in terms of cost.

Q. *The advertised figures, as I understand, for the shuttle are ten or eleven million dollars per launch. If we up that to, say, 15 million per launch just to be on the safe side, it would cost a total of about twenty five billion dollars to lift your 50,000 tons to low Earth orbit.*

A. A previous comment estimated that forty billion dollars would encompass the whole transportation system. That may be about right.

SECTION II: PRODUCTION

1. Process Chemistry for L5

Philomena G. Grodzka
Lockheed Missiles & Space Co.

Introduction

The practicality of inhabitable space capsules will be determined in part by the practicality of chemical processing of lunar, asteroidal, cometary, and planetary ores to obtain essential structural and life-support materials. Nonterrestrial consumables production is required to minimize both the mass of material removed from the Earth and the cost of transport to extraterrestrial destinations. The logical source for materials for L5 is the Moon, that body being closest at hand. In order to arrive at a decision as to the feasibility of processing lunar materials, we must first review the data on the chemical and physical nature of the lunar soils. The review will enable us to deter mine whether the principles of existing processing technologies are adequate to handle lunar processing or whether new technologies must be employed.

Summary

The chemical and physical compositions of lunar soils, as they are now known, are reviewed. Under the ground rule that no material other than hydrogen will be brought from Earth, it is concluded that aluminum and titanium extraction from lunar soils by existing technologies (that is, by means approximating those used on Earth) is infeasible. Metal extraction by direct electrolysis of molten lunar soil, however, appears to be a feasible, although as yet undemonstrated, alternative. Another feasible alternative appears to be production from lunar soils of glass and ceramic construction materials. Two routes appear promising for the production of oxygen from lunar soils. One involves direct reduction with hydrogen of ilmenite in lunar soils to produce water, iron, and titanium dioxide. This method, however, is not viewed as practical for the production of metals. Electrolysis of molten lunar soils is another method which appears promising and warrants further investigation. Electrolysis would have the advantage of producing not only oxygen but also metals.

Chemical and Physical Nature of Lunar Soils

The lunar materials carried back to Earth by the Apollo astronauts can be classified into four main types. The four categories are (Ref. 23, p. 7):

Type A: Basalt rocks – fine grained, vesicular crystalline igneous rocks

Type B: Gabbro or microgabbro rocks – a medium grained, vuggy crystalline igneous rock

Type C: Breccia or microbreccia – an agglomeration of Types A and B, mineral particles, glassy spherules, etc.

Type D: Fines or an assortment of rock particles less than 1 cm in diameter.

Type A and B rocks consist mainly of the minerals pyroxene, plagioclase and ilmenite as shown in Table 22.

Table 22. Approximate Percentage of Minerals in Type A and B Apollo 11 Rocks (in Volume %) Ref. 23, p. 48

Mineral	Type A Range	(Basalt) (Average)	Type B Range	(Gabbro) (Average)
Pyroxenes	50-59	(53)	45-51	(46)
Plagioclase	20-29	(27)	29-37	(31)
Ilmenite	10-18	(13)	10-14	(11)
Chromite-ulvöspinel	1-2	(1)	0-0.1	(0.05)
Troilite	.05-1.3	(1)	0.1-0.5	(0.3)
Iron	.01-0.1	(0.04)	.01-.05	(0.03)
Olivine	Trace-7	(3)	0	0
Cristobalite	Trace-1	(Trace)	4-6	(5)
Pyroxferroite	0	0	0.5-2	(1)
Others	1-7	1-7	4-8	(6)

The general chemical compositions of pyroxene, plagioclase and ilmenite are as follows (Ref. 24, p. 33):

Pyroxene $(Ca, Fe, Mg)_2Si_2O_6$

Plagioclase $(Ca, Na)(Al, Si)_4O_8$

Ilmenite $FeTiO_3$

The chemical composition of pyroxene and plagioclase are variable depending on the relative amounts of the indicated interchangeable elements. Solid solution formulation is another factor contributing to composition variation.

Relative mineral abundances vary from place to place on the Moon. For example, the "marias" or seas which are seen from Earth as dark patches contain the minerals plagioclase, olivine, pyroxene and ilmenite. Terrestrial volcanic basalt contains, for comparison, the minerals plagioclase, olivine and pyroxene. The lunar highlands, or light-colored regions, consist mainly of anorthosite, which is a rock comprised primarily of plagioclase $(CaAl_2Si_2O_8$; Ref. 25, p. 136).

This cursory discussion is meant to indicate the considerable variation in physical and chemical compositions of lunar soils. Obviously both compositions of the input materials will determine the nature of the extraction processes. For example, big heavy rocks will need to be crushed for subsequent handling; electrostatic interactions in lunar fines may make collection and handling a problem; low-grade ores are to be avo f possible for obvious reasons; and the chemical nature of the source material will dictate the subsequent method of treatment.

The specific cases of extraction of aluminum, titanium, and oxygen are considered in the next section. It should be mentioned that these discussions are based on information presently available on the physical and chemical compositions of lunar soils. Obviously, only a very minute portion of the Moon has been explored, and future discoveries may completely alter the conclusions reached here. The two discoveries that would have the most impact on the present conclusions are: (a) the presence of water in either bound or free condition, and (b) mineral deposits of a completely different nature than what have been discovered to date.

Feasibility Considerations for Various Chemical Processing Technologies

Aluminum. On Earth aluminum is obtained primarily from the ore bauxite, which is essentially the compound $Al_2O_3 \cdot 2H_2O$. High grade bauxite has the following approximate composition (Ref. 26, p. 9):

A_2lO_3	60%
Fe_2O_3	22%
SiO_2	2%
TiO_2	2%
H_2O	12%

Bauxite is processed on Earth by treatment with sodium hydroxide (NaOH) to produce pure alumina (Al_2O_3). The alumina is then dissolved in cryolite $(AlF_3 \cdot 3NaF)$, and the aluminum separated by electrolysis, i.e., the well-known Hall process. Alternate methods for separating aluminum from its oxide have been sought to circumvent the huge power requirements of the Hall process, but to date none has succeeded. The recent Toth processes (Refs. 27 and 28), however, may be "winners".

Bauxite differs considerably from the lunar

anorthosite ores, which are the aluminum-bearing ores on the Moon. Their chemical compositions are as follows:

Bauxite	Anorthosite
Varying mixtures of	Varying mixtures of
$Al_2O_3 \cdot H_2O$	$Na\,AlSi_3O_8$ albite
$Al_2O_3 \cdot 3H_2O$	$Na\,AlSi_2O_8$ anorthite
Minor other compounds	Minor other compounds

High grade anorthosites typically contain about 25-28% Al_2O_3 (Ref. 29).

The U.S. Bureau of Mines and others have been exploring ways in which to extract alumina from low-grade ores, including anorthosites, for a number of years (Refs. 30 through 33). A method that has been demonstrated both on laboratory and pilot plant scales involves a sintering treatment with sodium carbonate and calcium carbonate (lime-soda sinter process). The general reaction can be represented as follows (Ref. 31):

$$CaAl_2Si_2O_8 + 3CaCO_3 + Na_2CO_3 \cdot 2NaAlO_2$$

$$+ 2Ca_2SiO_4 + 4CO_2\uparrow$$

and

$$NaAlSi_3O_8 + 6CaCO_3 \rightarrow NaAlO_2 + 2Ca_2SiO_4 + 6CO_2\uparrow$$

The reaction products are further treated to obtain alumina or Al_2O_3. The other referenced processes involve treatment with sulfuric acid. Sulfuric acid treatment is applicable to low-grade bauxite ores and clays. Clays are essentially hydrous aluminum silicates, which again differ considerably from the anorthosite minerals. Treatment of anorthosites with sulfuric acid is not viewed as a feasible digestion method because of the limited solubility of anorthosite minerals in acid. The solubility apparently can be increased by first converting anorthosite to a glass. This route, however, is as yet unproved technology and would appear to suffer from the same general objections as are next raised (Ref. 34).

Returning to the lime-soda sinter process, it is evident from the reaction equations that large amounts of calcium and sodium carbonates are required. A glance at a table of lunar elemental abundances (Ref. 24, p. 117) shows that calcium and sodium carbonates will not be readily made on the Moon. Aside from this fundamental obstacle, secondary obstacles exist to adopting Earth-bound

technologies to lunar and space environments. First of all, extraction processes conducted on Earth handle materials that are in contact with air and moisture to some degree. Grinding and handling operations, therefore, do not run into problems such as cohesive binding of small particles. Such problems can be anticipated on the Moon. Most Earth extraction processes, furthermore, depend on copious amounts of water for the various leaching, flotation, and washing operations. Water, of course, will be in short supply on the Moon. Also, lunar and space environments have different gravity environments than Earth. Heat and mass transfer modes and rates, therefore, will be very much different from those on Earth. Equipment designed for Earth use, as a result, will not be suitable for use on the Moon or in space.

Titanium. Although one of the most surprising aspects of the lunar rocks and fines is their high titanium content, most of the titanium is present as ilmenite or $Fe\,TiO_3$. Ilmenite constitutes about 10 to 20% of the various lunar rocks. On Earth the usual source of titanium is rutile (TiO_2), which constitutes about 25% of the ore from which it is obtained. The rutile, after separation and concentration from its ore, is treated with carbon and chlorine to form the compound $TiCl_4$. The tetrachloride is then treated with magnesium to form an impure deposit of titanium metal. The metal must be further treated to eliminate the impurities.

The U.S. Bureau of Mines has conducted research on the synthesis of rutile from domestic ilmenites (Ref. 35). In the reported process ilmenite concentrates with a titanium dioxide content as low as 33 percent by weight have been treated to produce a crystalline substitute for natural rutile suitable for direct chlorination. The process involves treating ilmenite charges with coke or carbon and a small quantity of lime. These ingredients are smelted together. Iron separates as pig iron, leaving a titania-enriched slag. The slag is subsequently treated with a phosphorous-bearing flux and oxygen to form rutile. A number of other methods of breaking ilmenite down into rutile and a separable iron compound have been suggested (Ref. 36). It is also possible to obtain rutile by reduction of ilmenite with hydrogen to produce iron oxide, water and rutile. This process will be discussed in connection with oxygen production in the next section.

The practicality of producing titanium on the Moon by the route

Ilmenite→Rutile→Titanium Tetrachloride→Titanium

appears dubious, however. First of all, on Earth ilmenite is separated from siliceous gangue either by a froth flotation or a magnetic method. Either method requires that the ores be crushed and ground. As pointed out previously, this operation, or handling of the lunar fines directly on the Moon, will probably present severe problems. Further, assuming that the transformation of ilmenite to rutile is handily accomplished, the Moon is not a good source for the chlorine which is needed for subsequent treatment. As in the case of aluminum, we are led to the conclusion that extraction of titanium from lunar materials by demonstrated Earth technology appears unpromising.

Oxygen. A number of previous studies have explored the means of extracting oxygen from lunar soils (Refs. 37-39). They include:

- Reduction of ilmenite with hydrogen according to the reaction

$$FeTiO_3 + H_2 \rightarrow Fe + TiO_2 + H_2O$$

Oxygen can be liberated at will by electrolysis of the water.

- Fluorine reduction according to the reaction

$$Lunar\ fines\ +\ F_2 \rightarrow metal\ fluorides\ +\ oxygen$$

The metal fluorides can be reduced to produce metals and potassium fluoride, which can be electrolyzed to regenerate fluorine. A similar process utilizing chlorine has also been suggested.

- Hydrogen sulfide reduction. Hydrogen sulfide will reduce oxides of iron, calcium and magnesium, which constitute about 35% by mass of the lunar fine. Metal sulfides and water are the products of the reaction. Sulfur can be regenerated from the metal sulfide.

- Carbothermic process. This process involves the following reactions:

$$Lunar\ fines + CH_4 \rightarrow CO + 2H_2O + metals$$

$$CO + 3H_2 \xrightarrow{catalyst} H_2O + CH_4$$

$$2H_2O \xrightarrow{electrolysis} 2H_2 + O_2$$

- Carbon/oxygen. In this process lunar fines are reacted with sodium hydroxide and carbon at 500°C in the presence of a nickel catalyst to form carbonates, carbon monoxide, and water. Further reactions include reacting the metal carbonates with acid to form metal chloride, carbon dioxide, and water. Carbon oxides from the preceding two reactions are reduced on an iron catalyst with hydrogen to form carbon und water. The water and the metal chlorides can be electrolyzed to generate oxygen, metals, and chlorine.

- Electrolytic reduction. Sodium hydroxide is used to dissolve the oxides at about 400°C. The solution is then electrolyzed to produce oxygen and sodium, which reacts with the oxides to form the metals.

It is the conclusion of one study (Ref. 38) that the hydrogen reduction process appears the most promising for oxygen production, even though a number of problems remain to be resolved. The method, however, is not seen as feasible for the production of metals.

An interesting study relevant to the present topic is presented in Ref. 40, in which the following route to oxygen production from various silicate minerals was studied:

$$Silicate\ Minerals + \underset{(C)}{Graphite} \rightarrow CO \underset{Catalyst}{\rightarrow} C + CO_2$$

$$CO_2 \underset{Photosynthesis}{\rightarrow} O_2 + Carbohydrates$$

Figure 65 shows the amount of CO formed in five hours as a function of the silica (SiO_2) content. It can be seen that minerals representative of those found in large quantities on the Moon (pyroxene, feldspar, olivine) are in the poor reducibility group.

Indicated Directions for Processing Development

The preceding consideration of the various methods for obtaining metals for structural purposes and oxygen for life support and water production indicates that Earth-bound technologies are probably inadequate to meet the needs of lunar processing. Two new approaches, however, appear promising for further research and development. The first is that of converting lunar materials into glasses and ceramics which can be utilized for construction purposes. The second is that of electrolysis in

82

molten silicate media. Some of the foreseen advantages and disadvantages of the two approaches are discussed in the following paragraphs.

Glass and Ceramic Construction Materials. The previous discussions of possible lunar extraction procedures highlight the difficulties of adopting Earth technologies to the environmental conditions likely to be encountered on the Moon and in space. Rather than try to "fight" the new environment, a more reasonable course would be to take advantage of the new circumstances and materials. This course, however, means that new technologies must be developed.

Glass and ceramic materials already abound in the lunar materials. Glass and ceramic materials, furthermore, could easily be produced on the Moon or in space by direct melting with concentrated solar energy. It appears natural, therefore, to explore the extent that these materials could be used for construction purposes.

Glass is already used in various forms for structural purposes. Whether it can substitute for metals in space construction, however, needs further investigation. Glass has the property of rarely failing under compression (Ref. 41), making it ideal for deep-sea vehicles, for example.

Theoretically glass should be very strong, but because of microscopic surface flaws, tensile strength for commercial glasses are in the range of 10,000 to 20,000 psi, compared with aluminum alloys at 85,000 psi and titanium alloys at 150,000 psi. A number of processing schemes have been proposed to take advantage of glass's compression strength. Sheets of glass can be strengthened by heating and then rapidly cooling to a temperature where plastic deformation is no longer possible. This treatment has the effect of putting the surface into compression and the interior into tension. Such tempering can more than double the strength of glass.

Another means of strengthening glass is by chemical treatment (Refs. 42 and 43). This process involves submerging the glass in a molten bath of the salt of an alkali ion. The bath alkali ions replace some of the glass alkali ions, and, being larger than the glass alkali ions, cause the surface to be put in a state of compression. Another technique involves overlaying a high-expansion glass with a low-expansion glass. A recent application has been to overlay glass to ceramic, which gives a high level of compressive stress in the glaze. Interestingly

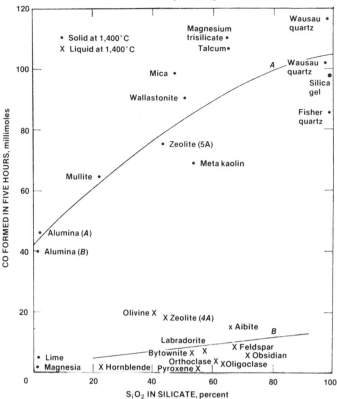

Figure 65 **Reducibility at 1400 C of Silicates as a Function of Their Silica Content (Ref. 40)**

enough, a microphotograph in Ref. 42 shows *plagioclase* crystals developing into the glaze-body interface, which results in a very strong bond between the glass and the ceramic.

Glass, incidentally, may be considered a perfectly elastic material provided that the stress is not large enough to cause fracture (Ref. 43); that is, the yield point and the fracture point coincide. Furthermore, glass can be formulated to withstand large thermal shocks.

The idea of utilizing ceramics as materials of construction is also not new. A cast basalt industry has apparently existed in Europe since about 1923 (Ref. 44). In this technology, crushed basalt rocks are fused in furnaces which are similar to open-hearth steel furnaces. The fusing temperatures are in the range 1320 to 1350°C. Crystallizing nuclei are introduced into the melt, and the melt is then cast. The physical properties of cast basalt are as follows:

Compressive strength	4000-5000 kg/cm²
Tensile strength	250-350 kg/cm²
	(3556-4978 psi)
Bending strength	400-450 kg/cm²

Mohrs' hardness	8-9
Abrasion hardness	0.06-0.08 cm^3/cm^2

Present cast basalt products include:

• Pipelines for pneumatic or hydraulic transport of waste rock in coal mines and for pneumatic transport of coal, coke, loose and powdered materials.

• Linings for hydraulic pipelines and channels, slag and ash conduits, and transport of dust.

• Tiles, form pieces, and special castings.

• Linings of floors which are exposed to mechanical and chemical stresses.

Recent developments in ceramics include materials for gas turbine engines, tools, wear parts and bearings, ballistic armor, optical and electronic applications (Ref. 45).

Electrolysis of Molten Lunar Soil to Produce Oxygen and Metals. Electrolysis was mentioned in the previous discussion in connection with the production of oxygen from lunar soil. The appeal of this method is that possibly the electrolysis could be conducted directly in molten lunar soil without the necessity of an intermediate separation process. A preliminary concept of a lunar electrolysis process consists of melting a pool of lunar soil with a solar concentrator, stirring in some soluble ionic salts, inserting a couple of electrodes, and then conducting the electrolysis with a device which converts solar energy to electrical energy. Conceivably one would require not even a container cell. The other equally appealing feature of the electrolysis techniques is that both oxygen and metals could be produced simultaneously.

Electrolysis in molten silicate media is a subject about which relatively little is known presently, although research momentum appears to be building. One study that is particularly relevant to the present discussion is presented in Ref. 46. Molten volcanic scoria, a material that bears a general similarity to basaltic lunar rocks, was electrolyzed to produce oxygen at the anode and a deposit of mixed metals at the cathode. The electrolysis was conducted at 1050° to 1250°C in boron nitride cells. A silicon carbide cathode and an iridium anode were employed. BaF_2 and LiF were used as the fluxing agents. Gases containing almost 14 volume percent oxygen were obtained. The average anode current efficiency was about 55 percent.

The electrochemical reactions by which oxygen and metals are produced are quite complicated. For orientation purposes, however, the following simplified reactions are presented:

$$Ti^{+4} + 4e \rightarrow Ti \text{ (Cathode)}$$

$$2O^{-2} \rightarrow O_2 \uparrow + 4e \text{ (Anode)}$$

Apparently some oxygen can also be obtained from the silicate anions in the melt via reactions typified by (Ref. 46):

$$SiO_4^{-4} \rightarrow SiO_2 + O_2 \uparrow + 4e$$

Obviously a number of further studies will have to be performed before the feasibility of electrolysis of molten lunar soils can be assessed. The concept, however, even now generates some ideas for evolving a practical process. For example, a first crude electrolysis as previously described could perhaps be conducted to extract oxygen and a mixture of metals. The mixture of metals could then be further separated by one of a variety of routes, depending on the composition of the deposit. Or, a controlled potential method could possibly be developed whereby one metal would be deposited at a relatively low voltage and another at a higher voltage.

A renewable supply of flux material may present a major problem with the electrolysis approach, because recycling is seen as prohibitively complex (Ref. 46). However, oxides such as CaO, Na_2O, and K_2O; or minerals such as apatite, $Ca_5(PO_4)_3(F,Cl)$; and whitlockite, $Ca_3(PO_4)_2$ possibly could be serviceable, although probably not very efficient, fluxes. The possibility should be investigated. Separation of the cited oxides from lunar soils should not present insurmountable problems. The minerals, however, although present on the Moon, may be somewhat difficult to separate from accompanying minerals. Another possibility is direct electrolysis of silicate melts in which ilmenite ($FeTiO_3$) is dissolved. Such a melt could perhaps be electrolyzed directly without the need for additional flux. Iron and titanium, however, would have to be subsequently separated.

As a final note, it should be mentioned that further research and development on molten soil electrolysis and glass/ceramic construction materials will have important consequences for Earth-bound technologies. The supply of high grade ores is running out or becoming increasingly more difficult to obtain because of increased world competition, and severe material shortages are anticipated in a number of areas (Ref. 47). Any advance in the areas of molten soil electrolysis and production of glass/ceramic construction materials, therefore, will be relevant not only for material supplies to L5, but also for meeting the materials challenges on Earth.

DISCUSSION

Q. You seem to be very discouraging about obtaining metals from the Moon even if we try to investigate technologies that aren't commonly used on the Earth. Would it be correct to say that chemical extraction of metals from the Moon will always require us to bring to the Moon materials from the Earth in masses comparable to the amount of metal we will get out?

A. The electrolysis methods I discussed appear to be quite promising. I think, though, that we will probably not take the technologies we have here on Earth and transport them readily to the Moon or L5.

Q. In an energy-intensive but materials-poor or product-poor environment, you would expend a lot of energy recycling such materials as CO_2. You won't throw that away; you would recycle it and start all over again. It would be much cheaper than taking it from the Earth.

A. I agree. I wonder how much effort would go into adapting an Earth-based technology, as compared with starting out on a whole new approach to the problem. I don't know how one can answer that question. Certainly it is possible to recycle, and perhaps the energy considerations won't be that great. Aluminum extraction by the Hall process is a tremendous consumer of energy here on Earth. Without any recycling, we use something like 20,000 kW-hr per ton of aluminum extracted from two tons of alumina. Even though theoretically we would have all the energy we would want on the Moon, I think it would still be a problem. To me, it would appear better to use that energy to melt a pool of silicate and do the electrolysis directly than to try to extract the alumina.

Q. The estimates that we have done so far indicate that about 4,000 MW-hr would be required to process some 80,000 tons of aluminum over a five year period. That's part of the energy budget, one hundred kilowatts, which was included in the first construction station.

But the main point is that if you are in an energy-rich, materials-poor situation, you do recycle. It looks to me that $FeTiO_3 + H_2$, cycling a couple of times with water electrolysis, seems to be enough to produce rather pure iron and pure titanium. Is that in error?

A. No. You can hydrogenate directly. However, the ilmenite is mixed in with the whole; it's usually about ten percent.

Q. But that is the magnetic part. Isn't the separation of ilmenite normally done by magnetic separation?

A. The ilmenite is separated from the rest of the materials by magnetic separation or froth flotation. You would have to concentrate your ilmenite. But it still seems to me that if you are going to use all of this energy, you could possibly use it more efficiently with a new technology than by trying to force an old technology into new clothes.

Q. Is the fact that the Bureau of Mines is even working on this subject an indication that the new technology is within a factor of five or ten of being competitive with the old one?

A. I get varying opinions on that, especially the lime-soda process. This is the process that has been explored most for getting aluminum out of anorthosite. My general overall impression from the conversations I have had with people at the Bureau of Mines and the Lunar Science Institute is that it is probably just marginal right now, but that given a more severe crunch for aluminum, it might become economically feasible.

Q. Can't we even distinguish yet between a factor of five and ten?

A. It is hard to say, for a process that is really not out of the development stage yet. I really can't give a good answer on that. The Bureau of Mines did have a program of development of extraterrestrial resources, the lunar materials.

They did a lot of studies with simulated lunar soils, and a number of the processes that I described came out as a result of that study. This reinforces my position that we should look to new technologies.

Q. *Do you have any estimate as to how long it would take to develop these new technologies?*

A. I think there is enough work going on so that it would not be all that long. For one thing, a lot of the lunar soil can be simulated by volcanic soil that can be found in Nevada, I understand. Also, it doesn't take big programs or a lot of money to do a great deal of research and development right here on Earth. I have indicated that the Bureau of Mines has done substantial studies. There are enough studies going on now, just for terrestrial applications (because we are running out of bauxite, for example) that I don't think it will take all that long to develop the new technologies we need for efficient extraction of lunar materials.

2. Industrial Development in Zero-G

Louis R. McCreight,
Space Sciences Laboratory
General Electric Company

Introduction

The idea for a Space Manufacturing Facility, and in particular the idea for obtaining raw materials from the Moon and using them to prepare solar power stations for generating electrical energy for use on Earth, has an appeal to the imagination.

It is my purpose to help to refine and further the idea by some comments and suggestions regarding the lunar resources and other space manufacturing activities. In essence, these are:

• We have much exploration to do on the Moon to find concentrations of the desired minerals in order to make lunar mining sufficiently attractive.

• A broader range of products (than solar power stations) would appear desirable and perhaps even necessary to make the economics of a space manufacturing facility at L4 or L5 more attractive. Some high value products in the latter area have been identified and are being studied as candidates for near-Earth-orbit, low-gravity space processing through the use of the shuttle in the 1980's and 1990's.

Lunar Mining. The Earth and its natural satellite, the Moon, are very similar in many respects and, of course, completely different in others. With respect to composition of the crust, they are on the average quite similar. However, with two exceptions, the recovery of natural resources is not attractive if one has to base the operation on averages. The ex-ceptions are the recovery of various gases from air and the recovery of certain salts from the oceans and some inland lakes or seas. In both of these cases, the ease of handling large volumes of fluids makes the operation economically viable. This is generally not so with minerals where the handling of large tonnages of solid materials is difficult and therefore expensive. It is therefore generally only practiced on the most concentrated available ores of the particular mineral desired. While there is no reason not to expect to find large concentrations of suitable ores on the Moon, they have not as yet been located. A major step in developing the space manufacturing facility will therefore need to be aimed at such exploration.

A recent paper (Ref. 48) and a report (Ref. 49) are of particular interest in supporting this view and relating it to the lunar mining situation. First, as Ehricke shows, the commercially exploitable concentrations of ores range from about 100 to over 10,000 times the background or average abundance of the minerals on the Earth. Next, the report by Nishioka gives estimates for the mining, mineral dressing, and refining costs of metals on the Moon as a function of mineral content in the ores. At a 1% concentration these costs may run $60/kg for mining plus $50-400/kg for dressing and refining. At 25% mineral content, the estimated costs drop to $2.50 per kg for mining, plus an additional $2 to $15/kg for mineral dressing and refining. These estimates are for large "commercial"-size operations (e.g. 4.5×10^6 kg/yr.) and of course also have large amounts of operating costs associated with them. For example, $250 x 10^6 for explosives is estimated in Nishioka's study. Ehricke's paper includes some novel uses of atomic bombs for this aspect of the mining operation, along with means of carrying out other desirable chemical operations and reactions simultaneously. These latter additional reactions are designed to yield directly such materials as oxygen, steam, various metals, and metallic compounds rather than just to loosen and break the rocks.

Ehricke's and Nishioka's excellent works contain many other details and references which the reader is encouraged to study if he desires further information. To these sources, one could also easily add other suggestions and refinements. Among these are, for example, the greater use of automation and solar energy in mining and refining lunar resources. Nevertheless, while a masterful job has been done, much more remains to make the operation viable. Among these are finding suitable ore concentrations, applying further technological innovations to help to lower costs, awaiting a sufficient market for materials and energy on Earth, etc.

In the latter area, improved materials which might be produced in an environment essentially free of gravity are worth speculating upon as a means of diversifying and broadening the operations in a space colony. This could possibly improve the utilization of materials, facilities, and personnel so as to hasten the day when the operations could become less speculative and more viable.

Products of Space Processing. For the past decade, ideas for utilizing the space environment to process materials for use on Earth have been under study. While space offers radiation, low temperature, solar energy, moderate vacuum with a tremendous pumping capacity, and prolonged nearly zero gravity, it is only the last item that is unattainable on Earth. There are many ideas for melting and solidifying materials, growing crystals, and performing various purification processes, all of which are affected by convection and sedimentation problems on Earth. All have in common the utilization of the low-gravity environment during the fluid phase condition (including molten, solution, suspensions, etc.) of the materials. Of these ideas a number of them were tried as simple experiments and demonstrations on the last few Apollo flights and then more elaborately on the Skylab. It was in the latter missions that there appeared some very solid

evidence for the ideas that more perfect crystals of electronic materials could be prepared by new melt and solidification techniques. Further experiments are scheduled to be performed on the Apollo-Soyuz Test Project (ASTP) in July 1975, and others, which can be performed in short times (5-15 minutes of zero-g), are to be tried on sounding-rocket flights over the next few years before the space shuttle is available.

Of all of the ideas, two general fields of materials and processes stand out as having both economical and technical justification for operation in zero-g. These are the preparation of specialty materials, especially the growth of some single crystals, and the preparation of certain biologicals. There well may be other products and processes identified from the research and development now underway. Conversely, there is a great likelihood that any particular product identified now may be eliminated from interest by new developments in the years before the space shuttle can really make space processing available. Nevertheless, it is likely that the basic processes of interest now will continue to be of interest. It should be remembered that only gravity-driven phenomena are attenuated; phenomena can still be driven, sometimes beneficially and sometimes detrimentally, by other forces and effects such as surface tension, diffusion, or heat transfer by conduction and radiation, in space as on Earth.

Inorganic Materials

From the inorganic materials field, there are potentially an almost infinite variety of compositions, forms and microstructures for which to consider processing in space. Even if one eliminates the low-value-per-pound, high-volume structural and building materials which are important members of this class, there are still many viable candidates and a great deal of interest in experimenting with them in space. These generally fall into two categories of materials and processes. First are the electronic materials which are generally, but not exclusively, desired in single crystal form. Secondly, there are innumerable compositions in which specialized melting and solidification are desired. Among the operations which are expected to be more easily achievable in space will be containerless melting and supercooling, as well as specialized solidification such as by unidirectional processes without sedimentation or thermal convection problems.

Electronic Materials. The use of the relatively

quiet controllable space environment to prepare materials for very high purity and perfection, especially in single-crystal form, was early identified as an attractive venture. Float zone refining and crystal growth in space as a means of preparing very large diameter crystals was first suggested by Pfann in 1958 (Ref. 50).

There are many other potential examples of materials in single-crystal form desired for research and exploratory development purposes. However, the most likely candidates for actual processing in space will probably be the semi-conductor and ceramic oxide crystals for electronic and electro-optical devices, which have very high value because of the important basic role they play in the performance of the device. Current examples include germanium, gallium arsenide, bismuth germanate, and lithium niobate.

However, to an even greater degree than in biologicals, one must be aware of the rapid changes in technology. For example, some oxide-type crystals identified only two to three years ago as being of potential interest for space processing studies are already now expected to be supplanted by thin films. While the thin films could conceivably be made more perfect in space, that is not too likely to be an economically viable process or product to consider. There are nevertheless some other specialty materials in crystal form which are likely to warrant further study and consideration for space processing. In particular, these seem to be melt-grown and solution-grown materials of both semi-conductors and other electronic or electro-optical materials.

Some of these were the subject of Skylab experiments and others have been considered in depth in a study for NASA (Ref. 51). Technical assessment has indicated that there are six areas of advanced applications where systems performance is directly dependent on the quality of the ceramic oxide and non-silicon semiconducting compound electronic crystals used. At the time of the study, these were computer memories, optical communications, opto-electronics, pyroelectric detection, surface acoustics, and ultrasonics. Space processing has the potential for providing crystals with the required perfection, size, and surface smoothness at high yields in production quantities to enable systems in each of the aforementioned areas to come close to their performance figures of merit.

Magnetic bubble memories, which operate on rare-earth iron garnet crystals, were expected to provide the greatest demand for high quality single crystals as of a few years ago. By the end of the decade, they were thought to fill the critical gap that exists between electronically and electromechanically addressable storage. They would complement semiconductor silicon crystal memories in computer structures, since the former is used in the fast memory section, and the latter for large storage in the bulk memory section. They may still fulfill these predictions, but in thin-film forms rather than bulk-crystal forms.

The next highest demand appears to be for high quality electro-optic crystals, such as lithium niobate, lithium tantalate, barium sodium niobate, bismuth germanate, lead germanate, bismuth titanate, gadolinium molybdate, lithium iodate, and triglycine sulfate. There are a wide range of compositions to process here, since devices based on electro-optic phenomena are being developed for use across the total range of the cited applications. The crystals are used as optical storage media and page composers in holographic memories, light modulators in optical communication systems, pyroelectric detectors in infrared thermal imaging systems, surface wave acoustic delay lines in radar, navigation and communication systems, and ultrasonic filters in the communications industry. The third highest demand will be for opto-electronic crystals such as gallium phosphide and yttria aluminum garnet, for light-emitting diode displays and high power crystalline lasers respectively.

However, to perhaps a greater degree than in most technical areas, progress is rapid and revolutionary in this field. Thus, magnetic bubble memories operating on oxide crystals may be supplemented by a thin film technology which can be implemented sufficiently on the ground. As of this writing, the melt-grown and solution-grown materials of both semiconductors and other electronic or electro-optical materials mentioned above remain of interest.

The ceramic oxide and non-silicon semiconducting crystals that will benefit from space processing are those grown from a liquid or vapor phase. The majority are grown by liquid techniques which include the Czochralski or melt growth technique, solution or flux growth, and the liquid-phase epitaxial growth of single-crystal films. In this study, solution has been interpreted broadly to include melt-grown crystals and liquid epitaxy from a flux.

89

It is generally agreed that there is a great likelihood of being able to prepare higher perfection crystals by solution-type processes in the absence of gravity-induced effects. If successful, the resulting more perfect crystals should be more valuable from either or both of two viewpoints. First, they should offer higher yields of usable crystals, and secondly, the higher perfection should offer better performance in applications. The benefit of higher yield is quite directly translatable into economic terms. However, any benefit due to higher perfection is more difficult to predict, but should be of great value in certain applications, so it is a principal reason for space processing experiments. Possible outcomes of such experiments include (1) a general improvement of space-processed crystals compared to the same compositions from terrestrial sources, and (2) a more intriguing possibility that some compositions will be improved more than others and thereby change the ranking of crystals being considered for an application.

Melting and Solidification. In space one can perform this most common of materials-processing steps free of containers. For very reactive or very refractory materials, this is an obvious advantage. In other cases, this freedom from containers may be more subtle. For example, the preparation of glassy forms of oxides which we normally see in crystalline form is possible when the container is not present to nucleate the growth of the crystals (Refs. 52 and 53).

This is one of the early ideas which has been postulated and examined in quite some detail with interesting results. The basic idea is to use oxides which normally do not yield transparent amorphous products here on Earth due to the ease with which they nucleate and crystallize on cooling in contact with a mold or crucible. By melting and cooling them out of contact with such surfaces, it has been shown possible to make some high-index-of-refraction glasses of such combinations as up to 20 percent calcia (CaO) and silica (SiO_2), plus 80 percent or more of any of the following oxides: Al_2O_3, Ga_2O_3, In_2O_3, La_2O_3, ZrO_2, HfO_2, Nb_2O_5 and Ta_2O_5. In addition, glasses from several individual pure rare Earth oxides have been prepared.

Many of these amorphous oxides have shown an index of refraction greater than 2.0, and some would be expected also to offer other useful properties, such as environmental resistance.

Another example may be from the monotectics

which exhibit the phenomenon of segregation of the liquids, on Earth, by virtue of density differences (Ref. 54). In the weightless environment this separation should not occur, and a matrix of one phase with dispersion of the other phase throughout should be obtained. Unique new alloys and intermetallic compounds with unique electronic properties may be prepared from melts of monotectic composition and hypermonotectic composition (Ref. 55). If thermal gradients can be adjusted across a freely floating melt, then directionally solidified composites could be produced. An example is Fe-Pb, which may have unique magnetic properties. Another example is Hg-Te, which forms the semiconducting intermetallic compound HgTe. Through supercooling melts of monotectic or hypermonotectic compositions, new intermetallic compounds, new alloy compositions, or amorphous materials may be formed. The chalcogenide glasses, SeSb, are other examples.

Yet another example has been demonstrated on Skylab as experiment M557 (Ref. 56), in which normally inmiscible alloys were melted and remained more intimately mixed upon solidification, with some interesting indications of superconducting behavior.

Another area of potential interest is the possibility of being able to purify melts by evaporating impurities from a containerless melt. This operation may make use of the space vacuum, although that would not be the primary rationale for performing the operation in space. This operation could then be followed by supercooling, with the likelihood of obtaining greater degrees of supercooling than are achieved here on Earth.

For many potentially valuable experiments one would like to have a gradient available for crystal growth by unidirectional solidification. This might initially be best done with a crucible to hold the melt; however, with careful control a containerless operation seems possible. In any case, numerous possible alloy experiments and potential products come to mind.

Unidirectionally Solidified Composites. Technologically valuable materials have been produced by controlled directional solidification of melts for many years. In the field of crystal growth, the development of the Bridgeman furnace technique and later development of floating zone refining techniques enabled specimens of high purity and high crystalline perfection to be produced. In the field of engineering materials it has been known for over a decade that directional solidification of alloy systems (non-eutectic) resulted in significant improvements in mechanical properties. Since 1958 intensive studies have been performed on eutectic and near-eutectic melts of metals, oxides, and salts because of the unique microstructures that can be developed in these systems under appropriate conditions. The microstructures consist of regular arrays of parallel lamellae of the different phases or of arrays of rods of one phase in a matrix of another. These mixed-phase composites have extraordinary potential for scientific and engineering developments in such diverse fields as high temperature metallurgy, unique optical and electro-optical systems, toughened ceramics, superconducting systems, and in organic and polymeric systems.

The central idea in what is called convectionless directional solidification processes is the attainment of very detailed control over the production of solid materials from melts. Weightlessness appears to make such control feasible because it can be used to suppress the random effects of convection, so the heat and mass transport effects that govern solidification become highly predictable. In most practical applications considered so far, control is exercised by producing a prescribed unidirectional temperature gradient in the melt so that solidification proceeds at a controlled and preferably constant rate.

Theoretical analyses of eutectic solidification show that the interlamellar spacing λ is related to the growth rate V by the expression $\lambda_2 V = \text{constant}$. Experiments have shown that significantly improved properties are achieved in materials with the finest interlamellar spacing, i.e. those grown at high rates in the presence of a steep temperature gradient G at the solidification interface. Investigations at General Electric's Corporate Research and Development Center, notably by VerSnyder and Guard and later by Cline and Livingston, have shown that highly desirable eutectic microstructures can be obtained by solidification of a wide range of alloy systems at speeds of up to 2 mm per second. Recent experience in the field has demonstrated that compositions appreciably removed from the eutectic point can be solidified if the growth rate V and associated temperature gradient G are high. This experience is of great practical importance, since most valuable technological alloys are off-eutectic compositions and contain alloying additives of diverse chemical nature.

Disturbances in the microstructural development during eutectic solidification have been attributed to convectional disturbances in the liquid phase. Theoretical treatments of eutectic growth generally assume that there is no convection in the melt. However, the effects of convection on development of cellular microstructures and of fault structures related to these instabilities in the liquid are well established. Experience in practical systems in terrestrial conditions has shown that growth rates for successful microstructure development are typically between 10^{-4} and 10^{-2} cm/sec. Cline and Livingston of General Electric have successfully solidified optimum microstructures from eutectic compositions at speeds up to 2×10^{-1} cm/sec. using high-purity alloy components. The achievement of high growth velocity may be related to the absence of impurities, since impurity concentration ahead of a solidifying interface is known to influence the breakdown of aligned microstructures and leads to supercooling and formation of cellular interfaces.

There are, of course, other eutectic compositions of interest besides the structural metals. Among these are some inorganic salts, and some super-conducting and possibly some semiconductor alloys which might benefit from and warrant the cost of zero-g processing. When considering the space processing of eutectic composites for turbine applications, cost is likely to be a major factor. Even though perhaps a much more rapid solidification rate could be attained in space which would (l) reduce the mold reactions, (2) reduce sedimentation of heavy alloy constituents and (3) reduce the present high investment in equipment to perform the process here on Earth, it seems unlikely that the benefits would equal the cost. Some critical experiments, however, may yield additional technical insight.

Biologicals

Biological products are very necessary in our health care needs. They are often difficult to make reproducibly because they are not well defined. This appears to be especially true of some which are concentrates of various body fluids. While there is some potential for ultimately finding the exact structures and functions of certain of these complex molecules to a degree that would permit synthesis, this seems unlikely for all or even a majority of such products. It therefore appears that separation or purification processes to obtain these products from natural sources will continue to be of importance. There are a number of basic well-known processes such as filtration, centrifugation,

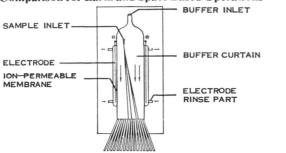

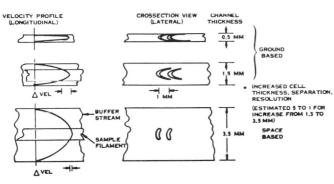

chemical reaction, and precipitation. There are also several other techniques used to prepare samples for defining the purity and performing various tests on the products. Among these, electrophoresis in its many forms or variations stands out as the principal and most elegant method for the analytical separation of complex biological mixtures. Although preparative fluid electrophoresis machines have been developed, they have never been very successful or widely used due to gravity-induced convection and sedimentation and the low through-put that results from attempts to minimize these effects. Staff members of the Wyeth Laboratories, Radnor, Pa., suggested in the spring of 1969 that effective preparative electrophoresis yielding relatively large quantities of product may be possible in almost zero-g conditions. Figure 66 shows the projected improvement by space operation of a fluid-flow electrophoretic separator versus the currently available Earth-based machines.

Electrophoretic separation processes may take many superficially different forms, but all are based on electrochemical effects that cause particles to take on electrical charges when suspended in aqueous solution. The nature of these charges is determined by the equilibrium between particle surfaces and ions in the solution, so that the charges are characteristic of the particles but also can be manipulated to some extent by changing the solution composition. Forces can be applied to particles charged in this way by applying an electric

field to the solution, and when this is done each particle will move along the direction of the field at a constant velocity such that drag forces exerted by the surrounding liquid are equal and opposite to the electric force on the particle. In general, therefore, each kind of particle suspended in a solution moves with a characteristic velocity determined partly by its chemical nature and partly by its size and shape when an electric field is applied, and particles that move at different velocities can be physically separated and separately collected.

Space flight conditions may benefit electrophoretic separation processes by suppressing convective effects in the solutions, but the main advantage appears to be that weightlessness makes it possible to apply these processes to heavy particles that could not be maintained in suspension by any means on the ground. This class of particles includes living human and animal cells, and several applications in medical research and therapeutic procedures have been proposed for pure preparations of particular types of cells.

Gravitational effects are even serious in all but the smallest analytical devices. Gels, paper, and starches, along with small dimensions, are often used to minimize convection and sedimentation in these apparati. In space, one should gain a significant improvement in both the resolution and through-put of a continuous-fluid electrophoresis apparatus primarily by being able to increase the cell thickness from the currently available 0.5 to 1.5 mm thicknesses to 4 to 6 or even 8 mm. This should minimize the wall effects (electro-osmosis) and thereby permit significantly greater resolution and greater through-put or reduced time to perform any given separation.

Other refinements may also become available, such as various focussing techniques to further improve the resolution, and various hydrodynamic flow ideas for improving the efficiency either in the form of through-put or the eventual need to reprocess some of the buffer solutions used in the processing.

As previously mentioned, centrifugation is a widely used analytical as well as preparative technique. It may also be susceptible to significant improvement if performed in the micro-gravity of space. Generally about half of the drive energy is transformed into heat by the frictional effects in the drive. This heat is conducted to the rotor and can cause convection within the rotor charge. There are also vibrational forces which can disrupt

92

resolution of separation. While there have been some excellent magnetically supported and driven rotors developed (by Beams), they may not be applicable to these problems. Thus, there appears to be a sufficient rationale to suggest including specially designed space centrifugation equipment aboard a space biology research facility to ascertain the possible benefits of a non-contacting support system for rotors in space.

There is also a potential need and perhaps a special benefit for performing lyophilization (or freeze drying) in space. It will likely be a necessary adjunct of the preparation of some biologicals as a means of preserving them. In addition, it may well be that performing lyophilization in zero-g may provide special benefits in permitting evaporation of the ice from all surfaces of a particle at a time. There are, of course, ways to suspend small ice/biological particles here on Earth, but usually only with other difficulties to overcome, or with a potentially detrimental effect.

Economic Considerations. The human value of more effective biologicals is of course impossible to measure. The economic value of freeing some 15,000 U.S. renal patients now on dialysis machines who might be helped by the preparation of purer erythropoietin has been estimated to be of the order of 1 billion dollars. Thus humanitarian and societal motivation in this area is unusually high, perhaps even greater than the basic economic value. Some simple projections for space processing of biologicals can be made based on certain assumptions.

It is presumed first that for efficiency and economy, as much of the processing as possible will be done here on Earth. Then only a reasonably pure concentrate will be taken to space for one more, or perhaps a few, processing steps. In addition, the large quantities of water normally used in biological processing are presumed to be recoverable and reusable in space so that this commodity will not need to be completely resupplied from Earth for each product. Finally, however, the general rule that each biological product should be prepared in isolation from other products in order to avoid cross-contamination is likely to be necessary. This may necessitate some special scheduling, but should not create any insurmountable problems.

Vaccines are the best-defined available product on which to base projections for the future. In the U.S., some 60 million doses of vaccine are used annually. If we utilize the World Health Organization's estimates of world population in 1990-2000 as 5 billion, and assume the same rate of vaccine application world-wide as is now current in the U.S., we project the need for about 1.5 billion doses of vaccine per year. Using a conservative average number of 100,000 doses per gram of active ingredient, we calculate the need for 15,000 grams of active ingredients per year. Many currently used and very fine biological products are at best quite dilute or impure (but not necessarily with harmful impurities). The purity may range from less than 1% to about 50%. This is assumed to be the starting material for a space purification operation. Therefore, the mass of starting material could range from 2 to 100 times the 15,000-gram final product mass derived above. Assuming a conservative average of 50, it is expected that some 750 kg of partially purified vaccines might be used as the starting material. In addition, some several hundred kilograms of water would be required. While vaccines generally cost about 20¢ per unit to produce, some examples of higher costs for greater specificity indicate that $1.00 per unit may be an acceptable value. This then indicates a $1.5 billion activity in vaccines alone, a fraction of which may require space operations.

The processing in space of some other biological products such as cells and the blood derivatives, while less specifically calculable, could easily exceed the estimates for vaccines by up to an order of magnitude in volume and value. In general, the products discussed below have been the subject of significant efforts to (1) purify them at all or (2) purify them with a reasonable yield. The most prominent include prebeta lipoprotein, erythropoietin, clotting factor VIII, virus subunit vaccines, immunoglobulin G, and viable human lymphocytes.

These potential products represent purification problems today in spite of a great deal of continuing effort. They are, however, in all likelihood not the products which will represent a challenge and a need ten years from now. They are discussed, then, more as examples of what might be done in the near future than as specific recommendations for processing in the 1980's or later on the space shuttle. In any case, the basic processing and the purification problems are expected to remain the same but for different products.

Lipoproteins. Lipoproteins represent a class of protein capable of transporting various types of important lipids throughout the body. They are heterogeneous and have been classified on the basis of density, ultracentrifugation flotation units, and electrophoretic mobility. The lipoproteins with a density greater than 1.063 are classified as high-density lipoproteins (HDL) and migrate electrophoretically near the alpha-1 globulins, just behind albumin. Lipoproteins with densities between 1.006 and 1.063 are classified as low-density lipoproteins (LDL) and migrate electrophoretically with the alpha-2 or delta globulins, depending on the substrate used..

Changes in the relative and absolute amounts of the various lipoproteins in serum are characteristic of a variety of diseases including nephritis, diabetes, hypothyroidism, and hepatitis. But the primary interest in the separation of lipoproteins stems from the relationship of prebeta lipid with coronary artery disease, the band becoming more intense and heavily laden with triglycerides following myocardial infarction (Refs. 57 and 58). The objective of an electrophoretic separation would be to obtain subclasses of one of the high density lipoprotein classes in sufficient quantity for analysis. A better knowledge of specific protein families within the ultracentrifugal flotation classes is important in the study of atherosclerosis.

Lipoproteins have been separated electrophoretically under a number of conditions. The most successful preparative separations have been carried out on paper (Ref. 59), but even these separations are rather marginal and the throughput extremely low. Free electrophoresis is clearly one of the most promising solutions to the separation problems, and the combination of high-resolution requirements and large sample size make consideration of zero-g processing attractive.

Erythropoietin. Erythropoietin is a hormone capable of increasing the total number and volume of circulating red blood cells in a normal animal. It is potentially of great value to patients suffering from renal failure or anemia. The treatment presently in use involves repeated transfusion of whole blood or red cells, either of which leads to a high probability of serum hepatitis and hepatic complications due to excess iron.

Some investigators have been able to accomplish partial purification of plasma and urinary erythropoietin by combining ion exchange, precipitation, and absorption methods (Ref. 60). However, the erythropoietin available for study still contains contaminating proteins, and while mice as test animals apparently tolerate the contaminants, humans are not so tolerant.

Relatively high purity erythropoietin ($\sim 50\%$) has been reported in the laboratory (Ref. 61) but only at very low yields. Since the amount of raw material is limited, the practical use of high purity erythropoietin will require other purification methods which minimize the loss of activity.

Gel electrophoresis has been used (Ref. 62) for purification of erythropoietin with some success and recovery of initial activity between 20 and 65%. There is, therefore, a reasonable expectation that free electrophoresis with its simpler recovery of fractions may prove to be a practical separation method. Assay of the material by *in vitro* and *in vivo* techniques would require about 0.1 mg of product, corresponding to about 40 mg of the dry material current available from NIH. At the usual dilution this represents about 4 ml of sample solution to be electrophoresed.

The potential consumption of safe, clinically effective erythropoietin is difficult to estimate since, as mentioned above, trials with humans have not been performed. However, if we estimate that 1.5×10^4 people may need the material and that two injections per week of 0.1 mg of material will suffice for each person, then some 60 kg of crude erythropoietin as presently available would have to be processed each year. This amounts to 6000 liters of diluted sample every year.

Factor VIII (Antihemophilic Factor). The usual methods for revovery of antihemophilic factor (AHF or Factor VIII) from fresh frozen plasma do not provide adequate amounts of Factor VIII concentrate to meet the needs of hemophiliacs. However, a number of unusual sources are available which can contribute greatly to the supply of this critically useful material. In a search for additional Factor VIII sources, the American Red Cross (Ref. 63) has investigated the use of frozen cryoethanol precipitate (cryo) made available as a discarded by-product of large-scale plasma fractionation. This material is removed from fresh frozen plasma in the first ethanol fractionation step in order to obtain more filterable fractions in the subsequent Cohn ethanol procedure (Ref. 64). The Factor VIII activity of cryo is preserved for many months in the frozen state, making it possible to stockpile large quantities for processing at a convenient time and location without interfering with the routine plasma fractionation.

Intermediate- and a high-purity Factor VIII concentrates for clinical use have been prepared on a large scale by cryoethanol precipitation, extraction of the precipitate with tris buffer, and fractionation with polyethylene glycol (Ref. 65). With fractionation of 100 liters or more fresh frozen plasma, the intermediate material shows a 30% yield and 14-30-fold purification.

Such "intermediate" and "high" purity materials are apparently useful in the treatment of hemophiliacs, but in order to keep a proper frame of reference, we must remember that "high-purity" Factor VIII contains less than 3% of Factor VIII while the "intermediate purity" material contains less than 0.3% of the active material (Ref. 66).

While electrophoretic purification of some of the suggested products (e.g., erythropoietin and lymphocytes) has received the enthusiastic support of most – if not all – of the corresponding experts, the same cannot truly be said for Factor VIII. In this case there is a difference of opinion between those who are or have been involved with the development and use of the current purification methods, and those whose business is medical research and its application to the welfare of the public. The U.S. Food and Drug Administration is actively investigating the effects on patients of the present Factor VIII. On the one hand, there is a material available which can be administered to hemophiliacs (at a cost of up to $20,000 per year) to prevent hemorrhage. On the other hand, the present methods of collection and isolation are never likely to make sufficient Factor VIII available for all 100,000 to 200,000 hemophiliacs in the United States, nor is it likely that the price will ever be reduced to an acceptable level.

In order to satisfy these objectives, a far better purification method must be found, or the nature of Factor VIII must be identified and a synthetic substitute be developed. The magnitude of the separation problem can be grasped by considering that from 3000 liters of human blood one might isolate 1.5 kg of the current "high purity" Factor VIII. This might be dissolved in 150 liters of buffer and electrophoresed to produce 15 g of pure material.

Virus Subunit Vaccines. There may be two reasons why viral structural components are or should be used for immunization:
(1) Cells utilized to cultivate the virus may produce, in addition to virus particles, unassembled viral structural proteins in excess. If at least some of these proteins represent the major contribution to the immunizing potency (with respect to induction of VN antibodies) it

would be unreasonable to isolate and purify the virus for use as the only component in a vaccine.

(2) The use for vaccination of morphologically intact virus, either infectious or rendered noninfectious by chemical or physical methods, may be connected with real and hypothetical dangers which justify the exclusive utilization of viral structural components for this purpose.

The main reason for using virus vaccines not containing intact virions is the fear that viral genomes might initiate a carcinogenic process in vaccines. To alleviate such fears with respect to the use of vaccines consisting of capsid components, absolute evidence must be given that they do not contain intact viral DNA or DNA fragments which might carry undesirable genetic messages (Ref. 67).

The problem of purification of virus subunit vaccines by free electrophoresis is mentioned because it represents a biologically unusual purification. while biologicals are sometimes called "high purity" when they contain 3% active ingredient and 97% impurities, the separation of the virus subunits from contaminating proteins must be absolute. Attempts to estimate the required improvement in resolution would be meaningless in the absence of experimental work on specific vaccines. Compare, for instance, the variety of results obtained by Sarkar (Ref. 68) in the separation of tobacco mosaic virus nucleic acid and protein by free-flow electrophoresis, depending on the particular strain of virus. With TMV-vulgare the two peaks were clearly separated by eight or nine product fractions which contained neither material.

Immunoglobulin G. There are five major classes of immunoglobulins which differ in structure and functional properties (Ref. 69). These classes are IgG, IgM, IgA, IgD and IgE. Each is composed of at least two types of peptide chains, light chains and heavy chains. The heavy chains are characteristic of the class of immunoglobulin while the light chains are common to all.

Immunoglobulin G (IgG), the major immunoglobulin found in most antisera, is a tetrameric molecule consisting of 2 light chains and two heavy chains. In the human at least 4 different sub-types of IgG heavy chains are found.

Multiple myeloma is a malignancy of the antibody-forming cells. Although many myeloma proteins react with antigens, the appropriate antigens for most are unknown. It is important to be able to separate a series of homogeneous antibodies directed toward known sub-determinant areas from the serus of a given animal. Studies of these may provide evidences of the manner in which antibodies are synthesized.

In the long run these studies will provide means for separating the various antibodies to a single antigen. Separated antibodies may have practical applications in cancer studies where antibodies which inhibit cell proliferation compete with those which enhance growth. In the treatment and prophylaxis of infectious disease, purified antibodies should be of great value. From the theoretical side, purification should allow structural determinations of antibodies to elicit their mode of action and perhaps help shed light on the mechanism of their synthesis.

We doubt that successful separation can be achieved on Earth by free electrophoresis. Residence times on the order of ten minutes are not used because the curtain flow is so slow that it lacks the stabilization inherent in a laminar flow system, the inevitable density difference between sample and curtain becomes a significant factor, and sample diffusion to the nearby wall creates unacceptable band spreading. All these problems are eliminated or alleviated in space, and long residence times should become practical.

Cell Populations. The electrophoretic separation of viable cells into functional subgroups dates back at least ten years. For example, Hannig (Ref. 70) reported the separation of viable tumor cells from normal cells in 1964. During about the last three years, though, the interest in such separations appears to have grown by an order of magnitude. It is now probably the most exciting and promising field of biochemical separations, and its possible scope expands almost daily, It may be possible to separate in a practical fashion urokinase-producing cells from fetal kidney cells (Ref. 71); insulin-producing cells from the other pancreatic cells; or generally, enzyme-producing cells from their inactive neighbors.

More far-reaching in its benefits may be the practical difficulties encountered in understanding immunological phenomena on a cellular level in the absence of a reliable method for fractionation of lymphocytes. Such a method must be specific and reproducible; the number of cells must be high

enough to allow them to be tested after separation; and the viability of cells must be maintained by the separation method. An optimal result of this method would be reached if differences in the physical properties which allow separation were also expressed by defined functions. In investigating immune systems, Hannig has succeeded in fractionating lymphoid cells from lymph nodes of the rat (Ref. 72), and localizing the antibody-producing clones in small defined fractions of the overall cell distribution. From these results, it might be concluded that there is indeed an indirect relationship between the electrophoretic mobility of cells and their functional properties (Refs. 73, 74).

A close relationship to the development of B-cells is shown by the hemopoietic stem cells. The hemopoietic stem cell is defined by two properties, the ability of self-renewal and differentiation into hemic cells. The majority of stem cells in bone marrow migrate with low electrophoretic mobility and represent the resting stem cell pool. There is good evidence that this resting stem pool is identical with the uncommitted stem cell. A minority of stem cells in the bone marrow migrate with high electrophoretic mobility, contributing to a population of high mitotic turnover.

The fact that T-cells and pluripotential hemopoietic stem cells in bone marrow could be electrophoretically separated suggested to Hannig that the transplantation of allogenic purified stem cells into lethally irradiated immunotolerant recipients could avoid a secondary disease. The hypothesis has been established by transplantation of electrophoretically separated bone marrow cells from a donor mouse into a recipient. All mice survived the X irradiation, as they were protected by uncommitted or committed stem cells. However, the mice which received fractions of high electrophoretic mobility suffered after some weeks from secondary disease which led to death, whereas the mice which received the bone marrow fractions of low electrophoretic mobility survived without any sign of disease for at least 8 months (Ref. 75).

Every year in the United States some 30-35,000 people die of malignant neoplasms, including neoplasms of lymphatic and hematopoietic tissue. If even one third of these were to be treated according to the above technique (i.e., 10^4 people), and the dose/mass ratios for mice and humans are assumed to be about the same, then some 10^{12} cells per year would have to be processed. At a concentration of 2×10^7 cells/ml (the usual concentration on Earth) this corresponds to 50 liters of cell suspension per year – a large but not impossible task for a small number of high-capacity flow units.

Particularly in the case of lymphoid cells, the principal improvement anticipated from free electrophoresis in space is an improvement in resolution. To our knowledge, no clean separation of fractions of lymphoid cells has been reported. One type of cell dominates the high electrophoretic mobility region; another the low-mobility region. The distribution of cells in the product fraction collectors strongly indicates the presence of several partially separated, but not resolved, groupings of cells. It is, of course, possible that there really is a continuum of cell types represented, and that they will not be separated regardless of improved resolution. The evidence available at this time, however, makes this hypothesis unlikely.

Conclusion

While the ideas expressed for processing high value products in space are still speculative, they nevertheless hold much promise for being both technologically and economically valid. As such they may provide a useful diversification and foundation for the development of the viable colonization of space.

It should be reemphasized that the individual products discussed may very well be displaced by others, even if the processes and general fields of endeavor prove valuable.

Acknowledgment

Both the work and reports of several associates in this field which have generally influenced this paper are gratefully acknowledged. In particular, the discussion of specific biologicals was prepared by Dr. Richard N. Griffin, who deserves much credit for defining the potential for preparative methods on these products.

DISCUSSION

Q. *When scientists and experts in the field of electrophoresis review the subject, they generally conclude that what you have just said is highly speculative and may not be true at all. A lot more money goes into space than into plain old Earth-bound applications. Perhaps the same effort devoted to Earth-based research might produce even better expectations.*

A. That's very true, but it's difficult to cover all the aspects of so complex a field in so short a time. As you say, there has been a lot of speculation and there has been a lot of argument as to which way to go on electrophoresis, whether it should be static or continuous flow. It is probably too big a subject to go into at this point.

Q. *Would space manufacturing of single crystals produce very strong crystal structures? Stronger than on Earth?*

A. I don't know about the increase in strength. What we are looking for primarily are improved optical properties.

Q. *Would zero gravity help in vapor deposition of carbon to make diamonds or other unique materials?*

A. We were quite involved in aluminum oxide whiskers about ten to fifteen year ago. We achieved material with a tensile strength that was something like 6.2 million psi. I'm not sure I can substantiate that, but I know that in many cases we were hitting up around two million psi without any great trouble. It was our impression, watching these whiskers grow with time, that gravity doesn't really affect them much. We think it's more a function of the transport of the vapors. There have been some movies in which iron whiskers would tip over and grow downwards. That's a gravity effect, but I think it was more like going after the nutrient in the gas stream. There was another corollary experiment on Skylab in which germanium selenide and germanium telluride crystals were grown by vapor deposition. Very high perfection and a large size crystal were achieved by growing it in space. Whether that is really unique, whether it couldn't be duplicated on the ground we can't be absolutely sure, but in any case, it was certainly a new result.

3. Production, Assembly, and High-Vacuum Fabrication

C. Mel Adams
University of Cincinnati

There are two broad frameworks for this topic: fabrication and manufacturing. Presumably fabrication would be of higher priority and manufacturing would come later. My discussion will try to make not too many assumptions about materials to be processed, being influenced by the obvious processes and processing involved.

The first subject of interest is the processing of solid materials, mostly metals and alloys, but not necessarily the metals and alloys we work with on Earth. There are application factors that may cause materials which are unsuitable for functions on Earth to work well in space. Materials can be processed in the zero-gravity and/or high-vacuum environment of space far more readily than on Earth. Solid objects can be transported back to Earth because of unusual properties, distribution of phases, or properties that we can't foresee from Earth today. The germane boundary conditions are that vacuum is available for processing, and so is low (or variable) gravity. The kinds of processing I will discuss involve the shaping of materials.

Grodzka discussed chemical processing in a previous paper, outlining several interesting procedures that are well advanced on Earth, although not yet commercial, for producing aluminum from low-grade bauxite. Because of impending shortages there will have to be changes, even for terrestrial extraction of aluminum from ores. Many of these schemes could lend themselves, with adaptation, to lunar or space environments.

Shaping is basically cutting, forming, and joining materials; in other words, metal fabrication techniques. Some things that we have learned and developed on Earth would appear to be applicable to space and certain other things not, either for reasons of energy or special fuel requirements.

Welding and brazing are different in some particulars in space than they are on Earth. Arc welding is the most important joining process used on Earth, but I doubt that there would ever be much arc welding in space because of the need for large amounts of consumables not available in space.

What kinds of heat sources would lend themselves to welding in outer space? I do not believe flames, like arcs, are viable. Two are likely: the electron beam and some manifestation of the laser. There has already been work on the use of an electron beam as a welding heat source in early Skylab experiments. Electron beam welding of metals is really not affected much by the absence or presence of gravity, but it has some things wrong with it that do need to be scrutinized carefully. First, it is generally constrained to operation in high vacuum. Although machines exist that do electron beam welding in atmospheric environments, they are not the kinds of machinery that I can envision having applicability in space. Second, there is a personnel hazard—a need for shielding of the operator from the X-rays produced. When a beam of moderately high voltage electrons impinges on any kind of a work surface, long-wavelength, soft X-rays are produced, of very high intensity, which can do biological damage.

The laser does offer the attraction of being usable in, but not constrained to, an atmospheric environment. Indeed, what little work has been done on vacuum welding with a laser beam on Earth makes it look like the vacuum is contributory to the quality of the joint, by reducing the energy input and increasing the penetration. The reasons for this are a little obscure, but the absence of an atmospheric environment in laser welding seems to be useful as far as the quality of the produced weld is concerned. That makes the laser look good; what makes the laser look not quite so good is that the energy conversion is far less efficient than it is with an electron beam.

The energy conversion picture with the laser is not clear. My understanding is that something like 20 to 30% of the input power can now be realized in actual kilowatts in the beam. This field is advancing rapidly, however, and even if there were a three-to-one loss in energy, because of the high intensity of the beam the total amount of energy required to accomplish a large structural weld would not be that great.

A distant possibility is the use of focussed sunlight itself. Although probably cumbersome, this approach would not be unworkable, at least with the lower melting-point metals. Calculations indicate that direct, focused solar radiation would be more than adequate for welding, say, 3 mm to 6 mm thick aluminum plate. Because solar energy is free energy this technique demands a closer look. It involves reflectivity, and in this particular part of the spectrum surprisingly little is known. It is not impossible that reflective and/or refractive systems could be made to work, for at least the lighter gauges of materials. I find this an attractive idea.

Another need for high-intensity heat sources is for severing, machining, and cutting. Actually, even here on Earth it is becoming less attractive to shape things by removal of material. The byword these days is to move it, not remove it. In making such objects as a cylinder head for an automobile, the productivity-oriented people worry how to expend less material – and energy – in the form of produced chips. Those reasons are multiplied in the space environment, of course, where all materials become worth so much more because of transport that there is considerable doubt whether there will be drill presses, lathes, shapers, or other conventional cutting tools.

New shaping techniques will be required. Severing and crude cutting, if they need be done,

will probably best be done with substantially forceless systems, corresponding roughly to the oxy-acetylene torch here on Earth. Again, either the laser or electron beam would probably be paramount. Solar radiation, with an oxygen assist, is another real possibility. It has been shown here on Earth that low total wattage lasers supported with oxygen can be used for severing, machining, shaping, or cutting of oxidizable materials, particularly iron-base and titanium-base materials. On ordinary steels and titanium alloys, very rapid clean cuts can be produced with a low-energy laser beam equipped with an oxygen jet, causing the material to be the fuel for its own cutting as is the case with oxy-acetylene torches. Whether or not focused solar radiation used with oxygen will be more attractive can be answered only by an in-depth economic analysis and considerable experimentation. In any case, thermal cutting processes are not noticeably affected by the presence or absence of gravity.

There is one other highly specialized but particularly space-adaptable joining process: capillary brazing. There was some exciting work done in Skylab. Brazing is basically a capillary process. In the absence of the competing influence of gravity, capillary and surface-tension forces are dominant, and some perfectly amazing things can be done with capillary flow arrangements. Much less attention needs to be given to matters such as the gap between the surfaces being joined or the smoothness of their finish. In other words, brazing could be a much more crude tool than it is on Earth, but yet quite workable in a low-G environment. On Earth, you have to machine parts to a pretty good finish and space them with pretty good parallelism (about half a millimeter would be the absolute maximum; usually it is quite a bit less than that, more like a twentieth of a millimeter). When you remove that requirement, brazing suddenly looks like a different process. Unfortunately, only certain kinds of materials are brazable, and aluminum isn't one of them. There are processes for brazing aluminum, but they are not truly capillary and they wouldn't have application in space fabrication.

Iron and its alloys are quite brazable, however, and so is titanium. Brazing, as a joining technique, would necessitate bringing certain kinds of materials like copper and silver alloys from Earth, and that is a serious constraint, unless we find the requisite metal deposits on the Moon.

Another important class of processes is liquid metal processing, e.g., casting. Casting, in the sense that a foundryman thinks of it here on Earth, involves some kind of a mold with a sprue, a delivery plumbing system into which the molten metal is poured. Actually, though, as practiced on Earth, gravity is more the enemy than the friend. Liquid metals have a kinematic viscosity quite a bit lower than that of water. The velocities they develop by falling only a few inches are enough to develop the kind of turbulence that causes considerable erosion of mold materials and much entrainment of air and mold gases. The highly uncontrolled fluid mechanics of casting on Earth is, in large measure, responsible for the technical troubles that foundry engineers have. The prospect of manipulating liquid metals, not at zero-G but in some system of controllable G, is most attractive.

The prospect of levitation melting is very attractive, especially for reactive metals like titanium, which is probably the most important example. But levitation melting could be extremely valuable in processing many of the alloys and metals of engineering technical importance to us here on Earth. It's always been our desire to melt metals without contact with an offensive and chemically reactive crucible. The prospect for doing this on Earth is rather remote. Electromagnetic levitation has been practiced; in the early and middle fifties, there were many publications in this area. The problem that couldn't be overcome was to induce enough energy to combat the gravitational acceleration without putting far too much energy into the material being processed. Temperature control was not adequate for this, and essentially defeated levitation melting here on Earth. It would have application in space, and it is a very attractive prospect.

Professor Flemings at M.I.T. has been working in recent years with the casting of "semisolids," in which he agitates alloys while cooling them to a state in which they are perhaps 40% solid and 60% liquid. He then impactively forces the material into a useful shape. The properties, the state of aggregation, and the phase distribution that can be produced in this process are remarkable. This technology seems to be made to order for space processing applications.

Another process, extrusion, is done on Earth with hot solid metal, high pressure, and heavy equipment. Extrusion in space, I think, could be done with much lighter equipment, something like extrusion of the kind that's done in the manufacture of gypsum shapes, plaster of Paris shapes, or ice cream.

The necessity for operating with low force systems seems to me to be quite real. This obviates forging, where momentum exhanges are very large. It's not that forging depends upon a one-G environment, but it is hard to imagine light-weight forging equipment. But going up to higher temperatures, dealing with liquid or semi-liquid systems, as has been shown so dramatically by Dr. Flemings and his co-workers, could make forgings much more readily producible in the space environment.

Finally, although I mentioned before that machining is unattractive because of its inherent wastefulness, lubrication and sliding-surface handling requirements of machining operations in space would be a further curse. Machining in vacuum tends to become welding in vacuum whether you want it to or not, as the tool becomes welded to the work.

In the non-metal area I want to echo Grodzka's sentiments. The utility of non-metals can be greatly enhanced by casting. There is some casting of ceramics and refractories here on Earth, but the refractory molds or crucibles needed to hold the liquid refractories present such a challenge that it has never really been a big industry. In the absence of gravity, it could be. Ceramics can be handled by levitation melting even better than metals, because they are not as conductive as metals, and coupling is easier.

The prospect of using raw, non-metallic materials, available solar energy, and very low energies for levitation support in a low-G environment is very attractive. This seems well within reality, and the prospect of using non-metals for engineering parts probably would be much more favored in the space environment than here on Earth.

DISCUSSION

Q. *The track for the lunar mass driver might be an I-beam which could perhaps be produced by continual extrusion, in long sections, from a continuous casting furnace on the lunar surface. Could you comment on production methods for manufacturing track on the lunar surface?*

A. I think continuous extrusion of semi-solid, at really quite low pressures, is quite possible. On Earth we would use a fixed, I-beam-cross-section hole in the gate of the extrusion die. In the handling of a semi-solid, on the other hand, we would use what are sometimes referred to as

Turk's head rolls, a dynamic extrusion method. This approach also lends itself to the producing of metal/non-metal mixtures, perhaps a metallic fiberglass. There are very few constraints on what kinds of things you can put together, including inmiscible or mutually insoluble phases, when one is granted the luxury of operating in low-G environments. But a continuous extrusion, a continuous casting operation, I find very imaginable, very real, and practical.

Q. *What about powder metallurgy techniques? Do you think they will find much application?*

A. Probably not in the shaping and making of parts, because the machines tend to be heavy and the force systems tend to be large. It would be nice, at least initially, to think in terms of systems requiring low forces.

In powder systems for chemical processing, even including the production of aluminum from bauxite, it is a different matter. Electrically augmented flames, direct chloride reduction, processes which are not attractive on Earth but lend themselves to operation in low-pressure environments, may well turn out to be workable on the Moon or in space.

Q. *In the use of solar energy for direct penetration welding, it seems to me that the size of the disc of the Sun makes that difficult, because what one wants is a tightly collimated beam. Laser welding, for example, offers such collimation, which far exceeds in welding capability the losses due to inefficiency of the laser generation process.*

A. That's right. This point is well taken and deserves amplification. The kind of weld that one could produce with solar energy, directly applied, would be as wide as it is thick. It would look something like an old oxyacetylene weld; it would not be one of these narrow, deep beads that you can produce with a laser. I think a laser is a far more attractive heat source for this application.

Q. *I have a near-term materials transformation problem. In the space shuttle, the only element which is expended is the propellant tank, which is composed of some thirty tons of 2219 aluminum. That thirty tons (per flight) is tantalizingly close to orbit and could, in fact, be placed in orbit quite easily if there were a use for*

it. *Do you have any thoughts on how we might transform that current liability into an asset?*

A. I would think that the energy requirement for converting that junk into something useful, per pound of aluminum, would be of the order of one hundredth what it would take, no matter whose scheme is used, to convert the "in situ" combined aluminum that you find on the Moon into metallic aluminum. 2219 is particularly convertible. It can be reused in its own state, or you could modify its composition quite readily in, say, a levitation melting device.

Q. *Returning to the question on powder metallurgy, suppose we were able to obtain powdered pure elements in particles as small as 200-500 angstroms in size. Wouldn't that provide an intrinsic advantage in processing over that which is possible on Earth?*

A. Potentially yes, because when you get down to particle dimensions of a few hundred angstroms, the available surface energy to make the particles stick together is immense. The prospect for producing consolidated shapes from that kind of material is very high, especially in the low-pressure environment. Of course, such particles are highly surfactant, so any benefits would be predicated on their being kept and processed in the low-pressure environment.

Q. *Do you see a possibility of using something other than standard machining techniques when you have tolerance specifications of, say one mil (.025mm) or less? Are there techniques for making things to those tolerances that could be used in a zero g environment other than lathes, milling machines, shapers, etc.?*

A. I'm not sure I have a good answer to that. Perhaps the basic forming process – extrusion, casting, etc., could be made more precise, bringing you closer to the final envelope. You could then finish up with something like a grinding operation, which doesn't require nearly so massive tooling and which doesn't involve accidental welding of the tool to the work. Moreover, I don't think that heat-source machining (e.g., with lasers) has been pushed anywhere near its ultimate limit. People have drilled holes with lasers, with impressive performance, but we haven't even begun to consider contour machining with high-intensity laser beams. Not only do I believe this is doable,

102

but you could readily achieve tolerances of the order of half a mil (about 0.01 mm) on parts whose gross dimensions were something less than 5 cm.

Q. Couldn't you eliminate some of the problems by just machining your tools inside the space stations?

A. Do machining in a shirt-sleeve environment? There's nothing wrong with that. It's just that if down here on Earth it's already becoming economically unattractive to do machining like we did twenty years ago, up there it must be even more so, so I don't see much in the way of big machines.

Q. What about small precision parts?

A. Certainly we would use machine tools for that sort of work, in the 'shirtsleeve environment'' just discussed. My earlier comments were directed toward production – manufacturing operations.

Q. It has been suggested that we might join or form objects by using "cold pack" instead of heat; i.e., shade the work pieces against the solar radiation and bond them together while cold. Would it be feasible to then take them out of the cold-pack environment, subject them to solar radiation, and not have them fall apart?

A. Cold welding, diffusion bonding, and pressure welding are more easily performed in high vacuum than on Earth. Gravity has nothing to do with it, but the atmospheric pressure does. High vacuum certainly does assist processes involving solid state bonding. These processes have been widely discussed in connection with space processing, and rightly so. One of the paradoxes may be, however, that I don't know how high the vacuum really will be around a large space vehicle. I understand that the particle density is relatively high around large vehicles, and you don't reach ultra-low vacuum until you get some distance away. If you want metals to stick together when you push them against one another, you need pressures lower than the order of 10^{-8} or 10^{-9} torr, which may not be conveniently available.

Q. You mentioned the possibility of manufacturing in space for delivery to Earth. Can you conjecture what sort of products might be favorable enough?

A. Yes, but I probably won't conjecture very cleverly. Right now I can think of only one almost trivial example. Years ago, there used to be quite a market for copper-lead bearings, a mixture of roughly 50% copper and 50% lead. They were quite tricky to make, because when you pour copper and lead in a crucible the lead all falls down to the bottom and the copper floats on top, like vinegar and oil. The technique was to shake the mixture violently and pour it very quickly into a chilled mold so it would freeze fast before it could fall apart again. The bearings were excellent, but the process was much too labor intensive and had to be abandoned. Now, copper-lead bearings are marvelous, but I don't know whether it makes sense to haul all the raw materials up there, make the bearings, and haul them all the way back down. But is *is* an example of something that could be done, trivial as it is.

Q. (Comment). Some of the products that you might consider are valuable ones; for example, crystals for electronic applications, biological separations, vaccines, many kinds of glasses, isotope separations. These are all very fine, valuable, human products.

4. Closed Ecosystems of High Agricultural Yield

H. Keith Henson and Carolyn M. Henson
Analogue Precision, Inc.

Abstract

The mass of a space farm can be reduced by using agricultural techniques which eliminate the need for soil, making it more feasible to grow conventional foods. The authors propose that human nutritional needs in space can be filled abundantly in conventional ways. The area and biomass requirement for the grains, fruits and vegetables of the proposed diet are computed to be 22 m^2 and 96 kg per person. Rabbits are found to be efficient meat producers, requiring 10 m^2 of photosynthetic area per person for feed. Biomass per person for meat production is computed to be 40 kg. With no additional photosynthetic area and with a biomass of 21.5 kg, agricultural and kitchen wastes will feed goats and chickens to provide milk and eggs. Total photosynthetic area per person would be 32 m^2; and total biomass, including water, would be 200 kg per person. There is reason to believe that the agricultural production of a space farm will be more stable than that of an Earth farm.

An integrated system is proposed to recycle waste materials, fix nitrogen, and maintain air quality. The concept is presented of building the construction site facility of material containing elements later required in Model 1, but not available from the Moon. A "first pass" design for a construction site facility based on the space farm area requirements is presented. Labor requirements for the space farm should not be excessive, and such work may provide recreation for the workers.

Introduction. This paper explores the potential for an agricultural system in space, hereafter called the "space farm." The parameters used are those of the construction site for Model 1. Farming on Model 1 itself, when completed, will be much easier (more area per person). Farming on the Moon will be much more difficult due to intermittent light. However, much of the information contained in this paper should apply to these other environments.

The merits of the space farm may be evaluated by linear programing, illustrated in Figure 67. Since a total resupply system generates a straight line, the breakeven point may be taken as a figure of merit for the space farm.

In order to get a short breakeven time, the mass of material shipped from Earth for the space farm, including biomass, must be kept to a minimum. Because the dominant part of the mass will be the enclosing structure, a design for a low-mass and reusable structure will be discussed. Because structure mass is area dependent, a strong effort will be made to minimize farm area.

Other parameters include an appetizing and high-quality diet, with protein and caloric content equal to that available to affluent people in the United States. Foods not commonly eaten, such as yeast or algae, will not be considered.

Low-Mass Plant Growing Methods. A problem recognized in earlier studies is that of soil mass. Fortunately, plants do not need soil. Successive experiments have shown that many plants will grow

Figure 67   How to Evaluate the Merit of a Space Farm

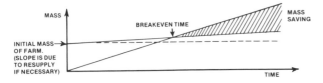

temperature control (Ref. 81). Reference 82 states that *Zea mays* fixed a maximum of 50 g/m^2-day with a 12-hour day under optimum field conditions. In a laboratory experiment, a carbon fixation rate of 30 g/m^2-day (24 hr) was raised to 90 g/m^2-day by optimizing CO_2 levels to 0.13% (Ref. 83).

Provisionally, we will consider attainable a plant

in sand, vermiculite, styrofoam, or nothing at all, provided they are supported and supplied with nutrients and water. The lowest-mass method the authors found is shown in Figure 68 (Ref. 76).

The plants are supported by styrofoam boards, and a nutrient solution is intermittently sprayed on the roots which hang below the boards. This requires only a small water inventory. A significant advantage of this method is that the roots may be harvested for animal feed. Some grains may require a different method, such as the conveyor belt technique proposed by John Richard Meyers (Ref. 77).

Human Nutritional Requirements. The basic parameters for the space farm are human nutritional requirements. These vary according to individuals, their activities, and culture. Recommended protein allowances per person, for example, range from 45 g/day in India to 85 g/day in East Germany (Ref. 78). Besides protein, people need calories, some unsaturated fats, vitamins and minerals. The amounts needed of these also vary. The conservative approach used here will be to provide a diet in excess of the highest recommended requirements and of familiar food. We will consider the area and mass requirements to grow grain, fruits and vegetables, meat and/or legumes, milk and eggs. Salt requirement problems will be considered in the waste recovery system.

Grain Production. Grain consumption in the United States amounts to some 120 g/person-day direct, and about 2,000 g/person-day indirect (Ref. 79). Much of the indirect grain consumption is inefficiently used to put fat on hogs and cattle. Animal fat, in large quantities, is not necessary in the human diet and may be detrimental to health. The overall food supply design presented here requires 500 g of grain per person-day.

How much area and biomass inventory are required to grow this? Reported dry matter yields range from about 10 g/m^2-day for wheat under average field conditions (Ref. 80) to 1,370 g/m^2-day for hydroponically grown forage under artificial 24-hour lighting, high ventilation and

Figure 68   Growing Biomass Without Soil, on Styrofoam

yield of 150 g/m²-day of dry weight and take a 50% loss due to various inefficiencies. This 75 g/m²-day figure has been calculated independently by others (Ref. 84). Using ~ 40% harvest ratio (Ref. 85), 16 m² should yield the desired 500 g/day of grain.

On Earth there has been no economic incentive for research into growing grains in enclosed optimized conditions. However, the cost of researching this subject would be low as it draws on existing greenhouse technology. Greenhouse yields for non-grains are commonly three times or more field yields per crop (Ref. 86).

The biomass estimates are based on average mass over a harvest cycle. Figure 69 shows various estimated growth curves (Ref. 87); the dotted lines show the average mass.

The estimated average biomass inventory per person for grain production is 70 kg (see Figure 69a).

Fruits and Vegetables. Vegetable production under partially optimized conditions on Earth is well-documented. Current commercial yields in a facility in Abu Dhabi, for example (Ref. 88), are:

Tomatoes (High yield)	82 g/m²-day
Cucumbers (High yield)	89 g/m²-day
Cabbage	47 g/m²-day
Radish	50 g/m²-day
Broccoli (Low yield)	28 g/m²-day

Without improving these figures, 6 m² will produce 500 g/day of tomatoes or other high yield vegetables. We would expect yields of melons to be similar to cabbage on the basis of their similar field productions, and yields of potatoes similar to those of tomatoes, on the same basis (Ref. 89). With unsupported roots, harvesting of potatoes might be automated like the collecting of eggs in a modern egg ranch.

Several improvements over current greenhouse technology may increase yields. A no-matrix culture allows a simple re-spacing of plants as they grow larger in order to use more efficiently the available area. Figure 68, cited earlier, shows how a plant can be "unplugged", or, alternatively, the growing surface can be tilted as the plants grow to change the area of sunlight intercepted. Also, day length, and to a lesser extent temperature, in the Abu Dhabi facility have been optimized. Considering these factors, it seems probable that production

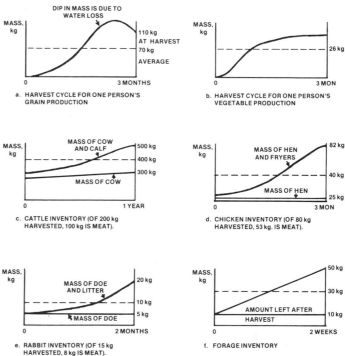

Figure 69 Estimated Growth Curves for Various Crops

a. HARVEST CYCLE FOR ONE PERSON'S GRAIN PRODUCTION

b. HARVEST CYCLE FOR ONE PERSON'S VEGETABLE PRODUCTION

c. CATTLE INVENTORY (OF 200 kg HARVESTED, 100 kg IS MEAT).

d. CHICKEN INVENTORY (OF 80 kg HARVESTED, 53 kg. IS MEAT).

e. RABBIT INVENTORY (OF 15 kg HARVESTED, 8 kg IS MEAT).

f. FORAGE INVENTORY

could be doubled. For space farm computations, assuming a wide mixture of vegetables with varying yields, we will use an average figure of 125 g/m²-day (wet mass assuming an average water content of 80%), or, from 6 m² area, 750 g/person-day.

An estimate for the required average biomass inventory (see Figure 69b) is 26 kg per person.

Animal Protein. Is it economically feasible to grow meat in the initial space farm, with mass and area at such a premium? First, as in grain, fruit, and vegetable production, the ideal animal must have high productivity in relation to biomass inventory. For example, only some 20% of the inventory of a herd of cattle can be harvested as meat per year, whereas 500% of rabbit inventory and 500% of chicken inventory (see Figure 69c, d, and e) can be harvested. Second, the productivity per unit area of animal protein must approach that of humanly usable vegetable proteins.

Because of their high reproductive rates and feed conversion ratios, chickens and hogs have often been suggested as the most efficient producers of animal protein for use in space. However, for efficient protein production, hogs and chickens require a diet also suitable for human consumption (Ref. 90), and the conversion loss is large. It is true that hogs in China are fed materials inedible to people, such as sweet potato vines and rice hulls, as part of their diet (Ref. 91). The remainder of the diet is composed of the same foods that people could eat and thus is still in competition with people. Their meat productivity on such a diet is quite low (Ref. 91). High-efficiency chicken production is based on animal protein from fish meal and animal butchering waste, soybeans, and grain. Again, because of competition with human diet, these animals will not be considered as major sources of protein for the construction site space farm.

Dr. Kenneth Olson, of the University of Arizona, has proposed the raising of alfalfa or other forage in a greenhouse environment for rabbit feed (Ref. 92). Alfalfa (a legume) produces high yields of balanced protein but is not a suitable protein source for people because of the fibrous content. With the addition of a little salt, alfalfa has been shown to be acceptable as a complete rabbit feed (Ref. 93). For reasons of palatability and yield losses, we will not consider extracting the alfalfa protein directly for human use.

One square meter will house a doe rabbit and her litters. The young are butchered every two months just before the next litter arrives. The productivity of this unit is approximately 143 g of low-fat and boneless meat per day. Feed requirement is on the average of 700 g/day dry mass (Ref. 94), requiring about a 10 m^2 area at 70 g/m^2-day. Using a multiplying factor of 4 between dry feed and live forage, the farm must produce 39 kg of forage every two weeks. Biomass inventory of forage would be about 30 kg. Biomass inventory for the rabbits and forage together would be 40 kg (see Figure 69 e, f).

In terms of protein production per m^2 per day, we estimate rabbits would produce 4 g, grain 4 g, and soybeans 6 g. It should be noted that rabbit meat can be cured like ham, and made into sausage and liverwurst; it is a mild-flavored meat that can be cooked many ways, even as rabbit-burgers.

This farm system generates food for two additional kinds of animal protein products at no additional cost in photosynthetic area. Ruminants can convert the waste materials, e.g., stems, leaves, and roots, from vegetable production into milk. Tomato vines, for example, are about 15%-24% protein, and, raised under greenhouse conditions, they can be fed to ruminants (Ref. 95). Cucumber vines, cabbage leaves, and melon vines are also valuable feeds. A reasonable figure for the mass of

vegetable and fruit wastes is 300 g/day dry mass per person. Assuming that most of the vegetables have high forage value, e.g., stems, roots and leaves of species such as tomatoes and cabbage, a ruminant could utilize an equal mass of low forage value material such as straw, sorghum stalks, etc., from grain production.

At this point, a comparison should be made between the two commonest domestic milk-producing ruminants (Ref. 96):

	Goat	Cow
Mass	56 kg	540 kg
Dry feed intake/day	2 kg	16 kg
Milk produced/day	5 kg	20 kg
Milk/feed	2.6	1.25

In summary, a goat will produce more than twice as much milk for a given amount of feed as a cow.

For an optimum utilization of these forages, goats, as well as cows, require some grain. The 500 g/person-day grain allowance contains 60 g of protein. This may be eaten directly or half of it (30 g protein) diverted as goat feed, for a total dry mass, including forage, of 850 g. This will return 2 kg of milk containing 64 g of protein with a better amino acid balance and higher mineral and vitamin content than the grain used as feed. Also, our space farm can now produce ice cream.

This system provides one goat for every 2.4 people, or a thousand goats for the proposed space farm.

For those who cannot digest the lactose in milk, or just for variety, cheese can be made with only a slight loss in food value. As for the culinary

Table 23.   Proposed Diet (Per Person)

Crop	Area	Biomass	Food Mass/ Day	Protein
Grain	16 m^2	70 kg	250 g	30 g
Fruits and vegetables	6 m^2	26 kg	750 g	10 g
Meat	11 m^2	40 kg	143 g	40 g
Milk	5 m^2	20 kg	2,500 g	64 g
Eggs	.5 m^2	1.5 kg	15 g	5 g
Total	32 m^2* 6 m^2**	165.5 kg	3,658 g	149 g

*Photosynthetic
**Non-photosynthetic

qualities of goat's milk, under conditions of proper feeding and sanitation, the flavor is as acceptable as that of cow's milk. Cream and butter can also be separated from goat's milk. Billygoats have a justifiably bad reputation in regard to their odor; however, artificial insemination for goats is a well-developed technology and eliminates the need for billies on the space farm.

The added biomass would be about 20 kg per person; added non-photosynthetic area would be 5 m^2.

Chickens can make eggs from leftovers on plates, kitchen waste, and butchering waste. These foods also have traditionally been fed to hogs as well as to chickens. Egg production is a more efficient food converter than pork and lard production. Three or four eggs per person per week could be generated with an addition of 1.5 kg of biomass and 0.5 m^2 of non-photosynthetic space. Aside from their nutritional value, eggs allow people to make cakes, waffles, omelets, mayonnaise, and many of the other amenities of life.

Table 23 summarizes the major components of the proposed diet per person.

Assuming low-calorie vegetables, such as radishes and cabbage, this diet contains 3,000 C. For a more active construction worker, a substitution of potatoes for most of the vegetables and soybeans for rabbit meat would raise the caloric intake to about 4,300 C.

The experimental evidence mentioned above regarding possible rates at which plants can grow dry matter is of special interest. If grain and forage production can be maintained at a rate of 150 g/m^2-day, given optimum CO_2 concentrations, light, temperature, humidity, and nutrients, the space farm could be cut down to a photosynthetic area of 19 m^2 per person. This subject is certainly worth further investigation.

Stability. A great deal of concern has been expressed about the "stability" of the space farm. We will define stability as the capacity of the space farm to continuously provide adequate food and air. Concern about this subject is certainly justified, as farm yields on Earth are highly variable from year to year and occasionally fail entirely. There are reasons to believe that the yield of a space farm will be more stable than that of an Earth farm.

It is instructive to look at the causes of yield variation on Earth and see which will apply to a space farm. Major causes are: weather, weeds, insects, rodents, and disease. Weather simply does not apply in space, assuming that engineers can solve the problems of temperature control.

The initial seeds for the space farm could be individually inspected to keep out weeds. If a few weed seeds did get through, the space farm area is small enough so that they would be spotted and removed. Simple fumigation of shipments from Earth should eliminate the insect problems. If an undesirable insect did get in, the procedures discussed regarding disease in this paper would deal with the problem. Alternately, low toxicity insecticides, of which pyrethrum and rotenone are examples, could be used. Rodents are even easier to keep out than insects, and we would not consider the problem further but for the fact that scientists will inevitably bring white mice and rats. In the event some escape, a cat may be necessary.

Disease organisms will be much harder to keep out or control, and will likely be brought in with each new shipment from Earth. The space farm environment is a rich one, and nature seems to have available organisms able to inhabit even the poorest of man-made environments – for example, jet fuel. The environment of a space farm is, in essence, that of a greenhouse on Earth. Molds and viruses have been troublesome in greenhouses, but a variety of control methods have been developed. Some of these, fumigation with methyl bromide for example, will not be acceptable in space. Other methods, such as steam sterilization, might be satisfactory. A number of horticulturists should be consulted on greenhouse disease problems and methods for their control. Mold problems are particularly troublesome in the high humidity conditions sometimes used in greenhouses. In space, the humidity may be made as low as desired by selecting the capacity of the water condensing system. For grain crops, moderately low humidity would be essential. In any case, the science of coping with micro-organism competitors and pathogens has a long history of development dating back to the time of Pasteur. The space farm would certainly stock vaccines, antibiotics, and medications. It should also be noted that bacterial and virus diseases usually attack a narrow range of hosts, sometimes even a single species or genotype. The stability of a space farm in relation to disease attack would be enhanced by growing a wide variety of crops and animals.

In many natural ecosystems, the biomass of

various species varies widely over time. The most commonly cited example is that of the rabbit and rodent populations of the far North. Natural systems have feedback loops which cause oscillation. A farm differs from a natural system in many ways, the most important of which is human control of the size and composition of the plant and animal components. This precludes oscillation, if the farmers are competent. The space farmers would plant a proper mix of crops for the anticipated needs, breed a correct number of rabbits to eat the forage planted for them, watch the system carefully, and take corrective measures when necessary in much the same way as is done on Earth.

Nevertheless, for those readers convinced of the general perversity of things (Murphy's Law), a number of fall-back positions are available. For one thing, the diet proposed is excessive; a substantial fraction of the crops could be lost and no one would go hungry. Also, there is a large safety margin in terms of stored food and seeds, food in process (cheese being aged), and standing meat inventory.

Let us assume a disaster, nature unspecified, that kills every plant on the farm but leaves the people and animals unaffected. What would be done in this case, which is similar to an Earth crop failure, would be to butcher all of the animals that stored or salvaged food would not feed for the next two weeks, and freeze or dry the meat. After cleaning up the mess, the farmers would plant the fastest growing seeds available.

The CO_2 content of the air would not reach a problem level for at least two weeks, even if nothing were growing. With planting, in one week the CO_2 level would be on its way back down. In two weeks, the forage production for rabbits would be back to normal, and in three months, the entire farm would be at normal production level. The two weeks of leeway before the CO_2 levels become uncomfortable would allow the ultimate fall-back position, help from Earth, to arrive.

Waste Product Recycling. There is only a small provision in the biomass calculations for inactive material. To maintain the high levels of CO_2 required for rapid plant growth and to supply the plants with minerals, the solid waste products from people, animals, and plants must be recycled rapidly. Incineration seems to be the fastest method to return material. Liquid wastes would be combined with the basic pH ashes and the acidic output of the nitrogen-fixing subsystem. Problems of

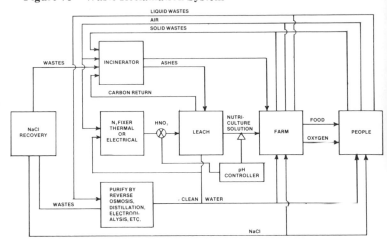

Figure 70 Waste Reclamation System

solubility, mentioned in early NASA studies (Ref. 97), probably stem from the low solubility of calcium and phosphorous compounds in basic solution. The solution formed of nitric acid and ashes makes an excellent pH-controlled nutrient solution for the plants. In a closed system, with no traps, the solid waste material will have all elements which the plants require except nitrates. An initial supply of salts will be necessary, but most of them would be supplied by the food initially brought from Earth. Figure 70 shows the flows in the waste recovery system. A problem may exist because nitrogen-fixing methods, both thermal and electrical, form nitrites as well as nitrates. Nitrites are somewhat toxic to plants.

A burner system serves another function – the maintenance of air purity. A large variety of unpleasant substances (hydrogen, carbon monoxide, hydrogen sulfide, ammonia, aldehydes, ketones, hydrocarbons, etc.) are formed as metabolic by-products or come from sources such as cooking. The technology for coping with these substances has been intensively developed over the last twenty years in connection with nuclear submarines. Some of this information is classified; the rest is available in NRL reports and BuMed reports.

The U.S. Navy has accumulated at least 22,000 man-years of experience in closed environments (Ref. 98). This has taught them to bring nothing into a submarine which is harmful after passing through a catalytic burner. Mercury and fluorinated or chlorinated hydrocarbons are examples of substances that must be excluded. Much of the data on submarines derived from U.S. Navy experiments in connection with sociological, psychological, and medical effects of closed environments will be directly applicable to space habitats.

At some point in the cycle, salt (NaCl) must be recovered, as it is used extensively in the intake of human food. Soap may prove to be another troublesome item to recycle. Although it is useful and easy to make from fat and ashes in the space farm, water containing it may have to be distilled if the concentration is detrimental to plants.

An Early Space Farm. The construction site facilities will be used until Model 1 is finished, a matter of some years, as a substantial industrial base must be set up to build Model 1. Even at only one-half kg per person per day, five years of supplies for 2,400 people will weigh 2×10^6 kg. Is it economical to lift enough material from Earth to make a space farm? The authors believe this to be possible, especially if most of the mass of the space farm is made of elements which must be imported from Earth for Model 1 anyway.

Using this concept, a "first pass" design for an enclosure for the space farm has been developed. The authors are not particularly skilled in this work, and before others quote the conclusions, the concepts and numbers should be verified, the cosmic ray shielding problem solved, and the design and assembly techniques for the space farm should be put forth in detail.

The dominant design factors influencing the mass of the space farm enclosure are the photosynthetic area and light levels required. For steady state conditions, the light input to the farm must be equal to the black-body radiation from it. At a temperature of 300°K and an emissivity of 0.9, each m^2 will radiate 410 watts. Maximum sunlight intensity on Earth is over twice this value, but 410 W/m^2 will require that the wall be about the same as the photosynthetic area. Active cooling would allow tiering of plant growing areas, as waste heat could be radiated at 1,300 W/m^2 if the temperature were raised to 400°K. On the assumption that passive systems are more reliable, a single level of photosynthetic area is proposed. Animal pens and work areas may be placed under the crop areas.

At 32 m^2 per person, the photosynthetic area requirement for 2,400 people is almost 8 hectares (80,000 m^2). An additional 20,000 m^2 will be allowed for walkways and other uses. Besides a 100,000 m^2 area, other parameters are as follows: Geometry is similar to Model 1, except for a crop-illuminating optical system which does not use

cylinder area for windows. No components will be used that are larger than 15 m in diameter or heavier than a space shuttle load. An internal air pressure of 2/3 atm (10 lb/in²) will be maintained. The main structural material proposed--carbon phenolic composite – while a fairly new material, is used today for golf club handles. It costs about $84 per kg, but the price is coming down and, compared with lift costs to L5, is low enough. Its main advantage is that its elements are reusable later for the biomass of Model 1. Characteristics are: tensile limit, 100,000 lb/in²; density, 1.4. It could be fabricated on Earth as hoops 45 m (147 ft) in diameter, and triple-looped (like a band saw blade) to 15 m for shipment to L5. An area of 50,000 m^2 per cylinder requires a length, not counting the end caps, of 354 m (1,160 ft). The end caps would be used for human habitation, as has been proposed for Model 1.

Simple calculations indicate a thickness of 9 mm (.354 inches) would carry the hoop stress, and 2.2mm (.088 in) would carry the end cap loads with a 100% safety factor. The longerons would be rolled up for shipment and the ends looped over and attached to end rings at L5. If some 1.5 mm (.060 in) of plastic were used to seal the air inside the cylinders, the total wall thickness would be 1.25 cm (1/2 in). Diffusion rates through the wall will have to be considered. The area, including end caps for one cylinder, is 56,000 m^2 (610,000 ft²), or 680m³ (24,000 ft³) of material. The enclosure would therefore weigh $.97 \times 10^6$ kg per cylinder. The volume enclosed by each cylinder is about 0.6×10^6 m³. Using an air density corresponding to 2/3 atm, the air inside will weigh 0.53×10^6 kg. Therefore, the mass of two cylinders for air and enclosures would be 3×10^6 kg.

The crop-illuminating optical system envisioned here concentrates sunlight into a beam that enters through a 15 m diameter glass window at one end of each cylinder. The beam is spread out by light scatterers down the cylinder axis. Assuming filters and losses reduce the effective solar radiation to 800 watts/m^2, the concentrator area outside the cylinder required for each one (see Fig. 71) will be 25,000 m^2, or 180 m in diameter. The power level in the beam, although high, is well within the limits for glass.

Figure 71 shows the assembly of farm cylinders and light concentrators. For scale, a 33%-efficient 40 MW power plant and a Model 1 ring are shown. At 10kg/kW, the power plant would weigh 0.4×10^6 kg.

Figure 71   Construction Site Facilities, Including Farm

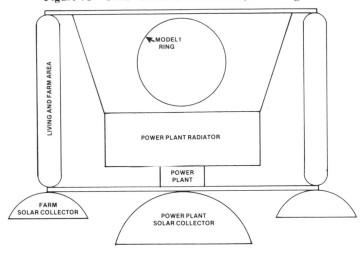

A low mass for much of the farm structure – plant supports, animal cages, plumbing supports, etc., and some of the optics – might be achieved by using wires or cables across the cylinder axis to build the structures in tension.

Including these structures, an estimate for the mass of the farm equipment, optics, windows, compression struts, pumps, fans, burners, pipes, ice cream makers, etc., is needed. Provisionally, the mass is estimated to be 0.9×10^6 kg. With the addition of the air and enclosure mass of 3×10^6 kg derived above, this results in a farm and living space total mass of 3.9×10^6 kg. The biomass, including people at 100 kg each, would weigh 0.73×10^6 kg, for a total of 4.6×10^6 kg and an enclosure to biomass ratio of 5.4:1. It should be noted that even if the space farm were not included in the construction site facilities, a substantial fraction of this mass would still be required for living quarters. Also, the morale of the construction workers on a diet of dehydrated and reconstituted food might leave something to be desired.

Human Lab Requirements for the Space Farm. Highly mechanized farming in the United States is full-time work for about 5% of the population. This may be a reasonable estimate for the space farm as well. While the level of mechanization will be lower, the lack of weeds and insects should compensate for this.

This farm proposal includes a lot of goats. Feeding and milking by hand will require 4 or 5 minutes per day per goat. At this rate, 10 to 14 people would be required. The meat supply will require butchering about 350 rabbits per day. At 10 minutes per rabbit, 8 people could do the work.

Both of the above time figures come from the personal experience of the authors.

Some, perhaps most, of the farm labor may come from volunteers working after regular hours. A large number of people like to raise animals and consider it recreation. An even larger number of people garden for fun. The space farm would be a gardener's paradise and would doubtless contain a few ornamental flowers from smuggled seeds.

One job the authors consider too tedious to attract volunteers is the hand-pollenization of vegetables. For pollinizing vegetables, several hives of docile bees should be included to complete the farm for a "land of milk and honey" (Ref. 99).

Acknowledgments

For help in researching this paper, the authors would like to thank Brad Barber, Ken Barnes, Bob Dennis, Carl Hodges, Merle Jensen, Ken Olsen and Don Whitehall of the University of Arizona; Ken Hanks, Subsistence Aquaculture; Gerald Driggers, Southern Research Institute; Eric Hannah, Princeton University; and John Billingham, NASA Ames Research Laboratory. Also special thanks to Anita Hanlan, botanist and editor, who must have read and commented on ten iterations of this paper.

DISCUSSION

Q. *You intend to increase the carbon dioxide and the amount of sunlight. Have you worked out what that would do to the heat balance of the colony?*

A. No. The heat sink problem has not been tested. The carbon dioxide should have virtually no effect on the heat balance in a space environment. It might on Earth, but even that's questionable.

Q. *The government recommends about twelve different nutrients and other items in the recommended daily requirements for adults, of which you discussed calories and proteins. I was wondering if in your program you considered other things like riboflavin, niacin, calcium, ascorbic acid, vitamins, and so on?*

A. There will be no problem with nutrients in the diet we propose. We are not talking about eating amino acids, pure carbohydrates or other artificial foods. Two pounds of vegetables a day, for example, have enormous nutrient value. How many people eat two pounds of lettuce and tomatoes a day? Of course you can increase that; e.g., spinach, chard, and other vegetables are quite favorable to grow. So to make available huge amounts of vitamins and minerals is no problem, assuming you recycle properly. As long as you are not heaping up a stack of garbage that isn't being recycled, you will keep the nutrients and the various trace minerals.

Q. *Did you assume twenty-four hour sunlight for the plants?*

A. No. I was assuming just the greenhouse productivity we get on Earth. But I would assume that we *would* grow for 24 hours in space.

Q. *We could certainly do that. But will the plants react normally and produce three times as much as they do on Earth?*

A. Not all plants. For instance, tomatoes take a complex of length of day and temperature to set fruit, but grains, for example, can grow very well under twenty-four-hour-a-day sunlight. It varies a lot, so we would have to make a choice of crops on the basis of what produces the best. A lot of research will be needed.

Q. *What do you do with dead peoples' bodies?*

A. I think we would have to obtain a release to allow them to be recycled along with everything else. I personally find that not at all unacceptable; in fact, I myself would much prefer it that way.

Q. *You said there would be 2 kg of inventory for every pound of person. I don't know what reasoning you used to get that number, but Earth for the last two centuries has been operating on a philosophy that there is all that biomass out there and we'll never make a dent in it. Now that philosophy is changing, and we want to treat the biomass with respect. But you would still need a reasonable buffer against catastrophe and inefficiencies. You might want to make that reserve ten times as great, so that things could go wrong and you could still get a product.*

A. You would have a problem with the huge masses just growing there. What do you do with it? Do you just chop it down and compost it without eating it? That's a problem.

If you wanted a buffer supply of food, say two months, you wouldn't want to have a monster biomass standing to achieve it. You could simply store freezable food for that period; in two months you'd be back in full production. Remember, we're not talking about a monoculture, like a bunch of chlorella. We have a diverse system; enough to be biologically stable – at least twenty or thirty different species. If, for example, all your animals died off, there would still be sufficient plant protein, according to the World Health Organization, to keep you from getting in bad trouble. You would change from optimum to minimal, but still adequate.

Q. *But if the entire world food crop died tomorrow, theoretically, everything would go with it. I think you are just as vulnerable.*

A. But in this habitat, if the wheat crop goes, two months later the new wheat crop is coming in again. It's a very short cycle.

Q. *But the rabbits haven't died with the wheat.*

A. You cut the population of your rabbits. You just butcher all the rabbits and don't breed them for two months, and then you start right up again with the remaining biomass.

Q. *My question also has to do with the stability of the system. Odum in Atlanta, as far as I know, operates the only closed, ecological system in the world, and the largest animal in it is a water flea. I think we ought to pay attention to the problem he points out: that stability requires diversification. He suggests that such diversification is necessary, that less than five percent, more like two percent, of the total biomass be available to humans. How does that compare with your system assumptions?*

A. Odum's is a stable *Earth* system. His figures are reasonable, and, I believe, testable. Will it turn out to be like an arctic biosystem, where there are fantastic fluctuations in the food, or like a tropical system, which has incredibly complex varieties of species, and the amount of food available in a square mile remains very constant as compared to fluctuations in the arctic environment? But in space, the environment is very stable. The sunlight is always coming in, you're maintaining it at the same temperature, and so on. We would really be simulating a tropical environment, only better.

Q. There's no possibility for disease?

A. Right. And there is no source for the diseases. Should a disease be shipped in inadvertently, it's going to kill maybe the rabbits, or maybe the goats, or maybe the wheat, but it's unlikely that you'll get one disease that will wipe out all three of them.

Q. I have a question about the esthetics. The bill of fare that you are proposing is certainly more appealing than distilled urine and chloraldehyde, but rabbit and spinach just wouldn't appeal to me night after night. What about the possibility for artifical flavorings and texturings which would give at least a fair verisimilitude of clam chowder, shrimp, roast beef, steak, among other things?

A. Some of those things are doable and some are not. You could probably manage the flavoring all right, but the actual growing of simulated steak has not been successful. However, growing shrimp and other seafood, if you have the water to do it, turns out to be very favorable.

This brings up a good point: can we get water locally, rather than from the Earth? Commercially on Earth, aquaculture can produce as much as ten thousand pounds per acre per year; that's a system that uses four species of carp. I was told that if you include fresh-water shrimp and clams and a few telopia to fill in the extra niches, you could get up to twenty thousand pounds per acre per year. The water mass is probably too much to make it worth importing the water from the Earth, though, so a local supply would be needed.

Q. Because the cost of the farming installation is very sensitive to total atmospheric pressure, could you reduce it below 10 psi? Also, NASA has estimated the resupply of the people in the construction system to be equivalent to 8,000 kilograms per person in 5 years. That is approximately forty times as much as the biomass which you have in your inventory. That means that you can afford to go up by a factor of ten in your biomass inventory and still save a factor of four over the NASA resupply estimates.

A. The atmospheric question is a good one. NASA uses seventy percent nitrogen to minimize chances of fire; once burned, twice careful. That *is* a real problem. But I would very much like to see the fire capacity computed on the basis of a quarter g, which I think is plenty adequate to orient plants, and the partial pressure of oxygen the same as we have on Earth, but with perhaps only five or ten percent nitrogen. There is no real reason why the farming area has to operate in the same atmosphere that you have in the living habitat.

Q. Do you have any fear about genetic drift? Perhaps from cosmic-ray damage?

A. In ordinary breeding, just from the fact that you have so many genes, any animal breeder can tell you that it is a constant battle to keep your animals from degenerating, because of the noise that enters into the system. So, I think genetic drift wouldn't be any worse than the natural tendencies on Earth.

Q. But that's the point. This is basically a closed system. You've probably got the worst possible conditions as far as cosmic rays are concerned.

A. There have been some experiments involving this. They put an unshielded nuclear reactor out in the middle of a forest, and it really cleaned house on various kinds of plants, but not on others. There is a lot of variation in the ability of plants to tolerate radiation. You could probably manage to pick plants that could stand more radiation and still be edible, but at the low radiation levels that people would worry about, plants are simply not affected. I believe the experiments showed hardly any effects at all below the ten roentgen per day level. I don't believe space radiation, even in a solar flare, would provide much more than that.

Q. I see the possibilities for bourbon, but I'm worried about the beaujolais. You touched briefly on the question of fruits; is there any possibility of forcing grapes?

A. Very likely, but grapes do require special treatment. Your wine after a few generations would probably be a little different than it was initially, but who knows? Perhaps it might improve!

5. Development of the Satellite Solar Power Station

Peter E. Glaser
Arthur D. Little, Inc.

The Potential of Solar Energy

Today, the application of solar energy is recognized as a promising alternative to meeting future energy demands, since the Earth receives prodigious quantities of solar energy (1.7 x 10^{14} kW are intercepted by the Earth). However, it is a widely distributed resource; one square meter of the Earth's surface exposed to direct sunlight receives the energy equivalent of only one kilowatt. Moreover, this energy is not easily convertible, and certainly is not "free." Thus, while solar energy is abundant enough to provide self-sufficiency and clean enough to satisfy the most ardent environmentalists, methods must be found for converting it efficiently and economically into useful forms.

One important drawback to the large-scale application of terrestrially based solar-energy conversion is the interruptions of solar radiation during periods of inclement weather or at night. These interruptions lead to a requirement for substantial energy storage capacity. Another drawback to the large-scale application of terrestrially based solar-generated power is that it will be economical in only a few locations. Consequently, terrestrial solar systems probably will be useful only in meeting peak demands.

These obstacles can be overcome when the solar energy conversion system is placed in synchronous orbit around the Earth where solar energy is nearly constant 24 hours a day (Ref. 100). Synchronous orbits are utilized today by communications satellites, and are ideally suited for the large-scale conversion of solar energy in a satellite solar power station (SSPS), such as appears in Figure 72 (Ref. 101); SSPS evolution appears in Figure 73.

The SSPS has the potential to provide an economically viable and environmentally and socially acceptable option for power generation on a scale substantial enough to meet a significant portion of future world energy demands.

The concept of the SSPS is based on the extension of existing technology and on the successful start of the development of an effective space transportation system, as represented by the space shuttle. The SSPS could use solar cells to convert solar energy to electricity on a nearly continuous basis. The electricity would be fed to microwave generators incorporated in a transmitting antenna located in direct line of sight on Earth, and there the microwave energy would be reconverted safely and efficiently to electricity. Additional SSPS systems can be established to deliver power almost anywhere on Earth.

The advantages resulting from solar energy conversion with the SSPS in synchronous orbit are as follows:

(1) The amount of solar energy available in synchronous orbit ranges from 6 to 15 times that available in areas receiving copious sunshine on Earth.

(2) The solar energy in orbit is available nearly

115

Figure 72 Design Concept for a Satellite Solar Power Station Based on Photovoltaic Conversion

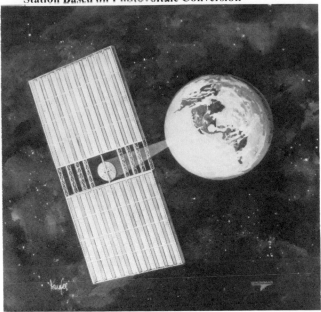

continuously except for short periods around the equinoxes, at which time the satellite will be shadowed by the Earth for a maximum of 72 minutes a day. Averaged over a year, this shadowing results in only a 1% reduction of the energy that would be available if the SSPS were continuously exposed to sunlight. Furthermore, the shadowing will occur near midnight at the receiving antenna site, when power demands are lowest. Therefore, energy storage is unlikely to be required.

(3) Synchronous orbit represents a favorable operational environment for the SSPS because

Figure 73 SSPS Configuration Evolution

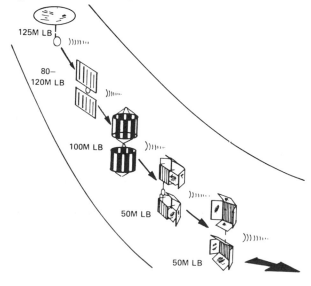

125M LB

80–120M LB

100M LB

50M LB

50M LB

zero gravity conditions and the absence of wind and rain and other natural environmental effects permit the deployment of large-area structures with minimal mass. Hence there is a marked reduction in the materials used per unit of delivered power. In addition, the space vacuum permits the operation of microwave generators and other components without the evacuated enclosures required on Earth. Moreover, because the SSPS in synchronous orbit is stationary with respect to a desired location on Earth, the microwave beam can be directed to most receiving antenna sites in the vicinity of major power users. These sites can be established on low-value land or offshore. Furthermore, because the receiving antenna is transparent to solar radiation and permits rain to reach the land below it, opportunities for multiple land use are provided.

(4) The environmental effects of the SSPS and the associated space transportation system are projected to be within acceptable limits. First, all waste heat associated with solar energy conversion and microwave generation can be rejected to space. Second, no waste products are generated. Finally, the microwave beam densities can be designed to meet international standards.

Technology Alternatives

Solar Energy Conversion. As originally conceived, the SSPS can utilize a number of approaches to solar energy conversion (Ref. 102): thermionic, thermal electric, photovoltaic conversion, and others likely to be developed in the future. Among these conversion processes, photovoltaic energy conversion was chosen as a starting point because solar cells represent a demonstrated technology as a result of widespread use in the space program. Solar cells are used widely in space power supply systems, whereas earlier efforts based on solar thermal and nuclear power were not as successful. In addition, ERDA's National Photovoltaic Program has as its objectives to develop low-cost reliable photovoltaic systems and to stimulate the creation of a viable, industrial, and commercial capability. The photovoltaic process, since it is a passive one, could reduce maintenance requirements and lead to increased reliability during the desired 30-year operational lifetime of the SSPS. Present communication satellites (e.g., INTELSAT IV) already have a projected lifetime of 10 years. Because the space environment is benign compared to the terrestrial

116

environment, it should be possible to extend the lifetime of solar cells beyond 30 years by processes such as annealing, or recycling in a space manufacturing facility.

Solar thermal conversion is of interest primarily because machinery operating on thermodynamic cycles; e.g.,the Brayton cycle, has had a long and successful history in terrestrial applications. Furthermore, the development of orbital solar powerplants could be based on the development of optical focussing systems and central receivers for solar thermal plants which could be adapted for use in the SSPS (Ref. 103). Novel techniques to achieve geometric perfection desired for the solar concentrators through active mirror-shaping controls are being investigated. If successful, these efforts will result in the large concentration factors required to achieve elevated temperatures for high thermodynamic efficiency. Progress in gas-bearing technology holds promise that the reliability of rotating machinery could be extended beyond the few thousand hours associated with most terrestrial applications of rotating machinery. Rejection of waste heat through active systems, including radiators, still poses a major challenge because of the mass required for a large-area space radiator and for operational reliability.

Thermionic energy conversion, which has been investigated in the space program but not yet applied, may be useful as part of a topping cycle in combination with a thermal conversion system.

Considerable technical and economic analyses will be required to establish which of the potential approaches for solar energy conversion will be optimal. However, the fact that there are several promising approaches to meet the requirements of the SSPS indicates a high likelihood that appropriate technology will be developed.

Power Transmission To Earth. There are several approaches for transmitting the power generated in the SSPS to Earth. Of these, the microwave method uses state-of-the-art or achievable technology to obtain high efficiency in generation, transmission, and rectification. Moreover, it promises to satisfy environmental requirements and safety considerations (Ref. 104). Microwave transmission and rectification technology is based on demonstrated results from commercial use and developments to meet military requirements. Mass production of more than one million microwave devices, serving an annual market of half a billion dollars in the United States alone, is indicative of the commercialization of the technology.

The transmission of power from orbit to Earth by laser, although receiving considerable attention, is not the preferred choice because of the low efficiencies associated with the conversion of electricity into laser power and the reconversion of laser power into electricity. In addition, the absorption of laser beams in the atmosphere, and by clouds, would reduce the overall efficiency of power transmission to an unattractive level.

The possibility of concentrating sunlight with mirrors placed in synchronous orbit to overcome the diurnal variation of solar energy on Earth has also been explored. Such an approach is unattractive because of the large area of concentrating mirrors that would be required in orbit to achieve a reasonable concentration factor at a location on Earth and because of the losses from absorption in the atmosphere.

SSPS Design Considerations

Solar Cells. Substantial data are available on the performance of silicon solar cells. Present silicon solar cells are about 200 microns thick. Efficiencies of 15% have been achieved and further increases in efficiency are considered feasible, even with reduced thicknesses. The present technology uses silicon solar cells mounted on rigid substrates with cover glasses bonded to the solar cell to achieve radiation shielding. Advanced technology based on a "roll out" blanket design which exhibits mass-to-power ratios of about 30 lb/kW have been fabricated. With improved fabrication techniques, reductions in thickness to less than 100 microns, and use of solar concentrators, a solar cell array mass of about 3 lb/kW is projected to be achievable in 10 years. These projections are based on reasonable improvements for single-crystal silicon solar cells and successful achievement of the goals of the National Photovoltaic Conversion Program being conducted by ERDA. The low solar array mass would be achieved through the use of plastic film to replace the cover glass, and is based on successful laboratory development of such solar cell blankets. Solar concentrators with Kapton film mirrors coated to reflect solar radiation onto solar cells and to filter undesirable portions of the solar spectrum are designed to reduce the area requirements for solar cells, and thereby their mass and cost. Figure 74 indicates the arrangements of solar cell arrays and concentrating reflectors.

A concentration factor of 2 will reduce the efficiency of an 18% silicon solar cell to about 14% at the operating temperature when heat rejecting

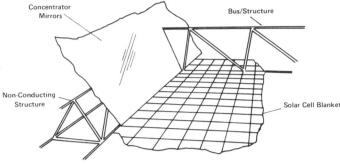

Figure 74   Detail of Solar Collector Array

Concentrator Mirrors

Bus/Structure

Non-Conducting Structure

Solar Cell Blanket

coatings are used for the solar cell array. Increases in solar cell thickness and lower efficiencies will be reflected in increased capital cost, because more material will have to be transported into orbit. The exposure to the space environment is projected to result in logarithmic degradation of silicon solar cells with a 6% loss of the original efficiency after the first five years. Micrometeoroid impacts are projected to affect 1% of the solar cells during a 30-year operational lifetime.

Recent progress in gallium arsenide solar cells has renewed interest in their use in the SSPS. The advantages of gallium arsenide solar cells are the higher efficiencies that have been reported at high concentration ratios and the lower susceptibility to degradation in the space environment. In addition, gallium arsenide solar cells may be produced at about one-tenth the thickness of silicon solar cells. Thus gallium arsenide deserves attention as an alternative solar cell material.

As a result of studies over several years, the design for the SSPS based on the silicon solar cell array configuration shown in Figure 75 has evolved. The two solar collector panels are designed to provide a power output of about 8500 MW, which results in an effective power output at the receiving antenna bus bar of about 5000 MW. A 100-meter diameter central mast and stiffened carried-through structure running through the assembly provide structural integrity. A microwave transmitting antenna is located between the two solar collector panels. The panels are arranged to face the sun continuously, while the microwave antenna will rotate once a day with respect to the solar collector in synchronous orbit. The solar collector panels are supported by both nonconducting and conducting structures which carry the power to the microwave generators via the central masts.

Rotary joints are provided at the perimeter of the central mast to allow rotation of the microwave

transmitting antenna. Dielectric materials, used for the continuous support structure, are transparent to the microwave beam. These joints are the only major continuously active components in an otherwise passive satellite.

Analyses of structural stiffness indicate that conventional analytical and structural design techniques are applicable to the SSPS. The structure of the SSPS will be subjected to thermal stresses and distortions induced by thermal gradients during the eclipses of the SSPS by the Earth's shadow for a short period before and after the equinoxes. The dwell time in the Earth's shadow will reach a maximum of 72 minutes during this period. Because the structure is so large, the thermal exposure cycle could cause it to oscillate; this possibility has to be evaluated in terms of

Figure 75   SSPS Baseline Configuration

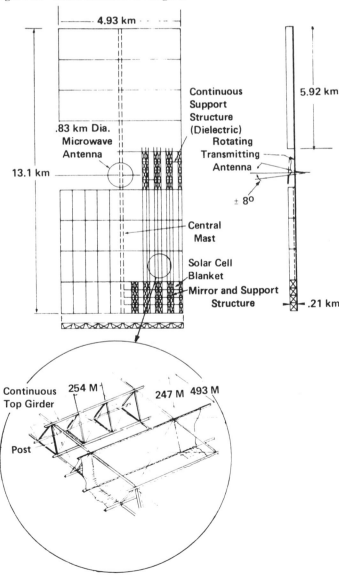

fatigue effects which could shorten service life. Although it is possible to select structural design approaches which will minimize the effect of such thermal exposure, more detailed evaluations of these effects are warranted.

The large structure required for the SSPS will be subjected to orbital perturbations (Figure 76), of which the gravity gradient will be the most significant. A reaction control system based on the use of ion engines (argon is one candidate propellant) will be required to keep the SSPS in the appropriate orbit and to assure that the solar collector panels point towards the sun within one degree, while the microwave antenna is directed towards the receiving antenna on Earth. To achieve the desired stationkeeping and attitude control for the SSPS about 100,000 lb of propellant will be required per year, depending upon specific orbital characteristics.

The mass of the SSPS, assuming that 5000 MW are delivered to the bus bar on Earth, in millions of pounds, is

Solar Arrays	27.29
Transmitting Antenna	12.22
Control System	.08
Rotary Joint	.37
Total System	39.96

The mass of about 8 lb/kW for the orbiting portion of the SSPS is remarkably low compared to that of terrestrial systems and is indicative of the advantages of placing the solar energy conversion system in synchronous orbit.

Microwave Power Transmission System. Figure

Figure 76   Orbit Perturbations

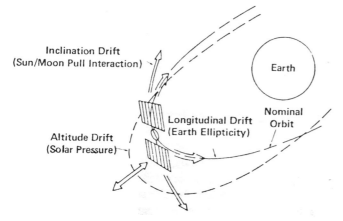

77 shows the functional blocks of the microwave power transmission system designed to transmit the electrical power generated by the solar energy conversion system to a receiving antenna on Earth, and the associated efficiency goal.

The device which is being considered for converting DC to RF power at microwave frequencies is a cross-field amplifier (amplitron). The amplitron uses a platinum metal cathode operating on the principle of secondary emission to achieve a nearly infinite cathode life. The DC voltage required for the amplitron is 20kV. A samarium-cobalt magnet provides low specific mass compared to that of conventional permanent magnets utilized in other microwave devices and makes it feasible to use such devices in the SSPS. Radiating surfaces, which will be operating at 420 to 480 K, are designed to reject waste heat, representing about 10% of the input power, to space. Pyrolitic graphite, because of its low density and high emittance, is being considered for the space radiators. A movable magnetic shunt is incorporated in the amplitron to regulate the output if the input current fluctuates. The movable magnetic shunt is the only element subject to wear. Considerations of specific mass, costs, and efficiency at specific frequencies have led to the selection of a frequency near 2.45 GHz, which falls within the industrial microwave band of 2.40 to 2.50 GHz. The output power level of the amplitron at 2.45 GHz exhibits a near optimum value when the output is about 5 kW (Ref. 105).

Space is an ideal medium for the transmission of microwaves; an efficiency of 99.6% is projected to be achieved after the beam has been launched at the transmitting antenna and before it passes through the upper atmosphere. Over the transmission distance of 38,000 km (23,500 miles), the curvature of the phase front of the beam will be very small; nevertheless, the front must be controlled with high precision to achieve high efficiency. To achieve the

Figure 77   Efficiency Chain

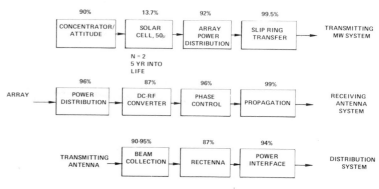

desired high efficiency for the transmission system, the geometric relationships between the transmitting and receiving antenna indicate that the transmitting antenna should be about 0.8 km in diameter, while the receiving antenna should be about 10 km in diameter (depending on latitude). The large size of the transmitting antenna is required to achieve a reasonable power density within the microwave beam at the receiving antenna for efficient conversion of microwaves into DC.

To reduce the dimensions of the transmitting antenna, the microwave amplitudes can be tapered from the center to the edge over the range of 5 to 10 db. The advantage of transmitting-antenna amplitude taper, as opposed to uniform illumination, is that it reduces the intensity at the center of the beam to less than 50 mW/cm^2.

To achieve the desired control of the phase front in the transmitting antenna, 18×18-meter subarrays are arranged into sectors to provide the required center-to-edge amplitude taper. Using a large number of small subarrays reduces the effect of attitude-control inaccuracies. Phase control electronics are provided for each subarray to compensate for subarray distortions which may be induced by thermal effects. The phased array waveguide approach is used for the subarrays to achieve very high efficiency low-frequency cut-off and reduced RF interference. Figure 78 shows the microwave generators and space radiators installed in a typical subarray.

A closed-loop phase-front control is used to achieve the desired high efficiency and safety essential for the microwave beam operation. A

Figure 78 Microwave Generators and Space Radiators Installed in Subarray

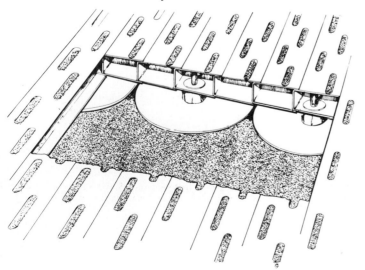

120

command and adaptive phase-front control concept is utilized. The reference beam launched from the center of the receiving antenna is sensed at each subarray and at the reference subarray in the transmitting antenna center. The central subarray transmits the reference signals to the subarrays over calibrated coaxial cables. The difference in phase between these signals which, for example, may result from the displacement of a subarray from the nominal reference plane because of thermal distortions of the structure, corrects the phase of the transmitted beam at the displaced subarray so that the required beam front is launched toward the receiving antenna. For a subarray of 18 meters by 18 meters, the maximum radiated power will be about 7 MW.

Aluminum has been selected for the wave guides, which have an overall thickness of about 0.5 mm. The subarray is divided into five-meter segments to limit the aluminum wave guide deflection over the 5-meter distance, which results in a beam power loss of less than 1% for the subarray.

The receiving antenna is designed to intercept, collect, and rectify the microwave beam into a DC output as efficiently as possible. The DC output will be designed to interface with either high-voltage DC transmission networks or to be converted into 60 Hz AC. The receiving antenna consists of an array of halfwave dipole antennas which rectify the incident microwave beam. Each dipole has an integral low-pass filter, diode rectifier, and RF bypass capacitor. The dipoles are DC-insulated from the ground plane and appear as RF absorbers to the incoming microwaves.

In principle, efficiency may approach 100% because the receiving antenna element and the microwave radiation are coherent and polarized in an orderly manner. Hence, the effective conduction cycle of the diode rectifer circuit and the reactive energy storage combine to produce a very high efficiency (up to 87% conversion effeciency has been achieved in the laboratory).

A receiving antenna based on the principle of halfwave dipole rectification is fixed and does not have to be pointed precisely at the transmitting antenna; thus, its mechanical tolerances do not need to be severe. Furthermore, the density distribution of incoming microwave radiation need not be matched to the radiation pattern of the receiving antenna; therefore, a distorted incoming wavelength caused by non-uniform atmospheric conditions across the antenna does not reduce efficiency.

The amount of microwave power received in local regions of the receiving antenna can be matched to the power handling capability of the microwave rectifiers. Any heat resulting from inefficient rectification in the diode circuit can be convected by the receiving antenna to ambient air, producing atmospheric heating which will be less than that over urban areas, because only about 15% of the incoming microwave radiation would be lost as waste heat. The low thermal pollution achievable by this process of rectification cannot be equaled by any known thermodynamic conversion process.

The rectifying elements in the receiving antenna can be exposed to local weather conditions. The receiving antenna can be designed to be 80% transparent so the land underneath the antenna could be put to other uses.

In the summer of 1975, tests of a 24-square-meter array of microwave rectifier elements were conducted at the NASA Venus antenna site at Goldstone, California, to demonstrate the effective performance of dipole rectification (Ref. 106). The transmitting antenna, which consisted of a 26-meter-diameter dish antenna, was located about 1.6 km (one mile) from the receiving elements. At a radiated frequency of 2388 MHz, incident peak RF intensities up to 170 mW/cm^2 have yielded up to 30.4 kW of DC output power. An average conversion efficiency of 82% was obtained at the receiving arrays under these conditions.

SSPS Transportation, Assembly, and Maintenance. The SSPS will require a space transportation system capable of placing a large mass of payload into synchronous orbit at the lowest possible cost. The cost of transportation, assembly and maintenance will have the most significant impact on the economic feasibility of the SSPS. Several approaches to achieving this objective are being investigated. It is highly likely that a two-stage transportation system will evolve, which will carry payloads first to low Earth orbit and subsequently deliver partially assembled components to synchronous orbit or possibly to an intermediate orbital altitude for final assembly and deployment.

The space transportation systems which are being considered are primarily an extension of existing systems. The potential systems, starting with the space shuttle now under development, vary from the use of a modified space shuttle to the development of a fully reusable liquid oxygen/liquid hydrogen heavy-lift launch vehicle with a potential 400,000-lb payload capability to deliver to low-Earth orbit. The current shuttle or its modification can be used for SSPS technology verification and flight demonstration and for transporting elements of the prototype SSPS into low Earth orbit. The cost for such a system, capable of lifting payloads up to 160,000 lb to low Earth orbit, is projected to be $100-200/lb. The heavy lift launch vehicle is expected to reduce payload costs to between $20 and $60 per pound for delivery to low Earth orbit.

The large mass of payloads will require about 60 to 100 flights for each SSPS assembled in synchronous orbit when an advanced space transportation system based on heavy-lift launch vehicles is used.

Ion propulsion, using solar power sources, could be used to transport a completely assembled SSPS from low Earth orbit to synchronous orbit. There is the option to transport to an intermediate orbit at 7,000 nautical miles. Chemically powered stages would transport payloads from low Earth orbit to this intermediate orbit, which lies outside the Van Allen Belt, and ion propulsion would transport the assembled SSPS to synchronous orbit. The cost for each flight will be strongly influenced by the feasibility of using ion propulsion for the orbit-to-orbit transportation and by the ability to reuse most of the components of the space transportation system for a large number of successive flights. Challenges inherent in the development of a low-cost, heavy-lift space transportation system are being explored (Ref. 107). The achievement of low-cost space transportation will be essential to the commercial success of the SSPS.

The large number of components, most of them performing the identical function, and the role of man in assembling these components require that the methods of assembly, packaging of components, assembly rates, and maintenance and repair support facilities required during the assembly and subsequent operational phases be carefully evaluated. There are two basic approaches to assembly:

(1) Remote assembly using ground controlled tele-operators.

(2) Assembly of components delivered to synchronous orbit by an assembly crew operating from a space station support base as part of extravehicular activities.

Assembly by tele-operators can be expected to be

less costly than assembly by work crews in synchronous orbit, which would require a space station for support of their operations. The choice between manned or tele-operator assembly will depend on the cost effectiveness of either approach. Tele-operators using remote assembly techniques should achieve assembly rates in excess of about 10 lb an hour, and would appear to be more effective than manned assembly, which would have to achieve rates of about 20 lb an hour to justify the cost of space stations and recycling of crews. It is highly likely that a combination of both manned operations and tele-operators will evolve, where man's most important function will be to exercise control over the assembly process.

With any major system such as the SSPS, the design criteria, materials choices, and data on component life and the expected operating conditions will determine reliability. Redundancy of components – for example, solar cells – will tend to reduce maintenance requirements. The cost of performing repairs has to be evaluated and compared with the option of delaying repairs and accepting the potential loss of revenue while achieving operational lifetimes consistent with cost analyses of the SSPS operation. The goal will be to evolve maintenance-free designs, particularly for the solar cell blankets and the microwave generator subsystems.

Space-Based Manufacture. The SSPS provides a unique opportunity to evolve manufacturing methods which are particularly suited for operations in space. The space transportation system, which will evolve to transport payloads from Earth to synchronous orbit, will have a substantially greater lift capability than even a space shuttle. However, this lift capability can be utilized appropriately only when the payload is designed to be mass limited rather than volume limited. Prefabricated beams (required, for example, for the microwave transmitting antenna structure) transported to orbit for subsequent deployment may be less desirable because packaging densities of about 5 lb/cubic foot are typical for folded and compressed designs for deployable structures. Thus available volume probably will be the limiting factor rather than lifting capacity if components are prefabricated on Earth.

The required high load factor could be achieved if fabrication and assembly were performed in orbit from appropriately prepared flat-rolled stock from which girders and other mechanical components could be produced by automated manufacturing techniques. With such techniques, the rolled stock would be formed into beams and girders and welded to form the mechanical structure, which is to be used in the subsequent assembly process.

A space "factory" – designed to serve as the production facility for succeeding SSPS – would be used for these purposes. Such a space-based manufacturing operation would permit assembly rates of about 400 lb/hr, allowing the most effective use to be made of the high-lift capability of the space transportation system, and thus greatly reducing the number of orbital flights. The potential of manufacturing in space has already been recognized and experiments in the Skylab mission provided important data on which future and more complex space manufacturing processes can be based.

Social Costs. The social costs of large-scale power-generation systems have to be established so the benefits of each specific system can be weighed against potential dangers to human health, destruction of valued natural resources, and the intangible effects which may influence the quality of life. Failure to take these costs into account will only lead to substantial impediments to the development of such systems, as was proven in such major programs as supersonic transport aircraft, nuclear power, and interstate highways.

The major social impact of SSPS operations would lie in:

• Resource allocations, including land management; energy requirements during construction, operations, and the energy payback period; commitments of resources; etc.

• Environmental effects, including waste heat disposal, interactions with the upper atmosphere, environmental modifications, noise generation, etc.

• Public safety, including long-term exposure under normal operations, effects on communications, safety issues under accident or abnormal situations, continuity of power generation and effects of interference with operations, etc.

Environmental Impacts. The operational phases

of the SSPS are projected to produce various environmental impacts:

- **Waste Heat.** Waste heat released at the receiving antenna site would be equivalent to about 15% of the rectified microwave power, which is substantially less than the waste heat released from energy production methods based on thermodynamic cycles.

- **Land Management.** Land use will be substantial, with about 100 square miles affected. However, the land could be devoted to productive uses because only about one-third of the land would be covered by the receiving antenna, which is a lightweight structure 80% transparent to sunlight and unobstructive to rain. Microwave radiation can be excluded from beneath the antenna, maintenance will be minimal, and transportation of supplies to the site will be infrequent compared to conventional powerplants. Offshore locations should be considered as alternative antenna sites. Land use for transmission lines could be reduced if receiving antennas were located in the vicinity of major users.

- **Resource Consumption.** Materials requirements will be limited largely to those which are in plentiful supply, such as silicon and aluminum. Each SSPS would require less than 2% of the yearly supply of critical materials, such as platinum, available to the United States.

- **Energy Consumption.** The energy required to produce the materials required during SSPS construction as well as the propellants to place it into orbit would be repaid – i.e., regenerated – in about two years of SSPS operation.

- **Atmospheric Pollution.** According to present estimates of space vehicle emissions, the multiple launches required to orbit the SSPS are not expected to add any significant amount of pollution to the atmosphere, and will be within allowable goals.

- **Ionosphere Interactions.** The microwave power density within the beam center is below the level where interactions with the ionosphere are projected to occur (50 mW/cm^2).

- **Microwave Exposure.** Exposure to the microwave beam can be controlled by providing suitable enclosures for the maintenance crew to work on the receiving antenna. Within 10 kilometers from the beam center the microwave power density would meet the lowest international standards for continued exposure to microwaves (Figure 79). The microwave beam directional system and the phase control achieved by means of a pilot signal beamed from the center of the receiving antenna preclude the deviation of the microwave beam beyond allowable limits. In case of failure of the microwave beam pointing system, the coherence of the microwave beam would be lost, the energy dissipated, and the beam spread out so that the microwave beam density would approximate communication signal levels on Earth. The effects on birds exposed to microwave power flux densities within the beam at the receiving antenna and the effects on aircraft accidently flying through the beam are projected to be negligible, but they should be determined experimentally.

- **Radio-Frequency Interference.** RF interference by the fundamental microwave frequency and its harmonics, turn-on and shutdown sequences, random background energy, and other superfluous signals resulting from specific design approaches for the microwave-generation devices could be controlled by filters, choice of frequency, and narrowband operation. Detailed and specific effects and impacts on radio astronomy services, ship-borne radar, and communication systems will have to be determined before the international acceptability of specific frequency allocations can be established. Preliminary investigations indicate that, for example, amateur sharing, state police radar, and high-power defense radar may suffer substantial interference if the 3.3 GHz frequency is chosen as the fundamental frequency.

- **Noise Pollution.** The noise from launch operations will be of concern in the immediate vicinity of the launch facility. Suitable location of the launch facilities and noise control during launches could reduce noise pollution to acceptable levels.

Economic and Social Implications. The SSPS represents a major technological development program. The scale of this program, even in the developmental stage, the financial and material

Figure 79   Microwave Power Density Distribution on Ground

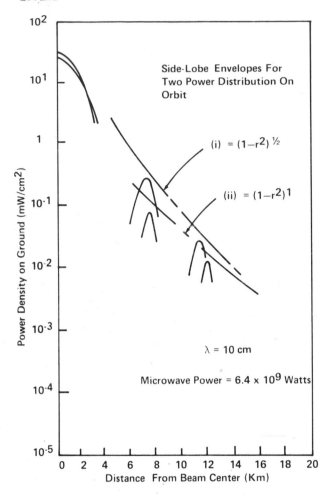

Side-Lobe Envelopes For Two Power Distribution On Orbit

(i) $= (1-r^2)^{1/2}$

(ii) $= (1-r^2)^1$

$\lambda = 10$ cm

Microwave Power $= 6.4 \times 10^9$ Watts

Power Density on Ground (mW/cm²)

Distance From Beam Center (Km)

requirements, the environmental impacts, the economic and social consequences, the international political significance, and the relationship to national and international energy programs place the SSPS in the highest rank of socially sensitive technological programs. It rivals nuclear fission and fusion, satellite telecommunications, and intercontinental aviation in significance.

The benefits and cost from a program as large as the SSPS will tend to be distributed nonuniformly and to concentrate in certain segments of society and the economy. Major effects of the SSPS development program can be expected to be felt by individuals, corporations, various institutions, even entire sectors of industry, who will react to the costs and the benefits as perceived by them. The political pressures generated as a result of these perceptions are likely to have a pronounced effect on the SSPS program, its ultimate success and the schedule against which it will be developed.

In addition to determining the economic viability of the SSPS, consideration should be given to assessing socio-economic impacts such as: energy self-sufficiency; balance of payments; trade balances; employment of capital and labor resources; effects on regional economics; direct, indirect and secondary impacts of industries; materials allocation; and energy requirements.

In addition the effects on the standard of living and quality of life, and institutional impacts on organizations, will need to be established. These issues are already receiving attention and are deserving of more detailed study as the SSPS development program proceeds.

The economic viability of the SSPS, in comparison with that of other alternatives, has been investigated to provide a basis for future decisions about a major SSPS development program (Ref. 108). The results of these investigations indicate that the SSPS is an option that continues to deserve serious consideration in comparison with alternative methods of power generation.

An operational 5000-MW SSPS would cost about $7.6 billion (Figure 80), or about $1500/kW. The largest cost element is space transportation, indicating that improvements in SSPS efficiency, particularly at the receiving antennas, and in mass reductions would be significant.

For an operational life of about 30 years the cost of power at the bus bar would be 27 mills/kWh. The expected life-cycle revenues will be about $35 billion for each SSPS, while operating costs will be $140 million per year (or $4.2 billion over a 30-year life cycle).

The revenues from a series of SSPS will be used to offset the development program costs – $20 billion for the development of SSPS technology and another $24 billion for the development of the space transportation system and related technology.

The SSPS development program costs could be repaid if 60 SSPS were operational by the year 2014, assuming that alternative system generation costs average 35 mills/kWh.

This number of operational SSPS will provide at least 10 percent of incremental installed generation capacity in the United States. A larger number of operational SSPS would be required to repay development program costs if alternative system

Figure 80 Unit Cost for 5,000MW SSPS ($1974 × 10⁹)

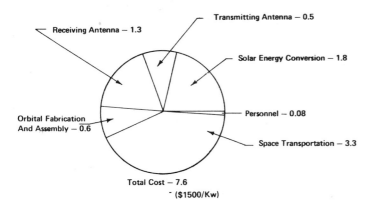

UNIT COST FOR 5,000 – MW SSPS
($1974 x 10⁹)

Receiving Antenna – 1.3

Transmitting Antenna – 0.5

Solar Energy Conversion – 1.8

Personnel – 0.08

Orbital Fabrication
And Assembly – 0.6

Space Transportation – 3.3

Total Cost – 7.6
⁻ ($1500/Kw)

generation costs were less than 35 mills/kWh between 1995 and 2014.

Figure 81 compares the range of projected generation costs for fossil-fueled and solar-terrestrial generation systems with those of the SSPS. A 5000-MW operational SSPS will be cost effective with fossil fuels at the projected bus bar cost of 27 mills/kWh. Between 1995 and 2025, coal prices are projected to rise as much as 5% because of increased production costs and costs for pollution control equipment. The relative price rise of oil is expected to be more pronounced; more importantly, it is unlikely to be available at any price after 2000 for large-scale power generation purposes.

Projected bus bar costs of terrestrial solar thermal and photovoltaic conversion systems range from 35 to 65 mills/kWh. Both of these solar energy conversion systems would provide mainly peaking power, whereas the SSPS will provide base load power.

Economic analyses carried out so far do not include the costs of social and environmental impacts. These costs would adversely affect the eonomics of most large-scale terrestrial generating systems and thus further enhance the overall economic attractiveness of the SSPS.

SSPS Development Program

The SSPS development program can be divided into three phases, as shown in Figure 82. During the first phase, the development of technology to meet performance and cost goals will proceed, and the technology will be verified to provide data on the performance of components and subcomponents

under expected operating conditions. The technology verification activities can be done on Earth, being supplemented only by those space experiments needed to provide data on specific system and component functions, potential interactions of the microwave beam with the ionosphere, and microwave frequency and beam power densities as they relate to biological effects criteria.

The critical technology development will be concerned with:

- Improvements in photovoltaic conversion including fabrication of solar cells

- The design of solar arrays and the performance analysis of large structures

- Techniques for manufacturing and assembling components in orbit

- System stability and control

- Microwave generation and transmission, including the development of DC-to-RF converters and filters, the development of waveguide materials, phase front control, control of the transmitting antenna attitude, control or suppression of radio frequency interference

- Mechanical systems, including rotary joints, slip rings, motor drives, and switch gears

Figure 81 Comparison of Range of Generation Costs Over the Period 1995-2025

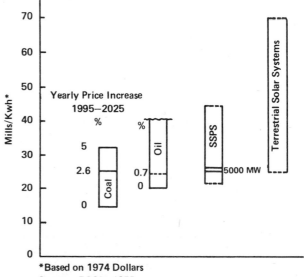

*Based on 1974 Dollars
Source: ECON, 1975.

125

Figure 82 SSPS Development Program Phasing

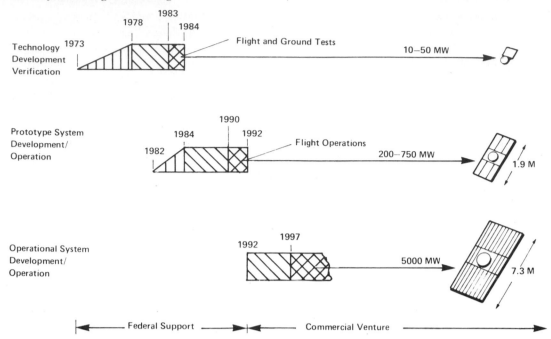

• Stationkeeping systems, including ion engine development

During this first phase, assessment of environmental and socio-economic issues should proceed in parallel. Analysis of these issues will provide feedback into the design and development process and help assure that the technology can be designed to minimize any adverse impacts.

At the end of the first phase, the subsystems and system functions would be verified in an orbiting test facility which may take the form of a space station. In parallel with the definition of the SSPS technology, the development, production, and operation of the space transportation system for materials, equipment, and personnel from launch through deployment for the specified mission orbit would proceed.

The development of the space transportation systems would include the development of the second-generation space shuttle, transfer vehicles between low-Earth orbit and synchronous orbit, orbital propellant storage, and maneuvering vehicles to transport equipment, materials and propellants to the vicinity of the assembly site. The development of the space transportation system would coincide with the assembly of a large prototype SSPS, which should be operated long enough to provide data and experience to guide the design of the full-scale operational unit of about 5000 MW.

After the successful completion of the second phase of the SSPS development program, the emphasis would shift to mass-producing SSPS, to provide at least 100 units by the year 2025. This development program is geared to achieve commercialization of the SSPS a few years before the year 2000 so this option for the large-scale use of solar energy can play an increasingly important role in the generation of power on a world-wide scale in the 21st century.

Conclusions

Since the concept of a Satellite Solar Power Station was first proposed in 1968, considerable work has been carried out on various aspect of the SSPS. The SSPS is now considered a credible option which, if successfully developed, could contribute significantly to meet energy requirements beyond 1995. Assessments are being carried out by academic, industrial, and government groups in the United States and abroad. The results of these investigations indicate that:

• The SSPS is technically and economically promising.

• The SSPS has the potential to be environmentally acceptable.

• An orderly incremental SSPS development program can preserve this energy option.

- Critical SSPS technology developments can contribute to other worthwhile endeavors in space and on Earth.

- Developments being carried out on advanced space transportation systems, solar energy conversion systems, and other related technology are supportive of SSPS development.

The SSPS represents an undertaking which, because of its magnitude, world-wide implications on energy availability, and potential for the industrial use of space, could benefit many countries. It should be in the common interest to obtain agreements on such aspects as suitable frequency assignment for the microwave beam, favorable launch sites for the space transportation system, and sites for the receiving antennas.

The successful implementation of the objectives of the SSPS should lead to the elimination of society's energy-related concerns. But even beyond this, it represents an opportunity to enter not only a new era of energy resource development but, in a broader sense, the first steps toward the industrialization of space and the extension of civliization beyond the confines of the Earth's surface.

What is required now is to proceed with the near-term development program for the SSPS so this option can be protected and so future decisions regarding the implementation of the full-scale SSPS development program can be based on hard data.

NASA and industry have the capability to undertake the SSPS development program. The commitment to this program within the technical community is growing. With the support of Congress and other elements of the Federal government this option could be established as one of the major initiatives to meet future national and world needs for energy.

DISCUSSION

Q. Even though the beam of microwave power reaching the Earth can be tapered to the point that it isn't dangerous to life near the edges of the antenna, it is in the electromagnetic spectrum that is normally used on the Earth for communications. Radio astronomers, for example, can see signals as faint as 10^{-29} W/cm². How much interference with communication and scientific research would be caused by this microwave beam?

A. We have recognized radio frequency interference as one of the very important environmental considerations. I'd like to refer you to what's called the Green Report (NASA CR 2357), where we discuss this. We have taken as a "given" that we will *not* interfere with radio astronomers, buy we may interfere with others, depending on the wavelength chosen. We will obliterate high-power defense radar, state police radar, and some amateur transmissions. We recognized that this is a tremendously important field. We've discussed it at length with communications people and with the Office of Telecommunications Policy, and they told us that if, indeed, this kind of satellite can be developed to be of benefit to the world, and we can show that not just we, but others will benefit, they are rather hopeful that international agreement on frequency assignments can be obtained. We may have to make choices: what is it that we really need from space, communication in certain bands or energy?

Q. Is our phased-array technology adequate for the antenna? Also, would you comment on the feasibility or the desirability of building a large paraboloid for transmitting, and perhaps using active structural control to achieve the desired contour.

A. The best knowledge that I have on this subject comes from the people who are most knowledgable in it – Raytheon. The phased-array transmission technology was already developed in 1963. Today that kind of technology is being used in installations in Alaska, which are five-story-high installations under the Cobra Dane program for the Air Force. The systems we need for the SSPS are really not too difficult for that technology to achieve. Whether the tradeoff between a phased array antenna and a paraboloidal antenna with various configuration controls would be better is exactly the kind of problem that I think ought to be looked at, because not enough work has been done.

Q. Would there be much heat created by the microwaves on the receiving antenna?

A. Yes. We've looked at it in some detail, because we were concerned about a "heat island" effect. Since we've already achieved 84% energy conversion efficiency, say 85%, there will be waste heat of 15%, which roughly corresponds to the waste heat release from an urban area. All we need is natural convection of air, and since it is over a relatively large area and most of the heat release will be in the middle rather than at the edges, we don't believe it will be a problem.

Q. *You mentioned that solar-cell costs could be brought down to about $.50 per watt or $500 per kilowatt. I have two questions: First, what if the cells were produced at the colony, and second, what is the cost now?*

A. The 50¢/watt is a goal enunciated by the Energy Research and Development Administration in their ten-year photovoltaic development program which JPL is just now starting to gear up, at a $7 million/year level. With regard to the lunar colony, I really don't have those numbers. I would say that we first have to learn how to make cheap solar cells on Earth and then translate it to what can be done there. I am rather hopeful that it *can* be done; O'Neill certainly has made a very convincing argument why we should use the Moon for raw materials, particularly when we have a large number of these satellites to construct over the next hundred years or so.

6.   Closed Brayton Cycle Turbines for Satellite Solar Power Stations

Gordon Woodcock
The Boeing Company

This paper discusses the construction problem of putting together a large power satellite employing turbine power generation. Various levels of technology have been discussed for power satellites; our current baseline is a near-term technology system. In other words, we think we know how to develop all the elements with only modest extensions of today's state of the art. Our purpose was to analyze the cost and economics of this system, and see how close it comes to being competitive with alternate sources.

Although large in scale, our baseline is a fairly conventional approach to the problem. We have not looked at the idea of manufacturing power satellites on the Moon or at the L5 libration point. If the lunar manufacturing concept can provide better economics, well and good. Anything that can improve the economics is, of course, favorable.

The concept employs a large solar concentrator that concentrates energy into a thermal cavity. Figure 83 is an illustration of one of these satellites. The satellite is eleven kilometers long, too large to compare it with today's space vehicles, but not much larger than the Golden Gate Bridge. The Golden Gate Bridge, of course, is much more massive; it's an earth-based structure. We can use very light structures.

The first reaction to so grandiose a concept, especially by the people who have been involved in managing large-scale projects, is illustrated in Figure 84. But to counter this typical response it is a good idea to think in terms of historical perspective.

When I graduated from college in 1954 our space technology was at the stage of the Viking sounding rocket (not the Mars Viking). The Viking rocket was the American version of the V2; it would go a little higher, but with a little less payload. The time frame that we are considering in satellite power stations is fifteen years. If you add fifteen years to 1954, you get 1969: a manned lunar landing.

The growth of technology that occurred over that time frame is comparable to the kind of growth we are now discussing. There are people who cite development "S-curves" – we are already on top of the S-curve, and it's really not going to get much better. I believe, however, that the programs NASA is currently undertaking with the space shuttle are putting us on a new S-curve, involving reusable systems and routine operations in space. That's the curve which is applicable to power satellites. You can't do it with expendable launch vehicles.

The concept discussed in this paper is similar in all respects to Glaser's except that we use heat engines for conversion of the sunlight to electricity. Right now it is hard to tell whether heat engines or photovoltaics is the best way to go. Present analyses indicate somewhat better economics with the heat engines, but it is about ten years too soon to make that choice.

One of the key factors in a heat engine system is the turbine inlet temperature one can achieve. Figure 85 illustrates the different kinds of applications. At the upper end of the chart are military aircraft, then commercial aircraft, then

Figure 83 A 10,000MWe Solar-Thermal Satellite Powerplant

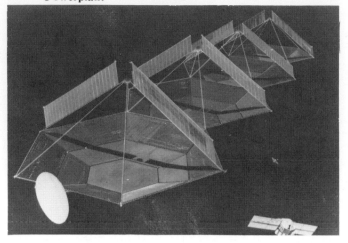

Figure 85 Turbine Inlet Temperature vs Time

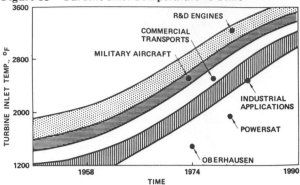

industrial applications and finally, down at the bottom, the data point for a 50 MWe closed-helium cycle turbine that is being installed in Oberhausen, Germany. If we postulate a curve from that data point, we can probably achieve about 1300 K (1900° F) turbine inlet temperature in an appropriate time frame to "freeze" the technology. The materials associated with this level, typified by columbium, are well enough understood to project a thirty-year life at these temperatures.

Another problem is how to achieve a reasonably efficient concentration of the sunlight. Many years ago, before the solar cell became the dominant method for generating space power, there were a number of attempts to configure thermal concentrator systems. All of them tended to get too massive at the concentration ratios of interest, except the one-piece reflectors. Since the satellite we

need is kilometers in diameter, it is not a one-piece reflector. And as Figure 86 shows, the inflatables, the petals, and the umbrella types all have very poor efficiencies. However, with a very large system, it appears practical to use many individually flat reflectors (heliostats), each individually steered to concentrate the energy into a central cavity, just as has been proposed for the central tower type of Earth-based solar powerplant.

With that approach, taking due account of the actual performance of reflective plastic films, we get the set of curves in Figure 87, which shows the achievable concentration ratio as a function of the geometric concentration ratio. We are currently using as a baseline about twenty thousand heliostats per concentrator, and need to get concentration ratios of two thousand or better to get reasonable efficiencies. These performance characteristics have been accounted for in the system described here.

Our baseline system is a ten thousand megawatt satellite; that's an arbitrary number, just as is Glaser's five thousand megawatts. Both are in the range of possible systems. The thermal engine satellite mass is estimated as sixty thousand metric tons.

Figure 84

Figure 86 Solar Concentrator Technology

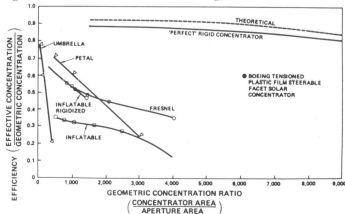

130

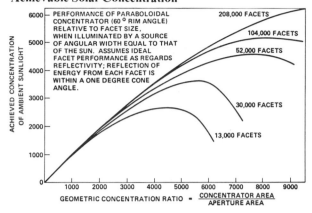

Figure 87 Number of Facets Used Influences Achievable Solar Concentration

PERFORMANCE OF PARABOLOIDAL CONCENTRATOR (60° RIM ANGLE) RELATIVE TO FACET SIZE, WHEN ILLUMINATED BY A SOURCE OF ANGULAR WIDTH EQUAL TO THAT OF THE SUN. ASSUMES IDEAL FACET PERFORMANCE AS REGARDS REFLECTIVITY; REFLECTION OF ENERGY FROM EACH FACET IS WITHIN A ONE DEGREE CONE ANGLE.

ACHIEVED CONCENTRATION OF AMBIENT SUNLIGHT

208,000 FACETS
104,000 FACETS
52,000 FACETS
30,000 FACETS
13,000 FACETS

GEOMETRIC CONCENTRATION RATIO = CONCENTRATOR AREA / APERTURE AREA

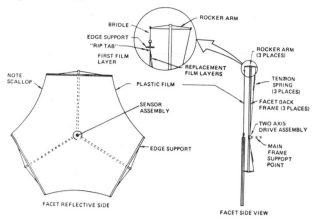

Figure 88 Typical Reflective Facet

The basic working unit of the concentrator itself is the plastic film reflector, shown in Figure 88. By using a three-point tension suspension technique, we can get by with low-precision hardware, just common tubing and angles. A very flat surface is achieved by stretching the plastic, making use of the principles of geometry rather than precision manufacturing. To increase the area of the facet, a hexagonal form is used instead of a triangular form.

Figure 89 is a photograph of a small test unit that was built. This illustrates the fact that space is an ideal environment. To use these plastic films on the ground, a bubble must be used to cover them, or the wind buffets them and the rain and dust ruin the reflective surface. The ground test unit of Figure 89 has a bubble over it, but the reflector is flat. It provides approximately the performance shown on Figure 87. The test reflector in Figure 89 is two meters across and weighs about half a kilogram. This is comparable to the mass used for estimating the space systems; note, however, that there was no particular attempt on this one to make its mass low.

In assembling a power satellite the first problem is to construct the heavy hardware: the cavity absorber, the radiators, and the main frame. Figure 90 is an illustration of a satellite assembly in low Earth orbit. The cavity itself is the object in the center; the turbomachines are clustered around it. Each turbomachine, with its cavity heat exchanger panel and its internal heat exchangers, is a single payload. The only fluid joints to be made in space are the connections from the turbomachines to the radiator. The assembly facility itself opens up like a bascule bridge to release the satellite when it is completely assembled. Figure 90 also shows some crewmen in the foreground and a space shuttle docked to the facility. The main frame structure in

this concept is launched in collapsed form and extended by a manned work vehicle. Its construction and that of the radiator assembly would probably be conducted in parallel. The next step is to put on all the reflectors. Remember that there are four modules of this satellite, one of which appears in Figure 90, with 20,000 reflectors on each one.

Figure 91 illustrates the deployment of the hexagonal reflector facets and their support arms. They are folded for launch, so that they can be packaged somewhat compactly, and then unfolded in space. Figure 91 also illustrates the "rosette" of seven facets on their support arms. First the arms unfold and then the facets can unfold. Each is thirty meters across, so the entire rosette would amply cover a football field of reflectors.

Aluminum is a practical material to use for structure. There are 200-300 kilometers of netlike structure installed in linear lengths to form the structural elements. Sending up completed beams doesn't make sense, because it is not likely that we will be able to get more than twenty to forty meters of length in the transporter's payload bay. Also, sending completed beams is like sending a box of empty beer cans; they take up a lot of volume and have very little mass. The space vehicle is volume limited rather than mass limited.

The assembly concept we have in mind, therefore, operates on the principle of the continuous "gutter" machine, adapted slightly to the production of low-mass aluminum beams. Starting with a flat roll of aluminum as produced by the mill (very dense, and consequently a mass-limited transportation problem) one can produce square beams of whatever length desired. We need them about two to three kilometers long. Figure 92 illustrates a work vehicle in orbit, manufacturing

131

Figure 89 Ground-Test Model of Plastic Film Reflector

Figure 91 Group Deployment of Reflector Facets and their Support Arms

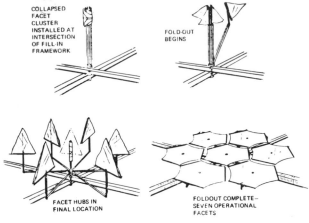

beams of the desired length to be attached to the structure. This is only one potential approach – an example of the way one might approach the problem. None of these concepts have been optimized yet to find the "best" approach.

Our suggested development program starts with experiments using the shuttle; there are a large number of experiments that one would wish to conduct. The program continues with the building of pilots plants, construction of facilities, development of launch vehicles, etc. Our rough estimates are that a 15-year development program would require non-recurring costs in the general vicinity of $60 billion. That does not buy the first satellite, but it completes all non-recurring investment required for the capability to produce one 10,000 MWe satellite per year and put it up into space.

Figure 90 Power Satellite Being Assembled in Low Earth Orbit

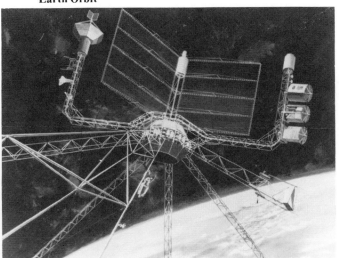

If we presume the placement of one satellite per year in orbit, this still leaves most of the emerging market (about 85%) for power production to prospective alternate forms of technology. That is, 10,000 MWe per year represents about fifteen percent of the predicted market. As each satellite comes on line, producing power at a cost of 25 mills per kw-hr, it produces a continuous lifetime revenue of about $2 billion per year. Thirty satellites in orbit generate revenue of about $60 billion per year. Using discount economics, to write off the $60 billion of development about a third of the total revenue stream is needed. This leaves about two thirds to buy satellites, which cost about $13 to $14 billion each (1975 dollars). We have not attempted to predict the rate of inflation.

The resulting cost tradeoff between hardware and transport costs is that if the hardware costs more to buy, there remains less left to pay for transportation. In our reference case, if we produce the hardware for about $130/kg, we leave about $65/kg to transport it. Note that the assembly and orbit costs are included in the $130/kg production cost, not in transportation costs.

We think that $130/kg is achievable; you can buy a 747 airplane for that, and a 747 is a more complicated machine than this power station, which although big, is really a relatively simple structure.

This then leads to some cost parameters for launch systems, as shown in the nomogram of Figure 93. The example illustrated in the nomogram shows that we can probably live with about $100/kg in transportation costs. If we were able to get as low as $40/kg, we might live with chemical propulsion to the high orbit. Figure 93 also shows that if we have a heavy satellite, such as the one just

Figure 92 Work Vehicle Manufacturing Square Aluminum Beams

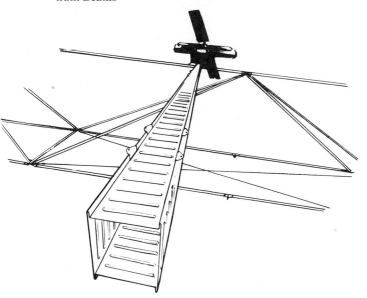

Figure 93 Low Orbit Transportation Cost Parametrics

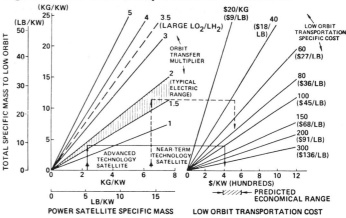

described, it is necessary to use electric propulsion, and we still need $40/kg.

The key to reaching $40/kg is total reusability. In the commercial airplane business, if it were necessary to paint the airplane between flights, it would double the cost of passenger tickets. So when I say total reusability, I mean just that. Nothing is changed between flights; you just refill the vehicle with propellant. One way to solve the thermal protection problem, for example, is to use water-cooled heat shields, filled with water every flight. There is a mass penalty, but it is much less expensive than having to replace a heat shield.

In summary, we believe the power satellite is a promising idea whether it uses heat engines or photovoltaic systems for power conversion. We think it is a massive undertaking, but based on the data we've assembled to date, it appears achievable. There seem to be rational concepts for most of the elements of the system; and not only are they understandable concepts, there are viable alternatives. The only function which appears to have no alternatives is the microwave power transmission, but that seems to be fairly well proven.

The economics of power satellites also appear acceptable. They will produce power at about the same price as fossil plants or nuclear plants, and probably much cheaper than ground-based solar plants. There are some big issues; e.g., the microwave power transmission. We've demonstrated very close to the required efficiencies over short ranges; the demonstration over long ranges is yet to be done. But there is nothing wrong with the theory, and it probably can work. Further, it leads to the definition of some good and useful experiments for the space shuttle program. Another issue is assembly in space: can we do it with a reasonable number of people? The low-orbit assembly facility (Figure 90) is manned with at least one hundred people, perhaps more. We do not manufacture anything in space, except the "gutter" machine products. Everything else is manufactured on the ground; the orbital facility is just for assembly. The final issue, of course, is whether or not we can really deliver on the low transportation cost.

I've only been very briefly exposed to the idea of manufacturing power satellites in space from lunar materials, but I do have a basic economic question on that subject: Can we afford to install the necessary facilities on the Moon and in space and still write them off economically with discounted economics? We found it was hard enough to write off our sixty billion dollars for conventional development.

SECTION III: HUMAN CONSIDERATIONS

1. Some Physiological Effects of Alternation between Zero Gravity and One Gravity*

Ashton Graybiel
Naval Aerospace Medical Research Laboratory at Pensacola

Introduction

The broad topic of this paper necessitates a selective choice of subject matter. I have selected the dual role played by the vestibular system in the lives of typically normal women and men. One role is the elegant manner in which the vestibular system functions under natural terrestrial stimulus conditions; the other is ease with which this system either provides unwanted information or is rendered unstable under unnatural stimulus conditions. The following discussion singles out those aspects involving the otolith organs and semicircular canals which cannot conveniently be neglected in making transitions between zero-gravity and one-gravity.

Background

The primitive character of the vestibular system in man accounts, in large part at least, for the almost incredible delay in discovering that sensory receptors in the inner ear serve functions other than hearing. This curious history divides into two with the publication of a report in 1870 by Goltz (Ref. 109), who drew his important inference from the studies of Flourens (Ref. 110), which showed that loss of equilibrium in pigeons followed sectioning of the semicircular canals. Goltz reasoned that if dis-equilibrium is caused by labyrinthine lesions, the same site must be involved with equilibratory function.

Before Goltz, what we now term vestibular side effects were, of course, well known; familiarity with seasickness and dizziness dates back to antiquity. Some of the earliest systematic observations were made by Erasumus Darwin (Ref. 111), who described in his "Zoonomia" (1794) the eye motions (nystagmus) and vertigo associated with rotation. Purkinje (Ref. 112) described a form of vestibular vertigo which he though had its origin in the cerebellum. Meniere (Ref. 113), who was familiar with Flouren's work, described the syndrome (deafness, vertigo, nausea) that bears his name, correctly ascribing the cause to labyrinthine disease; formerly, this syndrome had been included under the term "apoplectiform cerebral congestion."

After Goltz, within a period of five years Mach, Crum-Brown, and Breuer (Refs. 114, 115, 116) developed the theoretical basis underlying stimulation of the mechano-receptors in the semicircular canals and otolith organs. The theory that the canals are stimulated by impulse angular accelerations was elaborated by Ewald (Ref. 117) and confirmed by Steinhausen (Ref. 118) and Dohlman (Ref. 119). Stimulation of the otolithic receptors by gravity and by impulse linear accelerations was demonstrated by Kreidl (Ref. 120), Versteegh (Ref. 121), and Tait and McNally (Ref. 122), among others. Barany deserves the credit for introducing tests of vestibular function into the clinic (Ref. 123).

*This research was conducted under the sponsorship of the Office of Life Sciences, Lyndon B. Johnson Space Center, National Aeronautics and Space Administration, Order T-5904B. Opinions or conclusions are those of the author, and do not necessarily reflect the views or endorsement of the Navy Department.

With regard to the etiology of the vestibular side effects, it was the philosopher William James who in 1882 reasoned that if Goltz's deduction was correct, "deaf mutes" (with loss of labyrinthine function) should not experience dizziness (Ref. 124). Among 519 such subjects tested, 186 were classified "not dizzy", 134 "slightly dizzy", and 199 "dizzy". James interviewed "many deaf mutes" about their susceptibility to seasickness because of the "high probability" that it was of labyrinthine origin. Fifteen, in other than the "dizzy" category, had been exposed to rough seas and none had experienced seasickness. Sjoberg's classical studies on motion sickness (Ref. 125) demonstrated that labyrinthectomized dogs no longer were susceptible to motion sickness and, incidentally, proved the correctness of James' presumptive evidence.

The Semicircular Canals and Otolith Organs

The labyrinth of the human inner ear comprises the cochlea, the organ of hearing, and the otolith organs and semicircular canals, collectively termed the vestibular organs. These are paired end organs with a common blood supply and a shared secondary lymph circulation; their mechano-receptors have similar histological features and are innervated by the vestibular division of the eighth nerve. These sensory organs are situated in hollowed-out channels in the petrous portion of the temporal bone (Figure 94, from Ref. 126), and, within the bony channels, the enclosed membraneous labyrinth is surrounded by perilymph and filled with endolymph. Thus, the sensory receptor mechanisms are protected from the effects of

Figure 94. Reconstruction of the membranous labyrinth and related anatomy. (From Reference 126).

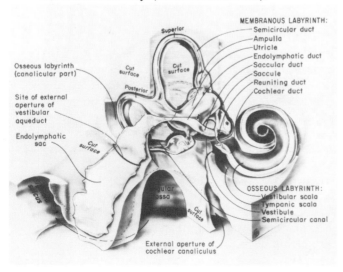

superimposed body weight by the bony labyrinth, and, by virtue of the contained fluids, receive additional protection from impact accelerations. Although protected from mechanical forces the mechano-receptors must respond slavishly to appropriate accelerative forces.

Figure 95. Cross section of well-preserved human ampulla (posterior semicircular canal) showing the crista with its sensory epithelium surmounted by the cupula. (Courtesy Professor Igarashi.)

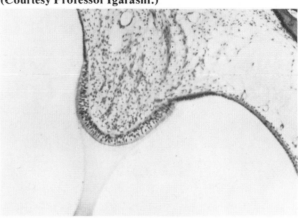

Figure 96. These drawings have been adapted from photographs taken in situ and published by Dohlman. A drop of opague oil has been injected into the simicircular canal and its position prior to (a) and after an accelerative stimulus (b) indicate changing relationships, i.e., endolymph flow with consequent displacement of the cupula.

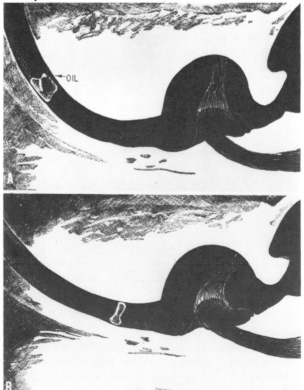

Figure 97. **Labyrinth of the left ear as viewed from the lateral aspect.**

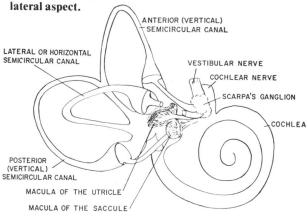

The Semicircular Canals. The orientation of the six semicircular canals with reference to the head is shown in Figure 94. It will be noted that, although the three canals on one side lie approximately in mutually perpendicular planes, only the plane of the horizontal canals even approaches being parallel to one of the coordinate planes of the skull, and even here the divergence is about 25 degrees.

A section through the ampulla of an exceptionally well-preserved human specimen is shown in Figure 95. The crista is a transverse ridge of tissue covered by a sensory epithelium containing hair cells, whose cilia extend into a gelatinous body called the cupula. The cupula, a meshwork of fibers, presumably collagen, extends to the roof of the ampulla completing a fluid-tight gate across the ampulla, hinged at the crista and free to move back and forth in reponse to movements of the endolymph. This apparatus constitutes the cupula-endolymph mechanism.

The cupula-endolymph mechanism is similar in man and fish. Its operation is illustrated by Figure 96, showing drawings made from photographs of the ampulla of the living pike. A drop of opaque oil was injected into a single canal and served to indicate any movement of the endolymph. Figure 96A shows the position of the oil droplet and cupula prior to stimulation. In response to angular acceleration the endolymph lags behind the movement of the bony and membranous canal, thus displacing the droplet and the cupula in a direction counter to the rotary motion (Figure 96B). The cupula-endolymph system, responding only to impulse angular accelerations in the plane of the canal, has been likened to a fluid-filled toris, with the cupula responding to movements of the endolymph in the manner of a spring-mass system with viscous damping. Based on the equivalence of gravity and

Figure 98. **a. A view of saccular macula from a squirrel monkey. Zonal structure is clearly seen. b. Schematic of zonal structure. c. High magnification showing crystalline structure of the otoconia (from Reference 128.)**

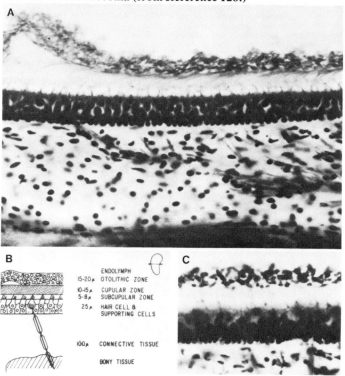

inertial mass, the semiconducter canals are gravity-independent for all practical purposes.

Under stimulus conditions that are natural for man, angular deceleration quickly follows angular acceleration and, inasmuch as the areas under the curves depicting acceleration and deceleration are the same, the cupular deflection is almost immediately restored to its natural position. For the reason that we can quickly rotate the head relative to the trunk, these start-and-stop accelerations are estimated to range as high at 700° per sec^2 during ordinary activities and far above 1000° per sec^2 for quick head movements. These high values may be compared with the threshold for perception of the oculogyral illusion, which is about 0.02° per sec^2. Stated differently, these high naturally-generated transient accelerations far exceed any that can be generated (or tolerated) during passive exposure in device or conveyance.

The Otolith Organs. The mechano-receptors in the two vestibular organs are similar, but the gross structure of the otolith organs bears little resemblance to that of the semicircular canals. The four curved macular plates on the inner walls of the paired utricle and saccule (Figure 97) occupy, without overlap, a significant portion of a sphere.

A cross section of the saccular macula of a squirrel monkey, which is similar to that in man, is shown in Figure 98 a and c, and a sketch of the zonal structure is shown in Figure 98b (Ref. 127). The otolithic membrane contains massive otoconia concretions of calcium carbonate with a specific gravity of about 2.7l, embedded in a gelatinous material. This membrane is the only tissue within the bony labyrinth that differs much from the specific gravity of the lymph fluids. The otolith membrane rests on the cupular membranes into which protrude the hair-like projections of the sensory cells, and it is the movement of the otolithic membrane relative to these sensory "hairs" or cilia that constitutes the effective stimulus to the organ (Figure 99, from Ref. 128).

It is important to make clear the distinction between accelerations that can stimulate the otolith organs and forces that can stimulate mechano-receptors serving touch, pressure, and kinesthesis. The latter are stimulated directly or indirectly not only by gravitoinertial forces but also by strictly mechanical (nongravitoinertial) forces.

The Biologically Effective Force Environment

On Earth. In this paragraph the concept of man's biologically effective force (BEF) environment is briefly developed in relation to life activities under terrestrial conditions and its general usefulness illustrated in connection with the unique force environments in aerospace flight. The need for a common basis in discussing and comparing these forces is best exemplified in comparing "life" in a weightless spacecraft and life on Earth. The purpose here is not to attempt a comprehensive analysis and synthesis, which would represent a large undertaking and even than be incomplete, but to set forth major guidelines which point to its further exploitation for practical or theoretical purposes.

Man's gravitoinertial force environment has its genesis in (a) gravity due to a central field factor, and (b) the inertial forces generated by the motions of "machine" or man or both in combination (Figure 100). Under ordinary living conditions on Earth, gravitational force may be regarded as a constant and the only force of sufficient magnitude to affect total body weight significantly. It is the force to which man has become adapted throughout evolutionary development and to which he is accustomed through experience. The addition of mutually perpendicular lines to the vector representing gravitational upright forms the spatial frame of Earth reference. When man is exposed in

conveyances and devices that generate accelerations or change his position with respect to the gravitational or gravitoinertial vertical, he is subjected to unnatural stimulus conditions that may range far beyond physiologic limits. These accelerations generate an external force field that, along with gravity, comprises the total *external* force field.

The inertial forces generated by the active motions of the body or parts of the body may be regarded as "immanent" forces inasmuch as they do not contribute to the external force field, but, of course, combine with it. These immanent forces are either of small magnitude or short duration, and derive their significance partly because they are associated with motions that change the position of the body with regard to the other components in the force environment, and partly because these forces are sufficient to stimulate specialized sensory receptors that provide information about body statics and dynamics. When gravitational, inertial, and immanent accelerative forces combine, they constitute a complex, dynamic pattern that varies as a function of time.

Although the equivalence of gravitational and inertial mass is the unifying principle underlying the gravitoinertial force concept, this simplicity gives way to great complexity when account is taken of the structural and functional characteristics of the body. Not only does the body lack uniformity, but

Figure 99. Sketch drawn from the electromicrographs of the fine structure of the utricular macula of the squirrel monkey. Two types of hair cells (HC 1 and HC 11). Two types of cilia (KC, kinocilia; St, stereocilia). (From Reference 128.)

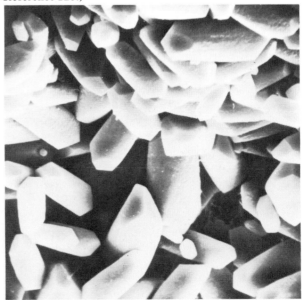

Figure 100. Man's biologically effective force environment under terrestrial conditions.

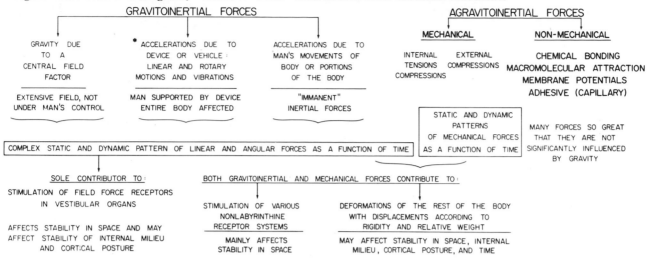

also a state of mechanical equilibrium in all parts of the body is never reached. Moreover, the vestibular organs stimulated in an unusal manner (even if the strength of the stimulus is small) may cause far-reaching disturbances after "amplification" in the central nervous system.

The agravitoinertial forces are much more difficult to identify and to measure in terms of a common unit than the accelerative forces. They assume great importance in a weightless environment, and a dichotomy may be drawn between agravitoinertial forces of mechanical and non-mechanical origin (Figure 100). With regard to the latter, further distinctions are possible, ranging between forces at one extreme that are so great that absence of gravitational force is of no practical consequence, and the other extreme when its influence is felt. All of these forces of mechanical origin are generated by tensions and compressions and, along with gravitoinertial forces, contribute to bodily deformations and to stimulation of non-vestibular mechano-receptors.

Zero Gravity Conditions. Under natural terrestrial conditions the force of gravity due to a central field factor is only part of our biologically effective force (BEF) environment; hence it is important to distinguish between weightlessness *per se* and man active in a weightless spacecraft. This difference, which may be very great, will be determined mainly by the role played by mechanical forces that are effective in countering the null-gravity state.

Figure 101 is an attempt to analyze the BEF environment in a weightless spacecraft. The

gravitoinertial forces are generated mainly by the motions of man and machine, although even in orbital space flight man will be exposed to a scalar gravitational potential, however small, and to a gravitational force while his mass is counter-supported. Immanent accelerations generated in the course of man's work and housekeeping activities contribute little to man's "apparent weight" but are important since they stimulate sensory receptors (directly and indirectly) and thus contribute to the flow of information to the nervous system.

The preservation of man's well-being in a weightless spacecraft is heavily dependent on agravitoinertial forces, which are of mechanical or nonmechanical origin. An analysis of the latter should be made in terms of their effectiveness at different organizational levels in the body. A table might be prepared indicating the forces operant at different levels; e.g., molecular, intracellular, cellular, and tissue levels. Cytochemical reactions involve forces (thermodynamic, bioelectric, and chemical) so great that they are "gravity independent."

The different organizational levels in cells and tissues at which gravity dependence appears as an influence have not been investigated systematically, but this information is important for two related reasons: first, to point out where preventative measures become necessary in the absence of gravity, and second, to point out the possibility that important alterations may occur in systems not primarily affected by weightlessness.

The *nonmechanical* forces just described are very largely out of man's control; hence, agravitoinertial

141

Figure 101. Man's biologically effective force environment in near-weightlessness.

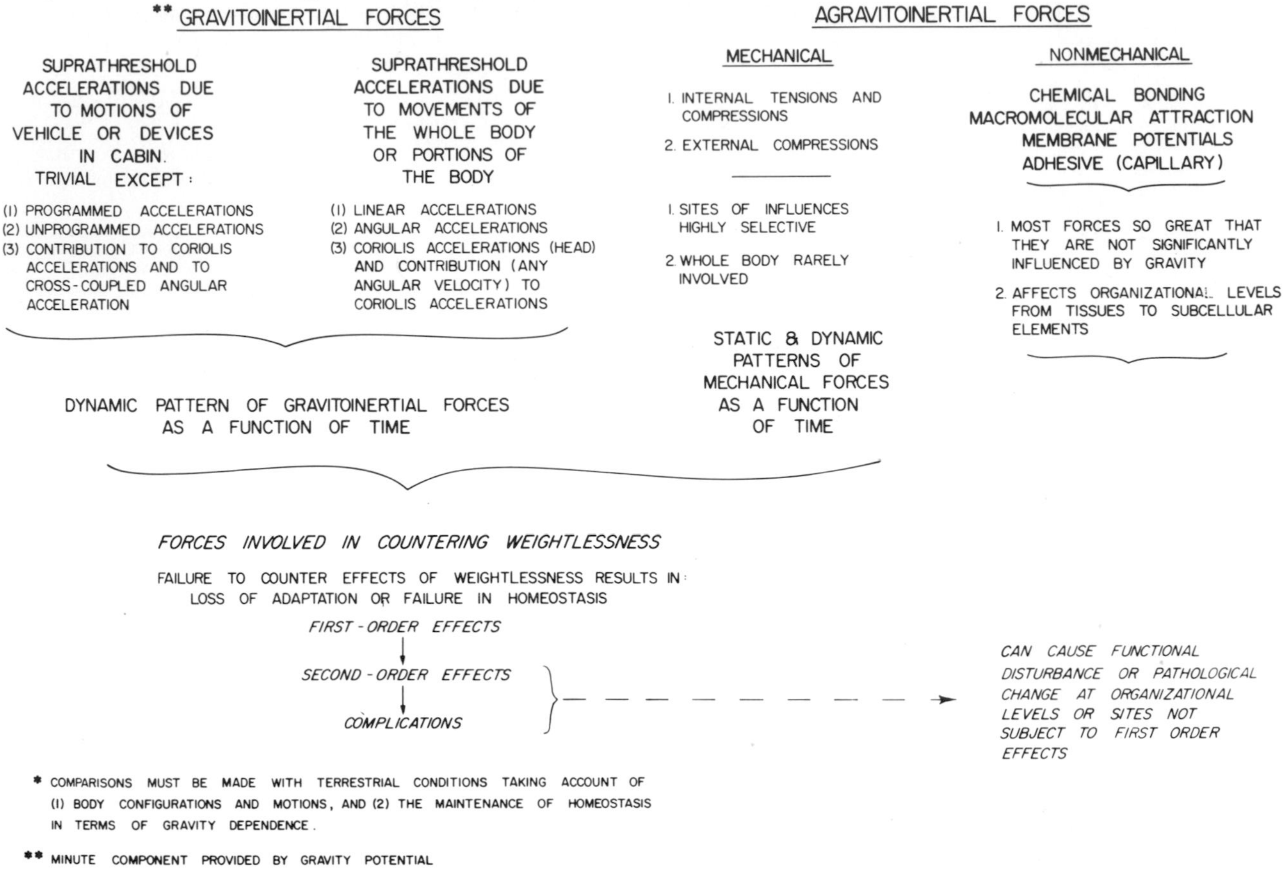

** GRAVITOINERTIAL FORCES

SUPRATHRESHOLD ACCELERATIONS DUE TO MOTIONS OF VEHICLE OR DEVICES IN CABIN. TRIVIAL EXCEPT:	SUPRATHRESHOLD ACCELERATIONS DUE TO MOVEMENTS OF THE WHOLE BODY OR PORTIONS OF THE BODY
(1) PROGRAMMED ACCELERATIONS (2) UNPROGRAMMED ACCELERATIONS (3) CONTRIBUTION TO CORIOLIS ACCELERATIONS AND TO CROSS-COUPLED ANGULAR ACCELERATION	(1) LINEAR ACCELERATIONS (2) ANGULAR ACCELERATIONS (3) CORIOLIS ACCELERATIONS (HEAD) AND CONTRIBUTION (ANY ANGULAR VELOCITY) TO CORIOLIS ACCELERATIONS

DYNAMIC PATTERN OF GRAVITOINERTIAL FORCES AS A FUNCTION OF TIME

AGRAVITOINERTIAL FORCES

MECHANICAL	NONMECHANICAL
1. INTERNAL TENSIONS AND COMPRESSIONS 2. EXTERNAL COMPRESSIONS	CHEMICAL BONDING MACROMOLECULAR ATTRACTION MEMBRANE POTENTIALS ADHESIVE (CAPILLARY)
1. SITES OF INFLUENCES HIGHLY SELECTIVE 2. WHOLE BODY RARELY INVOLVED	1. MOST FORCES SO GREAT THAT THEY ARE NOT SIGNIFICANTLY INFLUENCED BY GRAVITY 2. AFFECTS ORGANIZATIONAL LEVELS FROM TISSUES TO SUBCELLULAR ELEMENTS

STATIC & DYNAMIC PATTERNS OF MECHANICAL FORCES AS A FUNCTION OF TIME

FORCES INVOLVED IN COUNTERING WEIGHTLESSNESS

FAILURE TO COUNTER EFFECTS OF WEIGHTLESSNESS RESULTS IN: LOSS OF ADAPTATION OR FAILURE IN HOMEOSTASIS

FIRST-ORDER EFFECTS

SECOND-ORDER EFFECTS

COMPLICATIONS

CAN CAUSE FUNCTIONAL DISTURBANCE OR PATHOLOGICAL CHANGE AT ORGANIZATIONAL LEVELS OR SITES NOT SUBJECT TO FIRST ORDER EFFECTS

* COMPARISONS MUST BE MADE WITH TERRESTRIAL CONDITIONS TAKING ACCOUNT OF (1) BODY CONFIGURATIONS AND MOTIONS, AND (2) THE MAINTENANCE OF HOMEOSTASIS IN TERMS OF GRAVITY DEPENDENCE.

** MINUTE COMPONENT PROVIDED BY GRAVITY POTENTIAL

---

mechanical forces assume great importance in a weightless environment since, to a great extent, they are under man's control and can be utilized in the prevention of zero-G asthenia.

When man is free floating or lightly restrained in the weightless vehicle, these agravitoinertial mechanical forces are minimal and, although important for the maintenance of homeostasis in the *milieu interieur,* are nevertheless of trival value in the maintenance of musculoskeletal fitness. We need no further experience to state categorically that man's general fitness would rapidly deteriorate in the absence of mechanical forces generated by physical exercise.

Slow Rotation Room Findings

A slow rotation room (SRR) in a laboratory environment (Figure 102) provides an excellent instrument for the study of vestibular side effects. In the SRR a person is not subjected to a stressful stimulus unless he rotates his head out of the plane of the room's rotation (Crewman 5), hence the situation differs from that in ships and planes where a person cannot avoid stressful accelerations

generated by motions of the vehicle. The cardinal advantages of such a room lie in (1) its habitability; subjects have remained in the SRR for over a month with experimenters in attendance, (2) the great range in strength of the stressful stimuli; especially cross-coupled angular acceleration that stimulate the semicircular canals in an unusual manner, (3) the experimenter's control not only over the stressful accelerations, but also other important procedural and environmental variables, and (4) the opportunity for measurements to be made with sophisticated laboratory equipment. Thus, when the possibility arose that space vehicles might be rotated to generate inertial forces it was immediately evident that we had a means of simulating the angular velocities over a greater range than that seriously considered for use in space vehicles aloft. Particular attention is therefore given here to prolonged exposures (Refs. 129-131) in which subjects carried out a variety of tasks and experiments dealing with the acquisition of direction-specific adaptation effects (Ref. 132). The minor problem of postural dysequilibrium is mentioned briefly.

Prolonged Exposure. Prolonged rotation in the

Figure 102. Responses to the force environment in a rotating room. Crewmen 1 and 2, in articulated molds supported by air-bearing devices, are "walking on the wall", simulating the orientation in a rotation spacecraft. Crewman 2, walking in the direction of rotation, becomes somewhat heavier because his angular velocity, hence centripetal acceleration, is increased and sums with the Coriolis accelerations generated. Crewman 1, walking opposite to the direction of the rotation, becomes somewhat lighter because his centripetal accelerations are decreased and the Coriolis accelerations must be subtracted. Crewman 3, walking toward the periphery of the room, is exposed to increasing levels of centripetal acceleration and constant levels of Coriolis accelerations. Crewman 4, standing, is demonstrating two phenomena: first, as he moves his arm or leg sideways, a tendency to veer backward, the so-called "giant-hand" nucleus. Within each of these projections there is a somatotopic localization.

g = Acceleration of Gravity	Vr = Radial Velocity
A cen = Centripetal Acceleration	ω = Angular Velocity of Rotating Room
A cor = Coriolis Acceleration	φ = Angle Between Gravitoinertial
Vt = Tangential Velocity	And Gravitational Upright

SRR affords the opportunity of studying the complete symptomatology experienced by subjects both during and after rotation and the effects of these symptons on their performance. In general, the higher the RPM, the more severe the symptoms and the slower the adaptation if individual differences are taken into account. Many additional but mostly minor or incidental factors must, however, be considered.

In brief, at 1.0 RPM even highly susceptible subjects were symptom-free, or nearly so. At 3.0 RPM subjects experienced symptoms but were not significantly handicapped. At 5.4 RPM, only subjects with low susceptibility performed well and by the second day were almost free from symptoms. At 10 RPM, however, adaptation presented a challenging but interesting problem. Even pilots without a history of air sickness did not fully adapt in a period of twelve days. Initially, they were forced to restrict their head movements to prevent severe nausea. After a few days they no longer experienced nausea and, consequently, no longer restricted their head movements. They continued to complain of drowsiness and fatigue, however, and biochemical measurements revealed an increase in the plasma level of the enzyme lactic dehydrogenase. Even highly motivated and relatively insusceptible subjects were not fully recovered after twelve days.

Table 24 summarizes the findings obtained on three subjects exposed for two days with the SRR rotating at 1.71 RPM (Ref. 129), the rotation period estimated for O'Neill's Model 2 (Ref. 4). One of the subjects, RG, who had suffered bilateral loss of vestibular function in adolescence, had no perception of rotation and was aware that the room was rotating only while walking, throwing darts, etc. Both the remaining subjects, who were less

Table 24. Observations on four human subjects exposed to continuous rotation at 1.71 RPM for two days in a slow rotation room.

	RG						RME						RLE					
	1st Day		2nd Day	3rd Day			1st Day		2nd Day		3rd Day		1st Day		2nd Day		3rd Day	
	AM	PM	AM	AM	PM	Post run	AM	PM	AM	PM	AM	Post run	AM	PM	AM	PM	AM	Post run
Completed dial test	YES	YES	YES	YES	YES	YES	YES	YES	YES	YES	YES	YES	YES	YES	YES	YES	YES	YES
General malaise	0	0	0	0	0	0	0	0	0	0	0	0	2	2	0	0	0	0
Sweating	0	0	0	0	0	0	0	0	0	0	0	0	2	0	0	0	0	0
Nausea	0	0	0	0	0	0	0	0	0	0	0	0	3	2	1	1	0	0
Vomiting episodes	0	0	0	0	0	0	0	0	0	0	0	0	2	1	0	0	0	0
Dizziness	0	0	0	0	0	0	1	0	0	0	0	0	1	1	1	0	0	0
Oculogyral illusion	0	0	0	0	0	0	0	0	0	0	0	0	YES	YES	YES	YES	YES	–*
Headache	0	0	0	0	0	0	0	0	0	0	0	0	2	2	1	2	2	2
Apathy	1	0	0	0	0	0	1	0	0	0	0	0	2	2	1	0	0	0
Hours slept during day	0	0	0	0	0	0	0	0	0	0	0	0	1	0	0	0	0	0
Change in blood pressure	0	0	0	0	0	0	0	0	0	0	0	0	0	0	0	0	0	0
Difficulty walking	1	0	0	0	0	1	0	0	0	0	0	0	0	1	1	1	0	1
Difficulty heel-toe	1	0	0	0	0	1	0	0	0	1	0	1	2	2	0	1	0	0

Scoring: slight = 1, moderate = 2, marked = 3
*Not done

susceptible than the average person to motion sickness, experienced mild symptoms and had slight difficulty in walking throughout the first day. The second day they reported that the initial symptoms had disappeared, but remained apathetic. R.N., the inside observer, experienced mild symptoms continuing into the second day, but these sumptoms had disappeared by the morning of the third day.

An experiment similar to the one just described but with the room rotating at 2.22 RPM yielded similar results except in the case of one subject, 33 years of age, who considered himself less susceptible than the average to motion sickness. He had never been seasick in small boats, but on two ocean voyages was seasick the first day of each. He was a rather sensitive, nervous person, although highly motivated in his desire to serve as an experimental subject. During the first stress test (execution of standardized head movements), he experienced nausea, vomiting twice, and afterward had a loose bowel movement. Following the test, he felt sleepy and restricted his head movements. He showed significant improvement by the second day, and on the morning of the third day felt well except for what he described as a "tension headache."

A major experiment was conducted at 3.0 RPM (Ref. 13) in which three enlisted men and one experimeter were exposed to continual rotation for two weeks. The duration of the run was set at two weeks to test for an undesirable secondary effects which might occur after the initial period of adaptation. The subjects and the on-board observer gradually adapted to rotation and only minor disturbances of a physiological or psychological nature were demonstrated.

Direction-specific Adaptation Effects. A rotating room can simulate the angular velocity of a rotating space station, and the cross-coupled angular accelerations generated during the execution of head movements are the same as on Earth, although modulating influences are different. Early studies indicating that adaptation effects acquired in a rotating room were direction-specific seemed to pose a serious problem in making sudden transitions between rotating and nonrotating parts of a space station, inasmuch as in adapting to one motion environment adaptation to the other would be lost. The problem, however, turned out to be less formidable than supposed. The immediate reason is found in the fact that acquisition of *long term adaptation effects* in a room rotating counterclockwise is associated not only with the acquisition of long term adaptation to clockwise rotation, but is also associated with no loss of adaptation to the stationary environment. There is, however, one "complication" that must be taken into account, namely, that *short term adaptation effects* are also acquired and these are direction-specific.

Figure 103 shows the force profiles used in conducting a study involving 38 young Naval flight officers (Ref. 132). They were required to execute 120 head movements at each one-RPM increase in velocity of the room between 0 and 6 RPM and,

144

Figure 103. Variations in a typical stress profile. The initial adaptation schedule (IAS) is followed either by a one-step return to zero velocity (a) or by a reverse IAS that follows immediately (c) or after a delay (d). A delay may also follow the initial IAS (b). The number of head movements executed at each "step" in this profile was 120 unless testing was aborted.

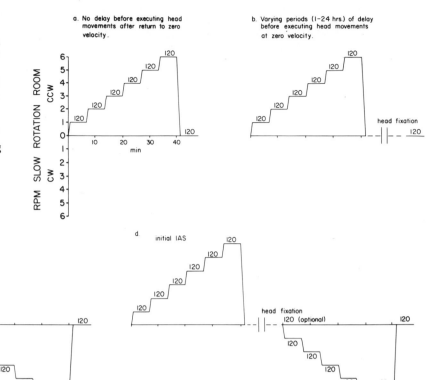

after a single-step gradual return to zero velocity, execute 120 head movements either immediately after the return or after delay periods varying from 1 to 24 hours unless, at any time, more than mild symptoms of motion sickness were elicited. A second stress profile differed by the sequential addition of an incremental adaptation schedule (identical to the first) in which the direction of rotation was reversed.

Figure 104 summarizes the measurements made

Figure 104. Stress profiles and motion sickness scores in two tests 6 days apart. In both tests the subject was symptom free during the incremental schedule. In Test 1 he was symptom free after executing head movements on return to zero velocity but 6 days later testing was aborted when the direction of rotation was reversed.

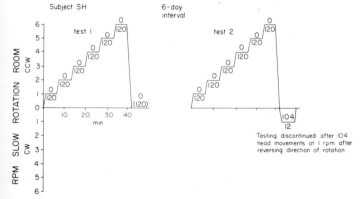

in the case of SH. In the first test SH was symptom-free, not only during the initial IAS but also during the challenge at zero velocity. The test 6 days later differed in that the direction of rotation was reversed immediately after completion of the initial IAS. The fact that testing was aborted after the execution of 104 head movements at 1 RPM demonstrates at once the greater challenge on

Figure 105. Stress profiles and motion sickness scores in two tests 9 days apart. In Test 1 the subject was virtually symptom free during the incremental adaptation schedule but testing was aborted while executing head movements after return to zero velocity. In Test 2, although mild symptoms were experienced at the end of the incremental schedule, the subject, after an 8-hour delay at zero velocity was virtually symptom free when the direction of rotation was reversed, indicating, in all likelihood, a decay in direction-specific adaptation effects acquired during the initial stress profile.

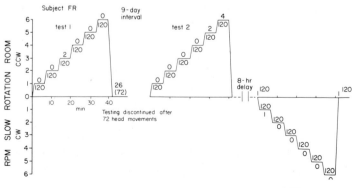

145

reversal compared with that at zero velocity and the fact that direction-specific adaptation had been acquired during the initial IAS. The great severity of the challenge after reversal of direction is a reasonable expectation.

Figure 105 shows the measurements made in the case of FR. In the first test direction-specific adaptation effects were demonstrated when testing was aborted during the challenge on return to zero velocity. Nine days later in test 2 FR was virtually symptom-free when the direction of rotation was reversed. The absence of frank motion sickness is explained by the 8-hour delay between the initial and reverse IAS. The fact that the head was fixed during the delay implies that the direction-specific adaptation effects occurred, to a large extent at least, spontaneously.

The exponential decay in direction-specific effects as a function of the delay period was measured systematically and is shown in Figure 106. It is seen that the decay in direction-specific effects took place (for most of the 22 subjects) within a period of 4 hours.

Postural Disequilibrium. Few systematic tests involving the acquisition and loss of ataxia have been conducted (Refs. 133, 134). Both normal subjects and subjects with bilateral labyrinthine defects (L-D subjects) experience ataxia in rotating rooms but gradually become adapted.

On cessation of rotation, both the L-D and the normal subject manifest ataxia which gradually disappears after walking until the initial perrotation baseline values for postural equilibrium are reached. During the period of ataxia, both feel that they are unstable with reference to a stable platform. One significant difference between the two is that the normal in contrast to the L-D subject tends to lose his balance on quickly rotating his head. It is obvious that nonvestibular somatosensory inputs contribute greatly to the postural disequilibrium manifested during and after rotation and that the vestibular participation in the case of the normal subject, while demonstrable, is of secondary significance. One difference between debarking after a voyage and leaving the SRR (after having adapted to walking) is that the dock seems to move relative to the passenger while the subject seems to move relative to a stable floor.

In one experiment (Ref. 134) a unique feature was the provision for subjects to walk and carry out their tasks while horizontal to gravity and at right angles to the axis of rotation. This ability to "walk along the wall" (crewmen 1 and 2 in Figure 102) was made possible by the use of air-bearing supports and custom-fitted articulated fiberglass molds. Efforts were made to ensure a degree of comfort and level of activity in the "horizontal mode" fairly comparable to that in the "vertical mode." Four subjects participated in two experimental trials involving habituation to the artificial force environment with the room rotating at 4 RPM. One pair initially in the horizontal mode was changed to the vertical mode in the middle of the prerotation period; in the second experiment they began in the vertical mode. The order was reversed for the second pair (Figure 107).

Figure 106. Decay in direction-specific adaptation effects as a function of the time elapsed between completion of a standard incremental adaptation schedule (and return to zero velocity) and execution of head movements at zero velocity. The first two points on the graph represent susceptibility scores obtained in Test 1 of the series, respectively, at 6 RPM and after executing head movements at zero velocity. Thereafter, each point on the graph (or circle in lieu of points) represents susceptibility scores obtained in subsequent tests. An exponential curve characterizes the decay trend.

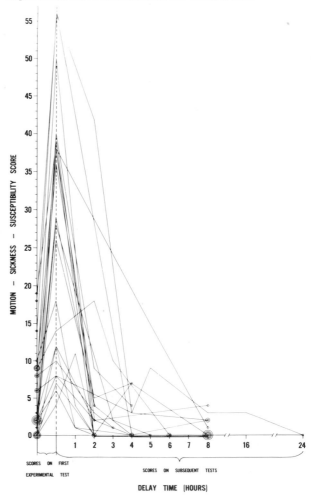

Figure 107 Approximate changes in level of symptoms of motion sickness and in postural disequilibrium in four young healthy subjects exposed to sudden changes in body orientation during continual rotation at 4RPM.

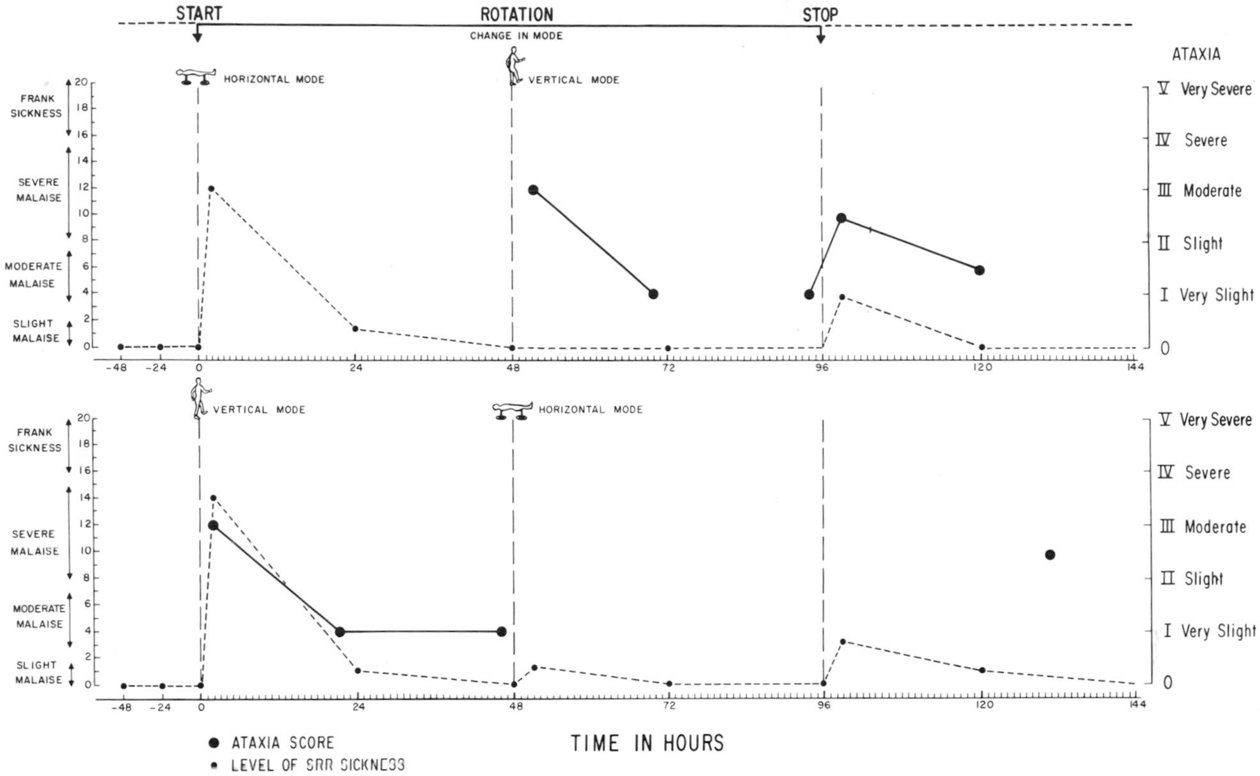

Susceptibility to motion sickness was not only similar in the two orientational modes but also "transferred" between the two modes. The adaptation acquired in the horizontal mode (ensuring freedom from symptoms of motion sickness) did not prevent ataxia on change to the vertical mode. Adaptation acquired in the "start-vertical" mode involved both motion sickness and postural equilibrium. Moreover, 36 hours after cessation of rotation, when the subjects returned to the upright, they were ataxic but not motion sick. If these findings are substantial, different mechanisms underly the acquisition and restoration of postural equilibrium in a SRR than motion sickness.

Skylab Findings

In view of the considerations discussed heretofore, we now consider two important Skylab findings: chronic motion sickness experienced by five of the nine astronauts in the first week aloft under operational conditions and, subsequently, failure to elicit motion sickness under experimental conditions.

Motion Sickness Under Operational Conditions. Figure 108 summarizes the findings under operational conditions. The horizontal lines reflect two things: first, where the astronauts were based

during the first week in orbit; although this indicates the opportunity for acquiring adaptation effects in the command module prior to entering the workshop, such important factors as the physical and mental activities of the astronauts are not indicated. Second, the thickness and continuity of the lines indicate the onset and probable disappearance of symptoms of motion sickness. The onset of symptoms is indicated fairly accurately. Recovery, however, involves first a loss of susceptibility to the eliciting stimulus, then spontaneous restoration through homeostatic mechanisms, and finally something termed 'convalescence;'' hence "disappearance" of symptoms is a vague indicator.

The vertical lines indicate when an antimotion sickness drug was taken and its composition. The administration of drugs increases the difficulty of diagnosing motion sickness; hence accuracy in diagnosis is greater in the absence of drug effects.

Under operational conditions the workshop provided the greatest opportunity up to the present time to reveal the great potentialities in weightlessness for limiting natural natural movements and encouraging highly unnatural movements often resembling acrobatic feats. Movies of the astronauts carrying out their tasks

147

and making transitions from one place to another best display the relatively large component of passive movement associated with active movements, with the opportunities for generating unusual patterns of vestibular stimulation and unusual or abnormal visual inputs.

In Figure 106 it is seen that none of the Skylab (SL)-2 crewmen were motion-sick aloft. The CDR who had not experienced motion sickness during the Gemini 5 and Apollo 12 missions was, in all likelihood, the least susceptible to motion sickness among the nine Skylab astronauts. He never took an AMS drug and was symptom-free under all conditions.

The SL 3 astronauts were quite confident before their mission that they would not become motion-sick in weightlessness and did not take AMS drugs as a preventive measure. The PLT experienced mild symptoms of motion sickness within an hour after insertion into orbit, the earliest diagnosis of this function disorder among space crewmen on record.

Figure 108. The horizontal lines reflect two things. First, the periods during which the Skylab astronauts were based in the Command Module and in the workshop during the first week in orbit. Second, the thickness and continuity of the lines indicate the onset and probable disappearance of symptoms of motion sickness. The onset of symptoms is indicated fairly accurately. The disappearance of symptoms, however, involves first, a loss of susceptibility to the eliciting stimulus, then spontaneous restoration through homeostatic mechanisms, and finally something termed convalescence; hence "disappearance" of motion sickness symptoms is something difficult to determine. The vertical lines indicate when an antimotion sickness drug was taken and its composition. The administration of drugs increases the difficulty of diagnosing motion sickness.

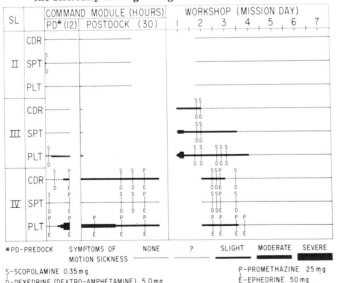

*PD-PREDOCK   SYMPTOMS OF .... NONE .... ? .... SLIGHT ... MODERATE ... SEVERE
                MOTION SICKNESS

S-SCOPOLAMINE 0.35 mg
D-DEXEDRINE (DEXTRO-AMPHETAMINE) 5.0 mg

P-PROMETHAZINE 25 mg
E-EPHEDRINE 50 mg

Subsequently, after transition into the workshop, symptoms included nausea and vomiting and treatment included restriction of activity and the use of AMS drugs.

During the activation of the workshop, about 11 hours into the flight, the CDR and SPT also reported the onset of motion sickness. Shortly thereafter the SL 3 SPT vomited. For three days the astronauts experienced symptoms of motion sickness which were intensified by movements and alleviated after taking the drug or restricting their movements. During this period their workload was lightened.

An interesting test was carried out on Mission-Day (MD) 2. The SPT executed standardized head movements for a short period and did not have any symptoms with eyes closed, but, continuing the head movements with eyes open, he did experience symptoms. Whether symptoms would have been elicited if the head movements had been continued with eyes closed is not known, but the visual inputs contributed to the interacting sensory stimuli and probably were of etiological significance.

In the light of SL 2 and 3 findings, the SL 4 crew were scheduled to take AMS drugs through MD3 and thereafter as required. Prior to entering the workshop the PLT experienced nausea and vomiting and was not free of symptoms during the first three days. The CDR reported "epigastric awareness" prior to meals, which may have represented susceptibility, and the SPT was symptom-free. It is interesting that all crewmen took AMS drugs during recovery and were symptom-free.

Motion Sickness Under Experimental Conditions. Stressful types of accelerations were generated by requiring the astronauts, with eyes covered, to execute standardized head movements (front, back, left, and right) while in a chair that could rotate at angular velocities up to 30 RPM. The endpoint was either 150 discrete head movements or a very mild level of severity of motion sickness. The tests were conducted on and after Mission-Day 8, by which time the astronauts were adapted to working conditions in the workshop. In all rotation tests aloft, the eight astronauts tested were virtually symptom-free, thus demonstrating lower susceptibility to motion sickness than on the ground. The amount of this decrease in susceptibility could not be measured because the "ceiling" on the test (30 RPM) was so quickly reached.

In view of this immunity a change in the procedure was instituted. This change was essential to determine whether the absence of responses was the result of complete insusceptibility or, in part, the consequence of adaptation to the stressful accelerations during the period of exposure to rotation. The latter was tested by reversing the direction of rotation immediately after 150 head movements had been executed in the initial direction of rotation. On MD 73, the CDR and PLT, and on MD 75 the SPT, remained symptomless during the bidirectional test procedure. Consequently, they were not adapting during the initial test.

Discussion. Skylab findings are clear-cut in two respects. The incidence of susceptibility to motion sickness was high among an elite selected group of astronauts, but after adaptation had been achieved the astronauts were alike in demonstrating under experimental conditions lower susceptibility to motion sickness aloft than on the ground. The importance of these findings for us rests in the manner in which adaptation is achieved on transition into zero gravity. If the mechanisms for acquiring adaptation are similar to those in the slow rotation room, for example, our problem is at worst trivial. On the other hand, if we are dealing with an etiologic factor in the nature of a homeostatic adjustment (such as a headward shift in body fluids), it is a reasonable expectation that restoration would quickly occur after return to one gravity, thus rendering the person liable again to experience motion sickness in zero gravity. Professional opinion ranges between these two extremes and may be briefly summarized as follows.

On transition into weightlessness few changes that are initiated during the transition are complete. Alterations such as hymodynamic adjustments, redistribution of body fluids, and changes in electrolyte balance that might affect susceptibility to motion sickness, either via the vestibular system or more indirectly, are at various stages along their time course. Even though the stimulus to the macular receptors due to gravity is lost, the question arises whether the physiological deafferentation process has stabilized. Only if symptoms of motion sickness are elicited while the head remains fixed would it be possible clearly to distinguish between a so-called "vestibular storm" (similar to labyrinthitis caused by disease or injury)

or the effects of an eliciting stimulus associated with activity. Among the possibilities mentioned, headward shift of fluid is the factor most often referred to as playing an important etiological role. A careful comparison between chronic motion sickness experienced the first week in orbit and in the slow rotation room reveal many more similarities than differences. It may certainly be conjectured that a unique predisposing factor exists in weightlessness, and intensive investigations are in progress to resolve the motion sickness problem prior to space shuttle missions.

Concluding Remarks

Physiological Aspects.

- Vestibular side effects including motion sickness would, in all probability, not pose a problem today; tomorrow, after the opportunity to conduct tests in Spacelab missions, the likelihood would be virtually nil.

- Based on Skylab findings the limiting factor probably centers in the preservation of bone. Preserving skeletal fitness may require that more than half of the time be spent in Earth-level gravity; the precise amount depending on body position and activity. Ensuring skeletal fitness should take care of other detrimental effects in zero gravity.

Preventive Medicine.

- A great opportunity would be present to raise the level of preventive medicine to a fine art.

- Longevity might be treated as a separate division of preventive medicine.

Scientific Opportunities.

- Determining the ideal level of simulated Earth-gravity poses an interesting problem that might be tackled in a cautious incremental fashion. One aspect would involve the desire or need to return to Earth. Another aspect, after the fabrication of true space ships, might involve adaptation to levels higher than Earth-gravity.

- Genetic research and other similar projects could be carried out without endangering mankind.

2. Meteoroid and Cosmic-Ray Protection

Eric Cabot Hannah
Princeton University

Meteoroids

In terms of visual impact, I suppose the most frightening type of disaster in space conceivable would be a ten-ton meteoroid colliding with a large colony, followed by explosive decompression and death for all inhabitants. Let me quickly assure you that that eventuality is only likely to be seen in future versions of movies such as "The Towering Inferno." The real meteoroid problem is basically one of identifying occasional minor leaks and repairing them in some economical fashion.

The first question to ask is: What is the flux of meteoroids of a given mass? Data come from three sources. The first and least satisfactory is photographic and radar observations from Earth, the second is measurement from space-based instruments, and the third is lunar impacts as measured by the lunar seismometer network

In the meteoroid mass range of a microgram to one gram, spacecraft sensors provide abundant data, and for masses above ten kilograms, the lunar seismic network is believed to have 100% efficiency. The Earthbound data are subject to large corrections, but agree with the NASA data at ten grams mass.

Figure 109 shows the distribution for meteoroid masses. I have not shown the Prairie Network data here, which is the Earth-based material, because it is subject to large corrections of an uncertain nature. The meteoroid structure most commonly found in space is a conglomerate of dust, bound together by frozen gases – a "dirty snowball" – as opposed to the stony or nickel-iron rock which reaches the Earth's surface after going through the atmosphere.

The second question to ask is: What effects would varying sizes of meteoroids have on a Model 1 colony? We can assume that anything heavier than about one ton would do very serious damage, for example, break one of the hoops. Somewhat less mass than this would probably result in a hole and extensive damage, but limited to the area of the hole. The main problem for the colony would be the immediate repair of the hole before much of the atmosphere could escape. Calculations by Daniel Villani at Princeton show that the leakdown time to 40% of the initial atmospheric pressure is eight hours for a hole two meters in diameter.

A more common occurrence would be the breaking of window panel by a small meteoroid. This would result in a leakdown rate of about one percent of the atmospheric pressure per hour. We estimate such window-breaking to occur from strikes by meteoroids having masses down to 0.3 gram. Below this mass value, the main problem would be a "sandblasting" effect on the windows, which, over many centuries, would reduce the transparency to light and would eventually necessitate resurfacing of the windows.

Table 25 lists possible meteoroid "disasters", showing the amount of time one expects before any specified disaster occurs. The one-ton meteor, which is the really catastrophic one, is a rare oc-

Figure 109. Cumulative Distribution of Meteoroid Masses.

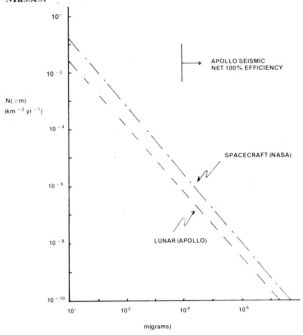

Figure 110. Cosmic-ray energy spectra of the more abundant nuclear species as measured near Earth. Below a few GeV/nucleon, these spectra are strongly influenced by modulation within the solar system. The different curves for the same species at those energies represent measurements at various levels of general solar activity, the lowest intensity being observed at the highest activity level.

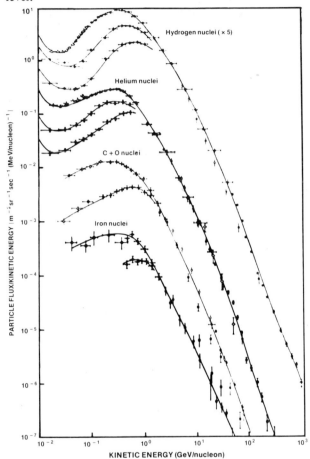

currence. Even 100 grams, which will break a window and perhaps create a good-sized hole if it comes through a metallic land-area structure, strikes only once in seven thousand years. The most frequent problem is the abovementioned 0.3-gram strike, once every three years. That produces only the minor problem of detection: has a panel broken? If so, where? And then getting to it and covering it up. Hence the risk to human life in space stemming from meteoroid strikes appears to be quite low in comparison to accidents and natural disasters here on Earth.

Cosmic Radiation

At the other mass extreme, we now consider the effects on people in space from the lightest particles: cosmic rays.

Streaming out from the Sun and inwards from the galaxy is a large collection of charged particles

Table 25. Risk Factors for Model I from Meteoroids

Mass	Time to Occur	Worst Effects
1 ton (metric)	2.5×10^8 years	severe damage
100 grams	7,000 years	10 hour leak-down to 40% of one atmosphere
0.3 grams	3 years	loss of window panel, 1%/hour leak-down

called "cosmic rays." Cosmic rays are predominantly protons moving close to the speed of light, but it is likely that every element of the periodic table is included in this onslaught.

Figure 110 shows how these various components vary with energy per nucleon. The lower curve branch for each species reflects the peak effects of the solar wind in "sweeping away" the less penetrating particles when the Sun is very active. For a point of reference, the rest energy (mc^2) for most particles is at about 1 GeV; above that point, where the curves start to slope down to the right, are relativistic particles.

When the Sun is at its most active stage, as when a giant flare or solar eruption takes place, then the cosmic ray flux contains massive amounts of added particles as seen in Figure 111. These added par-

Figure 111. Energy spectra from several moderate-size events compared with the galactic cosmic-ray spectrum.

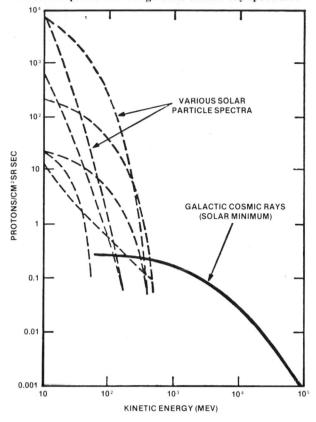

VARIOUS SOLAR PARTICLE SPECTRA

GALACTIC COSMIC RAYS (SOLAR MINIMUM)

PROTONS/CM²·SR SEC

KINETIC ENERGY (MEV)

more slowly moving particles are the most damaging. In the extreme relativistic energy region, the damage effects are basically constant. At the low-velocity end, the particles are removed by "electron pick-up," which neutralizes the charged particles.

The annual radiation dose that the general cosmic ray background gives an unshielded person, aside from the occasional solar flare outburst, is about one rem per year. This is not a high level of radiation: perhaps about twice what jet flight crews receive annually and only about one fifth the government's recommended dose for radiation workers. If the total dose were the only relevant radiation variable, then the problem would reduce to the simple issue of providing solar flare monitoring and intensive shield areas to be used only during the several hours of solar flare activity.

The problem, however, is more complex, because included in the general cosmic-ray flux are substantial amounts of totally stripped iron nuclei. When a fully stripped iron nucleus is traveling below about half the speed of light, its ionizing power is several thousand times that of minimally ionizing protons. At this level of ionizing power, the passage of a single iron nucleus through the body destroys entire columns of cells lying along its trajectory. The total amount of energy dumped in

ticles stream out of the Sun and cause the massive ionospheric disturbances that disrupt communications and create strong aurora effects. For lightly shielded structures, solar flares constitute a serious danger to personnel.

Cosmic ray particles endanger human beings because the passage of charged particles through tissue causes the breaking of chemical bonds. The damaging power of a charged particle is closely related to its "ionizing power", which measures how many chemical bonds per unit of body mass are broken and thereby gives at least a rough measure of the tissue damage sustained and the chances of genetic mutation.

Figure 112 plots the ionizing power of protons in silicon dioxide as a function of proton energy. Since the units of ionizing power are in units of mass traversed, the same numbers are reasonably accurate for all low-atomic-number (Z) matter; for example, human tissue. This basic curve also holds for any ion species when the vertical axis is multiplied by the ion's Z^2.

The essential result is that the ionizing power increases as the particle energy decreases, so the

Figure 112. Ionizing power of protons in silicon dioxide.

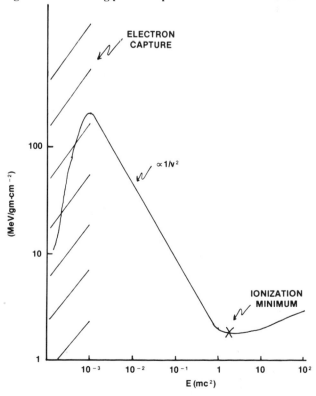

ELECTRON CAPTURE

$\propto 1/v^2$

IONIZATION MINIMUM

(MeV/gm·cm⁻²)

E (mc²)

the body by the particle is small, but its concentration is intensive over localized regions of the body. We don't yet know how bad this form of radiation is in terms of increased rates of cancer, for example, but we can calculate the loss of non-reproducing cells, such as spinal-column nerve cells, that any given exposure will cause. As an example, a recent article in *Science* has estimated that the Apollo 12 astronauts, during their two-week voyage to the Moon, lost between 10^{-7} to 10^{-4} of their non-replaceable cells, e.g., neurons. Projecting these data to a two-year mission to Mars and back, the fraction of lost cells could reach several percent. These effects, applied to young developing organisms such as children, could prove far more catastrophic.

Thus we must set a dose limit for exposure to heavy ion radiation for the Model 1 colonists. We have arbitrarily chosen the limit to be a dose equal to the amount the Apollo 12 astronauts received in two weeks; i.e., if a colonist is expected to live in Model 1 for thirty years, we must provide enough shielding to guarantee he will not accumulate the Apollo 12 dose until thirty years has passed. This brings us to the issue of practical shielding in the early space colonies, which lack the intrinsic shielding mass the later models will possess.

The first method of shielding is simply to use compacted Moon rock to surround the living quarters with spot shielding. The shielding calculations, including such factors as nuclear fragmentation, particle slowing-down, and creation of secondary radiation, indicate that 132 g/cm^2 of Moon rock would protect again the heavy ions and create an annual dose of about 3 rem.

But even though mass can protect human beings from cosmic rays and even solar flares, it is not a very effective or elegant way to achieve protection. Among the awkward aspects of mass shielding are the following:

- It adds considerable mass to the protected structure over and beyond the purely structural requirements for mass. Succintly, "mass is money."

- At the required thickness of around 150 g/cm^2, cosmic ray secondaries are produced copiously. Thus, adding mass causes the year's dose of overall ionizing radiation to go to about 3 rem, when an unshielded environment would only cause about one rem per year.

- The peak flux of iron nuclei occurs for velocities very close to the speed of light. Adding mass slows down these particles to below half the speed of light, the point where tissue damage becomes very serious. Thus, even though we add mass specifically to stop the iron flux, in a sense it only makes the basic problem, the elimination of slow rather than fast particles, more difficult.

We therefore conclude that simple mass shielding of cosmic rays would not be either economic or effective.

Examining other alternatives, we recognize first that it is the slow particles, both the iron cosmic rays and solar flare protons, which cause the most damage to human beings. Hence moderate magnetic fields could do the shielding job. A magnetic field distributed in space can protect against both iron nuclei and solar flares if its intensity multiplied by its spacial extent is around four tesla-meters. For objects with dimensions of the order of kilometers, peak field intensities needed are only of the order of a hundred gauss, spread over such dimenions.

As a concrete example of such an "active shield" approach, I have calculated roughly the parameters needed for a magnetic deflector which consists simply of coils of superconductor on the endcaps of a Model 1 cylinder. Table 26 shows the parameters of such a shield. Four hundred gauss, since people are not made out of iron, is not a very bad field to live in. The peak energy is a little high, however, and protection must be provided against an energy short-circuit through a single point. An attractive feature of such a field is that after the 90-second power-up period, no further energy is required to sustain the field.

A more detailed sample design for a magnetic

Table 26. Model I Magnetic Deflection System Parameters

Parameter	Value
Radius of endcap coils	100 meters
Central field strength	377 gauss
Current in coils	6×10^6 amps
Required mass of super-conductor	470 tons (metric)
Field energy	9×10^9 joules
Field creation time at full power station power level	90 seconds

Table 27. Toroidal-Geometry Station Shield System Parameters

Parameter	Value
Major radius of station	100 meters
Minor radius of station	10 meters
Number of conduits	63
Superconductor mass	38 tons (metric)
Current in conduits	3×10^5 amps
Field Energy	2×10^7 joules
Field creation time	20 seconds
Magnetic pressure	-14.3 pounds per sq. inch

shield postulates a toroidal space station with a major diameter of 200 meters and a torus cross-section (living-quarters) minor diameter of 20 meters. Surrounding the living space are 63 superconducting conduits which carry current parallel to the toroid's major circumference. This geometry produces very little magnetic field inside the living-quarter tube by symmetry, but it does create a very strong field outside the tube walls. It is this outside magnetic field which diverts flare protons and cosmic-ray iron nuclei away from the living spaces. This geometry has a further advantage in that since it surrounds the living quarters with a cold environment (to keep the superconducting system cold), any gases leaking out from the interior would be cold-trapped. Since they would freeze to the sides of the wall, they would eliminate atmosphere leakage problems from the station structure, a major consideration for resupply.

Table 27 shows the parameters of such a shield system. It requires only about 38 metric tons of superconductor mass to provide the shielding required, since the actual superconductor need only have a radius of about 6 mm.

The field energy is 2×10^7 joules and it takes twenty seconds to establish, assuming ten kilowatts per person for a thousand people. The last parameter in Table 27 is rather interesting. "Magnetic pressure" is the result of the interaction of the currents flowing in the conduits with the outside magnetic fields they create, causing an inwardly directed pressure which squeezes the tube. At 14.3 psi, if the station's internal air pressure were one Earth atmosphere, the magnetic pressure would very nicely balance the internal pressure. This numerical agreement was purely coincidental.

In summary, I think it is safe to say that careful attention to engineering can overcome the problems of meteoroid and cosmic-ray protection, even in the early space colony "construction-shack" models.

DISCUSSION

Q. What's the strength in gauss of the second field that you described?

A. I assumed that the field was distributed across a hundred meters. At four tesla, that's 40,000 gauss-meters. The central field is then 400 gauss, but as you get in closer to the actual superconducting wire, it increases inversely with the radius. So there is a very strong field right at the superconducting conduit, limited, of course, by the maximum field which does not destroy the superconducting property. That's what determines the superconductor's radius. For niobium-tin, with a safety factor of two, that's about ten thousand gauss.

Q. This field is supposed to slow down the slow-moving particles. Why doesn't it slow down fast-moving particles and make them slow?

A. "Slow-down" isn't quite an accurate description. All the field does is make the particles go in circles. A slower particle goes in a smaller circle than a fast particle. A very fast particle would be bent slightly by this field but nevertheless will come zipping right through. A slow particle would be bent enough so that it would turn away. To be honest, I haven't done detailed trajectory analysis to see exactly how the turning will go, but I think for a dipole field, for a hoop like this, the particles would zip down the center quite freely. I wouldn't want to live in the center of the torus, but the particles would be nicely diverted away from the living area in the outer circumference.

Q. Did you look at long-term effects of the field interacting with the Earth's field?

A. I believe that L5 is sufficiently far away that there's no Earth field left. But there will be effects of the solar wind and other phenomena. I have not tried to estimate these. This was just a crude, quantitative estimate to show that at least it's feasible to think in terms of using low-mass active shields.

Q. Does the magnetic field have any implications for docking maneuvers and supply ships?

A. If they are made out of anything with steel or iron it has considerable consequences. I assume, though, that most space ships would use non-magnetic structures.

Q. *Will the inward magnetic-field pressure tend to cause structural instabilities — buckling — of the wall?*

A. I never seriously thought about using the field to balance off the atmosphere. If it takes more mass to hold off the field pressure than to hold the atmospheric pressure, it's obviously not worthwhile. In this case, it would appear that the two forces cancel each other, so the structure can take it nicely.

Q. *It seems to me you have the wrong sign on your magnetic pressure. There is a theorem that the integral of tension times volume to contain a magnetic field is given by the energy of the magnetic field. If you have pressure contained on the one hand, and the magnetic field contained on the other, they will add, not subtract.*

It might be that the tension around the small ring is reduced, but the tension around the large ring certainly isn't. It is not a gain.

A. Yes. I was discussing only the hoop strength of the minor diameter.

Q. *Some years ago we pointed out that you gain a very large advantage in the magnetic field effect if you use that field to hold electrons in orbit along the magnetic field lines. This develops high voltages, of the order of several hundred million volts, to do exactly what you want — accelerate the slow particles without affecting the large particles. That is, your field will trap electrons to create a potential with the space vehicle which will be several hundred MeV above the surroundings. The decelerating electric field is enough to accomplish the effect that you wanted.*

A. That sounds very interesting.

Q. *What temperature do the superconductors operate at? Did you look at what kind of radiator area you would need for heat rejection? Heat loss is a big problem in a ring station to begin with. To keep the superconductors cooled, you'd need a huge radiator area.*

A. I was assuming about half the critical tem-perature for niobium tin, which, I believe, is around 18K. It is no real problem to hold 4K. I was assuming that there would also be use of super-insulation to minimize heat leaks. I haven't looked at the detailed refrigeration problems.

Q. *Why don't you wait until the heavy nuclei have actually penetrated a moderate mass shield, perhaps 100 g/cm. A field of about a kilogauss would then turn the nuclei, with a radius of the order of a meter or so, and send them back into the material as many times as is necessary.*

A. There's a problem there, because the flux of the slow particles is actually much below the flux that move at about the speed of light. So if you use 100 g/cm^2 you've nicely succeeded in slowing down the peak flux to where it hits with much more damage potential than it had to begin with.

Q. *Since your space station is rotating, would you be creating some low-level synchrotron radiation? You'd have, in effect, a little pulsar up there.*

A. Since the rotation is axially symmetric with the field, I don't think so. There *would* be some interesting electromagnetic effects. For example, the collapse of the field in the event of a short-circuit has some interesting effects, but I think at very low frequencies.

Q. *Why not just use an electron gun to accelerate the electrons enough to put them into an escape orbit?*

A. You cannot do that, because the conductivity of space is too high. It would require too much an energy load. However if you reduce the conductivity immediately around the space vehicle with a magnetic field, by a factor which is equal to the number of times an electron revolves around the vehicle's dimension between collisions, squared, then you can, in fact, charge up the vehicle with a relatively small accelerator.

Q. *Would we have the opportunity to turn this device off now and again, for achieving docking maneuvers?*

A. Yes, it takes only twenty seconds to establish the field. Or you take a few minutes; that wouldn't be a problem.

Q. *Would it charge the ship up?*

A. I suspect there would be some sort of resistive divider between the ship and the central hub.

Q. *Would this field affect communications between Earth and the satellite?*

A. If it starts picking up its own Van Allen belt, there could be some interaction. But I don't think that's a problem, because we were able to reach the Apollo astronauts through the Van Allen belt.

Q. *Your shield focuses particles, primarily protons, and protons are hydrogen. Would it be of any advantage to use your field as a solar wind catcher?*

A. The solar wind flux is quite low, because the particles move at very slow velocities. You would need to sweep an area thousands and thousands of kilometers in diameter to scoop up an appreciable amount of hydrogen.

3. Diversity, Survival Value, and Enrichment: Design Principles for Extraterrestrial Communities

Magoroh Maruyama
Portland State University

This subject is based on three fundamental notions:

(1) The basic principle of biological, social and even some physical processes is increase of heterogeneity and symbiotization.

(2) Diversity has a survival value for several reasons.

(3) Diversity contributes to a higher rate of cultural evolution.

The Three Basic Notions

Heterogenization and symbiotization as the basic principle of biological, social and some physical processes. So far there have been two phases of the development of mutual causal models in engineering, biology, operations research, and systems science, and the third phase is about to emerge. The first phase was characterized by deviation-counteracting, equilibrating mutual causal models by means of negative feedback loops. This phase began in full scale during the Second World War when radar, anti-aircraft artillery, and computers were hooked up in a mutual causal system. The second phase was characterized by differentiation-amplifying, heterogeneity-generating, evolution-creating mutual causal models by means of positive feedback loops (Ref. 136). This phase began in the 1960's and initially drew much interest from biological scientists because of the fact that these models could do what Shannon's theory of information could not do, i.e., increase structuredness and complexity. Shannon's information theory, similar to the theory of thermodynamics, was to proceed on a different paradigm which I call "random process paradigm" or "random influence paradigm", and it could only account for loss of information, but could never generate information, The most it could do was to combat loss of information by error-correcting methods based on various forms of negative feedback. As mathematician Stanislaw Ulam has pointed out (Ref. 137), complex patterns can be generated by means of simple rules of interaction (Refs. 136, 138), and it takes more amount of Shannonian information to describe the generated pattern than to describe the generating rules; i.e., the amount of Shannonian information increases in these processes. It is this feature of the differentiation-amplifying mutual causal models that drew much interest from embryologists and geneticists in the early 1960's. In the late 1960's some sociologists began applying these models to the study of social evolution and social change (Ref. 139). In addition to the creative and generative features of mutual causal processes, there is also a possibility of runaway situations. This feature was first pointed out by Gunnar Myrdal (Refs. 140, 141), and more recently received much more elaboration and publicity by Jay Forrester of MIT and his school.

The third phase of the development of mutual causal models, which has hardly begun, will have to deal with the mathematical methods or heuristics to hook up heterogeneous elements into symbiotic networks. In the biological evolution, the species which are symbiotic survive more than those which are not, and unsymbiotic ones have a higher probabilty of dying off. By the way, "survival of the fittest" is not "survival of the biggest" or "survival of the strongest," as average Americans tend to interpret, but rather "survival of the most symbiotic."

But in the social process we do not wait for people to die off. We must identify which combinations are symbiotic and which are not, and recombine unsymbiotic ones into other networks in which they will be symbiotic. Suppose Individual A has three alternative ways, a_1, a_2, a_3, to implement his goal, and Individual B has five ways b_1, b_2, b_3, b_4, b_5, to implement his. Then there are fifteen combinations of $a_i b_j$, some of which may be symbiotic. If none of the fifteen is, then A and B must be separated into different networks. On the other hand, those who are now separate may be symbiotic if they are together. We do not yet have mathematics to deal with such combinations in a large society.

Regardless of whether we have mathematics or not, it is now recognized that the basic principle of biological and social processes is heterogenization and symbiotization. Even some physical processes have these characteristics. Recently there has been much interest in the phenomenon of self-organizing noise by means of resonance.

Survival Value of Diversity. Diversity has survival value for at least three reasons: (a) symbiosis; (b) resource utilization; (c) catastrophe contingencies. The traditional western (European and American) logic and paradigm preached ideology of unity by similarity, considering differences as sources of conflicts. This amounted to the ideology of homogenization, standardization, religious and technological universalism, missionarism, and ethnocentrism. On the other hand, the new scientific paradigm is "symbiosis thanks to diversity." For example, the animals convert oxygen into carbon dioxide and the plants do exactly the opposite, and by so doing they help each other. Incidentally, it is interesting to note that the philosophies of American Indians, East and West Africans (but not North Africans), Far East Asians, and Eskimos are similar to this new scientific paradigm. However, Islamic, Hindu and Chinese philosophies, which westerners often refer to as "Eastern" philosophies, are much closer to the western philosophies than to Sub-Sahara African,

Japanese or American Indian ways of thinking, which are more markedly based on the principle of symbiotization of heterogeneity (Refs. 142-144).

Another example of the survival value of diversity is the heterogeneity of species in a coral reef or in a tropical rain forest. The heterogeneity enables maximum utilization of solar energy and diversification of food requirements. If all species ate the same food, there would be a food shortage. And diversity allows for a higher probability of survival in case of catastrophes such as radical change of environment.

Heterogeneity and Rate of Cultural Evolution. In 1931 Wright pointed out how the speed of biological evolution is related to the ratio between the mutation rate and the size of the population (Ref. 145). When the mutation rate is low and the size of population is large, the interbreeding between mutants and "normal" individuals, or between mutants of opposite directions, tend to cancel out the mutations, and the speed of evolution is very slow. When the mutation rate is very high and the size of population is small, there is much inbreeding effect, which tends to amplify the mutations rapidly, and evolution may take place so fast that the species has no time to adapt to the existing environment or to seek a new environment, nor time to work out new types of relationships between individuals. The whole species may become extinct. When the mutation rate is moderate and the population size is neither too large nor too small, mixture of stabilization and change takes place, and random drift occurs; a change may be amplified for a while, stabilization takes place, then another change in a new direction takes place, etc.

A faster rate of evolution occurs when the total population is divided into isolated independently evolving subpopulations, which are connected with occasional interbreeding. In other words, heterogeneity between subpopulations contributes to a higher rate of evolution.

Wright's theory holds true when the Mendelian law is operative. Cultural intercourse does not always follow the Mendelian law. For example, an idea can be communicated to many individuals at the same time; a new idea may be ignored by the receiver; the established persons may purposely suppress new ideas, etc. Nevertheless, the notion that heterogeneity contributes to a higher rate of evolution holds true even in the case of cultural evolution.

And needless to say, cultural heterogeneity enriches human life.

What We can Learn from Existing Cultures

There are many different patterns, forms, and styles of life in the world under different living conditions and different philosophies of social organization. Not to learn from them would be unscientific, and unwise and uneconomical as well. There are 13 areas for consideration:

(1) Effects of day, night and seasons.

(2) Shelter, clothing.

(3) Food.

(4) Proxemics.

(5) Time structure (working hours, week-system, etc.).

(6) Principles of architecture and landscaping.

(7) Different logics.

(8) Different paradigms of life.

(9) Principles of community structure.

(10) Family structure.

(11) Sex relations.

(12) Decision processes and administration.

(13) Matching between individuals, between individuals and jobs, individually optimal rate of communication, activities, etc.

Effects of day, night and seasons. Laboratory experiments have shown that many species of animals maintain diurnal and annual cycles in their biological activities and processes even if they are kept under constant temperature and light conditions. Humans who are transported from one time zone to another in a jet flight show some physiological disturbance.

However, there are human populations who live and have lived in geographic areas which lack diurnal or seasonal cycles. Eskimos who live north of the arctic circle have no nights during the summer and no daytime during the winter. On the other hand, those who live near the equator have no appreciable change in the length of daylight during the entire year. The Balinese calendars ignore completely the 365-day cycle, and instead use the 210-day cycle and 420-day cycle which are mathematically derived (the product of four prime numbers 2, 3, 5, and 7).

Traditionally, the Eskimo's life is not regulated by the 24-hour cycle: for instance, when they go to hunt, they often hunt four or five days without sleeping, and then sleep two or three days at a stretch. Likewise, they may hunt for a few days without appreciable amount of eating and with eating time unrelated to the 24-hour cycle, and then fast for a few days without interruption. This indicates that the 24-hour cycle is not an absolute necessity for the human species.

As for the seasonal cycle, the most extreme seasonal climatic variations are found in polar areas and in the inland areas of large continents in lower latitudes. These areas have four seasons, even though any of the four may be very short or very long. In these areas the life of people is regulated by the seasonal cycle: there are busy seasons (harvest seasons, fishing seasons, etc.) and relatively idle seasons. In many cultures the idle seasons were used for festivals or for organized sexual activities. There are also seasons of high intercommunity activities due to easier transportation, and seasons of relative isolation due to transportation difficulties. For example, for Eskimos the winter was the time for traveling because snow on land and ice on the ocean served as unlimited highways. On the other hand, summer was the time for camp settlement and less mobility.

Tropical areas lack the seasonal variations in the length of daylight. However, many of these areas have rainy seasons and dry seasons which form an annual cycle. This cycle is of importance in agricultural communities, but less important in fishing communities.

Shelter and clothing. Human adaptation to the climate by means of shelter and clothing has extremely varied forms. Traditionally, the Alaskan Eskimos lived in half-underground houses covered with dirt, which is further covered by snow in winter. This provided an extremely efficient thermal insulation, and a small seal-oil lamp was sufficient to keep the indoor temperature at 90°F (305°K). Most males lived completely naked indoors, and most females wore only a narrow band around genitals. When it was necessary to sleep in an unheated temporary shelter such as an igloo, an efficient way to keep bodies warm was to sleep naked, many people together, in one wide bed made by sheets of animal skin. It was important to have more layers of animal skin between the floor and the bodies than over the bodies. The outdoor clothing of Eskimos was made of animal skin. Seal hunting required a great deal of body immobility for a prolonged period on frozen ice, but animal skin clothing was sufficient for Eskimos. It is interesting to note that the Eskimo principle of sleeping warm was widely practiced among the ordinary people in medieval France, where the entire family slept naked in one large bed.

Other examples of human adaptation to cold weather can be found in the southern end of South America, where some humans lived entirely naked in cold rains at freezing temperatures, and in Australia where today many tribes live completely naked even in winter.

On the other hand, many populations who live in hot but dry areas cover their entire body to keep radiation heat out. But most of the tribes in the Amazon area, which is very humid and warm, live completely naked.

Interesting examples can be taken also from those who live in temperate zones: the traditional Navajo women in Arizona could live with exactly the same clothing throughout the year, where the summer temperature reaches above 100°F (311 K) and the winter temperature sinks far below freezing.

Food. The Eskimo food consisted almost entirely of animal meat and internal organs, with some berries harvested in summer. Large variations are found in the amount of liquid intake and outlet in different cultures. The Japanese have a higher amount of urine output than the world average, probably due to two reasons: eating rice instead of bread, and use of dried, salted or sauce-treated fish, which must be accompanied by liquid intake.

Proxemics. The spatial patterns between individuals or for an individual's activities vary from culture to culture. For example, physical crowding is more tolerated in other cultures than in the American culture. In the American culture, a close distance between two individuals, of the same or opposite sex, is interpreted to have sexual intention.

In many non-hierarchical cultures, people sit in a circle even in offical meetings, and the American

pattern of seating in rows before a podium is unthinkable.

Americans tend to define space in terms of walls and enclosures. In other cultures, for example in Bali, space is defined around something rather than inside something. The traditional Japanese considered the indoor as a continuation of the outdoor, and houses had removable walls (sliding partitions).

The American concept of privacy requires one enclosed, lockable room for each individual, while in other cultures privacy is achieved by a thin paper screen, or privacy is found "in the bush" rather than in the house. In some cultures privacy is achieved by simply turning off the lamp, or by looking in another direction. In the Navajo culture, a man was not supposed to look at his mother-in-law, and had to look in another direction. In some cultures there were no secrets or visual taboo, and the concept of "privacy" did not exist.

Americans require sound-proofing for individual space, while Japanese do not "hear" the conversation taking place behind a paper screen. Americans also require olfactory insulation.

The American idea of putting a toilet in the bathroom is shocking in many cultures, while Americans are shocked by mixed public bath.

If a large Japanese family traveling in the United States is assigned several rooms at a hotel, they may nevertheless sleep together in one room, getting rid of the bed if necessary.

Time Structure. Christians have a seven-day week. On the other hand, the Balinese have several types of weeks running concurrently: 2-day week, 3-day week, 5-day week, 7-day week, etc. These different cycles "heterodyne" at regular intervals (though not at different frequencies, but at common multiple intervals), and you have a 105-day anniversary, 210-day anniversary, 420-day anniversary, etc.

Most Americans eat three times a day. There are cultures in which the number of meals per day is 1, 2, or 5. In France and in Italy, the largest meal of the day is the noon meal, and the "lunch break" lasts 2 to 3 hours.

Most American have weekends. Traditional American Indians work without a weekend, but take time off whenever a relative or a friend comes to visit. Many Japanese companies give paid menstruation leaves to women workers, recognizing the physiological cycle.

American workers are put to work on the assumption of homogeneity of time, and are expected to work in the same way summer or winter, morning or afternoon, pregnant or menstruating.

Principles of architecture and landscaping. Esthetic principles vary from culture to culture. Some of the Islamic designs are characterized by intricate repetitions of minute details. The European Vitruvius principle also achieves its design unity by repetitions of similar elements. There is also frequent use of "subdominant" patterns which, in a miniature form, repeat the "dominant" pattern. Many of the French and Italian gardens as well as ancient Chinese city designs are geometric and symmetrical. All these are based on *homogenistic principles.*

On the other hand, the Japanese gardens and flow arrangements, and English gardens to a great extent, avoid repetitions and redundancies, and create harmony of dissimilar elements. These are based on *heterogenistic principles.*

Another contrast can be found between the two concepts "sappari" and "kudoi". In Japan repetitiousness, whether in design, in poetry or in human behavior, is considered "kudoi" (heavy, overdone, obnoxious) and is avoided. The contrary of "kudoi" is "sappari" (fresh, clear), and is a very important consideration in Japanese esthetics. The architectural designs by Walter Gropius and Frank Lloyd Wright as well as the Swedish glassware are sappari, while the "art nouveau", the Gothic design, and psychedelic paintings are kudoi.

There are also different basic numbers in different cultures. In Navajo, the basic number is 4. In Sioux, the basic numbers are 4 and 6, corresponding to the four directions of west, north, east and south, with sky and earth sometimes included as two additional dimensions. The Japanese flower arrangement is based on various principles of making a composition out of 3, 5, 7, or 9 different elements. Many Japanese designs use a triangle of unequal sides as a basic layout, often with secondary triangles added which should be dissimilar from the main triangle.

Also important is the contrast between the contextual principle and the individualistic principle. For example, in the Japanese architecture there has been, and there still is, a great deal of concern in harmonizing the building with its surrounding environment. On the other hand, many of the American architects tend to regard the building mainly as an expression of its or his individuality unrelated to other surrounding buildings. Le Corbusier had another philosophy. He thought that man-made buildings should not imitate nature; to do so would mean lack of respect for nature.

Another consideration is that, as mentioned earlier, the Japanese regard the indoor as a continuation of the outdoor, and minimize the barriers between the outdoor and the indoor. This principle was adopted by Frank Lloyd Wright. The traditional Japanese house is like an astronomical "black hole", designed to suck the outside into the inside instead of proclaiming its presence against the outside. Where the outdoor is not readily available, as in urban areas, the Japanese employ techniques to create a perspective of the outdoor. One evening while traveling in Japan, I came upon an inexpensive inn, and decided to spend a night there. It was cramped between other inns. Next morning I inadvertently walked into a wrong direction from my room, and was surprised to see a corner of a large, beautiful garden opening up around the next room. My steps were naturally drawn to the garden. But as I approached the corner, what looked like an entrance to a large garden turned out to be a small recess in a wall, no deeper than ten inches. There was no garden at all. A multi-floor restaurant in Tokyo has a foot-wide shelf outside very other floor, on which two-floor-high trees are planted. Viewed from the inside, these trees give an illusion of a forest. Viewed from outside, the building looks like a tree-covered mountain. A large building in another Japanese city has an exterior surface which looks like a Yosemite cliff, complete with a waterfall. There is also a ring-shaped kindergarten building, whose sloped exterior sides are covered with grass, giving an appearance of a hill when viewed from outside. In Portland, Oregon, there is a tall building which looks like a gigantic redwood trunk by virtue of its strong vertical lines along the entire length of the building and slanted windows at the top and at the bottom. The Russians have perfected a technique to reproduce immense outdoor scenes in a small wall recess, with changing lighting to create sunrise, sunset, and various weather and seasonal effects. It is also conceivable to make such recesses on the exterior walls of a building for the enjoyment of pedestrians.

Another cultural comparison can be made

regarding the principles of the use of rooms. In the American house, most of the space is taken up by furniture such as beds and tables, and different rooms are required for different furniture. In Japan, on the other hand, the furniture is removable and the entire space can be used by people, not by furniture. Furthermore, since the furniture is removable, the same one room can be used as a living room, a dining room, and a bedroom, resulting in enormous economy of space. This consideration may be important in extraterrestrial communities.

Different Logics. Many Americans know only one type of logic: the Aristotelian deductive logic, and believe this to be "the" logic. However, there are many other types of logics. I do not mean multivalued logic or fuzzy logic, which are nothing more than variations of the Aristotelian logic.

One of the drawbacks of the deductive logic is that it prohibits "circular reasoning". Until recently the deductive logical order was often confused with the causal order in physical, biological and social processes. As a result of this confusion, the concept of mutual causality (A and B cause each other: many things cause one another) was tabooed in spite of the fact that mutual causal relations are abundant in biological, social and some physical processes. As I have already mentioned, mutual causal processes can increase differentiation, heterogeneity and complexity, and make evolution and growth possible. Without mutual causal relations, such processes are impossible. Philosopher Hans Reichenback, who did not recognize mutual causality, had to introduce a teleology (the future determining the present) in order to explain growth and evolution (Ref. 146).

Another drawback is that the deductive logic leads to hierarchical social structure, dictatorship, aristocracy, elitocracy, technocracy, bureaucracy, etc. The deductive logic cannot see any alternative order of society. The only alternative conceivable within its logical limitation is anarchy or numerocracy (majority rule, domination by quantity). However, once we recognize other types of logics, other alternatives become possible. For example, the mutual causal logic enables us to conceptualize a network system of mutual interaction.

One of the most serious drawbacks of the deductive logic is that it fosters homogenistic thinking, belief that differences create conflicts,

belief in the existence of one truth, one ultimate God, etc. As these are very basic problems, let me comment on them one by one.

The logic of the Mandenka tribe (Ref. 143), who live in West Africa, is heterogenistic. According to this logic, it is homogeneity, not heterogeneity, which creates conflicts. They say: "If you force individuals to be similar, the only way left to them to be different is to get on top of one another. This creates conflicts." There is a great deal of wisdom in this. Furthermore, the individual in this tribe goes through different phases of tasks and functions in the society: adolescents are assigned certain specific tasks; those between 30 and 35 are assigned administrative and caretaker functions of the tribe; those older are given less demanding tasks, etc. By going through these different phases, the individual learns to see the same situation from different points of view, and to understand individuals in different situations. The individual becomes heterogeneous in himself, and becomes capable of poly-ocular vision. They are skeptical of westernization mainly because the system of specialization brought by the Westerners will lock each individual in one task, and he will become incapable of seeing other persons' points of view.

Likewise, the Japanese think in poly-ocular vision. Americans, who believe in the existence of one truth, will inevitably ask: if you have different views, which one is right? But consider the following: in the binocular vision it is irrelevant to raise the question as to which eye is correct and which is wrong. Binocular vision works, *not* because two eyes see different sides of the same object, but because the *differential* between the two images enables the brain to compute the *invisible* dimension. The binocular vision sees more than twice the monocular vision: it sees the invisible dimension. When there are different points of view, Americans tend to say: "Let's ignore the parts on which we differ, and work on the parts on which we agree." Well, if you cut down the binocular vision to parts on which two eyes agree, what is left is much less than the monocular vision. For the same reason, insistence on the "objective" parts on which everybody agrees is a tremendous impoverishment of our vision, even though many people would consider this as the "scientific" thinking. We can say that the "objective" parts are the most insignificant parts of our thinking. The Japanese do not even bother to find out "objectivity", because they can go much further with cross-subjectivity.

Throughout the planning of our extraterrestrial communities, I can predict that many hours will be wasted on the arguments as to who is right and who is wrong. Let us keep in mind that these hours can be used constructively if we know how to make use of the differentials.

The belief in the existence of one truth, one universal formula for happiness, etc., is very common among engineers. On the other hand, theoretical physicists who appreciate the hypothetical nature of physical theories, and mathematicians who understand the axiomatic basis of mathematical theories, are less prone to blind belief in one formulation. I may add that the belief in one truth is an aspect of what is called 'monopolarization'' (Ref. 147). Monopolarization is a psychological need to seek and hang onto one authority, one way of doing things, one explanation, one god, etc. Tendency for monopolarization is particularly strong among those who have been brought up in the family system with one father figure. In other family systems such as extended family, communal rearing of children, or periodical exchange of children between families, there is less tendency for monopolarization. It is not an exaggeration to say that the belief in one truth is a psychological hang-up from having been brought up in the nuclear family system.

Further discussions on different logics can be found in Ref. 142, for example.

Different paradigms of life. The word "culture" is used in social sciences in the sense of philosophy and pattern of life shared by a number of interacting individuals. It does not mean fine arts, music, and literature as is the case in many European countries, nor entertainment facilities and restaurants, as is the case among urban planners in America. "Culture" includes life style, but it goes much deeper. It also goes further than what is commonly called "social value system," which consists of the preferential order in which the community members rank various physical, psychological, ethical, and esthetic qualities. More basically, "culture" means cognitive and behavioral structure with which a person interacts with others and interprets the universe. It is more like "philosophy of life" or "paradigm of life." Some examples may be helpful.

- Example A: Life is cut-throat competition. The stronger takes advantage of the weaker. Success depends on effects. If someone is unsuccessful, it is his fault because he is not making the necessary effort. Outdo others or you will be a loser. People who are equal to you are your competitors. People who are different are your enemies. Life is a zero-sum game: what someone gains is what someone else loses. Life is a constant competition.

- Example B: Life is a harmony of mutual relations. Life is a non-zero-sum game. People can help one another and gain from one another without anybody necessarily losing. Different people can contribute different talents to one another. Some people are born and live under disadvantaged conditions, and they should be helped.

Note that "culture" is not a geographic concept. Within the same community, within the same office or even within the same family, you can find people belonging to different cultures. This is obvious in the case of generation gap. Example A stems from the hierarchical, competitive logic, while Example B is based on the mutualistic logic. There are many other paradigms of life stemming from other different logics:

- Example C: Everybody should earn his living. He can work as much as he wants or as little as he wants. But he must be self-sufficient. He must save for his rainy days. He does not need to help others. Do your own thing. Everybody minds his own business.

This is an individualistic, isolationistic paradigm. This paradigm is closely related to the logic of probabilistic independent events (Ref. 142). It is different both from hierarchism and from mutualism. There may be also several different paradigms based on one logic. An example is Example D, which stems from the hierarchical logic but is different from Example A:

- Example D: Life is exploitation. I have been exploited. I am a victim. It is not my fault. Rich people should give me what they owe me. I will go begging for a dime on the street, not because I am starving, but because I am entitled to the dime.

An example of a paradigm which is based on the mutualistic logic but is slightly different from Example B is:

- Example E: I tend to have surplus. There is no

need to save for rainy days because when I am in need, someone will help me. So I keep giving away my surplus.

It is interesting to note that seemingly similar or identical behavior may be governed by different paradigms stemming from different logics. Compare the following with the preceding example:

- Example F: I keep giving things to others because I want to have power over others. Others, who want to receive things from me, would have to obey me. I keep showing off my ability to give, because those who have not yet received anything from me would obey me in the hope of getting something from me.

- Example G: I give things to others because I want to be famous for being generous. I do not expect anything in return. I just want to be a generous man. I am a good guy and a do-gooder. I am superior to others.

Both examples are based on the hierarchical logic, even though the behavior may look identical to Example E, which is based on the mutualistic logic. As these examples show, culture cannot be identified from or defined by behavior and other observable manifestations only. The paradigm underlying the behavior, and the logic underlying the paradigm, must be understood.

The design of extraterrestrial communities does not have to be based on the paradigm and the logic which we are familiar with. We need to examine a wide range of paradigms and logics for their possible use in extraterrestrial communities.

Principles of community structure. There are, and can be, many different principles of community structure. We give here three principles as examples: *hierarchical, individualistic* and *mutualistic*. Theoretically, it is possible for each of the three to be either homogenistic or heterogenistic. In fact, a hierarchical community is heterogeneous in the sense of vertical stratification. But philosophically it tends to be homogenistic for the reason that hierarchism is related to deductive logic. A mutualistic community has no vertical stratification, and allows for horizontal heterogeneity. As discussed before, mutual causal processes are more capable of producing heterogeneity than the process of random independent events (individualistic systems). It is also useful to discuss the distinction between *Gesellschaft* structure and *Gemeinschaft* structure

in terms of horizontal mobility as they are relevant to heterogenization and homogenization. Related are also two different textures of heterogeneity called *localization* and *interweaving*. Let us discuss them one by one.

First, about the notion of hierarchy. The word is used with different meanings in different fields of specialization. In physical sciences, the word is often used in the sense of unit organization: for example, atoms make a molecule; molecules make a biological cell; cells make a tissue; tissues make an organ; organs make a body, etc. This type of ordering is called "hierarchy."

On the other hand, in social sciences the word "hierarchy" is used in the sense of power structure: who has power over whom. A hierarchical society has a vertical power structure: somebody is at the top, and some people are at the bottom; in between, there are chains of command.

If the physical science definition of "hierarchy" is used, then all communities are hierarchical. However, when the social science definition of hierarchy is used, there are communities which are not hierarchical. Let me first give an example:

The Navajo universe consists of mutual relations between several types of beings as well as between beings within the same type: humans, animals, supernaturals, ghosts and natural forces (Refs. 152 and 153). Humans can manipulate supernatural and natural forces by using appropriate formulas, and these forces can influence humans; animals can influence people, and people can influence animals; etc. There is no hierarchy in terms of the direction of influences. Among humans, there were no hierarchical organizations before the white government made Navajos organize the tribal council and other organizational structures. There were no chiefs in the sense of political authority. Old men and women as well as people with experiences were sought out as advisers when occasions arose, but those who sought their advice did not have to obey them: they could ignore the advice or change the advisers. White people often mistook these advisers as chiefs or leaders.

No one, either human or supernatural, is perfect, omnipotent or omniscient. In fact, such concepts do not exist in the Navajo epistemology. There are not even the concepts "good" and "evil". The Navajo concept closest to our "good" is "nice". Each of the supernaturals can be both beneficial and dangerous to humans, depending on the circumstances and the way humans behave toward them. Each medicine man has his limits of ability, and even the respected medicine men "go dry" unless they know some harmful witchcraft. Talented speakers are pleasant to hear, but too much talking spoils its own beauty. Drinking is enjoyable. But too much drinking results in loss of reasoning power and in dangerous mistakes. There is no concept of punishment. The man who causes damage or kills someone is not punished but is made to repair the damage or to take care of the family of the dead man. If someone behaves against the usual custom, no one prohibits him, but people feel sorry for him because some misfortune will certainly result from the misdeed due to the disturbed harmony in the universe.

The purpose of life is to maintain harmony and to enjoy beauty and pleasure. The Navajos live scattered over a wide area. But when a family shears wool, plants vegetables, harvest crops, or builds a house, relatives and friends come great distances to help, even though the concept of "paid labor" is gradually changing this traditional pattern.

The cooperativeness of the Navajos is not based on a belief in the unity of society, on obedience to a supreme order, or on a centralized coordination. On the contrary, their cooperation stems from their respect for the individual. Their universe consists of informal interrelations between individuals and between clans. Even a child possesses his own livestock and is free to dispose of his own property in any way he wishes. Men and women are equal, and each person chooses his own way of doing things. For example a husband may choose to own a horse and his wife may choose to own turquoise necklaces, or vice versa. When they travel together, one may ride his horse and the other may walk.

An inevitable skepticism which most white Americans raise regarding non-hierarchical social systems is that hierarchy is necessary in a large society, and that non-hierarchical systems work only in small societies. (Here the word "hierarchy" is used in the sense of power stratification, not in the sense of organization units.) But the Navajo society has a population size of 150,000 on the reservation alone. This is about one-half of the size of Dayton, Ohio, or Portland, Oregon. It is fifteen times the size of all Model 1 communities combined together. The geographic size of the Navajo reservation is 24,000 square miles, equivalent to four or five New England states put together. But even if future extraterrestrial communities become much larger and more complex, the size and the

complexity is not an obstacle in extending non-hierarchical principles because we can mobilize computer and communication technology.

The Navajo society is at the same time individualist and mutualistic: individualistic in the sense of allowing maximum individual freedom; and mutualistic in their cooperation. Let me illustrate:

In order to maintain harmony with other beings in the universe, one must know the complex workings of these beings and their forces. Ignorance causes mistakes, and mistakes bring misfortune and illness. Therefore knowledge is virtue. Since the purpose of Navajo religion is to maintain harmony, knowledge is religious. There is no separation between science, religion, ethics and esthetics in the Navajo culture.

The ceremony called "sing" exemplifies this inseparability of science, religion, ethics, esthetics and even economics, fun, social activity and psychological outlet. A "sing" is called for when someone becomes ill. A usual sing takes three days to perform, but some may last nine days. A sing is an occasion for a large, enjoyable social gathering. People who hear that there will be a sing will come from a considerable distance. They contribute whatever food they can; those whose crops were plenty bring more, and others less. But everybody can eat as much as he wants. There are games, dances, and other activities, though recently these extra activities are increasingly omitted.

For the patient, the feeling that so many people care for him is as much a part of the cure as the curing ceremony itself. The medicine man traces the sources of illness to some mistakes in the maintenance of harmony, and performs corrective measures which require highly complex and precise knowledge and formulae, as well as artistic skills in singing, sand-painting, etc.

An atmosphere of intense concentration dominates the ritual – not a concentration which can be called solemnity, supplication or humility, but rather like a concentration of an engineer operating a complicated machine. Minutely prescribed details have to be followed. But just as engineers take a break during their work, moments of relaxation, even joking, often punctuate the Navajo rituals. If a medicineman-apprentice is present, he may make many mistakes in singing. This often causes good-natured laughter both on the part of the apprentice himself and the audience.

The sings are frequent. During the summer there are one or two sings every week within one's reach. Therefore a Navajo can find frequent sources of food, social contact, and psychological outlet.

In addition to the contrast between the hierarchical, individualistic and mutualistic principles, it is useful to discuss the distinction between the homogenistic and heterogenistic principles. We must also distinguish between homogeneous and homogenistic, and between heterogeneous and heterogenistic. For example, the American society has been heterogeneous in its population, but ideologically it has been homogenistic with its concepts of melting pot, assimilation and standardization. Canada has been much more heterogenistic than the USA, with its official recognition of at least two cultural groups and two languages. Recently heterogenism began to emergy in USA, especially in the forms of ethnic movements and counter-culture movements, but some aspects of the ethnic movements and much of the women's liberation movement are aiming toward homogenization of the entire society.

Here it is important to distinguish two opposite concepts of social integration: one is homogenistic, and the other is heterogenistic. A non-white person who wants to move into a white neighborhood in order to behave like a white person is aiming at homogenistic integration. On the other hand, a Japanese who wants to move into a white neighborhood and build a Japanese house is aiming at heterogenistic integration. This distinction is relevant to the design of extraterrestrial communities: do the planners consider it sufficient to let all ethnic groups settle in the same sort of housing, or do they plan for different types of housing for different ethnic groups?

It is also important to consider two different principles of heterogenization: *localization* and *interweaving*. In localization, each of the heterogeneous elements separates itself and settles in one locality. Chinatown in San Francisco is an example. In localization, heterogenization increases between different localities, but each locality becomes homogeneous. On the other hand, in interweaving, each of the heterogeneous elements is not localized, but is interwoven with others. In this system the accessibility to different elements increases. This system creates no great differences between localities, but within each locality there is a great diversity. In an interwoven system, it becomes easier for the individual to heterogenize himself or to become something else than what he was. For example, a white person may eat Chinese food on Sunday, Italian food on Friday, learn Judo on Wednesday, etc. He may also become a full-time Tibetan monk. All these involve the concept of *Gesellschaft*, as will be discussed presently.

The German sociologist Tönnies made an important distinction between two types of social systems: *Gesellschaft* and *Gemeinschaft* (Ref. 148). There are many differences between the two, but what concerns us here is the difference that it is easy to move in and out of a *Gesellschaft*, but it is difficult to do so with a *Gemeinschaft*. *Gesellschaften* allow for horizontal mobility of people between them. For example, one can relatively easily change jobs between companies or agencies in USA, while it is more difficult to do so in Germany or in Japan. In this respect American companies and agencies are more of *Gesellschaften*, and German and Japanese companies are more like *Gemeinschaften*. One of the characteristics of a *Gesellschaft* is that it can amplify its eccentricity: those who do not like it will leave, and those who like it will join and stay. It can also easily eliminate non-conformists. Thus, homogeneity tends to increase within a *Gesellschaft*, though heterogeneity may increase between *Gesellschaften*. At the same time, a *Gesellschaft* may become very intolerant toward non-conformists.

There is an interesting relationship between the fact that the USA began as a colony of *voluntary* immigrants and the fact that its past philosophy and ideology has been homogenistic. USA simply began as a *Gesellschaft* with a slogan: "If you like our ideology, you are welcome. But if you do not like our ideology, go back to where you came from." Thus began the policy of assimilation, and immigrants were eager to become "standard Americans."

A *Gemeinschaft*, on the other hand, must deal with non-conformists differently. It must either suppress non-conformists or accept them. Thus, it may become either homogenistically totalitarian or heterogenistic, depending on its policy and philosophy. These are very important considerations in the design of extraterrestrial communities. The degree to which you make the extraterrestrial communities *Gesellschaft*-like or *Gemeinschaft*-like makes a great difference in the degree of homogeneity or heterogeneity they attain. As discussed earlier, there must be heterogeneity between communities as well as within each community.

However, heterogenization is only the first step.

The fact that heterogenization took place does not determine what the interrelations are between the heterogeneous elements. There are many possible types of interrelations:

Type	Gain	Loss	Remarks
Hierarchism	some persons	some persons	-
Separatism	-	-	No interaction
Symbiosis	all persons	no person	positive-sum
Parasitism	some persons	some persons	zero-sum
Antibiosis	no person	some persons	negative-sum
Mutual Antibiosis	no person	all persons	negative-sum

What we must avoid are the last three types. What we can experiment with are the first three types. Since Model 1 will have four different communities, a possible suggestion is that three of these communities can try the three first types respectively, and the fourth community can try the interweaving of the three types.

Family Structure. A usual American family consists of a father, a mother and their children. This type of family system is called the nuclear family system. In many cultures a family may include grandparents or other blood-related relatives. This is called the extended family system. In some cultures, such as West Alaska Eskimos, children move between different families from time to time. Though there is no established name for this system, let us call it the children-exchange system. In some cultures children may be disciplined by specific relations such as uncles, but not by their biological father or mother. Israel and Russia have a system of raising children collectively by child specialists away from the homes of the children's parents during the working hours of the parents. This is commonly called communal rearing of children. In USA, many young people are experimenting with alternative family systems. Some examples are commune and multi-marriage, in which several adults of both sexes live together with their children; lesbian colonies, in which there are no adult males and women live with their children (women go out for a date to get pregnant); male homosexual households with adopted or borrowed children; etc.

There are also various ways to produce blood-relations or non-blood relations which are called family. For example, in a tribe in Kenya, if a man is impotent, he asks one of his relatives to fertilize his wife, and if a woman is sterile, she may bring another woman into the household to obtain a child. An Eskimo may sleep with another man's wife in order that his children and her children become "cousins" who help one another as such. Americans practice adoption to obtain children. Artificial insemination is practiced in some countries.

Since we are already familiar with the nuclear family system, let us discuss applicability of other family systems to extraterrestrial communities. Undoubtedly many people would want to maintain the nuclear family system, but many would also want to explore other alternatives.

We have already mentioned one disadvantage of the nuclear family system: people who are reared in the nuclear family system have a tendency for mono-polarization. They tend to have a psychological need to seek and hang onto *one* authority, *one* truth, *one* theory, *one* god, *one* way of doing things, etc., and if they face many theories or many ways, they feel insecure until they make up their answer as to which one is right and which one is wrong, or which one is better and which one is inferior. They also have psychological monocular vision. And they tend to assume that their logic or their belief is the universal logic or universal belief, and try to advertise it or impose it upon others. They also tend to misinterpret and reduce others into their own logic. A typical misinterpretation is: "Different religions worship the same god by different names." They cannot see the difference between polytheistic harmonism and monotheistic homogenism. (A Christian missionary came to an African tribe whose universe consisted of harmony of 360 gods. Their religion was this harmony. They welcomed the missionary's god expecting that the new god would be a part of the harmony. But the missionary told them that their gods were wrong and there was supposed to be only one right god. Can you see how unharmonious *his* god was?)

Sex and Love. Contraceptives have separated sex from pregnancy. As more women choose to remain unmarried, sex and marriage become separated. And as professional and geographical mobility of people increases, love and marriage become more and more separated.

In the traditional American society, love,

marriage, sex, and pregnancy occurred inseparably in that sequential order. Now that this pattern is breaking down, we may need insights from other patterns in other cultures.

For Eskimos, marriage and sex were separate: marriage was for economic activities, and sex was for enjoyment. A hunter needed a wife to process the skins of the animals he hunted. A skillful hunter needed several wives to keep up with his hunting output. If his wife was pregnant, a hunter borrowed someone else's wife to go on his hunting trip. Visitors were sexually entertained by their hosts' wives. In long winter nights, Angmagssalik Eskimos of East Greenland who lived in semi-communal long houses played the game of "putting out lamp."

For Marquise Islanders, marriage and sex were also separate. Before marriage, girls could enjoy sex with many men. But after marriage they had to confine their sexual activities to their husbands. On the day of wedding, they bride gave a sexual farewell party to her old friends: she lay down, and her old friends lined up for their last intercourse with her. The longer the line, the prouder the bridegroom.

On the other hand, there were tribes which had sexual taboos between the husband and the wife on certain occasions such as religious ceremonies, important hunting trips, or fishing days.

As for love, the American concept of love used to require constant verbal and nonverbal demonstrativeness (kissing, or saying "I love you") as well as some exclusive feeling (I love you more than anybody else). But the younger generation is redefining the concept of love. In many other cultures, love consisted of something other than such demonstrativeness (Ref. 149) or exclusivity of feelings (Ref. 143).

New conceptualization of love and of sex has not yet crystallized in the American culture. More exploration and experiencing are needed, and will undoubtedly go on in extraterrestrial communities.

Decision Process and Administration. The principle of "American democracy" involves two logical fallacies: first, it is based on majority rule, which amounts to domination by quantity and imposing of homogeneity, disregarding and discriminating against minorities; second, it is based on "voting for your own interest," encouraging the disregard of others' interest. This promotes non-contextual thinking, competitiveness, and partisan-mindedness.

Most Americans propose the consensus system as an alternative to the majority system. However, the consensus system tends to be also homogenistic if it assumes that everybody should to the same thing.

Another system is the system of elimination of hardship on any single individual. This system is practiced by Navajos. Sitting in a circle, each person expresses his point of view, and alternative solutions are explored until a way is found which does not cause hardship on any individual and at the same time allows individual diversity for all persons.

Let me illustrate how the three systems produce three different solutions for the same problem. Suppose we have to decide whether or not to build a bridge over a river. If people disagree, we cannot build just half a bridge. We must build either the whole bridge or no bridge at all.

The majority system will count the votes, take the majority decision, and forget about the minorities. This is considered democratic.

The consensus system will listen to the minorities, and work hard until a unanimous decision is reached and everybody agrees.

The hardship-on-nobody system is concerned not so much with whether to build the bridge or not, but more with what to do for those who will suffer from any hardship, no matter which way the decision goes: i.e., if the bridge is to be built, some people may suffer from it. Then a way to alleviate the hardship must be found. If the bridge is not to be built, some other people may suffer from the lack of the bridge. Then a way to alleviate their hardship must be found.

The first two systems will be happy as soon as the decision is reached either to build the bridge or not. They do not have to be concerned about the elimination of the negative consequences of the decision. The third system is more concerned about the elimination of the negative consequences of the decision than the direction of the decision *per se*. The third system has more respect for each individual than the first two systems.

In a large society, consensus is difficult to reach, even with the help of computers and communication technology. The third system, on the other hand, is less difficult, and should be feasible with the currently available communication and computer technology.

Nevertheless, I suspect that the voting system would continue for a while until the no-hardship-on-anyone system becomes established. If the voting system is to continue, then the majority has the responsibility of taking the minorities' points of view into consideration when they vote. The so-called "minority problems" are really the majority problems as long as the voting system continues. It is no longer permissible to "vote for your own interest" only. The majority has the duty to understand the minorities' situations. In a long run, this will require more communication, education and information than the replacement of the voting system by the no-hardship-on-anyone-system.

However, there is another reason for promoting the understand-others policy. It is the consideration of symbiotization. As I mentioned, there is no methodology yet for symbiotization of heterogeneous elements. Before we can find symbiotic combinations, we must understand each of the heterogeneous elements.

The matching problem. Needless to say, individuals vary in their taste, abilities, and even in their optimal rate of communication. No culture is "healthy" or "unhealthy" for everybody. Each culture is healthy for those whose tastes, abilities and rate of communication match it, and unhealthy for others (Refs. 150, 151). High-communication individuals will suffer in a low-communication community, and low-communication individuals will suffer in a high-communication community. The same holds for the matching of individuals to jobs, or individuals to individuals.

Successful matching requires availability of variety, and availability of variety depends on the number of different types of communities as well as the degree of heterogeneity within a community. Also certain types of facilities require a certain size of population. For example, a symphony orchestra cannot exist in a small town. A university cannot be built in a very small village; etc.

There is also the problem of size vs number. For example, many areas of the Midwest USA have a large number of small colleges, each with 1,000 or 2,000 students. They all have libraries with more or less the same basic books. In a way this large number of small colleges creates heterogeneity. But in another sense, a small number of large universities can create more heterogeneity, especially in the variety of library books, or in the variety of departmental subjects.

The planning of extraterrestrial communities will have the same problem. Certain types of heterogeneity can be maximized by having a large number of small communities. Other types of heterogeneity can be maximized by making a small number of large communities.

There is also the problem of horizontal mobility (migration between communities) of individuals in order to increase matching. Then there will be the problem of the *Gesellschaft*-syndrome of localized homogeneity and intolerance.

All these must be kept in mind for long-range planning, and we will never have answers until we actually will have tried out different systems. All we can do is to keep our minds open and to keep experimenting.

Some Suggestions for the Design of Extraterrestrial Communities

In the sociocultural design of extraterrestrial communities, we do not know definitely whether an idea works or not until we have tried it out, because there are many more variables in social processes than in physical processes. But we must begin somewhere. Here are some suggestions, which of course are tentative and subject to change.

As discussed, heterogeneity between settlements not only increases the probability of the survival of the human species, but also increases the speed of the cultural evolution, as well as enrichment of human life. Furthermore, since we do not know which social systems work well and which do not until we have actually tried them out, we need to experiment with several different social systems. Hence our first consideration in the design of extraterrestrial communities is that the first initial communities are to be based on four different types of social and cultural principles. There are many possibilities for the choice of the four types. One suggestion is:

	Basic principle	Elements	Decision process
Community A:	hierarchical	standardized	majority rule
Community B:	individualistic	insulated	as it happens
Community C:	symbiotic	heterogeneous	find symbiotic combination; eliminate hardship on any single individual.
Community D:	interwoven	interwoven	combination of all above.

The hardware aspects of the communities reflect these different principles:

• **Community A:** There is zoning to separate living areas, working areas and recreation areas. All living units are alike except for some variation in size to allow for different sizes of families. All living units are made of standardized parts. Living units are grouped together in identical highrise buildings. People are divided into age groups, occupational groups, etc., in such a way that each group is homogeneous. Members of the same group are housed close together. Since living units are concentrated in a small area, a large area can be reserved for recreation facilities. Recreation activities which require large areas, such as glider flying, sky-diving and golf, can be accommodated.

• **Community B:** Each living unit is insulated against others in terms of sight, sound, and smell, and is as self-sufficient as possible. Each unit is either for a single person, a couple, or a nuclear family. The size of each unit in Community B is considerably larger than in Community A for the reason that most of the recreation in Community B is individualistic and takes place within the living unit. Each unit has a garden space, but there is very little public recreation space in the community. Within each living unit, everything is adjustable to the individual taste. The house has movable partitions, removable windows, removable roof, etc. Protection of privacy is a major concern in this community.

• **Community C:** Housing areas, working areas and recreation areas are mixed. There are houses as well as apartment buildings. Houses are all different, based on different design principles taken from different cultures and from different types of family structure including communes. Each apartment building is different, and within one building, each apartment is different. The overall design principle is harmony of diversity. Different elements are placed in such a way as to make harmony. Likewise, people of different ages, different occupations, different ethnic groups, and different cultures are located mixed in the community, but care is taken to place close together people who can help one another. For example, old people who love small children are placed near families who need babysitters. On the other hand, antagonistic combinations are avoided. For example, noisy people are not placed near people who like tranquility.

• **Community D:** Superficially this community resembles Community C. The overall principle is the same as Community C. However, there are elements within this community which are taken from Communities A and B. There are some homogeneous pockets as in Community A, and there are some large insulated self-sufficient units as in Community B.

Let us keep in mind that these four communities within Model 1 are within the visiting distance of a few minutes from one another. Therefore people in Community A who would like to eat exotic food once in a while can visit Community C for a dinner. On the other hand, large-scale recreation facilities are available more in Community A than in Communities B and C, and those in Communities B and C may go to Community A for such types of recreation.

The second consideration in the design of extraterrestrial communities is how to select the immigrants for each type of community. Hence the immigrants must be selected for each type of extraterrestrial community by means of psychological tests and other criteria.

Even though each community type has no *a priori* discrimination against any race or occupation, it may turn out that people in certain types of occupations or from a certain cultural background tend to prefer a certain type of community. For example, engineers who like standardization may tend to prefer Community A. People from communist countries may also prefer Community A. Texans and ranchers might prefer

Community B. West Africans might prefer Community C, etc.

Care must be taken to ensure that the psychological tests are not ethnocentric. For example, it is well-known that the IQ test measures white middle-classness rather than intelligence. Interculturally applicable psychological tests must be developed. They cannot be developed by American anthropologists and psychologists alone. We need participation of psychologists and social scientists from all cultures in the development of such psychological tests.

The third consideration is people's residential mobility between communities. We must avoid certain *Gesellschaft*-syndromes and *Gemeinschaft*-syndromes. Thus the regulation of migration between communities should be neither so strict that it suppresses individuals, nor so loose that it accelerates the eccentrization of each community and consequent intolerance for nonconformists.

4. Architectural Studies for a Space Habitat

Ludwig Glaeser
Museum of Modern Art

Before one can reasonably speculate on what the environment of a space habitat might be like, it is essential that the function of that habitat within the total system of the space colony be defined. Hence this presentation, tempting as it might have been to the architects in our group, is not full of images of the fabulous interiors of space habitats; such an approach would be premature and even misleading.

This report, of preliminary work in progress, is concerned largely with defining the function of the architectural environment within the total system of the space colony. From that definition, we attempt to delineate areas and methods of research necessary to arrive at a detailed design program. Only with such a program in hand may one begin to consider the full range of design tasks, from environmental systems to hardware specifications, for the construction of space habitats.

In considering the architectural aspect of space habitats, we should start with the question: In what sense is the function of the environment significant to the total colonization effort? If one can solve the difficult technical problems of constructing a satellite at L5, placing it in permanent orbit, and providing it with a self-sustaining ecological system, then aren't the problems involved in architectural design less critical? It might be assumed that in order to determine the architectural requirements of the colony at L5, all we need to do is to assemble its prospective population, have them decide what kind of environment they would prefer – high Alpine or subtropical island, for example – and then proceed to solve the technical problems of simulating such preferences. What could be more idyllic, or, if you wish, utopian, than the prospect of an existence in pollution-free environments, with weather made to order and landscapes on demand? While contemplating such a prospect is attractive, it is far too simplistic a view of the actual challenge.

Our fundamental concern is with the creation of an environment which is wholly artifical, and therefore inevitably more limited than anything encountered on Earth. This environment must not only be capable of attracting colonists to live in space, but also must be able to sustain their non-heroic day-to-day existence for years at a time. It is our basic assumption that unless one can provide such an environment, the solution of all other technical issues upon which this project rests will be in vain.

The architectural environment, as we conceive it in broadest terms, must include all the physical elements which are to occur between the shell of the satellite envelope and its population. This comprises not only shelter, but also furniture, utensils, even clothing. The shell and the population each represent a set of "givens", and each responds to certain requirements of its own, which must be brought together into one functional system. It is the primary task of the architectural environment to mediate and adjust these two sets of requirements to each other. To clarify these requirements, we should first consider some of the salient characteristics of the population and the shell, and the kind of constraints they are likely to impose on each other.

While later models are projected to accommodate much larger populations, which in their composition would be more representative of our urban societies, Model 1 clearly imposes the most constraining conditions with regard to population characteristics. Not only does it host the smallest population, but that population will be living in the greatest isolation, and in what can only be considered an experimental situation. Admittedly Model 1 may appear to distort the conditions of later models, but still it offers the best basis for our environmental criteria. Its inhabitants, or their children, are among us; we know their life-styles and values. Furthermore, since the success of Model 1, socially as well as technically, is essential to the construction of later models, the selection of its personnel and the establishment of their modes of interaction are perhaps more critical. For these reasons we will deal with the characteristics of Model 1, while observing its relationship to later models.

In certain significant respects, we might expect the characteristics of the population of Model 1 to differ from those of later models. To begin, the motivation and commitment which they bring to the colonization effort will have to be strong. They will be the first to engage in such an enterprise and they will be alone. They will have to be highly skilled and in all likelihood possess a multiplicity of skills. They are therefore likely to be well-educated, with a wide range of interests and experiences; in short, people who demand variety from their environment, and who might subsequently take adversely to a non-stimulating, regimented existence. The daily social life and the industrial tasks assigned to the colony will impose routine and social structure, which are likely to prove significant in the way the colonists adjust to life in space and to each other.

The satellite population will be confronted with a range of unprecedented perceptual phenomena, the effects of which will have to be examined systematically in a series of model experiments. To mention only a few:

- The internalized space and its scale distortions

- The cylinder curvature, which at least in Model 1 will be relatively perceptible

- The almost unpredictable quality of the light, reflected by the solars into the interior, which will probably, more than anything else, determine the visual perception of the shell configuration and of the imposed environmental elements

- The composition of the atmosphere and its proposed pressure of 2-3 psi, which is likely to affect hearing

- The mechanically controlled day-and-night cycles and the artificial climate, which will have an impact, even on a physiological level.

As we have suggested, the role of the architectural environment is to mediate between the given conditions of the shell and the existential requirements of its population. This role needs clarification, since certain characteristics of the shell, its atmosphere, gravity, etc., were already introduced in response to specific physiological requirements which have to be met in order to maintain a population in space. There are, however, other requirements of primary concern to us, which relate to the individual as an effect-responding, cognizing organism; in other words, which reflect the totality of his physiological, social and cultural endowments.

Conceptualizing the role of the architectural environment as a mediating mechanism, we can say, to the extent that the satellite environment is perceived as different from the native environment of its population, the potential exists for the development of stress reactions. We understand stress, following Glass and Singer's definition, as "the effective behavioral and physiological response to adverse stimuli." In man, the interpretation of stimuli as adverse may involve higher cognitive processes, as he is not responding exclusively to stimuli, but relies as much on his interpretation of associated information or cues. In any case, a major source of potential stress is the extreme novelty of the environment, reinforced by the perceived isolation of life in space.

All reactions to stress constitute a process of adaptation, which may be accomplished either by physiological adjustment, by cognitive mediation, or finally, by the alteration of the environment itself, so as to remove or diminish its stress-producing effects. These alternatives may be employed simultaneously, with a considerable amount of interaction between them. It is clear, however, that each alternative represents different kinds of potential costs, in terms of reduced performance, personnel replacement, or in remedial construction of the environment.

The given shell, an unadorned, large void, is obviously a potentially stressful environment by virtue of its initial lack of environmental stimuli. To be sure, the structures necessary to house and maintain the population, the facilities for agriculture and manufacturing and the variety of people themselves are sources of stimuli. However, in this wholly artificial environment, stimuli will have the desired effect only if all major environmental components are developed and programmed with this end in mind. The question which this unique environmental situation raises is, therefore, how it should be supplemented in order to alleviate the potential for stress.

The most immediate answer might seem to be to take the Earth environment most agreeable to the prospective satellite population and simulate that environment in space. The implicit assumption behind such an approach is that an Earth-like environment, especially an ideal Earth-like environment, far from being stress provoking, would act as a positive inducement for space colonization. This may be true, but the validity of this assumption cannot be accepted out of hand. Aside from the technical problems, the simulation of an Earth-like environment raises a number of conceptual questions: should it be attempted down to the last elusive detail? If we cannot achieve total simulation, what is really essential in an environment and what is considered by its inhabitants as extraneous? Must we simulate it literally, with real spreading oaks where the scenario calls for it, or can we substitute a styrofoam oak or perhaps a stylized one made of titanium mined on the Moon; perhaps a hologram of an oak will do? These alternatives are raised only half in jest, for they convey the very serious problem of any form of simulation, and that is, how will the satellite inhabitants react to it? Will it indeed provide an environment which alleviates the sense of estrangement that comes from living in such isolation from the Earth? Will it provide sufficient variety to keep its inhabitants' perceptual and cognitive processes "in tune"? It may well be that the very artificiality of such a simulation approach would be a source of stress in itself – the stress of a schizophrenic existence in which the inhabitant is asked to accept the illusory as the real.

While this question awaits an empirical answer, let us consider a completely different approach to the stress adaptation problem. Rather than attempting to adjust the physical environment to suit the conceptions and habits of a population raised on Earth, why not shift the process of adaptation to the cognitive level? That is to say, we might train people to adapt by fully utilizing their physiological and cognitive resources. There is an array of modern techniques and old techniques at our disposal, from bio-feedback (to alert people to the development of stress); to transcendental meditation (to cope with it); or, if you prefer, operant conditioning (to adjust to it). Such an approach might not only be attractive in terms of avoiding the inherent problems of simulation, but also in terms of providing optimal predictability about the behavior of the inhabitants, and therefore the greatest relability in designing facilities which could meet their needs satisfactorily. However, this approach also raises the specter of creating a society designed to fit the constraints of life in Model 1, but potentially ill-suited for life in larger models or on Earth, not to mention the negative influence on the recruiting of future satellite populations.

While both approaches may have a place in the process of stress reduction, and hence in environmental design, their effectiveness appears limited by too many preconceptions. Man does not necessarily respond to an unprecedented situation with innovative solutions, and we have therefore tried from the beginning to neutralize preconceived ideas and established formulas in order to remain as open as possible to new approaches. The one we favor at present does not involve the literal transplantation of stimuli, but would generate them out of its own creative potential in great variety. This approach considers the architectural environment as an open-ended opportunity system, one capable of facilitating the greatest number of activities in space with the greatest amount of flexibility in time. It offers, in our opinion, the closest possible fit between the habitat and its population, which will undoubtedly undergo continuous changes in number and composition.

From the construction phases to the time of full occupation and possible emigration to new satellites, we can always count on a population of high mobility. Accordingly their environmental requirements are likely to change over time; for example, in the initial periods the pressure to adjust to the new situation is such that an environment with the least additional variety may be the most desirable. After a time, however, the unavoidable routine of their isolated existence may prompt a need for change and variety to maintain optimal interest and vitality. Equally significant, however, is the flexibility with which the open-ended approach can accommodate the various social systems that are likely to develop in the satellite colonies.

Obviously, the basic production task which the colony will perform, be it manufacturing or energy production, will in itself generate sets of social interactions, which, together with other manifestations of social life, will ultimately result in social systems. The architectural environment must not only support their functioning, but insofar as these systems evolve over time, provide the opportunities for their emergence and establishment. To be precise, the role of the environment in this respect is not deterministic but only facilitating, inasmuch as the presence of certain kinds of spaces may invite the occurrence of certain kinds of activities. Conversely, the absence of certain spaces — for example, informal public space – may act to discourage certain activities. In keeping with an open-ended opportunity approach we would suggest that, rather than attempting to plan a single environment which anticipates and details all possible needs, we should allow for the development and alteration of space over time. The realization of such an open-ended system imposes reciprocal requirements on both the mechanical infrastructure of the shell and the social interaction of the population. On the other hand, mechanical details must be designed to accept flexibility needed in relocating facilities, and on the other, social governances must be developed to direct and control the alteration of the environment.

Considering the technical requirements to support a flexible environment (in particular, of creating difference-sized spaces), flexibility suggests some form of modularization and standardization. Modularity may be further assumed on the basis of transferring structural loads to the cable network of the shell. Similarly, standardization of construction may be assumed on the basis that most of the components will have to be manufactured at the colony under restricting circumstances. There is, by the way, no reason why an environment assembled from standardized elements must be monotonous, as the contrary has been demonstrated by a sufficient number of cases. Finally, the open-ended system has the particular advantage of providing an ideal experimental situation, which would allow us, by continuously monitoring the Model 1 evolution, to obtain a maximum of information about the design requirements for future colonies.

To summarize our argument at this point, we have defined the role of the architectural en-

vironment as a mediating mechanism adjusting the needs of the population to the characteristics of the shell. Mediation has been considered in terms of stress reduction and environmental opportunities. Areas of potential stress range from physiological to social reactions to the environment. The adjustment process of adaptation may take three forms, physiological, cognitive, or environmental. Our concern has been primarily with the design of the architectural environment as a means to alleviate stress and to maintain the health and vitality of the space colonists. While several design approaches were explored, emphasis was placed on one, which treats the satellite environment as an open-ended system.

This paper in no way constitutes a program for design; it merely indicates areas of research upon which such a program must be based. While the experimental literature dealing with psychological reactions to large-scale novel environments, or with social interaction under conditions of isolation, is substantial, much of it is only indirectly related to the actual conditions of space colonies. Further insights may be gained from historical analogies with other colonizing efforts, and specific data obtained from contemporary task communities working in isolation, where one could draw particularly on the subjective experience of the individual members.

While this survey of environmental data sources is underway, other research efforts will be made in specific areas, such as structural engineering, where we will seek information about the behavior of various construction materials and the suitability of various construction methods under space conditions. As a by-product, we intend to compile a catalogue of questions, which although unanswerable at present, indicate areas requiring further research in other disciplines. Our main objective, however, is the formulation of a detailed program for the design of an L5 satellite environment, and the development of precise criteria for the execution of such designs, which we ultimately hope to commission from a number of architects.

DISCUSSION

Q. I think that your approach is unduly pessimistic, because the first ten thousand people aren't going to be average people. They will be the people who want to go the most; and there are considerable more than ten thousand people in this country alone who would just love to go.

178

A. I'm sure that the number of adventurous people is as unlimited today as it has been in past periods of history; there is certainly a substitute in space for gold in California. But it was our approach to see the problem as a whole and in its full range, not only in view of Model 1. And even with Model 1 you have not only the initial motivation, but the subsequent periods of routine, where the whole stress situation will slowly make its impact.

Q. *It would seem to me that the idea of an "open end" approach is absolutely necessary. What is the minimum rate of change of the various responses necessary to keep the economics of the situation from becoming a cost and still satisfy the population? Are there any terrestrial analogies in various modern societies that would give some guidance to the rate of change of the various individual and psychological problems? Does the rate of change of such phenomena as rock music or dance variations in New York versus that in a small town give some handle on this? Is this a field of research?*

A. It is certainly a field of research. The question cannot really be answered at the moment, because of so many unknown factors. We don't know what kind of system we'll adapt; it depends upon the manufacturing facilities that might exist on the colony. On the other hand, to establish a proper rate of change, we will have to go much deeper into the composition of the population and their mobility.

Q. *There is an analogy in history: Pitcairn Island. People landed, they sunk their ship, and they kissed the world goodbye. A group of people just moved in, adapted to what they had, and built an idyllic existence for some time. Are there any corollaries like that in your field that would help?*

A. As I pointed out in my paper, there are historical analogies which will give us some clues, but there isn't really anything comparable in terms of the environment. Even in Pitcairn Island there was air, a horizon, Earth soil and fauna, and many other things we take for granted.

Q. *Has there been more than just cursory thought given to how people respond in different specific areas or how people change which would have relevance to the question here?*

A. Not to my knowledge.

Q. *When you talk about the isolation factor, have you taken into full account the probability of a communication network and the possibility of frequent travel between Earth and the colony?*

A. We have been speculating on the relation between each cylindrical colony and its other twin satellite, and what differences there should be in their environments. It should have a completely different environment. But the initial isolation is still a sensation which nobody really knows – to be in a container with nothing but space around you. It is not like being in a space vehicle in process towards a goal. You will, however, still have a lot of links with Earth, so it isn't a simple problem to evaluate.

5.   New Options for Self-Government in Space Habitats

Richard Falk
Princeton University

The plausibility of space habitats is the most genuine foundation for the recovery of hope for civilization that I know about, both in the sense of restoring confidence in the future and in restoring our conviction that science and technology can contribute positively to the general cause of global reform.

There are three principal points that crystallize a political consciousness for space colonization. The first is the real importance of non-American participation, particularly Third-World participation, in the early stages of thinking and planning the project, to avoid any adversary attitude. The second is to establish an important role either for the United Nations or some other international organization, under public or corporate auspices, to take the project as far and as early as possible out of the general pattern of geopolitical rivalry that has so often in the past doomed what might otherwise have been promising new initiatives. Our experience both with space and with Antarctica suggests that it's never too early to try to establish that kind of global orientation. The third point is that the project should evolve in the spirit of benefiting the common heritage of humanity, rather than as a proprietary initiative of a single country, region, or constituency of any kind. The real acceptability of this effort depends on its recognition as something that benefits the world as a whole.

It is difficult to project feasible options without making quite a number of restrictive assumptions about the earthly auspices and the context surrounding the establishment of space habitats. If space colonization is projected early in the next century, it is impossible to provide restrictive assumptions which are also realistic. Intervening developments on the national and global levels are likely to be of such an extraordinary magnitude as to make assumptions that now seem plausible appear, in retrospect, highly implausible. Therefore, our weak capacity to predict the international political environment likely to exist in the period 1996 to 2086 constitutes a major constraint on any sort of conjectures that one might make at this point.

A second caveat in defining political structures is that the early experience with space habitats will influence decisively the choice of options for the self-government of subsequent habitats. That is, a rapid learning experience can be anticipated, which would be likely to confirm or reverse the options chosen for the earliest experiments in this kind of space living.

With these two caveats in view, I make the following eleven assumptions; at least a few of them will have to be correct:

- No major intervening global catastrophe will occur.

- Nothing comparable to global unification will occur to overcome the political, cultural, and economic diversity presently associated with the world state system.

- The degree of national diversity that now exists or has existed in the period from 1950 to 1975 will be sustained over the course of the 21st century.

- There will be considerably improved international mechanisms of coordination, as well as a generally more positive attitude toward human solidarity.

- The United Nations will be generally far more important as an autonomous actor than it is at present, or else it will have been replaced by a new general-purpose international organization that enjoys greater autonomy and possesses larger capabilities in functional areas than we presently associate with the United Nations.

- A specialized global agency concerned with space settlement will emerge as a significant participant in any national or intergovernmental project for space settlement, and an appropriate international legal framework will evolve.

- The global interest in space settlement will be guided by a series of widely-supported goals: to reduce population pressure; to secure economic well-being for all peoples; to protect individual and group human rights; to minimize large-scale violence; to protect ecological quality and stability; to conserve and augment scarce and expensive resources; and to regulate technological innovation.

- There will be many more non-state actors of transnational and supranational character active in shaping global policy, and generally, national governments will be much less important in that period than we now regard them to be.

- The space habitats will be established in conformity with international space law and accorded substantial internal autonomy, and they will be generally subject to control from Earth, but they will not be absorbed into the state system, either as colonies or as additional sovereign entities.

- The space habitats will not be in a position to inflict harm, that is, wage economic or political warfare against the Earth, nor will any given habitat have the capacity to harm another, except possibly its sibling cylinder.

- Adverse developments on Earth of a non-military kind cannot imperil the well-being of the habitat program once it becomes self-generative, so that therefore the whole structure of these kinds of space habitats will be largely autonomous of the Earth once the early phase of creating their self-generating capacity has passed.

These eleven assumptions proceed along relatively optimistic lines about global trends. Alternatively, it is quite possible and even likely that by 1996 the level of global disorder and confrontation will have produced a world system much less conducive to this kind of optimism, one that would instead exhibit far more violence, terror, and repression than is characteristic of the 1970's. However, in an exercise of this sort, it is almost impossible to take such a possibility into serious account, because the specific features of such a negative world setting would dominate the kinds of options for self-government that were chosen for the first series of space habitats and for the entire project. Thus, if one approached the problems of the world in a highly Darwinistic way, exactly the opposite of the way that most of the authors have proposed or assumed, then it would seem almost certain that the conventional image of the colonization of space would actually occur and that those parts of the world that were the most powerful and technologically proficient would consider these habitats merely to be extensions of their own areas of geopolitical or national dominance.

In considering the options for self-government, it seems to me useful to set forth four shared values that would provide an agreed framework and that are congenial to most images of global reform on the Earth, and therefore wouldn't create early notions of antagonistic developments in the habitats:

- A commitment to the minimization of violence

- A commitment to the economic well-being of all residents or all settlers in the habitats

- A guaranteed level of social and political justice

- A commitment to the maintenance and improvement of ecological quality

These values constitute broad, normative perspectives whose various modes of implementation could express distinct visions of how to administer a particular space habitat. At the same time, this sort of value consensus would facilitate communication on Earth about the form which these habitats might take, who is to live in them, and how the settlers would be selected or recruited. It is essential that an interactive learning process between space habitats and planetary society be created at the earliest possible time. This would give further credibility to the notion that space habitats are a continuation or a higher evolution of Earth culture, rather than something that is subversive or antagonistic to it. In this respect, these space habitats could be conceived as metaphors or models for new governance options on Earth. Perhaps, for instance, a transnational movement might take shape to create Earth-adapted habitats resembling in social, economic, and demographic form the most successful space habitats. This could also provide a simulated Earth experience for what the characteristics of the space habitats themselves would be.

In addition to the normative framework that would provide a kind of ethical orientation to the creation of self-government structures, certain elements of a constitutional order should also be established as guidelines for all space habitats:

• Effective procedures of checks and balances to avoid undue concentration and abuse of power

• The protection of minimum human rights

• The guaranteed provision of life-support needs

• Minimization of the bureaucratic role and the intrusion on the private lives of the inhabitants of the habitats

• Intensive participation by the settler citizens in the authority structure that emerges

These shared features of space habitats would ensure that positive experiments are undertaken. Obviously, some of these experiments might fail. The form of governance is only one, and not necessarily the most important, ingredient of social, economic, and political success. The character of the population, their levels of skill, cohesion, mutual trust, and affection are likely to be decisive, but the character of the governing system agreed upon can reinforce the positive prospects, if the system is well adapted to the social and economic characteristics of a given habitat.

One exceedingly important variable seems to

concern issues of habitat safety as it bears on the perceptions and experience of these early communities. If the habitats are deemed exceedingly vulnerable to destructive behavior, then reassurances against social deviance would likely be given an exceedingly high priority. Such a priority would both influence selection and screening procedures used to determine who the settlers would be and also the policing mechanism used to guard the habitat against either irresponsible or malevolent anti-social behavior. If internal security concerns become prominent, it is likely that they would produce undesirable levels of surveillance and conformity within the habitats, making the governance system highly coercive and omnipresent. Such an atmosphere seems so politically undesirable that it places a very high engineering premium on establishing habitat conditions that do not appear to be – and are not, in fact – vulnerable to sabotage, negligence, or accident. What I have in mind here are the vulnerabilities to the ultimate survival of a habitat or a pair of habitats. This issue of the safety of a habitat is important in terms of the objective characteristics of how vulnerable it is, but even more so (especially in the early stages) in how vulnerable it appears to be, because that will definitely shape the way in which the whole habitat would be structured.

In one sense, projecting options for space habitats is one way to realize the philosopher's dream of creating a civil society from the state of nature. As such, it involves both a challenge and an opportunity to design a just society. However, the constraints on what can be accomplished in space will reflect the realities of such an endeavor's auspices on Earth. In view of these realities, it seems essential to urge experimentation with diverse modes of governance that reflect the preferences of the founding citizens of individual space habitats. Indeed, one might imagine a process of space colonization whose initial phase would be a constitution-building one, with minimal constraints set only along the lines indicated by the normative and procedural agreed-upon framework that I have suggested.

It is essential in this early phase that the settler-citizens of a particular habitat undertake a relatively long-term commitment to live there, and that the optimal population be a good deal larger than its original band of settlers, so that new children born there would have a large role in shaping the early experience of a habitat. In this way, it is easy to envision a constitution-building process taking place on Earth as part of the preparation for the creation of a particular habitat.

The main types of positive options for self-government, which call attention to the particular organizational motifs that obviously need to be combined in any given space habitat to take account of the various priorities accorded the notion of self-government by those who were going to live in that particular habitat, are as follows:

● Minimum governance. How could you organize a space habitat so that it has as little internal bureaucratic structure as possible? How would one adapt, for instance, a town meeting format to the setting of a habitat? Could one limit the governmental functions to exceedingly small roles, such as protecting the safety of the habitat and insuring communication with Earth and other parts of the total habitat system?

● Highly decentralized or cantonal governance. Official institutions could perhaps be entrusted with a somewhat wider range of functions, but decentralized in such a way that no real, central executive authority emerges within a habitat. Organization could be in districts of regional level with a rotating chief executive, to take the kind of global politics that has proved divisive in most Earth contexts out of the life of these habitats.

DISCUSSION

Q. *One thing that you and Maruyama left out in these considerations is the extreme productivity per person involved in the construction of these habitats. By the time we are making Model 4's, there will be a population of ten or a hundred thousand million people producing the equivalent of New York City in 6 years. This means that each individual has a fantastic amount of power and judgmental authority. He's actually like a window at the top of a vast pyramid of capability, and he's serviced by a system of data processing that will be beyond any capability we can conceive today.*

A. That's a fundamental question. The power and the potency of each individual, if he or she is genuinely capable of producing that kind of wealth, must of course be considered, but so also must the level of sophistication that one needs to participate successfully in that kind of community. There are a lot of problems in having too much power for individuals or groups and knowing how to organize that power so that it doesn't destroy the moral and political fabric of the community. If this makes the habitat accessible only to ultra-sophisticated people, it will engender very strong negative responses in the world. Your suggestion of an elitist way of evolving these habitats is clearly one possibility, but I would regard it as a negative scenario of the future. If social Darwinism really does prevail in the decades ahead, as it is quite likely to, then the habitats *will* be a further evolution of that kind of elitist world system. But I think that would accentuate the distortions of the world's system rather than overcome them. What I am saying is that equity is more important than efficiency in thinking about self-governance, and that we shouldn't be misled by the assumptions of a materialistic civilization to think that what's so great about these space habitats is that they will be so productive from a wealth-creating perspective.

● Creation of a just governance system. This would involve not worrying so much about the bureaucratic structure and about the relative problems of abusing power as much as trying to achieve just arrangement of material and non-material goods for all those settler-citizens who participate in the life of the settler community. The goal here would be to devise the ideal social contract between the settlers and the auspices that arranged for building the settlement.

● The vocational motif. Each particular habitat should be used to evolve as far as possible a special human dimension, whether it be culture or science or medicine or sports or whatever. As an artificial community, it should try to create the ideal conditions for one-sided development. This could have very exciting possibilities in terms of the interactive learning process between the space communities and the Earth.

Let me conclude by noting that these suggestions about new options are obviously very preliminary. At this stage this sort of speculation, which needs to be undertaken by a wide diversity of people proceeding from many different backgrounds, can do more than give substance to the rich exciting opportunities for political innovation that are a central feature of the whole vision of a large number of relatively self-sufficient space habitats. It really is essential that one get similar speculations from Indian peasants, African tribal leaders, and Latin-American businessmen. The goal is to try to understand the vision of what these space habitats might be, by utilizing the dominant perspectives that are active in the life of the planet Earth itself.

6. Organizational Possibilities for Space Habitat Realization

Konrad Dannenberg,
University of Tennessee

Before we can plan an actual organizational form suitable for the operation of a space colony at L5, it appears necessary to define the total scope required to accomplish a project of this kind. We must focus during the early phases of this project on improvements in the quality of life for mankind here on Earth to make the program acceptable to the nation or to the world. We must "sell" this program, not only to the United States, but to the world in general. Furthermore, it should be organized on an international basis, since space habitats have the capability to solve global problems.

It must also be realized that a mere demonstration of technical capabilities will not suffice to get the program underway. Our early activities must be responsive to such human needs as sufficient food supplies, eradication of poverty and disease, prevention of pollution, and conservation of critical resources. All these issues cannot be postponed to the year 2000.

Other authors in this volume have shown that the colonization of space is technically feasible, and I will assume that they are basically correct. We must now find a program management concept which will accomplish the nontechnical goals I have touched on. In some cases, this may mean that we must close our eyes to the most cost-effective management in order to do the things which are really for the benefit of mankind, since these are not always completely compatible.

Immediate improvements in global conditions can be obtained by broad implementation of educational and health services programs. These will definitely have to be different in the less developed world than in the developed countries. On the other hand, even in the less developed countries, the need for education and health services is just as great as the direct need for physical aid and fiscal assistance, so we must certainly do both. The program content of any early phases must be such that it will educate the global population to redirect on-going efforts to optimum use of our existing resources. We must help them to get through the next twenty-five years or so.

The programs must be designed to aid in the generation and distribution of food and health services, and last but not least, they must sell the global populace on the idea that our proposed approach is not just another space venture, another space program, but that it is vital to meet mankind's long-range needs.

With these thoughts in mind, the program to be administered by the proposed "organization" I was asked to describe to you is herewith defined to include an early planning activity. This is something that should be done on a much broader – worldwide – basis than holding conferences at Princeton.

Satellite communication and educational programs must be utilized to the maximum degree and should help in defining these goals for mankind. It is furthermore proposed to invite world-wide participation in the U. S. space shuttle and in the European Spacelab programs to include student experiments. This would generate enthusiasm throughout the world and develop broad participation, not solely by aerospace specialists.

Earliest possible exploitation of capabilities in space manufacturing and, particularly, solar energy conversion in space should be studied jointly and should be demonstrated as to potential capabilities in early shuttle flights. These are not, to my knowledge, planned at the present time, and I would propose to add certain phases to the ongoing NASA programs. All these activities will lead automatically to space habitats and eventually to a colony of the type discussed here.

The challenges of such a visionary program will provide to mankind great incentive to join hands as a "team". Such unified efforts might eventually lead to the greater benefit of all: that we understand each other, that we know a little bit what the other fellow has in mind, and that we have appreciation for each other. This appreciation and understanding will, hopefully, educate man about the benefits of cooperation. We still have to lay the groundwork for this phase. To realize this latter benefit will require planning for joint and international programs with widest possible participation.

In my discussion of these possibilities with other people, the most frequently asked question was: "If we can do all these great things in space, why can't we do at least some of them also down here on Earth?" We should implement a number of the types of approaches that were discussed here. We should set up some of our communities to work under the critical conditions which we will find in space. We should establish some of the intensive agricultural activities. Some of these programs will even be revenue-producing. These wide-ranging efforts may easily double the program cost; however, we should not draw back from them. Many of them may bring real financial benefits, and certainly the spirit of mankind will be uplifted to a great extent.

All of these activities have the desirable characteristics of large-scale involvement by people. We should find the potential for use of unskilled and even unschooled labor. All workers don't have to be PhD's with aerospace backgrounds. The early people we send out to the colonies will be the same type. Broad educational, vocational, and health services programs will equip the trainees to progress within the program and to eventually become space colonists, or to return to their home countries and prepare additional generations for these future activities.

Because of these educational benefits, the cost for this portion of the program should be borne by the sponsoring agencies of the sponsoring nations, and should not necessarily go into the colonization project operation *per se*. We should plan for an international program, and for that reason, I propose that any such organization should really be attached to the United Nations. This proposal is made in spite of the known problems and difficulties of the United Nations, but let us not forget that an newly established agency may have the same problems.

In recognition of this situation, it is proposed that one of the early activities of the project operation manager be the question of how an efficient arrangement can be found for the long run. I propose a phasing in such as was done in INTELSAT. The final attachment should be to the United Nations, but maybe we can find an intermediate solution in the meantime; one suggestion is the creation of a bicameral system, which would establish a separate "Service Agency". It is hoped that enough nations would recognize the benefits of such operations and would be willing to delegate such major fiscal powers to such a Service Agency.

I would propose that we initially start with relatively simple things, like an international educational communications system, similar to INTELSAT operations but concentrating on education. It would not be the same operation as INTELSAT, as they are in the business to handle commercial, official TV traffic.

I further propose that we use ATS-type satellites, which can broadcast directly into homes. Some of the nations are reluctant to accept these, so we would have to move carefully and make the right arrangements for this kind of broadcasting. On the other hand, it is an efficient way of giving education to billions of people; we would initially start with millions. Some of you may know that the ATS-6 (formerly the ATS-F) is on its way to India, and will be turned over to India within the next few days. It will broadcast into five thousand Indian villages. So, we could probably educate, with this proposed system, something like five hundred thousand people in one big swoop. Even if such a satellite costs quite a bit of money, the cost per pupil is relatively low, and even a relatively poor country like India should be able to pay the cost.

It will probably be necessary to obtain from all the countries who want to use these kind of services an indication of interest. I have already had a number of indications from countries other than India which would be interested in using similar systems. They should, of course, pay according to their capability to pay, perhaps as measured by their gross national products. It comes out that the U.S., at least, could pay, in the first year of operations, for one of the ATS satellites, a cost of fifty million dollars. It is much more expensive than the COMSAT-type satellites, but it has a larger capability. If we could charge these nations and have them keep on paying fifty million per year, we would have quite a good revenue from these activities.

If it is really possible to create power from space in a relatively early time interval, then we could definitely up the percentage of the gross national product from the nations. I see easily that we could charge something like ten dollars per head. If we were able to send power to one billion of the world's population (it is now close to four billion), at, say, $10 per person per year (a very cheap power source!) we can have annual returns up to $10 billion.

In the long run, as the power usage grows, we might be able to raise this per capita cost for electric power to higher levels. I am, therefore, not too much concerned if the final cost of the project exceeds $10 billion per year. Such costs can be raised if the projects return to mankind specific benefits of education programs, health services programs, and eventually, of course, electric power from space.

In order to conduct such a program, a strong project organization is needed. In INTELSAT, COMSAT apparently took a really strong hand in running the program, at least during the early years. And, of course, a project manager should have at his disposal some relatively strong groups in the area of operations. These are essentially education operations in the early phases, and may go to power operations in later phases. He should have a group to do the world-oriented planning, as well as administration of the project. I see, basically, about six boxes in this organization which would, eventually, report to the United Nations.

As a first step, I propose that we go to one of the specialized sub-agencies of the United Nations.

Since I have stressed education, I would propose UNESCO. One of my co-workers is going to take up with UNESCO officials what their interest would be to get such a planning phase started. I would propose that under UNESCO we set up a group which would undertake the overall long-range planning and which would come up with recommendations for specific activities that can be "bought" by many people. As an international program, I would expect to invite, and get participation from, the Russians, the Chinese, and other uncommitted countries which are not participants in INTELSAT.

I would like to remind you that the present communication satellite of the type I propose, ATS-6, is on its way to East Africa. It will be stationed over East Africa and will broadcast into India. They will start recording in June of this year and tests will be conducted for about one year's operation. Positive results from these tests will become avaliable for appraisal and review so that we can enhance considerably the desires and plans of what we think should be done in these areas.

In my opinion, it is not too early to start now. More detailed plans and, particularly, the principal resolve to go ahead are required. I personally think that the United States should take the lead, by a contribution of what I call "seed money".

Step number one would be, for example, to leave the ATS-6 satellite with India. Our present plans are to take it back and use it over the United States. Then, of course, we would be in a position to charge India for its benefits. They have already installed a relatively expensive ground system which they can only use for one year if our present plans to return ATS-6 to the U. S. are pursued.

I understand that Fairchild Industries, which built this satellite, has another one in storage. Why not put it into this program and maybe sell it to the Shah of Iran? There are some indications he might be willing to pay for it, and if he continues to pay, roughly, $50 million per year, we have something that can be put into both our planning activities and our future activities.

I also specifically propose that the United States build a few more satellites of this type, because otherwise we will have to wait for the arrival of the shuttle. These satellites will, of course, be carried into space by the shuttle, but I do not think we should wait to build them until 1980 when the shuttle is flying.

I am convinced that once we really solve the problem, and can handle it technically, of getting electric power from space down to Earth, we can build up sizable resources, which I hope will not flow into a private enterprise but will be used to keep on supporting a project of this type. This, then, would be beyond the responsibilities of UNESCO, and for that reason I see, eventually, a direct tie-in to a new UN-type organization: perhaps a bicameral system as I mentioned earlier. In such a system we could earmark the monies which are being provided so that they can only be used for the educational programs, for the health services programs, and for the power program. They will not be available for the peace-keeping mission. That's the basic principle of the bicameral system, to be sure that the funds are so clearly subdivided that they cannot be misused.

DISCUSSION

Q. What is the ATS satellite?

A. It's an Applications Technology Satellite. It's basically a communications satellite, but it has a larger capability and it can do direct broadcasting into a home-receiver-sized antenna. You need an antenna which is about a meter in diameter, and you do not have to go through a rebroadcasting station like our present educational TV systems do.

Q. Is it possible to use it for transmitting two-way TV?

A. Yes, it is a two-way link. ATS-6 has been operating over the United States for about a year, and it has been very successful. There were quite a number of educational programs. A major one was to explore continuing education for our thousands of teachers, but it has turned out that this was not the main long-run benefit. The medical people were so enthused by ATS-6 capabilities that the Veterans' Administration hospitals are using this means now to consult with specialized doctors, who don't have the time to travel to Los Angeles and consult

directly, but who can give consultation by means of ATS-F. That's what India is very much interested in. Many people here do not realize how little transportation is available in India. Some of the five thousand villages were selected because they are not tied to any railroad, nor to any streets, so there is really no way to get there. For that reason, they have no teachers at all. The teaching programs for these villages are on a very primitive, simple basis, appropriate for television communication. And they need it very badly.

Q. Since there are many applications for these satellites, as you said, could you explore the possibilities of selling all these services to the various countries?

A. I would not want to compete with private ventures. Some of these things really should be conducted on a private business-type basis. They certainly could be done by COMSAT, for example.

Q. You are concerned about generating money for this project, to bring benefits to man as soon as possible. Could we tap some of the enormous funds which are to be spent on energy in the next ten years by Western Europe, the United States, and Japan? A joint public corporation/energy project could be set up for those who might want to participate. The less developed countries could also be involved, certainly as potential customers for cheap energy.

A. Yes, this can be done. I think we will find many customers willing to make a down payment and to wait a year or two until the system is available. Like INTELSAT, we should deal with entire economies, not with the individual customer. These aggregates – a country or a region – should then make their own local distribution. The project therefore would be responsible, as INTELSAT is, only for the space-based equipment; each country would provide its own receiver stations.

7. International Law and Outer Space Stations

Edward R. Finch
Finch and Schaefler

I will deal principally with the three major treaties that deal with space: the 1967 Treaty (also known as the "grandmother" treaty), the 1968 Treaty, and the 1972 Treaty. Earlier, the United Nations General Assembly *Resolution 1721*, in December 1961, had commended to the Member States the principles that:

- International law, including the United Nations charter, applies in outer space

- Outer space, including celestial bodies, is free for exploration and use by all States in conformity with international law and is not subject to national appropriation.

The 1967 Treaty, *The Treaty on Principles Governing the Activities of States in the Exploration and Use of Outer Space, Including the Moon and Other Celestial Bodies,* is now in full force and effect, ratified by many nations. This treaty originated in the United Nations. From it has sprung all of the bilateral agreements and many of the executive agreements now in effect.

Article I of that treaty declares that there shall be freedom of scientific investigation in outer space and that States shall facilitate and encourage international cooperation in such investigation.

Article II states that outer space, including the Moon and other celestial bodies, is "not subject to national appropriation by claim of sovereignty by means of use or occupation, or by any other means." It sets to rest the fears regarding claims of sovereignty such as taking effective possession of portions of any celestial land mass such as the Moon. "Permanent" Moon mining scientific stations, therefore, are clearly permissible, with notice, and also will be subject to what comes out of the 1975/76 negotiations on the New Moon Treaty. The Moon is no doubt the present likeliest candidate among celestial bodies for a permanent space station. The launching State or the launching organization is liable for the space station and responsible for it, as well as for any damages caused or for any contamination caused on the surface of the Moon; and the launching state or the launching international organization retains jurisdiction of the same, under existing international law.

Article III provides that a nation's activities in the exploration and use of outer space shall be in accordance with international law and in the interests of maintaining international peace and security. Now, the United Nations charter obviously overrides this and applies to what we do in outer space. These interests are clearly advanced by the scientific and cost advantages of weightless outer-space laboratory research and manufacturing in space station laboratories *if* we assume that the scientific advances therefrom will be available for the benefit of all mankind by way of ultimately reduced cost to Earth consumers plus the new scientific, medical, and biomedical products, alloys, crystals, or whatever the station may produce. We assume that they will also be available to those who have not contributed to the station, either financially or by participation. Space shuttle transfers of materials to, and products from, space station manufacturing laboratories present no problem if the three major treaties are complied with, particularly the 1967 Treaty.

Article IV of the 1967 Treaty prohibits the stationing in outer space of any object carrying nuclear weapons or any other weapon of mass destruction. That prohibition extends to installing such weapons on celestial bodies or in outer space in any other manner. Clearly, then, outer space stations or space laboratories cannot be armed, and since they will not be armed, there is no violation of the '67 Treaty.

To assure that celestial bodies are used exclusively for peaceful purposes, Article IV also prohibits the establishment of any military bases or the testing of weapons or the testing of materials which would be useful in weapons. The treaty does, however, permit the use of military personnel for scientific research or any other peaceful purposes, as well as the use of any equipment or facility necessary for the peaceful exploration of celestial bodies. The Moon mining facilities must be engaged in Moon soil and Moon sub-soil research and exploration. Research and exploration are constantly referred to in these treaties, and it is very important that any space station or mining station established on the surface of the Moon be engaged in, and be contributing to, research in a very substantial form, as well as gathering Moon material to take back to L5.

Article V expressly regards astronauts, the people, as "*envoys of mankind*" and provides that in the event of accident, distress or emergency landing on the territory of another State or on the high seas, they shall be given all possible assistance, including safe return. On celestial bodies, astronauts of different States are to render all possible assistance to one another. The proposed New Moon Treaty provides that all personnel on the Moon shall be "astronauts" for the purpose of the application of this Article V and for the purpose of the application of the Rescue Treaty, the 1968 Treaty.

Article VI places international responsibility on a State for its activities in space, whether by governmental or non-governmental entities. Non-governmental entities must have authorization from participating States and "continuing supervision" by the State concerned.

Article VII provides that the launching State and the State from whose territory or facility an object is launched shall be internationally liable for any resulting damages to the persons of another State.

Jurisdiction and control, from a legal point of view, are retained by the State on whose registry the object is launched. As far as military personnel are concerned, they would be under the Uniform Code of Military Justice and they would still be subject to the jurisdiction of the United States. For civilians, we would have to amend the *United States Criminal Code, Title 18*, to cover the commission of crimes in outer space, in a space station, on the space shuttle, or on celestial bodies by persons who are not members of any Armed Service, whether it is Soviet, United States, or any other country.

This could be done very easily by Congressional action, extending certain criminal jurisdictions, just as they did to passengers aboard aircraft of United States registry while over the high seas. That was done in 18 United States Code, Section 7, subdivision 5. The laws of the United States must apply if it is solely a United States Moon mining facility.

Article IX concerns the application of the principle of cooperation and mutual assistance among States in their exploration and use of outer space. On pollution, we have definite treaty commitments; we cannot contaminate the Moon. As to safety in outer space, we have to provide for a means of safety for any facility at L5, no matter whether it has one village or two villages, or how it is ultimately determined to be constructed. If we do not do that, we might be in violation of the '67 Treaty. I can very well remember on the extra-vehicular activities (EVA's) many of our astronauts were distressed when they lost even one screw in outer space and it completely got away from them. So we do have to worry about safety from the point of view of a space colony or, as I prefer to call it because of the semantic language in the existing treaties, a space station.

The 1967 Treaty provides for informing the Secretary General of the United Nations, as well as the scientific community and the public, to the greatest extent feasible and practicable as to the nature, conduct, locations, and results of a State's activities in outer space. This the United States has consistently done. We have lived up to our treaty obligations. We follow this out, particularly in outer space, because outer space has been an area of new frontier, a new territory, where we have been able to reach agreements with the Soviets because it is in their pragmatic interest to do so.

In addition to the reporting, the United States pressed for inclusion of a very strong launching requirement. We also report to the Secretary General of the United Nations every launching that we make, and the Soviets have been doing this too. Their reports are very brief; they don't tell too much about the launch vehicle or the payload; they just say investigation of the upper atmosphere or something like that, but at least they do announce that something is on the way.

The 1968 Treaty's legal title is *The Treaty on the Rescue of Astronauts, the Return of Astronauts, and the Return of Objects Launched into Outer Space*. This is the treaty that creates the unconditional obligation to help and return people promptly and safely.

The 1972 Treaty, called the 1972 Liability Treaty, is entitled the *1972 Convention on International Liability for Damage Caused by Space Objects*. This assures recovery to a national of a State for injury to his person or damage to his property from another adherent State's space activities. The present legal mechanisms that exist for setting up an international agreement permitting use of lunar materials are found in the existing treaty organization structure. For outer space, historically, this has been in the Legal Subcommittee of Peaceful Uses of Outer Space of the United Nations (COPUOS Committee).

The New Moon Treaty (NMT) is one of the draft treaties before the COPUOS Committee. Six provisions applicable to space stations are currently near U.N. COPUOS decision. These are:

- General provision of the applicability of international law

- Requirement of reporting to the Secretary General of the United Nations, once for space missions of less than sixty days, or seriatim if you are in outer space for more than sixty days, the time, purpose, locations, orbital parameters, apogee, perigee, duration and so forth of the mission, and including scientific results

- Measures to prevent the disruption of the existing balance in the Moon environment by contamination or extra-environmental matter

- The placement of any radioactive materials on the Moon, whether for research or scientific purposes or not, and the purpose of such placement

- Obligation to inform the United Nations Secretary General concerning areas in the Moon for special scientific interest (prior to actual utilization) for consideration for designation of such areas as international scientific preserves

- Obligation to inform the United Nations Secretary General and the international scientific community of any indication of organic life on the Moon, or phenomena discovered in outer space which could endanger life or health.

It is obvious that the nations participating in the discussion of the current U.N. draft Moon treaty are seeking to establish under an international regime:

- The orderly and safe development of Moon natural resources and other celestial bodies for the common heritage of all mankind

- The rational management of those resources

- The expansion of opportunities in the use of those resources

- The equitable sharing in the benefits derived from those resources.

I would like to postulate certain assumptions on which I will further apply the content of the treaties outlined:

- We will try to keep weapons systems out of outer space stations

- The principal source of energy will be solar, for internal use in living in space stations and in laboratory, manufacture and research therein

- The stations at the L5 location will not be self-governed initially.

With these assumptions, the United States would be in full compliance with the 1967 Treaty and the other existing treaties in the project which we have been discussing, and it definitely would be another step in the advancement of science for the common heritage of all mankind.

I have already discussed contamination, but I would like to make a couple of further assumptions which I think fit in with the existing framework of international law:

● There will be a common language in space. Apollo-Soyuz, launched July 1975, has proved this. I've heard it in Moscow, I've heard it in Washington, and I've heard it in New York; you've got to have a common language base. The Apollo-Soyuz project has been a very good testing ground for space station construction.

● The space stations will have to operate either on a line-of-staff basis or on a commune principle with a mayor, deputy mayor, staff, etc. This assumption arises from the fact that you have life-support problems, and therefore you need to regulate the community. If you have as many as ten thousand people in one space station, you have to have some sort of a system such as we have on a large, isolated base or in a large, isolated tribal community structure. You have to have free food, free dental facilities, free medical facilities. You have to be able to communicate with Earth. And, because of the initial requirements for life support, from the point of view of the framework of existing international law, you are going to have to live within the jurisdiction of the launching sponsor.

On May 24, 1972, we have entered into a bilateral agreement between the United States and the Soviet Union. That bilateral agreement was not approved by Congress, but it is a very key agreement. There is no legal requirement that Congress approve bilateral agreements, but executive agreements and bilateral agreements are just as binding, legally, on the United States, because we are a government of laws and not of men. Therefore I refer you to Article IV of the executive agreement of the United States and the Soviet Union of May 24, 1972. It reads:

"The Parties will encourage international efforts to resolve problems of international law in the exploration and use of outer space for peaceful purposes with the aim of strengthening the legal order in space and further developing international space law and will cooperate in this field."

Signed by President Nixon and Chairman Kosygin, it is in full force and effect. The citation is TIAS 7347.

The United Nations needs to take a broader and longer-ranged approach to its role in outer space

matters beyond those suggested by the outer space powers to date, by guaranteeing the interests of the less technically oriented countries and by ensuring equitable access of utilization and information from the new technologies. The U.N. should be able to remove many of the fears of the developing countries and the member States which manifest themselves most frequently in efforts to limit a technology's full accomplishments.

Technology and scientific advancement can be retarded if international law does not keep step with the progress of science, whether it be in the project at L5 or in any other project. As examples of that, I would further call your attention to the current national territorial restraints which are being brought up by some of the developing nations in regard to the ERTS project, now called LAND-SAT, and then the geopolitical restraints on the Direct Broadcast Satellites (DBS).

When space station manufacturing in outer space is ready, I am hopeful that international law will be ready, *if* we can get the current draft Moon Treaty and the other proposed treaties satisfactorily completed in the U.N., adopted and ratified by the necessary State parties, and into full force and effect. Then we shall see that, for outer space stations for peaceful purposes, law and science can move forward together for the benefit of all mankind.

DISCUSSION

Q. *You speak as if the treaties were inviolable and absolute. Yet we know the Soviet Union has several times put weapons in orbit in the form of Fraction-Orbit Bombardment Satellites (FOBS) and has tested those devices. We at one point had a Military Orbital Laboratory (MOL) project which was a military base. How does that fit in with the treaties?*

A. Interpretation of the treaty depends on how you define where "outer space" begins. This has not yet been resolved. Because FOBS has a very high apogee and a very low perigee, you can't say that that is technically a treaty violation. It's a question of semantics.

Q. *What will be the interpretation of the 1972 treaty if we start disassembling the Moon?*

A. As long as we set up a scientific, legal preserve, engage in Moon research, including subsoil research, and we make the information available to the Secretary General of the United Nations if we come up with any findings in the anlysis of the Moon soil, I don't think there's a violation.

Q. *But if we were bringing the material back here for mining purposes, wouldn't there be an objection to our exploitation of that resource?*

A. Not necessarily. Nobody objected when the Apollo and other projects brought back lunar materials. In fact the Soviets displayed them in Leningrad, and they had blocks of people just waiting to walk by and take a look at them.

8. The Intelsat Arrangements

Gus J. Rauschenbach
COMSAT Corporation

On October 4, 1957, the U.S.S.R. launched Sputnik I and Earth had its first artificial satellite. During the balance of that year, another Russian satellite, Sputnik II, was launched and immediately thereafter, the first U.S. satellite, Explorer. Thus began the Space Age. There then followed, during the years 1962 and 1963, a series of U.S. communications satellites: TELSTAR, RELAY and SYNCOM. These satellites demonstrated to the world that the so-called natural barriers that had separated people from the beginning of time – the oceans, the deserts, and the jungles – could be bridged by satellites hovering over the Earth, and that these satellites would enable people to communicate with other people in the very distant parts of the world by means of speech and the projection of visual images. Beginning in the year 1965, vast areas of the world benefited from the commercial utilization of outer space by means of the communications satellite.

In the case of satellite communication, the basic technology itself requires extensive international cooperation. Essentially, the act of communicating through outer space involves the transmission of a signal from an Earth station to a satellite, which, in turn, relays it to a second Earth station. It is then redistributed via the terrestrial network that is available to a given geographical area. This requires cooperation on the part of a number of people and on the part of a number of countries.

The technology also requires a second form of cooperation, since satellite communications, which are a form of basic microwave radio transmissons, use one of the most valuable resources available to man – the electromagnetic frequency spectrum. This is a limited resource, and if it is widely used, there must be agreement between all countries for its allocation among the competing users, including satellite communications.

There is another fundamental difference between satellites and other means of long-distance communications which emphasizes the need for close cooperation on a global basis. Satellites are capable of connecting any point on Earth with all those other points to which the satellite is mutually visible and without linkage through any other country.

This technology may make it imperative for international cooperation to take place. Men must preserve this necessity and respond to its challenges in a timely manner. In the field of outer space, we have seen many effective responses, at the United Nations level, the domestic level, and in international agreements.

In *Resolution 1721* of the United Nations General Assembly, which was unanimously adopted September 20, 1961, the declaration was made "...that outer space and celestial bodies are free for exploration and use by all States in conformity with international law and are not subject to national appropriation."

This principle of the freedom of outer space, which is so essential for the use of outer space for commercial purposes, was reaffirmed in the resolution adopted unanimously by the General Assembly of the United Nations on December 13, 1963, entitled "Declaration of Legal Principles Governing the Activities in the Exploration of Outer Space." In addition, the U.N. declaration stated two principles of particular relevance to the organization and operation of a global communications satellite system:

- States bear international responsibility for national activities in outer space whether carried on by governmental agencies or by non-governmental entities

- The activities of non-governmental entities in outer space require authorization and continued supervision by the State concerned.

Our government responded to the challenge with the Communications Satellite Act of 1962, which states the policy and purpose of this country in these words:

> "The Congress hereby declares that it is the policy to establish in conjunction with other countries as expeditiously as practicable a commercial communications satellite system as part of an improved global communications network which will be responsive to the public needs and national objectives, which will serve the communications needs of the U.S. and other countries and which will contribute to 'World Peace and Understanding'."

That act created the Communications Satellite Corporation and provided that it should be the U.S. participant in the global satellite system. It did not, however, attempt to dictate the form or content of the international agreements under which the system would be established. This was left to be worked out in the course of international negotiations.

It is fair to say that among those many factors that had to be considered by those engaged in establishing an international organization in this field, the economic aspects were given at least equal weight with the political factors. It is my belief that this equilibrium contributed greatly to the shaping of an organizational structure which has been responsive to the many interests, and yet able to move ahead efficiently with its operational responsibilities.

In considering possible international arrangements, it was found useful to conceive of the global system as consisting of a single space segment and a number of Earth segments. A space segment includes all of the satellites used in the system and the tracking, command, and control facilities required to control the operation of the satellites in orbit. The Earth segments comprise the stations located in various countries which are used to transmit and receive telecommunications traffic through the satellite.

Negotiations were undertaken initially with countries whose potential use of communications satellites was of such magnitude that their participation in the global system seemed desirable from the outset. We found that there were countries which, like ours, felt that the space segment should be jointly owned and financed by participants from all of the major regions of the world, and that the extent of each participant's investment and consequent ownership share should be related to its potential use of the global system. It was also agreed that the various Earth segments of the system should be separately owned and financed by the telecommunications entities, public or private, which were authorized by the using countries. This distinction between the formal ownership and financing of the space segment on one hand and the Earth segment on the other is basic to an understanding of the international arrangements.

The negotiations culminated in the framing of two interrelated agreements which were opened for signature on August 20, 1964. Together the agreements established an international partnership for the financial ownership and operation of the space segment of the system. The first, entitled *Agreement Establishing Interim Arrangements for a Global Commercial Communications Satellite System*, was an agreement among governments. The second, called the "Space Agreement," was one which could be signed either by the governments themselves or by telecommunications entities, public or private, designated by the governments signing the first agreement. When these agreements were first opened for signature, they were signed by the United States and thirteen other countries.

The first of the two interrelated interim agreements established certain basic political and economic principles and goals to which all of the signatories are committed, as well as the organizational and financial framework of the partnership.

The Interim Agreement established a governing committee, the Interim Communications Satellite Committee, which had the overall responsibility for the design, development, construction, establishment, maintenance, and operation of the space segment of the global system. It also provided that the Communications Satellite Corporation act as the manager in the design, development, construction, establishment, operation and maintenance of the space segment.

The space segment was owned in undivided shares by the signatories to the special agreement in proportion to their respective contribution to the cost of the space segment. The Communications Satellite Corporation, as the United States participant in this joint venture, was initially obligated by the agreements to contribute 61% of the capital required for the establishment of the space segment during the interim period, estimated at the time to be $200 million. The initial investment quotas of all the Western European countries totalled 30.5%, with the remaining 8.5% divided among Canada, Japan and Australia. As additional countries became parties, the quotas of previous signatories were reduced *pro rata* to accommodate the quotas of all parties within the total of 100%. Thus we ended up with a majority of the countries having quotas of less than 1%.

It was decided to limit membership on the Interim Communications Satellite Committee to representatives of each of the participants or groups of participants having an ownership interest and a financial commitment of at least 1.5%. Each member of the committee had voting power in proportion to his ownership share of the organization or organizations he represented. Although the COMSAT Corporation had more than a majority of votes by virtue of its investment quota, the agreement specified a number of important subjects on which decisions required the concurrence of a number of parties in addition to the COMSAT Corporation – the necessary accumulation of votes being such that countries located in several major geographical regions of the world had to be in agreement.

The following aspects of these arguments are worthy of special note:

- The concept of an international cooperative enterprise with widespread membership for the purpose of sharing the exploitation of new resources for the economic benefit of all mankind.

- The effort to reduce national rivalry in a new field of economic activity by the concept of a single global system instead of competing national systems.

- A form of organization which recognized the diversity of national economic systems by permanent participation of either public or private entities on behalf of the signatory countries.

- A form of organization which provides for a wide disparity of investment and ownership reflecting the probable extent of the use of the system by the various participants and which takes this factor into account in the decision-making process.

All the foregoing relates to the INTELSAT Interim Arrangements – the initial agreements under which the consortium was formed. On May 21, 1971, representatives of the member governments of INTELSAT adopted a set of what we call "Definitive Arrangements," which constitute the present "Operating Agreement."

The Definitive Arrangements are the Operating Agreement under which INTELSAT now operates. They consist of an Intergovernmental Agreement with 3 Annexes, including an Arbitration Annex and an Operating Agreement with Annex. Under the Definitive Arrangements, INTELSAT is a judicial entity consisting of four organs. These are an assembly of government representatives referred to as the Assembly of Parties, a Meeting of Signatories to the Operating Agreement, a Board of Governors similar to the earlier Interim Committee, and an executive or management organ headed initially by a Secretary General and subsequently by a Director General. COMSAT will continue as manager under contract for six years, specifically rendering technical and operational management services. Other management activities shall be the responsibility of the Secretary General and thereafter the Director General.

Investment in INTELSAT by the signatories is based on their use of the space segment of the system, with adjustments to be made annually. COMSAT's investment has dropped to 33.6%. This reflects the fact that the traffic out of the U. S. has become a smaller percentage of total world traffic as more countries make increasing use of the satellites.

Voting in the Assembly of Parties and Meeting of

Signatories is on a basis of one country – one vote. Voting on substantive matters in the Board of Governors is by weighted vote with a limitation that a single Governor may not cast more than 40% of the total votes or veto a Board action.

The United States concentrated its efforts on the distribution of functions and powers within the INTELSAT hierarchy, arguing that the responsibility for the design, development, construction, and operation of the space segment must rest with the Board of Governors, where decisions would be taken by weighted vote based on investment. Any arrangements that would risk the major investor's interests by one member-one vote actions, perhaps by less than 15% of the total investment of INTELSAT, was completely unsatisfactory to the United States.

The opposing view conceded the need for the Board of Governors' responsibility for the establishment and operation of the space segment by advocating the reduction of COMSAT's voting strength in the Board of Governors. This view also urged giving the Assembly of Parties, composed of representatives of each of the governments, the power to establish general policies and objectives of INTELSAT, to receive and act on complaints, and to exercise any residual functions of the organization as the principle organ of INTELSAT.

Extensive negotiations were conducted on this issue in the autumn of 1970, and a compromise was reached on the distribution of responsibility and power within the INTELSAT hierarchy. Pursuant to that compromise, no organ may interfere with the exercise of the powers or responsibilities of another organ except where the Agreement specifically provides.

The negotiated package provides for an Assembly of Parties composed of all parties to the Intergovernmental Agreement. It is empowered to consider general policy and long-term objectives of INTELSAT, and to formulate its views on these matters to the other organs of INTELSAT; however, it is not itself empowered to decide these matters. It has the power to confirm the permanent management official, the Director General, who is appointed by the Board of Governors. The Assembly of Parties meets every two years unless it decides otherwise. Each Party has one vote, and

Figure 113. Current Intelsat Organization.

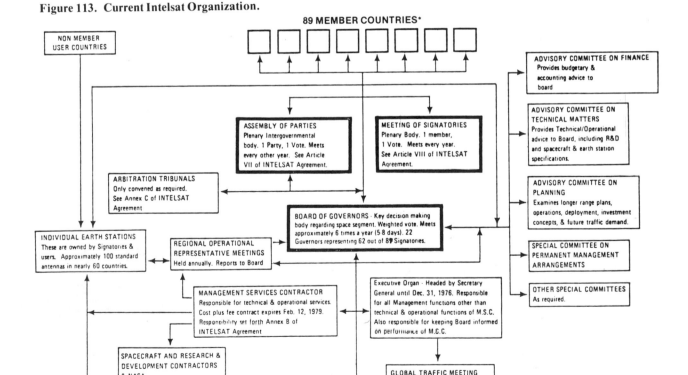

• Governments are Parties to INTELSAT. Agreement Signatories, i.e., the operating entities, adhere to Operating Agreement. Parties and signatories provide representation to INTELSAT meetings, own their own earth stations, pay for share of space segment they utilize. Five Signatories currently are or will shortly be providing Tracking, Telemetry, Command & Monitoring services under contract to INTELSAT. These include: Australia (Carnarvon); Brazil (Tangua); Cameroon (Zamengoe); Italy (Fucino); U.S. (Andover & Paumalu).

substantive matters must be decided by at least two-thirds of those present and voting.

The Meeting of Signatories is the body which supervises the Operating Agreement. Among its functions are the power to initiate any amendments to the Operating Agreement and to decide upon any increase of capital ceiling, the latter upon the recommendation of the Board of Governors. It can establish rules for access by Earth stations to the satellites, for allotment of satellite capacity, and for charges for the use of satellite capacity. Each country has one vote in the Meeting of Signatories. Like the Assembly, the Meeting of Signatories can act on matters of substance only by a vote of at least two-thirds of those present and voting.

The functions of the Board of Governors are those of supervising the running of the satellite system, including procurement, operations plans, standards for access to the system by Earth stations, terms and conditions of the charge for use of satellite capacity, and the approval of research and development projects, to name a few. This body supervises the Manager. It's the Board's job to see that as a telecommunications system, INTELSAT functions efficiently, reliably, and looks ahead to the operating and technical problems of the future. The Board of Governors can increase the capital ceiling up to 10% beyond the $500 million stipulated in the Operating Agreement. The Board may also appoint, subject to confirmation by the Assembly of Parties, and remove from office, the Secretary General and the Director General.

The final part of the package is the management entity. Under the 1964 Interim Agreements, COMSAT serves as the Manager of the system. It was apparent from the outset of the negotiations that to have an internationalized manager was a broadly supported aim of a number of nations, and this was one of the first issues to be settled in the Definitive Arrangements.

The United States proposed that COMSAT should continue to manage INTELSAT under contract arranged by the Board of Governors and subject to replacement at the end of any contract term. The opponents argued that management, including technical and operational functions, should be internationalized from the outset of the Definitive Arrangements in a Secretariat of IN-TELSAT, headed by an international civil servant. They argued that a permanent international organization should not rely for its management

upon a private international entity, and that the interest of COMSAT, as the United States investor in INTELSAT, conflicted with the obligations of COMSAT as manager of INTELSAT. At the same time, it was recognized that COMSAT's demonstrated expertise in technical and operational matters was unmatched. This was a significant factor to many of the developing nations who depend, to an increasing extent, on satellite service to provide them with reliable international communications.

The compromise provided that :

Table 28. INTELSAT: The International Tele-communications Satellite Organization (89 Countries)*

Afghanistan	Lebanon
Algeria	Liechtenstein
Argentina	Luxembourg
Australia	Malagasy Republic
Austria	Malaysia
Barbados	Mauritania
Belgium	Mexico
Bolivia	Monaco
Brazil	Morocco
Cameroon	Netherlands
Canada	New Zealand
Central African Republic	Nicaragua
Chile	Nigeria
China, Republic of	Norway
Colombia	Oman
Costa Rica	Pakistan
Cyprus	Peru
Denmark	Philippines
Dominican Republic	Portugal
Ecuador	Saudi Arabia
Egypt, Arab Republic of	Senegal
Ethiopia	Singapore
Finland	South Africa
France	Spain
Gabon	Sri Lanka, Republic of
Germany, Federal Republic of	Sudan
Ghana	Sweden
Greece	Switzerland
Guatemala	Syrian Arab Republic
Haiti	Tanzania
Iceland	Thailand
India	Trinidad & Tobago
Indonesia	Tunisia
Iran	Turkey
Iraq	Uganda
Ireland	United Kingdom
Israel	United States
Italy	Vatican City State
Ivory Coast	Venezuela
Jamaica	Vietnam
Japan	Yemen Arab Republic
Jordan	Yugoslavia
Kenya	Zaire, Republic of
Korea	Zambia
Kuwait	

*As of May 8, 1975.

● COMSAT would furnish technical and operational management services to INTELSAT under contract for six years after entry into force of the Definitive Arrangements.

● A Secretary General would be responsible for the administrative and financial aspects of the management of INTELSAT.

● Both COMSAT and the Secretary General would be responsible directly to the Board of Governors and neither would exercise any supervisory role over the other.

● The Secretary General would be superseded on December 31, 1976, by a Director General who would be responsible thereafter for all management services.

The Definitive Arrangements provide that at the end of COMSAT's six-year contract, the Director General shall let a contract to one or more competent entities for the technical and operational functions to the maximum extent practicable, with due regard to cost and consistent with competence, effectiveness, and efficiency.

Both the International Agreement and the Operating Agreement contain provisions for their amendment. It became apparent that these nicely balanced provisions in the Agreements might prove to be lost labor if the amendment process was not made reasonably arduous. The United States proposed that the amendment process should require the final approval of a substantial majority of the Parties to the particular agreement, who also represent a substantial majority of the investment in INTELSAT. In almost the final hours of the conference a compromise was reached, pursuant to which an amendment could enter into force upon the final approval of either a minimum of two-thirds of the Parties, who are at least two-thirds of the investment shares, or of 85% of the Parties without regard to investment, providing that the necessary approvals were forthcoming within a fifteen-month period of time. This compromise, making steep but not impassable the path to amendment, was accepted by the conference after several cliff-hanging days of crisis.

You can readily see the problems that were involved in putting this consortium together. I'm very pleased to report that regardless of the complications, regardless of the problems that we had in putting it together, there exists today a consortium consisting of 89 separate nations (Table 28) all pulling in the same direction, all working together. The bills are put out once every thirty days, and we don't have a single one of the 89 nations in arrears in its payments. The system (Figure 113) operates right now to an efficiency of 99.94% and probably gives us the finest telephone and telecommunications system that you'll find anywhere.

SECTION 4: GOVERNMENT ACTIVITIES

1. Summary of Problems of Greatest Urgency

Robert F. Freitag
NASA Headquarters

As we take our first, real, halting steps in space, the ability to provide a proper focus is one of our greatest problems. The theme of the activities described in this Conference serves that purpose; i.e., to find a course of action to achieve "permanent occupancy of space".

In the first sixteen years of the space age, progress has been rapid. We have made great strides toward understanding the environment, we've adapted man to be able to make short excursions into space and to perform useful and effective work. We have achieved easy access into space for men and machinery and, with the advent of the space shuttle near the end of this decade, we will achieve a major goal for easy return from space for men, women, and materials. At the same time, we hope to improve the efficiency of space operations so that their cost effectiveness will be better. The next major goal is to achieve permanent occupancy of space and from there move on to many of the things that have been described in this Conference. Much attention is being devoted to this goal by the NASA in the United States, and by the Soviet Union. The introduction of the European Space Agency into this field by their selection of the Spacelab as their first major contribution in the exploration and occupation of space is a significant step.

It may seem conservative for us to suggest (see the next paper) that we select as our interim goal, our first step in this direction, a four to twelve-man space station by the 1985-1987 period. Studies and technology for developing ways and means of moving in this direction are underway, but certainly they are not at a level at this time that will assure early success on a large scale. The concepts and approaches for building and operating a near-Earth-orbit space station on a moderate scale are well known, certainly for an Earth-supported station. The needs for achieving a lunar base are somewhat less defined, but the results of the Apollo program give us a sound basis for design efforts in that area. the underlying base of space transportation is perhaps the most advanced system under development. Yet in all these cases, we're depending upon a backlog of technology that evolved in the Saturn/Apollo effort of the late 1960's.

It is the area of supporting technology, involving new concepts of engineering, biological, and sociological systems, that we might approach with the greatest caution. Today's expansion into space does not possess the great backlog of technology that we had, say, in the early 1950's, when we embarked on the ballistic missile program, the early space booster program, and the design of spacecraft. That unusual coincidence of the early '50's, which saw several dramatic breakthroughs or maturing of research that brought us the transistor, the inertial platform, the digital computer, high-performance rocket fuels, and high-temperature materials, and at the same time the bold willingness to undertake the management of large enterprises such as Apollo—that unusual coincidence is not with us today on the same scale. The past year—the past ten years—has seen somewhat of a regression of this bold research. In fact, if anything, we are often confronted with "negative breakthroughs", such as the problem of utilizing today's technology in the framework of environmental constraints or the essential need of conserving resources.

These constraints, however, could turn out to be new needs which will stimulate space research in the areas of the special concern of this conference. Perhaps one of the avenues of great urgency that confronts this conference will be to identify and to stimulate those technological courses that will yield the greatest leverage to the ultimate goal of permanent occupancy of space. The one fundamental problem that every enterprise of this nature faces is getting the program approved. Obviously there is no pat formula, else we would be inundated with projects of great merit that have been unable to get the blessings of the omnipotent "they" who approve these sort of things. It is difficult to predict the magic chemistry that brings about a "critical mass" or a national consensus, but there are certain patterns that seem to hold promise of success.

I have observed that the most common element that brings support to large space programs is the simple and objective characteristic: "Why is it good for the U.S.A.?" There is no single ingredient of this characteristic; it can be national security (as differentiated from national defense), or economic strength, or national growth, or world prestige, or world leadership, or response to a threat, whether it be economic well-being or basic survival. These factors tend to transcend the more materialistic consideration insuring a good return on an investment. Still, most programs do have to show good, practical benefits to the man on the street; if they do, they will have an advantage over other programs which support, for example, the simple goals of technology advancement or scientific venture. In recent years, there has been an increasing trend to put emphasis on cost benefits, as in the case of the shuttle, resulting in the need to justify ultimate uses; unfortunately, like the case of the airplane, these ultimate uses can never be predicted accurately.

In the decades of the '60's there was a great spirit of adventure attached to the space program. The elements of exploring the unkown, pressing back to the frontiers – technological, physical, and sociological – received strong support. There was also a vicarious attachment that was stronger than most people realized. However, as competition for national resources became keen, payoff benefits became dominant. Today, still, there are the same elements of experimentation and exploration; for example, the Apollo-Soyuz test project, in which dramatic new efforts in international cooperation are being pioneered and tested. In space transportation, where the western European nations are sharing a major element of this venture, we find another manifestation of this exploration virtue. It is interesting that this characteristic is appreciated more outside the United States than within; perhaps it's our over-familiarization with the space effort, or perhaps it's other nations' appreciation of the possibility for "One World" that space holds.

I should not downgrade the significance of the need to demonstrate practical benefits. The "higher virtues" do wear thin, and a lasting economic or sociological benefit needs to be present to sustain the effort over the long periods that are characteristic of a large space program.

One ingredient, more than any other, that has carried us to where we are today is the fact that man has been involved. Not only is man involved as an operator and a passenger aboard the spacecraft, performing all those tasks that require his intellect and dexterity, but in the broader, more humanistic considerations of mankind, he is reaching out to achieve new purposes heretofore unknown. Certainly this basic consideration is one of the points that has captured the imagination of those reviewing the propositions discussed at this conference.

One of the technical problems to be solved which we who have looked at the concept at NASA feel is quite significant is the potential for developing a closed ecological system in space. Much is yet unkown in all the areas of interaction associated with the development of such a closed ecosystem. Algorithms must be developed to define the basic supporting relationships between people, animals, plants, and micro-organisms, and to define the conditions under which this ecological closure can exist. This area could prove to be the single most demanding technology, from the standpoint of time, to be developed prior to the realization of a habitat in space.

There are two basic steps to be followed in developing the closed ecosystem in space: the significant research on micro-scale simulations on Earth, as a first step towards developing the algorithms, and further definition and actual experience with a closed ecosystem in space, either the lunar base or the construction base at L5. Once the elements of a closed ecosystem are understood from Earth-based research and experimentation/simulation, the real test will come when the ecological closure is tried in space under those conditions that cannot be duplicated on Earth, specifically the lower or artificial gravity and the severe environment. These initial facilities in space will have to provide redundant environmental areas, both closed-loop artificial and natural environments, during this "bootstrap" time period, until the ecological closure is totally understood.

It is difficult, if not impossible, at this time to predict the time period for ecological closure in space, since the biosphere within the space manufacturing facility will be at least six orders of magnitude more sensitive to change than that on Earth. This estimate is based upon the atmospheric volume per person: on Earth the post-2000 population will be eight billion; in space it will be ten thousand. The specific volume on Earth is approximately 300 billion cubic feet; in the initial space habitat it will be 200 to 300 thousand cubic feet per person. The aspects of contamination toxin must be well understood, since now on Earth, with its huge mass of biosphere volume, concerns about the ultimate capacity of the biosphere to dilute and disperse toxic concentrations to acceptable levels is gaining much attention. The definition of the ecosystem for the space habitat, with its comparatively microscopic size, will have to be very thorough to assure the safety of the initial inhabitants of space.

Lunar material transportation and collection is a second major problem. The current approach to construction of the space manufacturing facility at L5, as well as subsequent supply of materials, is based upon lunar materials shipped from the Moon by a mass launcher. This mass launcher, called a Transport Linear Accelerator (TLA), launches a steady stream of material from the lunar surface to L5. While this method provides a relatively low cost method of launching materials from the Moon, alternative methods for both launch from the Moon and collection at L5 will have to be examined; for example, more conventional space transportation systems that are refueled from lunar-produced oxygen and Earth-based (or possibly lunar) hydrogen. Both alternatives will have to be evaluated from both an operational and a cost standpoint. We should also consider other alternate mass transport, such as fusion-driven transports or laser-powered rockets, as Kantrowitz has suggested.

Materials processing, discussed in several previous papers, is one area that will demand substantial effort, not only to develop the technologies for producing materials suitable for space habitat construction, but also the type and location for the processing facility. The purpose for the processing operation is to minimize the resupply requirements from Earth and to maximize the utilization and effectiveness of a lunar mining base and the L5 construction base personnel. The location of certain materials processing plants might be dictated by the level of gravity; for example, certain aluminum production techniques could not be used in less than one Earth gravity, as has been discussed. The storage volume required for unusable slag or gangue from materials processing could tend to drive these functions back to the lunar surface. The requirements for the habitat structure demand that the technology developed for structural materials processing provide high strength-to-mass materials with a minimum of Earth-based materials resources used in the processing. The overall area of materials processing requires concentrated evaluation as early in the concept evolutionary process as possible, since these parameters will have a strong influence on the design concept and on the transportation requirements.

The development of either automated, manned, or mixed construction technologies for the assembly of large structures in space is yet another area of space habitat development that has at best a marginal base to start from. The development of these technologies will proceed either through programs of large-structure assembly in low Earth orbit, to gain experience to be used in the assembly at L5, or through potentially longer-range assembly programs at L5. Significant design and development activities will be required to define the assembly techniques and the operational system requirements for the assembly of the habitat.

Another significant area is the design of the habitat: cylinders, connecting structures, mirrors, etc. It is very important to understand the basic system; that is, much better understanding is needed of the numbers and types of specialized machines and devices required to construct and operate a permanent facility in space without dependence on the industrial capacity and resources of the Earth. Definition is required of assembly yards, docks, and other specialized space bases and stations which will be necessary to develop, fabricate, and assemble the tools and machines needed to construct a self-sustained manned facility in space. These tools include, of course, the computers and computer software which have been discussed in previous papers.

One of the more significant aspects to consider is the habitat structural design requirements. These will be very critical throughout the entire system; certainly the atmospheric pressure and the gravity levels chosen for the habitat are two of the most important design drivers of the entire habitat concept. Serious concerns must be raised about the proposed use of pure oxygen in the initial habitat. The low atmospheric pressures afforded by the use of oxygen is attractive, as is the lack of need for transporting nitrogen from Earth, but the use of pure oxygen for an atmosphere is unacceptable from long-term physiological and safety stand-points. Atmospheres using nitrogen can also be at low pressures – 7 to 8 psi – and are far safer. Further, the selection of both pressure and gravity levels may be dictated by manufacturing or other activities within the habitat.

A much better understanding needs to be developed of the genetic effects of increased radiation dosage over long periods of time and of the detailed shielding requirements implied. This could be done on Earth or in low-altitude orbits, but again, is such a long-range experiment that it clearly paces any commitment to full-time space activities.

A few comments on the status of current activity are appropriate. Figure 114 gives some perspective of the nation's space program over its first two decades. There have been only three major decision points in the entire continuum: 1955, 1961, and 1969. In 1955, Mr. Eisenhower initiated the program; in 1961, Mr. Kennedy moved it from the "research" phase into the "operational" phase and initiated such efforts as Apollo, the COMSAT Corporation, the two-billion-dollar-a-year defense program, and numerous other civil satellite

Figure 114. Space Activity & Planning Cycle.

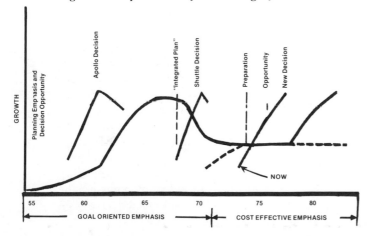

programs; and in 1969 a major change of emphasis was decided upon by Mr. Nixon, and we moved from an expensive goal-oriented effort to a more cost-effective approach which resulted in a phasedown of the Apollo exploration, the initiation of the shuttle effort, a re-emphasis of application systems, and the institution of broad programs of international cooperation.

Accompanying each of these decision periods was an intense period of study of advanced programs and alternatives. Now, in the 1974-1976 period, there is another intensive re-evaluation of our space options of which this conference is an integral part. NASA is conducting its "Outlook for Space" study, the DOD its "New Horizons 2" study, and the committees of Congress and others are gathering data and conducting reviews of all possible courses of development.

These considerations (see Figure 114) lead to the conclusion that the nation will be facing another critical decision opportunity in the 1976-1977 period. That decision will be very much more of the nature of the 1961 decision, in which the question will be asked, "How do we utilize the new capabilities that we have under development?" It is necessary also to ask the parallel question, "What new courses are open to us?" now that low-cost, routine transportation in and out of space is about to become available.

Currently, firm plans for the shuttle operational period are based only on using the shuttle essentially as a "manned booster". We must open our minds to the new potential of using the shuttle as a spacecraft. To this end, extensive study and technology efforts for means of providing habitats or permanent space stations are underway. Similarly, the means for delivering and assembling large structures in space are currently receiving an increasing share of the budget. Techniques for on-orbit operations, for maintenance, resupply, refurbishment on a continuous basis, are getting prime attention. This groundwork of systems and operations is paralleled by the necessary investigations in the life-sciences area to ensure that long-duration flight and effective utilization of man is not a restriction. However, the level of effort in these areas is minimal.

Meanwhile, feasible mission areas in this new era of space flight are getting an equally intensive look without the earlier constraints of miniaturized operations for long-duration flight or the short-lived, one-shot manned operations. Many of these have been discussed in prior papers: space power concepts, production in the weightless and high-vacuum encirnoment, and even Dannenberg's "University in Space". These are just a few of the possibilities that we will study as this decade comes to a close.

The concepts evolving at this Conference are most timely. Our collective jobs will be to insure that we are on the right approach, that our perspective remains logical, and that we are successful in bridging the gap from today's minimum level to tomorrow's necessary scope, whatever that will be.

DISCUSSION

Q. *Do you feel that NASA can generate, in house, the amount of governmental support necessary to get substantial U.S. involvement in the development of the L5 project, or must we have other additional lobbying thrusts?*

A. I believe that general support will depend strongly upon a two to three year study of all the alternatives. The opinion-making people within NASA will then begin to influence the opinion-making people outside of government. I cannot predict whether other agencies or interests will grasp this solar power opportunity.

Q. *For a demand-dependent program, do you see any other space-development projects that might have the potential of an L5 colony for recapturing widespread public support of bold exploration?*

A. There are a lot of possibilities. One which has been alluded to in this conference is a pure international space station, strictly for the sake of proving that space is a place where we can bring people together. It might be good, after the Apollo-Soyuz launch this summer, if the Russians were to come back and say, "that was rather nice, let's do something else."

Q. *Most of the activities mentioned so far could be done right here on Earth. Are there any really unique activities for space-based facilities?*

A. Space activities in order to be truly practical must achieve something that cannot be achieved on Earth. The international example that I used is a good example. We are achieving a mode of cooperation with the Soviets on Apollo-Soyuz that's beyond anything we have been able to

achieve in any of our other large-scale relationships. When they had an accident on the booster recently, they were on the Hot Line almost immediately, giving us a complete explanation. This is a degree of "opening up" that hasn't been achievable anyplace else. This is the kind of activity that has high visibility and that says to eighty or a hundred nations that international cooperation *is* possible. I have no way of knowing how much in the way of national resources should go into a thing like this.

Q. *It seems to me that there has been an unhealthy preoccupation with cost-effectiveness. The principal need of our people now is emotional, not material, and I think we need to go back to goal orientation.*

A. I think the goal of cost effectiveness was driven by many things. You must recall that in 1969, we were in the middle of the Vietnam War, with a "guns *and* butter" policy. We were spending $30 to $40 billion every year, and still trying to maintain "business as usual" at home. Everyone knew that we were riding for a fall on inflation. Mr. Nixon was obviously preoccupied with two things: end the war and stop the inflation. An emphasis on cost-effectiveness was a natural consequence of this environment. Perhaps when these decision points arrive in the '77 or '78 period we may be able to deal more properly with "the human spirit." I don't know.

Q. *The 1961 decision was based upon an emotional need: our apparent loss to the Soviet Union in technical achievement. The goal we picked was to be first to the Moon. We are suffering now from an emotional problem that relates to "guns and butter," for the Viet Nam war, a perception that we have no future, and a perception that we have been wasting resources. NASA would be well-served to find that the goal is to make things more productive. Don't you (NASA) serve yourself badly by talking about programs that involve "motels in space" or other non-productive activities rather than finding something that would meet this emotional need?*

A. I do not disagree that a great emotional need was part of Mr. Kennedy's decision, to save us "face". But far more significant was the resulting seven years of research on this new environment of space which gave us the capability to build navigation satellites, weather satellites, communications satellites, and all the other practical uses of space. We don't have that today. We have lots of opportunity, but not the backlog of new technology that goes with it. I *do* support a strong goal-oriented program, but I do not know whether the national consensus will accept it.

2. Developing Space Occupancy: Perspectives on NASA Future Space Program Planning

Jesco von Puttkamer
NASA Headquarters

The purpose of this paper is to discuss selected NASA planning aspects of potential future manned space flight missions, and their evolutionary relationship to both presently formulated near-term developments and such far-future undertakings as space colonization, space industrialization, and manned planetary exploration.

The basic question is whether we can initiate some actual work on technology right now, without being too specific about the long-term goal, and still be reasonably sure that we are headed in the right direction. It is not my intent to hazard a guess as to the needs, relevancies, or social payoff of future programs, but merely to discuss missions and early development work which I judge to be critical for the most probable missions. This deliberately naive approach therefore does not consider major uncertainties resulting from such aspects as politics, social goals, ecological and resource constraints, synergistic effects, future discounting, and nonlinear variations.

We are now entering a new era of applications-oriented space operations based on the space shuttle.

During the eighties, the space transportation system (STS) shown in Figure 115, which Davis addressed earlier, will replace the less flexible and more expensive expendable rockets in the nation's launch-vehicle stable. The space transportation system consists of three elements: the space shuttle, the Spacelab and the space tug, the latter preceded in time by the interim upper stage (IUS). The Spacelab is being developed by the European Space Agency for participation in the 1980 period.

This system will be our baseline, from which we will start our analysis. In developing the space transportation system through relatively near-term commitments, NASA is obviously preparing for a long-range future. But would the STS, in its present form, be useful to a long-range future? We will address this problem later.

To make the most effective use of space is the overall goal of the space program (Figure 116). Whatever we will do in space in the next decades, our main goals will be to understand and make best use of our Earth, to explore the solar system, to investigate and understand the universe, and to continue to provide the capability for man to operate effectively in the space environment.

But what is beyond the STS? What could the space program be like in the later 80's and in the 90's? Most importantly, will there be any goals additional to the ones outlined here?

In order to define some of the major directives underlying future space program planning and to relate them both back to current/near-term activities and forward to potential future way-stations that may have a high probability of leading to long-distance goals, we must start with an unconstrained listing of desirable future activities grouped around

Figure 115. The New Space Transportation System.

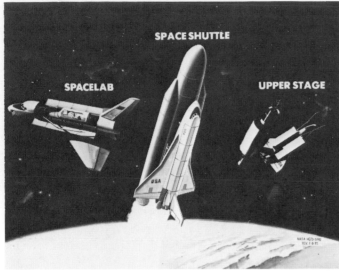

a set of postulated overall goals. By defining this unconstrained or "blue sky" type of listing, we can then add one planning constraint after the other, and this way lower our sights towards the more mid-range and near-term activities required.

This unconstrained listing, Figure 117, assumes an infinite horizon. To provide a rough ordering in time, the future initiatives are assigned to an arbitrary sequence of increasing penetration of space by man, characterized by:

• Permanent occupancy of near-Earth space

• Permanent occupancy of near-Moon space

• Full self-sufficiency of man in Earth-Moon space

• Permanent occupancy of heliocentric space

Under each of these major initiatives, I have listed some of the prime sources and stations we have studied throughout the years.

Under "permanent occupancy of near-Earth space" are listed such things as space station, space base, propellant depot and service station, and the orbital launch facility, to achieve the first goal.

Under "permanent occupancy of Earth-Moon space" are such things as geosynchronous solar powerplants, the manned geosynchronous space station or platform, the orbiting lunar station, and so on.

Under "full self-sufficiency of man in Earth-

Moon space" are the Earth-orbit space community, the Earth-orbit space city, the lunar colony, and the L4/L5 colony.

Then it goes on to such things as Mars orbiting stations, exploration of the asteroids, comet exploration, planet engineering program, heliocentric orbit installation, and even interstellar expedition, under "permanent occupancy of heliocentric space."

This, of course, is an unconstrained listing, and at this time has not yet been examined as far as technology requirements and intermediate way-stations are concerned. The total view presented by this chart becomes more useful to us if we put it into a specific time frame.

Figure 118 shows the results of an attempt to make the sequence of man's progress in space more manageable by reducing it to three major steps, or way-stations, here identified as Phase 1 through Phase 3, covering a time horizon of something like the next fifty years. The three phases are defined as those points in time when man achieves:

• 100% permanent occupancy in near-Earth-orbit space (Phase 1)

• 100% permanent lunar surface base (Phase 2)

• 100% self-sufficiency in space (Phase 3)

Each of these steps is reachable in certain sub-steps or certain sub-goals; the attainment of each signifies a certain percentage of the overall goal. These are generally S-curves and, as you know, the

Figure 116. NASA Program Thrusts.

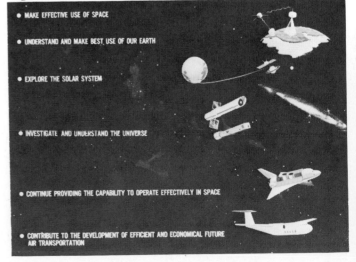

Figure 117. Future Space Scenarios ("Infinite Horizon").

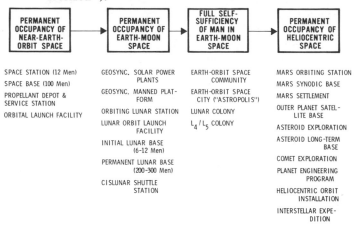

Figure 119. Evolution of Space Community in Earth Orbit.

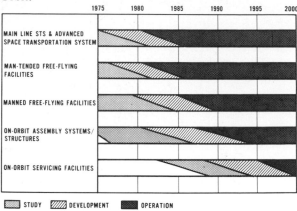

accepted theory of technology or the progress of man's potential is supposed to follow an S-curve: a slow beginning, then a rapid increase as we overcome the first initial problems, and then a flattening out as we approach the point of saturation. Then, when we reach that point, somebody else will have already developed a new S-curve and progress goes on.

Referring first to Phase 1 in Figure 118, we see that in order to attain the level of that phase, primary goals will have to include the completion of the space transportation system and its range of payloads. Other primary goals are biomedical research to establish man's physiology in space, a permanent space station in low Earth orbit, and the necessary tools and procedures to assure man's usefulness in space.

If we accept the chief goal of Phase 1, certain subgoals may be defined that might become general

program planning objectives necessary to reach the Phase 1 level (Figure 119). Here are defined five major thrusts consisting of the development of:

- The space transportation systems

- Man-tended free-flying facilities

- Manned free-flying facilities

- On-orbit assembly methods for systems and structures

- On-orbit servicing facilities such as payload hangars

The major thrusts have been redefined in Figure 120 as:

- Development of man-tended free-flying facilities, which will lead to payloads which are automated, but which are tended by men during regular visits; e.g., a large space telescope

- Development of manned free-flying facilities which eventually will lead to a space station

- Development of operational techniques, systems, and facilities for on-orbit assembly

- Development of the baseline STS/Spacelab systems capabilities and their evolution toward further systems.

Possible evolutionary steps in this process are indicated in Figure 121. Again you see the four major thrusts, now identified as systems including things like the Long-Duration Exposure Facility and the Earth Observation Satellite.

Figure 118. Way-Stations of Man's Progress in Space.

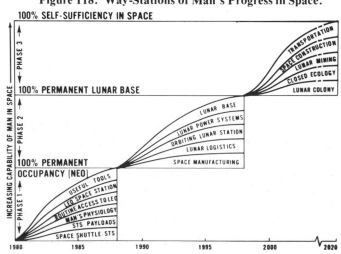

Figure 120. Evolution of Four Major Manned Space Flights and Candidate Program Elements.

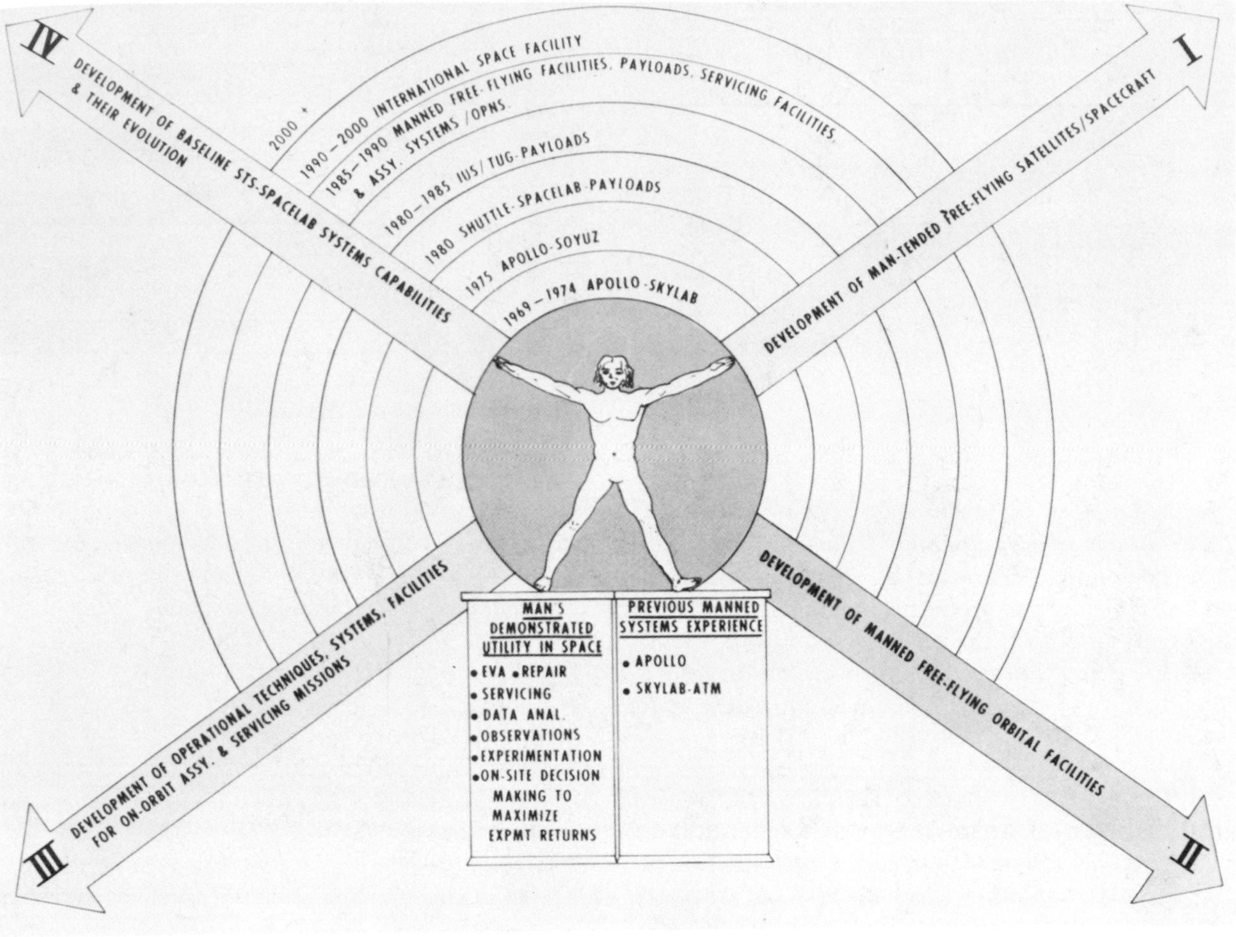

The relevance to specific Phase 1 type missions of specific space systems currently under development or planning is indicated in Figure 122. This is a cross-impact matrix in which some of the major space missions of the first phase are defined as:

- Spacecraft placement and retrieval: low orbit and high orbit

- Spacecraft maintenance and repair

- Short-duration multidiscipline lab

- Long-duration multidiscipline lab and orbital base

- Assembly of large structures

- Logistics supply and waste disposal

These are logical steps we consider as necessary but also sufficient requirements for developing Phase 1 capability. As shown here, all positive correlations are given equal weight. If the total

number of correlations at the intersections are assumed to provide an indication of relative importance of the system to the overall goal of Phase 1, it can be seen that next to the baseline STS and its extensions (SEPS and LLV), the manned orbital systems and mobility devices rate highly.

A typical modular approach to a manned orbital system is shown in Figure 123. A crew of approximately six men would be required to operate a facility of this type.

Figure 124 shows one version of an early Earth orbital facility, circa 1984, consisting of a two-man habitability module with an attached general purpose laboratory section. The shuttle is shown delivering a space processing module which will stay up there for sixty to ninety days. Also shown is the shuttle docking module, used for space station crew exchanges, and a basic Spacelab pallet in the cargo bay with an experiment of its own.

Figure 125 shows the possible evolution from the early concept toward larger and larger space

Figure 121. Evolution of the Earth Orbit Space Community.

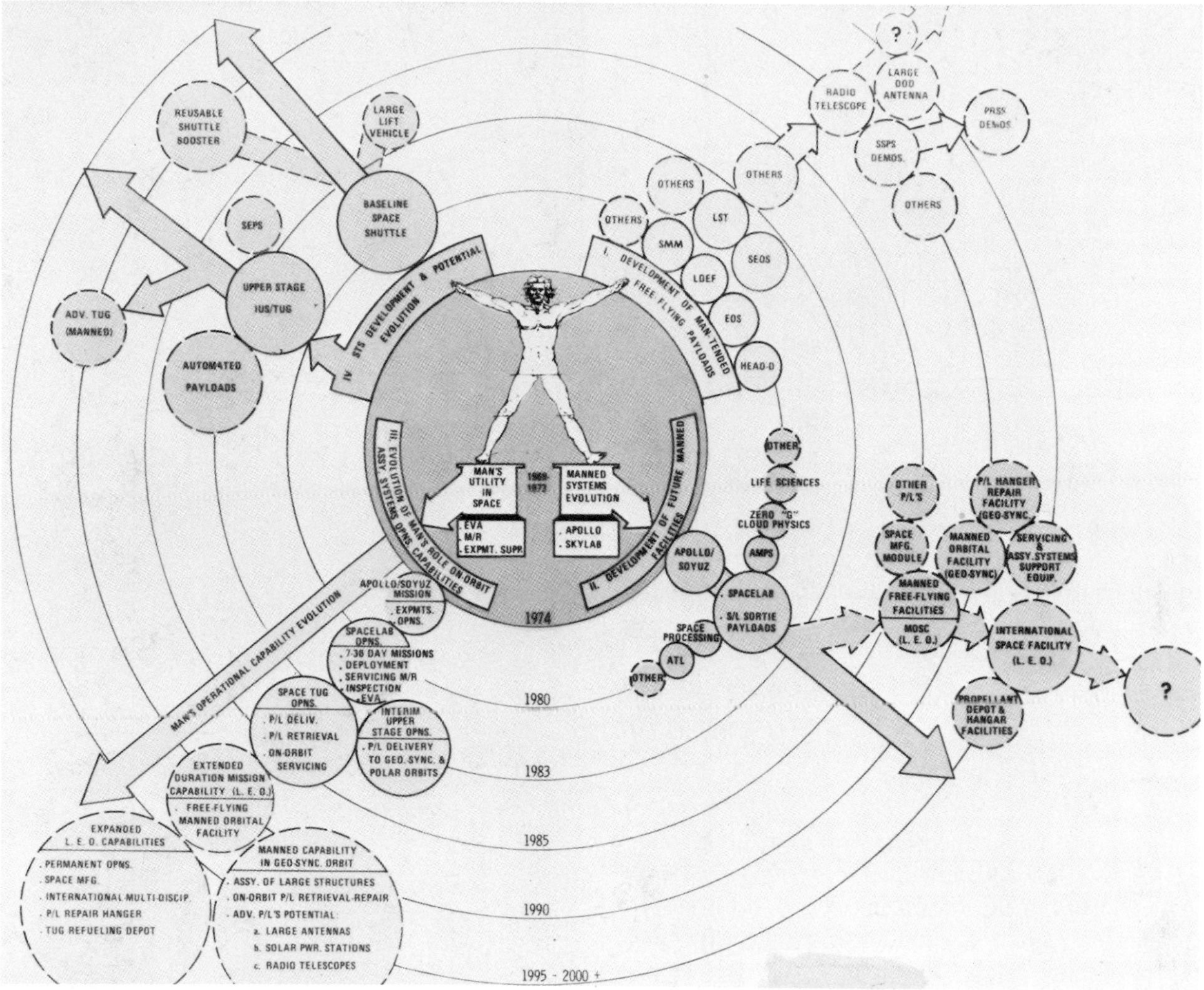

facilities. This is Phase 1 of a further evolution.

Figure 126 shows a larger facility including a payload repair hanger, two cargo modules, a large solar array for collecting solar energy, and also a propulsion system which generates low thrust with a solar-electric ion engine for boosting into high orbit. These space stations would then be useful for developing the Phase-3 thrust of men developing on-orbit servicing and maintenance capabilities.

Typical program costs for achieving Phase 1 are shown in Figure 127, based on recent projections by the NASA Marshall Space Flight Center. The space station costs reflect the development and production costs for the modules. The area labeled 'STS Operations'' includes the delivery costs for the modules and an assumed nominal experiment program. Costs to develop experiments and payloads and to fund payload-related mission support operations are not included.

Proceeding now to Phase 2, the next chief goal of the 1988-1998 period may be the achievement of the 100% permanent lunar base. Primary goals necessary or desirable to reach that capability include such disciplines as space manufacturing capability, lunar logistics and orbiting lunar stations and lunar power systems, and then the actual Lunar Base.

The potential development of space manufacturing leading to space industrialization is shown in Figure 128 based on current thinking at Marshall Space Flight Center and in industry. Starting in 1980, when the shuttle and the Spacelab become operational, we concentrate first on research and development in zero-g, then later, as we go into the 1990's this portion loses its dominance and we go into testing of operation. Later we go into limited commercial manufacturing, i.e., items of limited quantity, and then eventually, hopefully by the years 1995 to 2000, we'll go into commercial space

Figure 122. Future Manned Earth Orbit Capabilities.

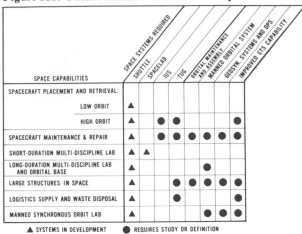

SPACE CAPABILITIES	SPACE SYSTEMS REQUIRED							
	SHUTTLE	SPACELAB	IUS	TUG	ORBITAL MAINTENANCE AND ASSEMBLY	MANNED ORBITAL SYSTEM	GEOSYN. SYSTEMS AND OPS.	IMPROVED STS CAPABILITY
SPACECRAFT PLACEMENT AND RETRIEVAL:								
LOW ORBIT	▲							
HIGH ORBIT	▲		●	●				●
SPACECRAFT MAINTENANCE & REPAIR	▲		●	●	●	●		●
SHORT-DURATION MULTI-DISCIPLINE LAB	▲	▲						
LONG-DURATION MULTI-DISCIPLINE LAB AND ORBITAL BASE	▲					●		
LARGE STRUCTURES IN SPACE	▲		●	●	●	●	●	
LOGISTICS SUPPLY AND WASTE DISPOSAL	▲			●				●
MANNED SYNCHRONOUS ORBIT LAB	▲					●	●	●

▲ SYSTEMS IN DEVELOPMENT   ● REQUIRES STUDY OR DEFINITION

Figure 123. Manned Orbital System Growth.

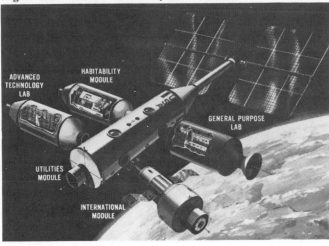

manufacturing in large, unlimited quantities.

Between now and 1980, we are doing research and development in one-g, in drop towers and on sounding rockets. We are also developing space experiments for flying on the space shuttle.

For the lunar logistics delivery, the prime element will be a lunar lander vehicle. A typical design, based on cryogenic propulsion, is shown in Figure 129, from a 1971 NASA study.

Figure 130 shows the design of an orbiting lunar station (OLS) from a previous study. It is a 6-8 man station orbiting the Moon in a polar orbit at 111 kilometers altitude, supported by logistics and resupply from Earth. Its purpose is to aid in the selection of suitable lunar surface base sites, to serve as base camp for sorties to the surface, and as an important support element in the lunar base program. For example, it would be required as a staging point for abort and rescue from the lunar surface or as an observation/communication center for lunar surface exploration traverses. You can see one of our lunar landing cars or lunar landing vehicles going down, carrying two "saddle bags," as we call them.

The next Figure, 131, shows a lunar surface base. This illustrates a construction approach for a semi-permanent outpost, utilizing basic modules derived from the Earth-orbit modular space station. These modules are carried to the Moon using an OTV, an orbit transfer vehicle. They are then assembled on the lunar surface, in this case for a crew of twelve men.

The next Figures, 132-135, illustrate various

Figure 124. Initial Space Facility Operations.

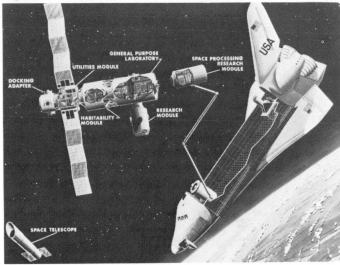

Figure 125. Space Facility Evolution – Phase I.

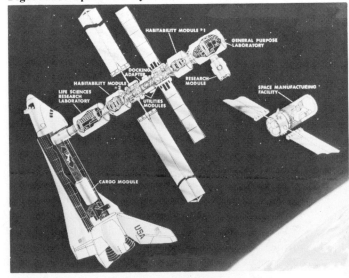

Figure 126. Space Facility Evolution – Phase II.

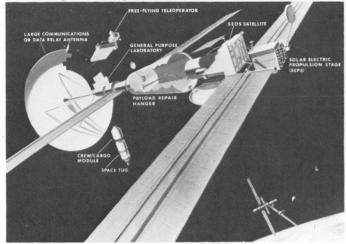

Figure 128. Space Industrialization Technology (Typical Development Forecast).

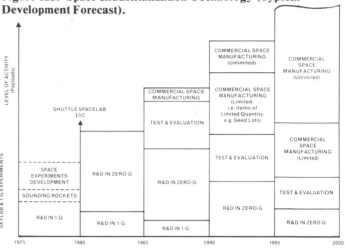

build-up phases of the lunar base into a larger colony with a high degree of self-sufficiency, utilizing lunar material for radiation shielding, meteorite protection, thermal control and construction, and extraterrestrial agriculture.

Figure 132 shows an agriculture module. Here we can see how we can bury our modules halfway in the lunar dust, which has been shown by Apollo experiments to be a perfect thermal insulator.

Figure 133 shows how the base is growing. We are using prime movers to move equipment around and we are assembling some construction covers for vessels using an eagle type approach. We might even be able to manufacture concrete on the Moon; there was an interesting paper in the Space Life Journal of the British Interplanetary Society recently.

Figure 129. Lunar Lander Tug Kilopound Propellant Capacity.

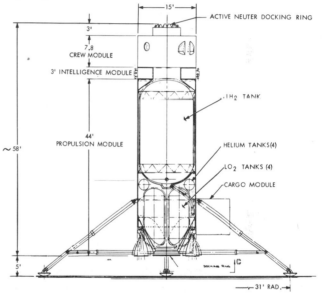

Figure 127. Total Program Costs to Reach Phase I (Uninflated 1975 Dollars).

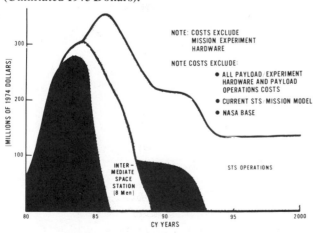

Figure 130. Orbiting Lunar Station (OLS).

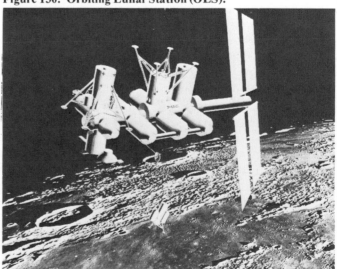

Figure 131. Lunar Surface Base: Modular Space Station Derivative Configuration.

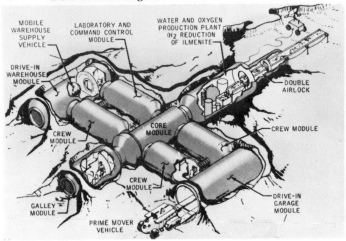

Figure 132. An Agriculture Module.

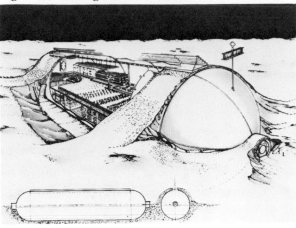

Figure 133. Lunar Base Expansion.

Figure 134 shows the base spreading still more. In the rear you can see how we are spreading out into a colony.

Figure 135 is the control center from which Figure 134 is viewed. This picture shows we have been studying the lunar base in quite some detail. These studies are available. They need some updating, but we would be ready to go without having to start from scratch all over again, if we were given the go-ahead.

The total cost to achieve this Phase 2 capability is shown in Figure 136, based on recent Marshall Space Flight Center estimates. Note that to achieve Phase 2, you first have to achieve Phase 1.

Referring again to Figure 118 and proceeding to Phase 3, we may define the chief goal of this step as man's achievement of 100% self-sufficiency in space. This new thrust would include such primary goals as a lunar colony, closed ecology, lunar mining, space construction techniques, and transportation to allow us to do our traveling out there. No cost estimates can be made with any hope of credibility at this time, but we are able to establish a rough ordering of relevance between the individual primary goals and sub-goals which will help us to clarify some of the interrelationships between the steps described up to now and their evolution towards some of the postulated distant future "megaprograms". Such a relevance tree is shown in Figure 137.

In this figure, the size of the circles is intended to give a rough indication of the relative magnitude of the effort involved in producing the system. The connecting lines, showing contributions and

predecessor-successor relationships, establish evolutionary paths of increasing functional capability. They are judged to indicate the most direct route from "time now" to the particular chief goal selected. Thus they can be assumed to represent necessary and sufficient conditions.

The "From Skylab" line coming from the past passes through the manned orbital systems concept

Figure 134. Continued Lunar Base Expansion.

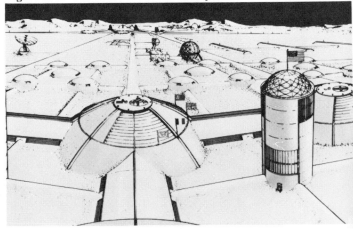

Figure 135. Control Center for the Lunar Colony.

Figure 137. Evolutionary Paths to Far-Future Space Endeavors (Relevance Tree).

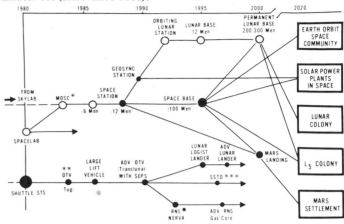

* MANNED ORBITAL SYSTEMS CONCEPT
** ORBITAL TRANSFER VEHICLE
*** SINGLE-STAGE-TO-ORBIT VEHICLE
• REUSABLE NUCLEAR STAGE

(MOSC) which is being studied at this time, goes through various stages of the "space station" to the twelve-man space station. It then branches out into some options necessary to proceed toward some geosynchronous station, which is a type of prerequisite for solar powerplants in space, the orbiting lunar station, the lunar base, and the permanent lunar base (one of the prerequisites for the L5 colony, and also for the lunar colony, if you prefer to select that option). Transportation systems would have to undergo certain evolutions. Note that the space station appears as a major prerequisite of all future options.

Having a general idea of the necessary way-stations or overall program elements, we now ask ourselves, "What will we have to do to achieve these capabilities? What are the technological prerequisites without which those utopias will always remain pipe-dreams?" Figure 138 summarizes the results of an assessment aimed at providing a preliminary answer. It lists an arbitrary choice of postulated far-future space endeavors, including:

• A near-Earth orbital space community, which is essentially a collection of facilities in various orbits around the Earth (i.e., a tourist center, hotels, maufacturing facilities) where each orbit and each sub-element of the community is in the most optimum orbit for its purpose.

• A space city, or Astropolis as Ehricke calls it, which is a monolithic type system in which you have all your facilities: tourist center, hotel, honeymoon center, whatever; all under one roof

• A lunar colony and mining base

• Solar powerplants in space

Figure 136. Typical Total Program Costs to Reach Phase 2 (Uninflated 1975 Dollars).

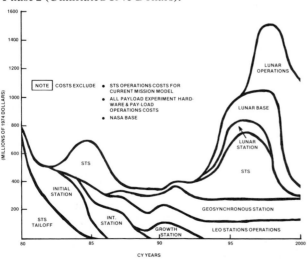

Figure 138. Typical Technological Prerequisites of Far-Future Space Endeavors.

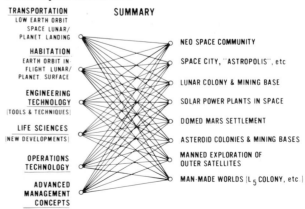

- A domed Mars settlement, which is a permanent settlement on Mars with a dome over it, such as a Buckminster Fuller dome, to protect the people from the radiation and also to keep the environment in

- Asteroid colonies and mining bases, such as the Apollo asteroids as proposed by Dandridge Cole

- Manned exploration of the outer satellites, such as the moons of Saturn and Jupiter, which seem to have atmospheres of their own

- Man-made worlds such as the L5 colony

On the left of Figure 138 are the prerequisite technologies. The figures indicates that within the set of future options inspected, nomatter which 'megaprogram'' future generations may decide to develop, the basic technology listed on the left side applies generally to all of them. Thus, one need not be too specific with regard to the particular long-distance focus in order to proceed with nearer-term technology developments. So, really, we can, for the purpose of near-term type planning, forget about the right side of Figure 138 for the moment and be pretty confident that if we go for the technologies on the left, we are headed in the correct direction and that they will provide what we are going to need eventually.

Prerequisite "transportation" for low-Earth orbit, space transportation, and lunar planetary landing is shown in Figure 139. Each positive correlation has equal weight. Eventually these, of course, would be weighted so that priorities could be established.

The same applies to the prerequisite of "habitation" shown in Figure 140. These are the enclosures in which people live. I have also included crew modules, because for some missions those crew modules become long-term habitation systems rather than transportation systems. They do mate with orbital transport vehicles in use.

"Engineering technology", Figure 141, includes everything which we need from orbit assembly and manufacturing to space processing, large volume/long distance communications, construction, orbital assembly in space or at the lunar or planet base, megawatt power systems, and advanced propulsion.

Figure 142 shows the "life sciences"

Figure 139 Typical Technological Prerequisites of Far-Future Space Endeavors (cont'd): Transportation.

PREREQUISITE: TRANSPORTATION		NEO SPACE COMMUNITY	SPACE CITY "ASTROPOLIS"	LUNAR COLONY & MINING BASE	SOLAR POWER PLANTS IN SPACE (ENERGY FROM EARTH)	DOMED MARS COLONY	ASTEROID COLONIES & MINING BASES	MANNED EXPLORATION OF OUTER SATELLITES	MAN-MADE WORLDS (L5 COLONY)
LOW EARTH ORBIT	"CURRENT" LOW-COST (Shuttle/STS)	●	●	●	●	●	●	●	●
	HIGH-VOLUME LOW-COST (Super-Shuttle)	●	●	●	●	●	●		●
	LARGE LIFT VEHICLE (Shuttle-Derived)	●	●	●	●				●
	LOW-THRUST STAGE (Ion Propulsion, SEPS)	●	●	●	●				●
SPACE	CHEMICAL ORBITAL TRANSFER VEHICLE (OTV)	●	●	●	●				●
	NUCLEAR OTV			●	●				●
	INTERPLANETARY SPACE VEHICLE					●	●	●	
LUNAR/ PLANET-ARY LANDING	LUNAR LOGISTICS TUG (People & Cargo)			●			●		●
	PLANETARY LANDING MODULE					●	●	●	

Figure 140. Typical Technological Prerequisites of Far-Future Space Endeavors (cont'd): Habitation.

PREREQUISITE: HABITATION	NEO SPACE COMMUNITY	SPACE CITY "ASTROPOLIS"	LUNAR COLONY & MINING BASE	SOLAR POWER PLANTS IN SPACE (ENERGY FROM SPACE)	DOMED MARS COLONY	ASTEROID COLONIES & MINING BASES	MANNED EXPLORATION (OUTER SATELLITES)	MAN-MADE WORLD (L5 COLONY)
EARTH-ORBIT SPACE STATION (12-Man)	●	●	●	●	●	●	●	●
EARTH-ORBIT SPACE BASE (100+ Men)	●	●						●
NEO PROPELLANT DEPOT & SERVICE STATION	●	●		●	●	●	●	●
ORBITING LUNAR STATION (OLS)			●					●
LUNAR BASE ELEMENTS			●					●
PLANETARY BASE ELEMENTS					●	●	●	
STANDARD CREW MODULE (6-Man)	●	●						
HIGH-VOLUME CREW MODULE (500 Passengers)		●				●	●	●

Figure 141. Typical Technological Prerequisites of Far-Future Space Endeavors (cont'd): Engineering Technology.

PREREQUISITE:	ENGINEERING TECHNOLOGY (Tools & Techniques)	NEO SPACE COMMUNITY	SPACE CITY "ASTROPOLIS"	LUNAR COLONY & MINING BASE	SOLAR POWER PLANTS IN SPACE (ENERGY FROM SPACE)	DOMED MARS COLONY	ASTEROID COLONIES & MINING BASES	MANNED EXPLORATION OF OUTER SATELLITES	MAN-MADE WORLDS (L5 COLONY)
	ORBITAL ASSEMBLY/MAINTENANCE/SERVICING/REPAIR	●	●	●	●	●	●	●	●
	SPACE PROCESSING & ZERO-G MANUFACTURING	●	●	●	●	●	●		●
	LONG-TERM CRYOGENIC STORAGE IN SPACE	●	●	●	●	●	●		●
	LARGE-VOLUME/LONG-DISTANCE COMMUNICATIONS	●	●	●	●	●	●		●
	LONG-LIFETIME RELIABILITY ASSURANCE	●	●	●	●	●	●		●
CONSTRUC- TION (Min. Pre-Fab)	IN SPACE (ZERO-G)	●	●		●				●
	LUNAR BASE			●					●
	PLANETARY/ASTEROIDAL BASE					●	●		
MEGAWATT POWER SYSTEMS	SPACE-BASED	●	●		●				●
	LUNAR SURFACE			●					
	PLANETARY SURFACE					●	●		
ADVANCED PROPULSION	ADVANCED CHEMICAL PROPULSION	●	●	●	●	●	●	●	●
	ELECTRIC PROPULSION (Ion Propulsion, SEPS)	●	●	●	●	●	●		●
	SOLID-CORE NUCLEAR REACTOR ENGINE					●	●	●	
	"EXOTIC" DRIVES (Laser/Fusion, Photon, Gas Core, Matter/Antimatter, etc.)					●	●	●	

prerequisites. They are very important, since we have no real handle yet on man's very long-term stay in space.

"Operations technology" is shown in Figure 143; what has to be done is to develop high-rate checkout, launch, and flight operations; to develop such things as multiple flight mission control, and so on. We are not able to do these things now; we have to learn to do business in a brand new way.

218

The last in this series of prerequisites is "advanced management concepts", shown in Figure 144. For the megaprograms of the future, management concepts will undoubtedly have to change radically, just as they have continually changed throughout history from the construction of the pyramids of Egypt and the Great Wall of China to the Apollo program and now the space shuttle.

The Apollo-type thinking will not apply to these undertakings, and even the phase program planning approach of the shuttle program may be inappropriate. In my opinion, it is wrong to compare these large programs of the future in any way to Apollo, both in terms of management approach and cost. There is simply no analog.

In conclusion, we are now ready to propose a rough program phasing schedule: Figure 145. Keep in mind that it takes eight to ten years to develop a system, that it takes three years for the budget cycle to get the go-ahead from Congress, that it also takes some time for contracting and procurement, and that those three cycles have to be properly phased and synchronized. Figure 145 therefore represents the most reasonable phasing details I can come up with.

This rough program phasing schedule starts at current (1975) activities and projects near-term (to three years), mid-range (to ten years), and long-range (to twenty years) to the far-term options beyond the twenty-year horizon. The activities are categorized as a Feasibility Study, which is our advanced study area; a Design Study, where you start drawing blueprints; Hardware Development, where you are cutting hardware; and an Operation period, where you are starting to fly.

For example, the manned orbital systems concept studies, currently under feasibility investigation, would enter the space station design phase in the near-term and the hardware phase prior to 1985 (mid-range), to become operation somewhere in the long-range time frame 1986-1995. These focuses diverge as we look further into the future, commensurate with our ability to predict. In the far-range there are the options I pointed out earlier, bringing us to the colonization of space.

Besides the space station, other initiatives that must be introduced as advanced studies in the near-term, meaning that we have to start them within the next three years, include the manned orbital transfer and lunar lander vehicles, advanced

Figure 142. Typical Technological Prerequisites of Far-Future Space Endeavors (cont'd): Life Sciences.

PREREQUISITE: LIFE SCIENCES (New Developments req'd)	NEO SPACE COMMUNITY	SPACE CITY "ASTROPOLIS"	LUNAR COLONY & MINING BASE	SOLAR POWER PLANTS IN SPACE (ENERGY FROM SPACE)	DOMED MARS COLONY	ASTEROID COLONIES & MINING BASES	MANNED EXPLORATION OUTER SATELLITES	MAN-MADE WORLD (L5 COLONY)
ENVIRONMENTAL CONTROL & LIFE SUPPORT SYSTEM, SEMI-CLOSED	●	●	●	●	●	●	●	●
ENVIRONMENTAL CONTROL & LIFE SUPPORT SYSTEM, CLOSED-ECOLOGY	●	●	●		●	●	●	●
RADIATION SHIELDING/PROTECTION	●	●	●	●	●	●	●	●
PHYSIOLOGICAL ADAPTATION PROCESSES	●	●	●	●	●	●	●	●
ADVANCED EXTRAVEHICULAR (EVA) SPACESUITS	●	●	●	●	●	●	●	●
ADVANCED EVA MOBILITY DEVICES	●	●	●	●	●	●	●	●
REMOTE-CONTROLLED MANIPULATORS	●	●	●	●	●	●	●	●
TRAINING/SIMULATION/INDOCTRINATION REQUIREMENTS	●	●	●	●	●	●	●	●
PSYCHOLOGICAL FACTORS OF LONG DURATION FLIGHTS	●	●	●	●	●	●	●	●
SOCIOLOGICAL FACTORS OF EXTENDED MISSIONS	●	●	●		●	●	●	●
EXTRATERRESTRIAL AGRICULTURE (Hydroponics, Aeroponics, etc.)	●	●	●		●	●	●	●

Figure 143. Typical Technological Prerequisites of Far-Future Space Endeavors (cont'd): Operations Technology.

PREREQUISITE: OPERATIONS TECHNOLOGY	NEO SPACE COMMUNITY	SPACE CITY "ASTROPOLIS"	LUNAR COLONY & MINING BASE	SOLAR POWER PLANTS IN SPACE (ENERGY FROM SPACE)	DOMED MARS COLONY	ASTEROID COLONIES & MINING BASES	MANNED EXPLORATION OUTER SATELLITES	MAN-MADE WORLD (L5 COLONY)
HIGH-RATE CHECKOUT, LAUNCH & FLIGHT OPERATIONS	●	●	●	●	●	●	●	●
MULTIPLE-FLIGHTS MISSION CONTROL	●	●	●	●	●	●	●	●
CONTINGENCY & EMERGENCY OPERATIONS	●	●	●	●	●	●	●	●
HIGH-RATE RECOVERY & REFURBISHMENT OPERATIONS	●	●	●	●	●	●	●	●
SPACE STATION/BASE OPERATIONS	●	●		●				●
LUNAR BASE OPERATIONS			●					●
SPACE PROCESS ENGINEERING OPERATIONS	●	●		●		●		●
SPACE CONSTRUCTION/ASSEMBLY OPERATIONS	●	●	●	●	●	●	●	●
LARGE-SCALE SPACE LOGISTICS OPERATIONS	●	●	●	●	●	●	●	●
SPACE TANKING OPERATIONS	●	●		●				●
EXTRATERRESTRIAL MINING OPERATIONS			●		●	●	●	
PERSONNEL RECRUITING & TRAINING OPERATIONS	●	●	●	●	●	●	●	●

Figure 144. Typical Technological Prerequisites of Far-Future Space Endeavors (Cont'd): Advanced Management Concepts.

PREREQUISITE: ADV. MANAGEMENT CONCEPTS	NEO SPACE COMMUNITY	SPACE CITY "ASTROPOLIS"	LUNAR COLONY & MINING BASE	SOLAR POWER PLANTS IN SPACE (ENERGY FROM SPACE)	DOMED MARS COLONY	ASTEROID COLONIES & MINING OF OUTER SATELLITES	MANNED EXPLORATION OF OUTER	MAN-MADE WORLDS (L5 COLONY)
VERY-LARGE PROGRAM MANAGEMENT	●	●	●	●	●	●	●	●
LARGE RESOURCES/ENERGY/GNP REQUIREMENTS	●	●	●	●	●	●	●	●
MULTIPLE INTERNATIONAL INTERFACES	●	●	●	●	●	●	●	●
MULTIPLE TECHNICAL/NONTECHNICAL INTERFACES	●	●	●	●	●	●	●	●
LARGE-SCALE CONFIGURATION CONTROL	●	●	●	●	●	●	●	●
LARGE-SCALE SYSTEMS INTEGRATION & MANAGEMENT	●	●	●	●	●	●	●	●
EXTENDED PLANNING "HORIZON"	●	●	●	●	●	●	●	●
LONG-RANGE COMMITMENTS (Budget, People, Facilities, Resources)	●	●	●	●	●	●	●	●

transportation concepts including the large lift vehicle and shuttle improvements, and preliminary definition work on commercial space manufacturing concepts and facilities within the overall complex of space industrialization.

DISCUSSION

Q. The bone resorption problem (calcium loss), which is certainly serious in zero-g, is probably going to be serious in the fractional g's of lunar

Figure 145. Potential Manned Spaceflight Program Phasing.

	CURRENT	NEAR-TERM (1975-1978)	MID-RANGE (1979-1985)	LONG-RANGE (1986-1995)	FAR-TERM FOCUS (1995+)
FEASIBILITY STUDY	• MANNED ORBITAL SYSTEMS CONCEPTS (MOSC) • UPRATED TRANSPORTATION • ORBITAL ASSEMBLY & MAINTENANCE	• ADVANCED TRANSPORTATION • LARGE LIFT VEHICLE • MANNED ORBITAL TRANSFER VEHICLE (OTV) • LUNAR LANDER • LUNAR BASE • SPACE INDUSTRIALIZATION	• SPACE BASE • ORBITING LUNAR STATION • SPACE SOLAR POWER SYSTEM • CONCEPTS OF PERMANENT SPACE OCCUPANCY • SPACE ENGINEERING DEVELOPMENTS	• MANNED PLANETARY EXPEDITION • PERMANENT SELF-SUFFICIENT SPACE HABITATION CONCEPTS (e.g. COLONIZATION)	
DESIGN STUDY	• IUS/TUG	• SPACE STATION • TENDING OF AUTOMATED PAYLOADS • GEOSYNCHRONOUS PLATFORM • SPACE TUG	• LUNAR LANDER • LUNAR BASE • SHUTTLE IMPROVEMENTS • LARGE LIFT VEHICLE • MANNED OTV	SPACE BASE ORBITING LUNAR STATION • SPACE SOLAR POWER SYSTEM	• MANNED PLANETARY EXPEDITION • SELF-SUFFICIENT SPACE HABITATS
HARDWARE DEVELOPMENT	• SPACE SHUTTLE • SPACELAB	• SPACE SHUTTLE • SPACELAB • IUS	• SPACE TUG • SPACE STATION • GEOSYNC. PLATFORM • TENDING OF AUTOMATED PAYLOADS	• LUNAR LANDER • LUNAR BASE • LARGE LIFT VEHICLE • ADVANCED SHUTTLE • MANNED OTV	• SPACE BASE • ORBITING LUNAR STATION • SPACE POWER PLANTS
OPERATIONAL	• ASTP		• SPACE SHUTTLE • SPACELAB • IUS	• SPACE SHUTTLE • SPACELAB • SPACE TUG • SPACE STATION	• LUNAR LANDER • LUNAR BASE • SPACE SHUTTLE • SPACE TUG • LARGE LIFT VEH. • MANNED OTV • SPACE STATION

gravity. It's going to be kind of tough to spin a lunar colony to produce artificial gravity. What do you think about this problem?

A. The loss of calcium from the bones is probably the only major concern the doctors have right now. A vigorous and extended long-term program in near-Earth orbit is necessary to give us more data. But to do medical experiments in space, it isn't sufficient to have an astronaut there; what we need is large populations of people, maybe up to a hundred, at durations up to several months. They can either be shuttled back and forth to get their total time in space, or they can be put up all at the same time and left there for several months. These trade-offs would eventually show us what is better: a large space base or a smaller space station with a lot more transportation in between.

Q. *Concerning your comment that we need not focus on L5 in short-term planning, do you feel that a long-term focus is necessary now in order to generate the government funding to support the necessary short-term planning, or do you feel that it would be counterproductive to have a specific focus on space colonization at this time?*

A. It is absolutely necessary to have long-term focuses – a whole lot of them. Whether long-

term focuses can be used convincingly to get funds is another point. The whole point of my paper is to indicate a possible way of establishing a phased approach to a long-term focus. It is, of course, just a first cut, and a pretty rough one, but you can't build a bridge without having a bridgehead. We have been working in a direction without really knowing what is at the far end. One of those ends is space colonization, as I have indicated.

Q. *If we select the L5 colony as a primary goal out of your "laundry list" and eliminate the excess baggage in the planning, how much could we compress the schedule?*

A. We *can't*. It's a minimum schedule. It's a "critical path" – the relevance tree. For *all* the programs suggested, including the L5 colony, we need the space station – the space base for a construction site – whether it looks like the one that Driggers suggested or the one I showed. A space station is needed to do preliminary developments such as space processing and medical testing. The space base for a hundred-plus people is required as a construction site at L5. A lunar base is also needed, as are the space transportation systems. The critical path for L5 is thus the one which goes from space station to space base. There are shorter-term developments for which you don't really need the space base; for example, if you want to fly to Mars, you don't need a hundred-man space base as a way station.

Please note, however, that the relevance tree I have shown is just my own opinion of critical paths. There may be alternative routes; I left them out for clarity. For example, there may be ways to go to the Moon without having to have a lunar orbiting station. You may be able to build power stations in geosynchronous orbit without having a geosynchronous manned platform first. Final decisions on which alternatives to select can sometimes come from analytical trade studies; sometimes it's just someone's opinion that makes the decision.

3.   Data Collecting Activities of the "Outlook for Space" Panel

William G. Stroud, NASA
Goddard Space Center

NASA has undertaken a year-long study called "The Outlook for Space", which is an effort to determine what role space flight might play in the American society as we approach the year 2000. It is a NASA-wide study, drawing on some twenty individuals throughout the agency, and with very strong input from external communities.

If there is anything we don't know, it's what the future is going to be like. Our actions today are severely constrained by our dim vision of the future. We therefore are attempting to identify what alternative events might happen in this nation that would affect its ability and its willingness to go into space and to associate those differences with the opportunities we have for space flight. This paper is a progress report on the study.

Table 29 lists the ground rules that were given to us by the NASA Administrator. The most important task was to figure out what space activities would fulfill our national goals and objectives. A major part of our problem has been trying to figure out where the nation is going. As you know, we are a nation of "ad hocers", and one of the things we've learned is that this may not be an adequate mode of operation.

Figure 146 is a flow diagram for the study, illustrating the strong role played by external inputs. We have inputs to identify the possibilities, the kinds of missions, the kinds of activities that we might do in space. We have external forecasting inputs: "How good will our solid-state physics be in the future? What will be our laser capabilities? What will the future environment be like? What is the public perception of future space activities?"

The basic flow here is simple: we go from "could do" (things that we are capable of doing in space), to things that we "should do" (because they, in some way, contribute to society), to what we "will do". What we "will do" cannot be specified by the Study Group, because what the nation will do will be determined by the policy, the amount of money available, the public attitudes, perceived threats, and other factors we cannot predict. The study therefore utilizes a "strategic approach", and we will deal with the future as the future becomes more and more clear. At that point you consider the "should do", and also the money, policies, thrusts, etc., to come up with the potential future programs. There will ultimately be a single program coming out of this activity.

Table 30 shows what kind of people and organizations we talked to; where our external inputs came from. We talked to all our bosses; that's obviously a necessary step. Then, NASA has a whole family of advisory activities: it has a Space Program Advisory Committee (SPAC), it has a Space Application Board (SAB) which is a part of the National Academy of Engineers, it has a Space Sciences Board (SSB) which is a part of the National Academy of Sciences and so on, and it has a Research and Technology Advisory Council (RTAC). NASA has always had lots of advisors, and we've consulted with them.

We also went to aerospace industry segments and

Table 29.   Study Objectives

- To relate goals and objectives of civilian space activities to national goals and objectives

- To develop unconstrained listing of desirable and practical civilian space activities

- To group activities around goals, objectives, and themes

- To define R&D tasks required by potential commercial and operational uses of space

- To identify social and economic national challenges which can benefit from space

What directions should the U.S. take in the civilian use and exploration of space in the next 25 to 30 years? Why? How?

other industrial input; Dr. Fletcher sent out some fifty letters to fifty different industrial organizations, soliciting their views.

We brought some of the futurologists in to help us figure out what the future is going to be like: Hudson Institute, The Futures Group, Forecasting International, and other well known organizations. We talked with about a hundred specific individuals: Gerard O'Neill, George Field (*Science*), Barney Oliver about CYCLOPS, Joshua Lederberg about the strategies or search for extraterrestrial life, and so on. Our basic format was to have the Study Group meet with these individuals.

We had an intensive and stimulating seminar at the Hammersmith Farm in Newport, Rhode Island, to which we brought some thirty people from all fields in an effort to determine their opinions of the world's problems and the way in which the world might evolve. We had people from Erickson of Yale, the psychologist who is interested in youth attitudes and values, practical physicists who had been working in the space program for some time.

We also drew on the Hudson data base, which is

Figure 146.   Outlook for Space: Study Approach.

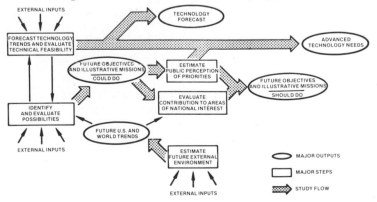

enormous. They subscribe to some one hundred and fifty polls and surveys, starting with Gallup and Harris. We also ran some of our own. We had Oklahoma State University poll some fifteen thousand high school and college students throughout the country to get their attitudes on what the challenges are that lie before the country and what role they see for space flight. We even ran some local polls in high schools in the Washington area, both inner-city and suburban.

The hierarchy we are using in the study is based on some thirteen themes for potential space activity. Figure 147 shows one of the themes: The Production and Management of Food and Forestry Resources. One particular objective within that theme would be to have space capability of providing global crop yield predictions.

We asked segments of the public to evaluate the contributions that that specific activity – a Global Survey of Crop Yield Predictions – would make to human knowledge, the exploration of the unknown, basic needs of the individual, national vitality, basic needs of humanity, national prestige and self-esteem, and opportunities for international cooperation. These are the categories of human needs or human interests as we have drawn them from our discussions with the various segments of the public.

The various segments of the public, listed on the left side of Figure 147, have been ourselves, the Study Group; Congress, as perceived by our Congressional Relations Office; and the public, as perceived by our Public Information Office. The Hudson data base was able to provide synthetic input from the academic estate; the responsible center, which makes up most of the bureauocracy; the provincial leaders, who are the mayors of our cities and the governors, and so on. Then we had the Oklahoma State University survey and the local high school surveys.

In this particular activity, there is almost unanimous agreement that the ability to conduct Global Crop Surveys would be a major contribution to the basic needs of humanity – food, shelter, etc.

Before I give a sample of the kinds of results that we are coming up with by using this type of analysis, which are in this basic format, I want to look at the Oklahoma State University survey (Table 31). This survey is interesting because it was supplemented by an enormous volume of individual remarks and comments that we received from the students, which give considerable insight into the thought that the students put on it. In their priorities of future national challenges, space comes out pretty low in their set of values.

In terms of priorities for space itself, for the next ten years, they are oriented practically: Earth resources, international understanding, defending our nation, developing space stations to manufacture materials, and, of course, understanding weather. There was strong rejection of the idea of monkeying with the environment, and no sympathy at all for shipping men out to Mars.

Table 32 shows the complete matrix of themes and specific activities versus the areas of national interest or benefit. Without any pretense that this is definitive at this time, we've attempted to identify objectives and rank them in priority in terms of their impact on the various aspects of national interest. This approach has generated some controversy, because people don't like to have somebody else set priorities for them and this chart, to a certain extent, does that.

The first theme in Table 32 has already been mentioned: Production and Management of Food and Forestry Resources.

The other themes are Prediction and Protection of the Environment, with all of the weather, climate and stratosphere activities; Protection of Life and Property; Energy and Mineral Exploration; Transfer of Information; Use of Environment of Space for Scientific and Commercial Purposes; Improve the Quality and Availability of Health Care; Earth Sciences; The Nature of the Universe (galaxies, quasars, expansion, nature of gravity, etc.); The Fate of Matter; The Life Cycle of Stars; Evolution of the Solar System; and Origins and Future of Life. These last few themes stress the

Table 30:   Outlook for Space: External Inputs

- NASA Program Offices
- NASA Advisory Activities (7)
  SPAC, SAB, SSB, RTAC, etc.
- Aerospace & other Industrial Groups
- Hudson Institute, The Futures Group, Forecasting International
- Specific Individuals - (100)
  O'Neill, Field, Oliver, Lederberg....
- NASA-Smithsonian Institution Seminar
- Public Surveys-Oklahoma State University; local

Figure 147. Example of Public Perception Matrix.

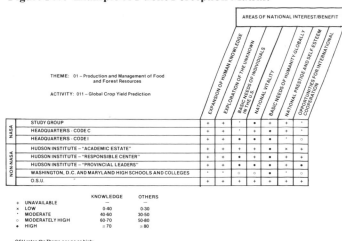

ability of space science activities to contribute to our basic knowledge, or our extension of knowledge. Some of them, like the last one, "Can we detect extraterrestrial intelligent life?" could have a strong impact, if we were to be successful in the next twenty years, on our feeling of prestige. Of course, it may turn out to be deflating; there may be a negative impact when we discover that there are people out there smarter than we are because they were able to communicate with us without our having been able to communicate with them.

Table 31.   Young People's Attitude Toward Future and Space (Oklahoma State University Survey)

Priorities of Future National Challenges

- Controlling world population
- Production and distribution of food
- Developing world peace
- Discovering and developing new sources of energy
- controlling inflation
- Protecting the environment

Space ranked 12 out of the 16 choices

Clear negative response on controlling the weather

Priorities for the next 10-20 years in space

- Explore and monitor Earth resources (*A clear first*)
- Develop international understanding through cooperative space exploration
- Explore the solar system and the universe
- Defend our nation
- Develop space stations to manufacture materials that cannot be made on Earth
- Understand weather phenomena and improve long range weather predictions from space

Ranking last were: • Modify weather
                          • Send men to Mars

223

Areas of National interest/Benefit

Legend:
- ✓ Low Contribution
- * Moderate Contribution
- + Moderate to High Contribution
- ● High Contribution

	Expansion of Human Knowledge	Exploration of the Unknown	Basic Needs of Individuals in U.S.	Basic Needs of Humanity-Globally	National Vitality	National Prestige & Self Esteem	Opportunities for National Cooperation
Theme 01; Production and management of food and forestry resources							
011-Global crop production	✓	●	*	+	+	*	*
012-Water availability	✓	●	+	+	+	✓	✓
013-Land use and environmental assessment	●	●	✓	*	*	✓	✓
014-Living marine resource assessment	✓	●	✓	*	*	✓	✓
015-Timber inventory	●	●	✓	✓	✓	✓	✓
016-Rangeland assessment	●	●	✓	✓	✓	✓	✓
Theme 02; Prediction and protection of the environment							
021-Large scale weather	*	●	*	+	+	✓	
022-Weather modification	*	●	*	+	*	✓	✓
023-Climate	*	●	*	*	+	✓	*
024-Stratosphere changes and effects	*	●	*	*	*	✓	*
025-Water quality	✓	●	*	*	*	✓	✓
026-Global marine weather	✓	●	✓	*	*	✓	*
Theme 03; Protection of life and property							
031-Local weather and severe storm	✓	●	+	*	*	✓	✓
032-Tropospheric pollutants	✓	●	*	*	*	✓	✓
033-Hazard warnings	✓	●	+	*	*	✓	✓
034-Communication-Navigation	●	●	*	+	*	✓	*
035-Earthquake prediction and warning							
Theme 04; Energy and mineral exploration							
041-Solar power	✓	●	*	*	*	*	✓
042-Power relay	●	●	✓	✓	✓	✓	✓
043-Hazardous waste disposal	●	●	*	+	*	✓	*
044-World geological atlas	✓	●	✓	*	*	✓	✓
Theme 05; Transfer of information							
051-Domestic communications	●	●	+	●	*	✓	✓
052-Intercontinental communications	●	●	●	+	+	✓	
053-Personal communications satellite	✓	●	*	*	✓	✓	✓
Theme 06; Use of environment of space for scientific and commercial purposes							
061-Basic physics and chemistry	*	●	✓	*	✓	✓	✓
062-Material science	*	●	✓	+	✓	✓	✓
063-Commercial inorganic processing	✓	●	*	+	✓	✓	✓
064-Production/isolation of biologicals	*	●	✓	*	*	✓	✓
065-Commercial processing of biologicals	✓	●	*	*	✓	✓	✓
066-Effects of gravity on terrestrial life	+	●	✓	✓	✓	✓	*
067-Man living and working in space	*	✓	✓	✓	✓	*	*

Areas of National interest/Benefit

✓ Low Contribution
* Moderate Contribution
\+ Moderate to High Contribution
• High Contribution

	Expansion of Human Knowledge	Exploration of the Unknown	Basic Needs of Individuals in U.S.	Basic Needs of Humanity-Globally	National Vitality	National Prestige & Self Esteem	Opportunities for National Cooperation
Theme 07; Improve the quality and availability of health care							
071-Physiology and disease processes	*	•	✓	✓	✓	*	*
072-Disease carrying insects	✓	•	✓	✓	*	*	+
Theme 08; Earth science							
081-Earth's magnetic field	*	•	✓	✓	✓	✓	✓
082-Crustal dynamics	*	•	✓	✓	✓	✓	✓
083-Ocean interior and dynamics	*	•	✓	✓	✓	✓	*
084-Dynamics and energetics of lower atmosphere	*	•	✓	✓	✓	✓	*
085-Structure, chemistry, dynamics of stratosphere/mesosphere	*	•	✓	✓	✓	✓	✓
086-Ionosphere-magnetosphere coupling	*	•	✓	✓	✓	✓	✓
Theme 09; The nature of the universe							
091-How did the universe begin?	+	✓	✓	✓	✓	*	✓
092-How do galaxies form and evolve?	*	✓	•	•	•	✓	✓
093-What are quasars?	+	✓	✓	✓	*	✓	✓
094-Will the universe expand forever?	*	✓	•	✓	•	✓	✓
095-What is the nature of gravity?	+	✓	✓	✓	✓	*	✓
Theme 10; The fate of matter							
101-Nature of stellar explosions	*	✓	•	✓	•	✓	✓
102-Nature of black holes	+	✓	•	✓	•	✓	✓
103-Where and how were elements formed?	*	✓	•	✓	•	✓	✓
104-What is the nature of cosmic rays?	*	✓	•	✓	•	✓	✓
Theme 11; The life cycle of stars							
111-Composition and dynamics of interstellar matter	*	•	•	•	•	✓	✓
112-Why and how does interstellar dust condense into stars and planets?	*	✓	•	✓	•	✓	✓
113-Nature and cause of solar activity	*	✓	✓	✓	✓	✓	✓
114-Corona and interplanetary plasma	*	✓	✓	✓	✓	✓	✓
115-What is the ultimate fate of the sun?	*	✓	•	✓	•	✓	✓
Theme 12; Evolution of the solar system							
121-What process occurred during formation of the solar system?	+	*	•	✓	✓	*	•
122-How do planets, large satellites, and their atmospheres evolve?	+	✓	•	✓	✓	✓	✓
123-How can atmosphere dynamics be quantified?	*	✓	✓	✓	✓	✓	✓
124-Origin and history of magnetic fields	*	✓	✓	✓	✓	✓	✓
Theme 13; Origins and future of life							
131-How did life on Earth originate?	*	•	✓	✓	✓	✓	✓
132-Is there extraterrestrial life in the solar system?	+	*	✓	✓	✓	+	*
133-What organic chemistry occurs in the universe?	*	✓	✓	✓	✓	✓	✓
134-Do other stars have planets?	*	✓	•	•	•	✓	✓
135-Can we detect extraterrestrial intelligent life?	+	*	✓	✓	✓	+	✓

This quick overview has not commented on where we think the technology base is going. Throughout the study, the group has placed great emphasis on "why": what are the compelling reasons for establishing an objective or a theme in terms of the space program, or how significant would be the contribution of meeting the defined objective to an area of national interest?

The Study Group as individuals (there are twenty different people in the group ranging from engineers and physicists to astronauts who have flown around the Moon) all believe that man will leave the Earth and will ultimately colonize space, provided he survives the next twenty-five years.

This attitude is not reflected in the Study; you didn't see anything about building a space station, building a shuttle, building a tug, building a colony, because those are the "hows", not the "whys". They answer the question, "How do you accomplish an objective in space", not "Why should we select this as an objective?" One impression of the Study Group is important: we feel that the first step towards the industrialization of space is the solar power approach, and that one of our objectives should be to initiate, in the next ten years, a space-based pilot solar powerplant. As far as space colonization itself is concerned, we think the question is: When will the national interest and the national means converge to make such a thing possible?

4. Planning for the 1975 NASA-Ames/ Stanford University Summer Study

William Verplank,
Stanford University

This paper is simply an announcement that the focus for studies of space colonization will shift this summer to California, as the theme for the Tenth Stanford/Ames Summer Study.

These summer studies are sponsored by both NASA and the American Society for Engineering Education (ASEE). The program basically has two goals: one is to give the participants experience in interdisciplinary design; the second is to produce a useful study. The participants are twenty faculty fellows: teachers from across the country. They consider a different problem every summer. Past projects have included the design of a manned lunar laboratory, a system for detecting extraterrestrial intelligence (that was the Cyclops report – it came out of a summer study), and other systems for monitoring air quality, synthesizing carbohydrates, and fighting and preventing forest fires. The problem to be considered this summer is the design of a system for the colonization of space.

One of the educational purposes of these programs is to spread the notion of systems engineering, which is rather well established. This concept started with some very successful courses at M.I.T., Stanford, and other universities. Initially concerned with space systems, they have, since then, developed into analyses of urban systems, transportation systems, and others. The Stanford/Ames summer programs spread the way to teach that kind of a course, and the best way to teach these teachers is to have them do a study. The

project is set up very much the way we would run the student courses; that is, we supply considerable background in terms of reading and speakers. My role before the summer consists of helping to define the problem, select the participants, and line up the inputs. During the summer, my role is more like that of a cruise director rather than a project leader; the participants are essentially self-organizing.

There is profession consultation and review, with considerable information-gathering from professionals. The study is located not at Stanford University but at Ames Research Center, where we draw quite heavily on the resources of NASA. During the study there will be several rather professional reviews, but its primary focus will be its report. It will be written essentially by the end of the summer and then edited and published, probably about the beginning of next year.

The topic of space colonization was motivated by O'Neill's *Physics Today* article, a talk that he gave at Ames, and the enthusiasm of Ames' Director, Hans Mark. We had over a hundred applications, from which we've selected twenty. We can have some influence on the way the program goes by selection of the disciplines of the participants. There will be four physicists, three mechanical engineers, three civil engineers, and one each of an architect, an electrical engineer, a computer scientist, a chemical engineer, an operations researcher, an industrial engineer, an economist, an anthropologist, and a sociologist.

SECTION V:
CONFERENCE SUMMARY

1. Concept Overview and Construction

Jerry Grey
American Institute of Aeronautics and Astronautics

Summary of the Space Manufacturing Facility Concept

The mechanism of developing space manufacturing facilities, as defined at this Conference, depends on the establishment of self-sufficient communities in space. There are two basic differences between this concept and previous "space colonization" conceptions. First, in discussing colonization in the past, people have always thought of colonizing the Moon or Mars or some other planet; the present concept is very different in that it projects the fabrication of totally man-made communities or facilities in stable orbits in Earth-Moon space called the L5 libration point. Second, the time scale discussed here is not sometime in the next century, but within the next few decades. That is, the initiation of a space manufacturing facility project could be undertaken in the very near future and, conceivably, a first-stage system might be in operation before the end of the century.

The key elements in this concept are:

• The availability of unlimited energy from the Sun

• The availability of materials not carried from the surface of the Earth at great cost, but transported initially from the Moon and subsequently from the asteroids

• The availability of a unique, beneficial environment, zero gravity, which tends to simplify and make possible many operations which are virtually impossible on the surface of the Earth

The characteristics of the space manufacturing facility as presented earlier by O'Neill is based on one important factor: that it be totally self-sustaining rather than depend on a continued resupply from the Earth. It requires capital investment from the order of perhaps twice the amount of the Apollo program up to perhaps as much as two tenths the cost of Project Independence.

It is important to put these numbers into the proper framework. The development of energy resources, which comes under the overall umbrella of what we call Project Independence, has been estimated to cost up to $600 billion over the next several decades. That is a lot of money; two tenths of that is $120 billion. On the other hand, that investment can pay off, according to some of the discussion at this conference, over a fairly short period of time.

Another basic characteristic of the space manufacturing facility is that it is not for astronauts. Although a number of highly trained technical people are necessary, the operation involves all of the skills and all of the characteristics of a somewhat advanced community that you might find on Earth. The system concept, further, over a long period of time, could act as a major source for population expansion for the Earth. In fact, in some of the more optimistic projections, space

231

habitats could serve to drain excess Earth population into the indefinite future.

Figure 1, cited previously by O'Neill, shows the general characteristics of the "Model 1" habitat. It consists of a cylinder approximately 1,000 meters long and 200 meters in diameter, with a collector for solar energy at one end and a powerplant to develop the energy. The hinged mirrors reflect sunlight into the cylinder through three large glass openings. The land areas of the habitat are on the solid portions of the cylinder. The cylinder is always aligned facing the Sun, so there is energy available continuously. The mirrors can be opened or closed to create artificial sunrise and sunset as they might appear on the surface of the Earth. In order to counteract some of the forces (Coriolis, etc.) caused by the cylinder's rotation, which generates gravity at the inner surface in a similar manner to that of prior space station concepts, each habitat unit would be composed of two such cylinders connected by tension cables and compression towers to balance out the forces.

Figure 2, also cited previously by O'Neill, shows what the interior might look like, somewhat foreshortened. Living quarters are located at the full gravity position at the outside surface of the cylinder; manufacturing facilities in the lower gravity regions. The center of the cylinder is the region of zero gravity. It is conceivable that the crop-growing area could be within the cylinder, but there also are regions outside the cylinder with their own crop-growing areas. The main point is, however, that this is a potential Earth-like environment in space. It can be as Earth-like as the colonists or inhabitants wish: if they prefer, for example, a four-hour day, that's possible; if they'd rather have a twenty-six-hour day, fine; if they like the twenty-four-hour day that we are used to, this can be arranged too. All the options are available and can be exercised as desired.

Figure 2 corresponds to O'Neill's so-called Model 1, the first habitat. Subsequent habitats could be much larger. Model 1 is designed for ten thousand people in two cylinders; the others can be much higher. The living density, the limiting factor, can be kept much more favorable than in the more crowded areas on Earth. In summary, space habitats are comfortable.

Science fiction? Perhaps. However, keep in mind that man requires three key elements: land – room to live; energy – one of the most important aspects of all life; and materials – to convert into the necessities and the luxuries of life. In space habitats, there is, literally, an infinite amount of available land. It will be costly initially, but eventually relatively inexpensive. The land is simply the land area of the cylinder. There is room in the stable L5 and L4 orbits for literally millions of habitats of this type. Land is available in virtually infinite quantity.

Energy is available in space in much larger amounts than on the surface of the Earth. In space, the insolation – solar energy – is approximately six times that available in July in Arizona; fifteen times that in middle America, and twenty times that in Boston. It streams, wasted, through space in these regions until utilized.

Finally, materials. The Moon has an enormous resource of the necessary materials for construction and sustenance of these habitats. With some reasonable projection, the cost of getting them is a fraction of that of raising them from the surface of the Earth. Initially, the Moon is a large resource, but over a long period of time, if we talk about tens or hundreds of millions of habitats, the asteroids form a virtually inexhaustible source of all the materials that are available on Earth.

There is one point that O'Neill mentions later, but which I think is necessary to bring out at this time: to make these colonies self-sustaining, they need some sort of continuing commercial communication with the Earth. There are products developed and made on the Earth which will be very useful or even necessary: generally objects of small mass but nevertheless valuable in trade. Therefore, the colonies should have their own products to trade, and produce for them a favorable balance of payments. The obvious product at the moment is energy: energy which, available in space in virtually unlimited quantities, can be sold to the Earth in exchange for whatever trade goods the colonies need or want.

Background

The background of the space manufacturing facility is not extensive, but it does go back far in time. The Russian astronautical scientist, K. E. Tsiolkovski, was probably the first to propose this concept in its current form. The bulk of current data comes from O'Neill's extensive and competent studies of the various characteristics discussed at this Conference.

In the historical sense, it is interesting to note that Arthur C. Clarke is known for his almost uncanny ability to predict future developments. For example, in 1945, twelve years before Sputnik, he had postulated in some detail the synchronous

232

communications satellite, the INTELSAT system discussed earlier by Rauschenbach. At about the same time that O'Neill was formulating the present space colony concept, Clarke wrote and published a fiction book called "Rendezvous with Rama". The characteristics of his habitat, which was not built on Earth, were very similar to those that O'Neill had postulated independently. It is interesting to see what will come in the future.

Goals of This Conference

Of the goals that O'Neill set up for this conference, some were quite ambitious and have not been achieved. They are, however, worth repeating in this summary:

(1) Search for problems so fundamental as to invalidate the entire concept

(2) Identify steps which have the largest elements of uncertainty about them and therefore require the greatest effort and further study

(3) Identify elements which are uncertain but which could be brought to a much higher degree of certainty by a relatively modest additional effort. These may be candidates for the earliest attack by additional but modest research efforts

(4) Bring together vital pieces of information from fields which have up to now been isolated

(5) Look for ways, not thus far explored, by which savings in time or cost of habitat construction or manufacturing processes could be made

(6) Explore ways by which, in spite of our imperfect human institutions, the construction of the first space community could be realized

(7) Identify intermediate steps in engineering development which could lead toward a space manufacturing facility while also serving other purposes

The two ground rules for this conference have been the following:

(1) To think in terms of an early time scale, which, given adequate priority soon enough, could see the first space manufacturing facility in place before the end of the century

(2) To restrict discussion to existing technology; that is, processes and materials which already exist or which can be proven feasible on the

basis of straightforward engineering practice

This latter ground rule is perhaps the key element which makes this concept of considerable interest to practical engineers like myself. Neither in O'Neill's prior publications nor in the conference discussions have I seen any basic barriers to the concept as proposed. I foresee difficult and challenging engineering problems, but it has yet to be shown that the concept is not feasible. That, I think, is perhaps the most significant conclusion of this Conference.

Construction

There are three needs for the construction of the first Model 1 space manufacturing facility: materials, energy, and the transportation systems required to get the hardware into the right place.

It is estimated that 98% of the materials requirement will be available from the surface of the Moon. Only 2%, and possibly less, must be transported from the Earth.

What is on the Moon and how do we get it? Heppenheimer discussed a concept called a "mass driver", a method postulated many decades ago, but nevertheless a novel method in today's environment, for getting raw materials from the surface of the Moon to the L5 location. Criswell talked about the lunar materials themselves; what is available, in what quantities, and how we can get at them. Drexler discussed the interesting possibility of utilizing the asteroids in subsequent operations.

The question of putting a "construction shack" in space for people to work from (basically a space station of the type with which we are familiar) in order to build the habitat itself, was discussed in some detail by Driggers. The primary transportation requirement – the launch vehicles necessary to lift the two percent of mass from the Earth – was discussed by Davis. Kantrowitz proposed the novel and interesting possibility of using lasers to power some of the ground-based rocket engines. Tischler discussed transportation in space: once we have gotten payloads off the surface of the Earth into low Earth orbit, how we get back and forth to the Moon, L5, and geosynchronous Earth orbits.

Transporting materials from the Moon was the first of these topics raised at this Conference. The initial thought was to use rockets; we know how to build them, we've put them on the Moon, we have launched them from the Moon. However, when one begins looking at the numbers, rockets turn out to be a rather difficult problem. They are massive, the tankage is large, they turn out to be expensive (in dollars per kg launched), and further, the rocket exhausts of propellants available on the Moon, over a period of time, would not only contaminate the Moon, but would create an atmosphere around the Moon – an atmosphere of not very pleasant gases at that. As a result of these considerations, but primarily of cost, the concept of using conventional rocketry has been more or less discarded.

The proposed concept is that of a "mass driver." Arthur Clarke postulated this kind of a device back in 1950: it is simply a linear induction motor. It has been used here on Earth for driving high-speed trains. It can readily be adapted, using magnetic suspension on a long rail, to throw chunks of lunar rock at L5. Although that concept is novel, the basic technology is quite well known. The linear induction motor is operating in many places in the world today over much longer tracks than we need to discuss here. The magnetic suspension concept has been developed to a fairly high degree of preliminary engineering refinement. The problem comes in applying it to the throwing of rocks from the Moon several hundred thousand kilometers away to the L5 location.

The "mass driver" for this application would consist of a long track, aligned in the proper direction in two dimensions in the proper plane of the orbit you want to throw rocks in to get them to L5. It might be a number of kilometers long, but in the lunar environment that is probably not a problem. There are, of course, some engineering problems to be solved.

The vehicle to carry the payload consists of a bucket mounted by magnetic suspension on the track, forming a linear synchronous motor. The payload consists of material mined from the Moon and mechanically refined, wrapped up and put inside a "burlap bag" (which might really consist of an aluminum net) placed inside the bucket. The bucket is then accelerated electromagnetically along the track and releases the payload off the end at a speed of about 2400 meters per second, which is the velocity necessary to reach the L5 location.

One problem is that of aiming. We aim spacecraft very well, but we can do that because we have a very expensive device on board called a mid-course correction system, meaning that when we are halfway there, we take a look and squirt out enough gas in the proper direction to steer the spacecraft where we want it to go. For the kind of mass throughput needed to supply L5 this would be prohibitively expensive. As a result, the mass-driver

"cannon" must be aimed precisely, so that when the material reaches L5 and the big bucket which catches it, that bucket does not have to be a thousand kilometers in diameter.

The principle initial problem is to get the payloads to leave the buckets at the proper speed, which is within one millimeter per second in a basic velocity of about 2400 meters per second. That might seem incredibly difficult, but it is actually only about a thousand times better than current ICBM's, the best operational systems we now have for cut-off of velocity. And the Moon is a lot easier to work on than the highly accelerating payload of an ICBM.

There are several approaches which can be used, some novel, some standard. Heppenheimer has identified the trajectories that might be used. There is a family of trajectories which go fairly directly, called fast trajectories, as well as a whole system of slow trajectories which are not particularly applicable. One basic point is that launch must be from the far side of the Moon.

Heppenheimer has suggested a concept for obtaining the necessary velocity accuracy: mounting a series of lasers along the track with accurate timing devices to tell how fast the bucket is moving along the track at any given time, and applying successively more accurate corrections until the payload flies off the bucket at exactly the right speed. This is a novel system which has a reasonable chance of working.

The bucket itself uses magnetic suspension to sustain it relative to the track in the two dimensions necessary to carry it straight and to keep it from wobbling, pitching, heaving and rolling as it goes off the end. The use of superconducting current loops to get the very high magnetic fields necessary is commensurate with the lunar environment.

When the bag of rocks finally arrives, after its journey through space, in the L5 area, we must catch it. Heppenheimer's term for the catching device is appropriate: "the Venus Fly Trap Mode". It is a container having two swinging doors which open, allow the pellet or bag of rocks to come in and strike a strong, flexible net at the bottom. The bag breaks, and the pieces are then swept out by gas to the processing operation. The optimum velocity at which these bags of rock might reach the trap is something like 400 meters per second, which is approximately the speed of an 18th-century naval cannon ball. It can be caught, but it is a problem that does need some further work.

234

Preliminary estimates of the cost of launching materials by the mass driver from the Moon to L5 run about one percent that of the cost of lifting them from the Earth. An important number, because when you talk about 500,000 metric tons, a factor of 100 makes an enormous difference in some very large costs.

What are we going to throw from the surface of the Moon? Criswell has indicated that the requirement of 500,000 metric tons, 98% of which must come from the Moon, is in the form of oxygen, titanium, aluminum, silicon and some iron, all of which are available on the lunar surface, which we now know rather well from the Apollo analyses. The biggest lack, however, is hydrogen – necessary for water at the habitat – some 5,000 metric tons. The other lack is nitrogen, which is needed for the atmosphere – about 1,000 metric tons of it – and also, conceivably, for fertilizing materials.

At the present time, we assume that nitrogen and hydrogen will have to be lifted from the surface of the Earth. However, Criswell has indicated that there is a great deal of hydrogen in the lunar soil; it has been pounded in by the solar wind for millennia. His estimates indicate that we could get the necessary hydrogen from the lunar soil by processing about sixty times as much lunar soil material as is necessary for the basic chemical constituents. Whether or not this is feasible requires evaluation. The fact that the lunar soil is largely powder, and therefore easily handled, makes the problem somewhat simpler. Should lunar hydrogen extraction indeed prove to be practical, it would reduce almost by half the necessary load to be lifted from the Earth.

Drexler indicated that the asteroids, which consist primarily of excellent steel (95% iron, 5% nickel) with traces of other beneficial alloying elements, constitute a long-term material source for the construction of the L5 stations. We do not want to extract materials from the Moon indefinitely. First, the Moon will not last indefinitely, and second we don't want to wreck it. Ultimately, we would go to the asteroids for the very large quantities of material needed to construct many thousands of habitats.

In addition, Drexler pointed out that a single asteroid, perhaps one cubic kilometer in volume, contains enough steel to last the Earth for ten years; at $100 a ton, which is the current price of steel, that asteroid is worth $700 billion. If we postulate thermonuclear pulse propulsion of an asteroid to a high orbit around the Earth, $700 billion in revenues covers a big investment – an interesting possibility for the future. It would need, as Drexler pointed out, acceptance of thermonuclear pulse propulsion by the public, and that might not be too easy. He points out, however, that the solar wind cleans up all the exhaust debris by blowing it out of the solar system.

The basic requirement for the space station that would form the "construction shack," as outlined by Driggers, is that it hold 2,000 people – a big construction crew, but we are talking about a big construction project. The crew members stay there from six to twelve months each; the shack must last for a ten-year period. The initial postulation is a 100-meter-diameter spherical working space with a pressure of half an atmosphere of 70/30 nitrogen/oxygen: a fairly comfortable shirt-sleeve environment; that is, space suits will not be needed while working.

The system must be fully self-supporting; that is; either it includes provisions for shipping food and other sustenance from the Earth, or a farm setup is required to grow food and necessary materials on the premises. Either way, the system must feed, clothe, and house 2,000 people over a ten-year period.

Driggers has developed the conceptual space station design quite extensively, as indicated in his Figures 14 through 27. Of his various overall configurations for the space station (and those of us who have been in the space business have seen literally hundreds of possible similar concepts) the one that looks as if it will work out best is called the double-spoked "H" combination (see Driggers' Figure 14).

The general configuration of the system (Figure 15) includes a power station and two facilities in one location. Each of the facilities includes a 100-meter-diameter working sphere and the central core with living and recreational quarters.

Driggers has detailed the central core (Figure 21), showing how the whole living-quarter section rotates so that a comfortable gravitational field is maintained for living conditions, while construction is done under the zero gravity conditions.

One requirement which is very important is that a solar flare shelter be provided within the system. When a solar flare is observed, everybody goes into the shelter until the flare passes (there is always plenty of warning before the flare radiation reaches

L5). It turns out that this requires a substantial amount of mass, and several alternative possibilities to a massive flare shelter have been suggested.

Driggers has also evaluated the tradeoff which determines whether or not we supply from the Earth or by farm, by plotting the total mass requirement as a function of years of station operation. For very large total masses, as the years of station operation increase, it becomes economical to build the on-board farm. Driggers showed his results in Figure 25.

Since transportation is the single most important cost element in the system, Driggers has optimized vehicle cost against number of flights, and has concluded that a shuttle vehicle capable of launching 150 tons to low Earth orbit would be best. His recommended launch schedule requires 31 launches in order to get all the necessary material into orbit.

His overall cost summary (see Table 10) is based on a total mass requirement in the neighborhood of 3500 metric tons for a single unit. The total cost of seventeen billion dollars covers operations for ten years. This order of magnitude is probably reasonably accurate, based on our current experience.

Turning to transportation, Davis has outlined our brief history in this area. Jupiter C, the first space launcher of the United States, was an old Army artillery rocket based on Redstone technology. Ten years later, Saturn V (1969), was a fairly elaborate, vertically launched vehicle, not economical by any means, but capable of putting 125 metric tons into low Earth orbit. Ten years later, 1979, we have the space shuttle, which will be capable of launching payloads to low Earth orbit on an economical basis; that is, it's supposed to pay for itself over a reasonable period of time. Now let's discuss ten years later: 1989.

The important point that Davis (of NASA) has made very clearly is that there are no technical barriers to carrying the payloads we are talking about. The only requirement is to establish a demand for the necessary launch capability.

Davis used Figure 41 to illustrate what some of these low-Earth-orbit launch vehicles might look like: the current space shuttle, which will carry 25,000 kilograms (25 metric tons); a heavy lift vehicle, which uses the same basic hardware as the shuttle and can launch 70 to 110 metric tons in its second modification); and ultimately a low-cost

heavy-lift vehicle to carry 250 metric tons. These vehicles are based on existing capabilities – all they cost is money, not new technology.

Davis has proposed a launch facility using the existing test stands at Cape Canaveral, possibly including an artificial fresh-water lake for low-cost retrieval of boosters. His estimates of operating cost for the low-cost heavy-lift vehicle run somewhere between $45 and $110 per kg. Its initial investment might be of the order of $8-$12 billion. These figures can be compared with those of the present space shuttle, which will probably have an operating cost over $650/kg, six to eight times as much, and an initial cost in the neighborhood of $6 billion.

The concept of using laser propulsion, as presented by Kantrowitz, is an exciting alternative which he estimates will cost about the same: the order of $65/kg into low Earth orbit. This is a new technology, but we can look at it as a promising opportunity.

The final aspect of the construction task is the carrying of the necessary hardware from low Earth orbit to the L5 station and the necessary material to the Moon. The requirements are to bring 10,000 tons to the L5 location (of which 1800 tons should be there by 1982, if we stick to O'Neill's proposed schedule) and 3,000 tons on the surface of the Moon.

Tischler has defined the difficulty of a space mission in terms of the velocity increment needed to get to the destination. Getting from low Earth orbit to lunar parking orbit has about the same velocity increment as getting from low Earth orbit to L5: about 4100 m/sec. It is then necessary to get from lunar parking orbit to the surface of the Moon, which is about half of that, and getting from the surface of the Moon back to lunar parking orbit, just a little bit less. About 700 m/s are required to go from lunar parking orbit to L5, and finally, 1750 m/s from L5 to geosynchronous orbit where necessary. These are important numbers to keep in mind in a general sense, not in great detail.

The method which has been postulated for doing this job is a two-stage rocket vehicle using oxygen/hydrogen propellants and two stages. The first stage achieves a very high elliptical orbit; the second stage then provides the "kick" needed to get to L5 or the lunar parking orbit, whichever is necessary. Tischler has described the necessary vehicles in some detail.

The performance of these orbit transfer vehicles is very important. Tischler has calculated that 10,000 tons at L5 requires 30,000 tons in low Earth orbit, roughly a factor of three for the propellants and the rockets necessary to get there. To put the 2,000 tons on the Moon, we need 6,000 tons in lunar orbit. To put the 6,000 tons into lunar orbit, 18,000 tons are needed in low Earth orbit. The overall requirement, then, is 50,000 tons in low Earth orbit.

Tischler made a very important comment about this number: 50,000 tons in low Earth orbit. He said, there is nothing surprising about that number; that is just one Saturn V launch a week. This statement by Tischler is a very important statement. He was a rocket research engineer in the Lewis Research Laboratory back when NASA was still NACA. During the time he was at NACA and NASA, he was more involved in launch vehicles and propulsion systems than perhaps anybody in the organization. As manager of the Low-Cost Shuttle Office, he tried to figure out ways of beating down the cost of the shuttle system. He has a long-time reputation as a practical, knowledgable, "hard-nosed" engineer. His statement has therefore convinced me that this is not an unreasonable thing to do. It is not even a high-frequency space operation, based on our projection for shuttle launches at the end of this decade. If we go to Davis's low-cost heavy-lift vehicle, it will require only one launch every two weeks over the time necessary to launch the system. Thus the required effort is really not anything extreme.

The three conclusions one would reach as a result of this brief summary are as follows:

• The space station, the "construction shack," is a conventional concept that NASA has been considering for some time.

• The launch vehicle requirement is one for which, as was pointed out by Davis, the technology is available. All we need is the demand.

• The space propulsion capability is, according to Tischler, not very much out of the ordinary.

These are very important points. Perhaps they are the key elements of the entire construction discussion.

Philosophical Commentary

The purpose of this review was to summarize the presentations at this Conference, and up to this point I have attempted to adhere to that assigned task. However, at this point, I would like to make known some of my own personal views on this subject.

I have been in the aerospace bsuiness for about thirty years. I have seen numbers of ideas come and go; I have generated a few of them myself. This whole concept of the L5 habitat is an idea whose time has come, although it is a challenging idea involving structural capabilities and other problems that we have not as yet, even in this Conference, addressed in necessary or sufficient detail.

There is a need on Earth for three things: energy, sufficient land to provide food, and a "frontier". We now have available to us a confluence of circumstances which offer a prospect for providing all three of these needs. We have already discussed the virtually unlimited supply of land and energy provided by the space colonization concept, but now, for the first time in history, we have the capability – even the familiarity – needed to achieve these needs. We have moved into space, and men have worked there – with confidence. The technology is available, and it is familiar technology. We have accomplished much of it already; all we need to do is extend it a little. It is not necessary to develop new science or new knowledge: the requirements for space colonization have been under attack in the U.S., at a $3-billion-a-year level or more, for the last fifteen years. We are familiar with the problems. That doesn't mean that they are not there; there are serious problems, but we are capable of solving them.

One of the things that is needed is a political commitment. In 1960, when President Kennedy said, "We will put a man on the Moon in this decade", there was a political commitment that made the job possible. Without that, nothing can be accomplished.

Also, we need money. Money comes partly with the political commitment, but in today's economy, it also comes from the necessity to demonstrate, beyond the shadow of an economist's doubt, that there is a long-range financial benefit. An enormous investment is needed. Nobody is going to make that investment unless it can be shown that it will pay off in dollars or human requirements. I believe that space manufacturing facilities can pay off in this way.

This is a project that the world needs and can do.

DISCUSSION

Q. In the "catcher" which receives the lunar material at L5, isn't it necessary to compensate for both the momentum of the incoming payloads and also any dispersion in their trajectories?

A. That subject was covered quite adequately by Heppenheimer, but not in my summary. Heppenheimer has suggested simply a pellet thrower, a slingshot if you like, which throws out a small fraction of the mass received in order to compensate for lunar-mass momentum.

Q. Is it practical to consider nuclear propulsion for some of the transportation requirements? Salkeld has stated in his paper that in order to achieve necessary cost reductions in the long term, a nuclear propulsion system will be needed.

A. That's a question which hasn't been resolved; I, myself, am not convinced of it but it is certainly a possibility.

Q. Is the 50,000 tons of payload you mentioned necessary to get the Model 1 space colony in place?

A. No. The 50,000-ton payload is necessary to bring the material needed from the surface of the Earth, but that is less than 2% of the mass of Model 1. That payload includes, incidentally, some very sensitive payloads, like people.

Q. What time period is suggested for transferring that payload?

A. Ten years.

Q. You mentioned up to $120 billion for Model 1 and perhaps $700 billion for bringing in an asteroid. Would you compare these with, say, the defense budget for a year?

A. The current annual defense budget is the order

of $90 billion. But we are discussing a twenty or thirty year project. $120 billion is not to be spent tomorrow, but over a 20-30-year period. In fact, $100,000 looks like a good figure to start some of the early research studies, and perhaps a few million dollars a year or two from now. If the prospects continue to look good, as they now do, the big money will begin to be spent perhaps 5 to 10 years from now.

Q. What are the real prospects for obtaining the major political commitment you say is necessary?

A. Having been involved in the energy business to a considerable extent, I believe a serious crisis in this area is going to come up very soon. Perhaps it will take another Arab oil embargo or something like that. Conceivably this could trigger the necessary political commitment. Unfortunately, though, if we wait too long – if we wait for the crisis before we act – there will be a series of tragic occurrences which will make past plagues and world wars seem mild in comparison. I'd rather see a reasonable, properly phased effort start now, at a relatively slow pace, to begin to prepare for that crisis.

Q. Was the $17 billion for the first station?

A. No, $17 billion was for the "construction shack" – the 2000-man spherical-design system. The overall cost of Model 1 is of the order of magnitude of $60 to $120 billion.

Q. What's the budget of the U.S. Department of Health, Education, and Welfare?

A. I'll hazard a guess at about $110 or $120 billion; I'm not sure. A lot of that is untouchable. To obtain the funding needed for a space manufacturing facility project, some major political commitment is necessary, and then beyond that a substantial commitment by taxpayers, by industry, or by nationalities is going to be essential.

2.   Production

Albert R. Hibbs
Jet Propulsion Laboratory

Materials

Lunar materials are primarily basaltic rocks, gabbros and breccias and a large number of lunar fines down to fine dust particles. There have been quite a number of surveys as to what minerals and elements exist in the lunar rock. The primary ones, at least from the lowlands or mares, are pyroxenes, plagioclase and ilmenite. Grodzka reviewed for us their chemical nature, pointing out that the plagioclase is a potential source of aluminum, not quite as nice to work with as the bauxite with which we are familiar on Earth. The highlands offer another source of aluminum: anorthosite. Ilmenite is a combination of iron, titanium, and oxygen. The concentrations of the above vary greatly from place to place.

We have had only a very small survey of the lunar surface, nothing like a geologic exploration. There is no way to know now whether there are mineral deposits which we might find (outcroppings of certain rich ores at one place or another). We must work with an average survey of the lunar surface. We know the composition of lunar samples to date, and we will assume that these are representative samples of the Moon.

There is no easily available hydrogen, although it was pointed out that there is surface hydrogen in the lunar fines which might be extractable, but we presume that any hydrogen necessary for processing will have to be brought from the Earth.

Grodzka compared processes with which we are familiar on Earth to those which would be necessary at L5 to handle the same materials. She emphasized the difference between bauxite, which we have on Earth, and anorthosite, which would probably be one of the best sources of aluminum on the Moon. Bauxite is fairly simple to deal with. It is alumina with water of crystallization. Bauxite, although a very good source of aluminum, is beginning to run out on the Earth. The United States imports 80% of its requirements. Aluminum cannot be extracted as easily from the anorthosite as it can from bauxite; however, there is a research program being carried on by the Bureau of Mines on the production of aluminum from this ore. There are a number of potential processes for producing aluminum from anorthosite; one, which uses sulfuric acid, seems to be inappropriate for the Moon. Another approach is to melt the ore and use electrolysis to obtain the aluminum, an energy-demanding process, but L5 will be rich in energy. The fluxes required may be difficult to obtain from lunar material, but they could be recycled. The Bureau of Mines has done some work on this already, and has done some work on close simulations of lunar material.

Titanium can be obtained from ilmenite. Grodzka suggested a method of reducing ilmenite to titanium and oxygen, a cycle involving hydrogen which is recycled in the process. It is an energy-demanding process, but again, L5 will be energy-rich.

An important point in refining materials is that we cannot simply apply unchanged, Earth-based technology to materials obtained from the Moon. The processes may have to be different. Studies will be required to decide which is optimum, given lunar conditions and given the conditions at L5.

Oxygen can be extracted by the reduction of ilmenite. There are also carbothermic reactions to obtain oxygen from many of the ores, with a cycling of methane through a system which results in the production of oxygen. Given the lunar materials, however, this is a very slow process. It can be quite rapid with Earth materials, but the minerals on the Moon are not of the type that permit this to be done rapidly.

One point that was brought out quite strongly was that the Moon is rich in various glasses and ceramics which we do not use too much on Earth. Basalt is used on Earth to make piping to carry corrosive and hot liquids, although it is not a very large technology. We use steel pipe more than basalt pipe, but the technology exists, and it would seem logical to explore at L5, where the availability of the material is great and where the energy needed to melt and shape it is available. Also, glasses have extremely important properties: glass does not fail readily under compression. Based on some of the experiments that were carried out in Skylab, it appears possible to produce in a gravity-free environment glasses whose surfaces are essentially perfect, without scratches or flaws. So we might even be able to get around the problem of tension failure of glass. Certainly it is something to be examined because of the availability of the raw materials.

Grodzka's conclusion was that lunar materials contain all the minerals we need, all the elements necessary for any of the types of processing that we wish, with the possible exception of hydrogen. Earth technology, with which we are familiar, may not be applicable to lunar materials. However, there are new technologies for use at L5, it is undoubtedly true that those technologies would be imported to Earth very rapidly, because we are running out of bauxite and we still have a lot of glass.

It was pointed out that the lunar samples are extremely variable; there have been some 15,000 non-redundant pages of analysis just on the samples we have brought back already. It has been a large project just to understand what the Moon is like; we have a long way to go in understanding the detailed structure of lunar minerals before we can really approach the derivation of metals from them in a sensible manner.

It was emphasized that energy-intensive processes, particularly electrolysis, are perfectly satisfactory, and that many of the materials necessary in the processes can be recycled. The possibility of using hydrogen to reduce ilmenite to titanium and oxygen was raised.

It was noted that the Bureau of Mines' motivation to carry out research on these rather marginal minerals was the need to utilize poor ores; they are becoming almost marginally worthwhile in Earth economics. We are really running out of the rich ores; we have to look around, even on Earth, for other processes. Development time on these new process was estimated at about 5 years.

Life Support

Carolyn and Keith Henson examined closed ecological and food supply systems. There is a time, measured in man-months in space, at which resupply becomes more expensive than self-contained farming. This time appears to be of the order of a few hundred man-months.

The Hensons' emphasis was on the possibility of very high intensity agriculture. For example, if you raise the carbon dioxide content of the atmosphere to the order of 0.1%, still acceptable to human beings, you might be able to up the production of food by a factor of ten. Also, temperature has a very strong effect. Using a greenhouse (and of course the colony *is* a greenhouse) to raise the temperature could raise the food production rate by a factor of ten.

There is also the possibility of using continuous sunlight. Fruit plants require photo-periodicity, but some grains and vegetables can put up with sunlight twenty-four hours a day and grow rapidly. Plants should be selected specifically for that characteristic.

The costs involved are largely those of the structures to support the farm. It was suggested that a tiered structure, layer upon layer, with mirrors bringing the light in, would be the most economical from the point of view of conserving both volume and mass of the structure itself. Dirt is not needed; there have been successful experiments in which plants were grown in styrofoam with nutrients added by having the roots sprayed regularly. Under these conditions, vegetables reached half of their growth in about 2 weeks, and grains in about 4 weeks. That is a very rapid growing period.

The farm can provide food for both humans and

animals. There is a lot of leftover plant waste after human consumption: stems, leaves and roots. Goats and rabbits can utilize these leftover waste products, producing rabbit meat, which has a very high meat-to-bone ratio, and goat's milk. Chickens could also be raised on garbage to produce eggs.

To provide enough protein for a stevedore, which is probably a good criterion considering the amount of work that a person will have to do on the first construction project, there would have to be about 200 kg of standing biomass, being continually recropped, harvested, and eaten. This is considerably less than the intensive agriculture practiced by various greenhouses, such as those now being built in Abodabe and Mexico, but it could be accomplished by using the concept of tiers, mirrors, twenty-four-hours-a-day sunlight, and rabbit meat.

Capillary brazing, a technique which on Earth requires reasonably fine spacing of the surfaces which are to be brazed, would be much simpler with the lack of gravity. Only certain kinds of metals are usable for brazing, and it may be necessary to provide these from the Earth.

Casting would also be simpler in a low-gravity environment than on the Earth. Casting on Earth is a problem because of the turbulence induced in the metal as it pours into the mold; turbulent eddies of the molten metal often result in rather poor forms in the resulting cast. This effect is not present in a low gravity environment.

There is also the possibility of using levitation molding; since no crucible is involved, none of the impurities which a crucible invariably introduces into a melt would be present.

A lot of work has been done in semi-solid manipulation, where an alloy is partially melted and the plastic mass is formed into the final shape. This would be particularly useful in a low gravity environment.

Ceramic melting in a zero gravity environment is easier to accomplish and makes it easier to control the final shape. Solar energy is particularly applicable to the melting of ceramics. On Earth ceramics are a problem to melt because they are highly refractory material; and the containers used must also be made of highly refractory material: containerless melting might be particularly useful in zero gravity.

The tracks for Heppenheimer's mass driver could be extruded directly on the Moon, using the semi-solid technique, from lunar materials. The availability of ceramics on the Moon would permit metal-ceramic composites with some very interesting properties, a field of technology that is just now coming into its own. Another potential high-quality source of materials, the metal in the leftover space shuttle tanks, could be salvaged. They appear to be a good source of materials for some of the early work.

Additional points to be considered are mechanisms to get rid of the excess heat produced by both the people and the farms, the possible need for a reserve food supply, in case something goes wrong, the stability of a system reduced to its bare simplicities, possible genetic drift, and the possibility for relieving the sameness of the diet by eventually growing fresh-water fish, shrimp, and clams, if sufficient water can be made available. None of these problems appear at this time to be insurmountable.

Manufacturing Processes

Some metal-shaping processes; i.e., joining, deforming, and cutting, are easier in space and some are harder, as one might expect. Welding and brazing were the two joining processes considered; the heat sources that seem most likely are electron beams and lasers. The electron beam is not gravity-sensitive, and it does need a high vacuum to work properly; it also requires that the person using it be well shielded, since there is a large production of X-rays from electrons impinging on metal.

Lasers work well in an atmosphere and a little better in a vacuum. They require much more energy than an electron beam. The possibility of cold welding must also be investigated. Adams also suggested the possibility of using focused sunlight, which can also produce welds for certain special processes; e.g., big, sloppy welds of heavy aluminum plate.

On Earth, cutting metal on a lathe or milling machine is beginning to give way to other procedures. It is a huge waste of material to cut a small item out of a big block. Even on Earth, and certainly in space, it would seem more logical to look at other ways of forming things rather than by cutting them. A serious problem associated with machining in high-vacuum environments could be the tendency for the tool to weld to the work; however, "cold-welding" might be a useful joining process. Lasers and electron beams can be used for cutting, particularly with oxygen, and high tolerances can be achieved by laser finishing or grinding.

3. Human Factors

John Billingham
NASA Ames Research Center

"Human Factors" have been defined as the entire range of human activities, all the way from physiological and medical to behavioral, including interactions of all types between people and their environment, and also governmental, social and political factors. This is a broader meaning of "human factors" than is normally recognized.

Physiological Factors

Graybiel described the medical and phsyiological problems of the rotating environment and what has to be done to be sure that people can go from one gravity to zero-g and back again. He described some of the basic work done in slow rotating rooms and other facilities to investigate the phenomena of disorientation and motion sickness caused by abnormal forces imposed in the space environment on the organs of balance and on the body as a whole. He found that the majority of people were able to adapt to the rates of rotation proposed by O'Neill for Model 1, which has the highest rate of rotation (some three revolutions a minute), and the smallest radius. Adaptation would be correspondingly easier in later models where the rotation rate is slower. These conclusions are qualified by the fact that they are based on the assumption that one can extrapolate from the rotating room situation to space space situations.

The loss of structural strength of bone, which occurs in weightlessness, is a major reason for having artificial gravity, and may require people to spend half of their time in the simulated one-gravity environment. At present, however, we simply do not know how much artificial gravity would be necessary to maintain the structural integrity of bone. During Skylab, there was a fairly continuous loss of calcium from the bones of the astronauts, not at a rate which became in any way alarming for the length of the Skylab mission, but which might well become a problem if projected for many months or years at the same rate. It is possible, however, to look at this situation from another point of view. We should keep in mind that developments could occur which would make it feasible to maintain the strength of bone without having to resort to artificial gravity. This has not been demonstrated, but just to show how important this is in relation to habitat design, if it were indeed possible to live for long periods at zero-g, one could imagine instead of a two-dimensional living area on the inside of the cylinder a three dimensional structure occupying the whole of the cylinder, with obvious major design and architectural implications. We should, therefore, keep our options open, although we should clearly select at this time the more conservative design of a habitat with artifical gravity, as O'Neill has done.

Graybiel did not touch on the subject of the atmosphere, which has a major potential impact on the design of the structure. The ideal specification would be sea-level air; that is, nitrogen, oxygen and carbon dioxide at normal partial pressures, as we have on Earth at sea level, and as was recommended some years ago by a National Academy of Science panel which looked at this problem. But one can consider oxygen and nitrogen separately. The oxygen should probably have the same partial pressure as at sea level, although there has been some discussion about reducing it to make the design of the habitat easier. It is certainly conceivable that a Denver oxygen altitude (1500 meters) might just be acceptable, but even that altitude can be a problem for people who have medical disorders such as cardiac problems, chronic respiratory ailments, or problems of those elements of the blood which are concerned with the transport of oxygen. A high-altitude environment would therefore require separate facilities for treating people who have these disorders, so that sea level oxygen partial pressure is indeed desirable.

People cannot live without inert gas (nitrogen, in the Earth's atmosphere) because there are some medical problems associated with its lack. For example, if the human lung collapses, a fairly frequent occurrence in the case of lung pathology, an obstruction may result. Under normal circumstances, alveoli (the terminal air sacs in the lung) remain expanded, because oxygen is absorbed rapidly into the blood vessels through active absorption. Nitrogen just stays in the alveoli and keeps them open. If nitrogen is eliminated, the lung collapses very rapidly. It is not possible to say how much nitrogen or other inert gas would be needed until extensive experimentation has been done. Some partial pressure of nitrogen or other inert gas, perhaps helium, lower than what we are breathing now, is almost certainly acceptable. Inert gas may also be needed for other purposes; for example, the prevention of serious fires. At the moment, the tendency is to have as much inert gas in spacecraft atmospheres as one can afford. Perhaps the compromise will be a near-normal oxygen partial pressure and an inert gas partial pressure reduced substantially from sea level, but not to a point where there is a significant increase in fire danger.

The radiation picture is fairly straightforward, although it needs extensive research. We do not yet know exactly what cosmic-ray particles traveling at very high energy do to individual cells. We do not know the long-term effects. There will be no immediate effect (the dose is so spread out in time) but there will be some life-shortening from a variety of causes. The question is, how much? We have to find out what causes life-shortening and be in a position to say what is acceptable. This type of research can be carried out mostly on the ground, at facilities like the Bevalac at Berkeley.

International Considerations

Rauschenbach emphasized two important factors which originally led to the formation of IN-

TELSAT: the disappearance of conventional physical barriers to communication, as the earliest Earth satellites came into operation; and the rapid growth of the communications technology which followed. There are some possible parallels with space habitats.

Based on the challenges of the United Nations resolution of 1961, declaring that international law applies to space, the United States responded with the Communications Satellite Act of 1962, creating a corporation which is directed at both national and international communications goals. Political considerations have on the whole not been allowed to hamper the development of what is now a very effective international body. One of the reasons was a heavy concentration on economic factors. The system was set up to have a space portion, owned jointly by a large number of nations, and ground segments owned and operated by the individual countries. There are 89 member countries, an agreed distribution of votes and responsibilities, an arbitration board, and a sophisticated and effective hardware system. In spite of the long duration of formation of the organization and the considerable difficulties experienced, INTELSAT has achieved a degree of solid progress not often achieved in the international sphere.

Rauschenbach noted four particular aspects of the corporation: it was an endeavor to cooperate on an international basis in order to use a new resource for the benefit of all mankind; it was non-competitive in nature; it allowed participation by private and public organizations, representing individual states; and there was a wide disparity of investment and ownership.

There is recent agreement between the United States and the Soviet Union in which the parties are encouraged to pursue efforts to resolve problems of international law and cooperation in space. But Finch suggested that the United Nations should play a much larger role: it should provide full information to all countries and guarantee their interests and access to the new technologies and capabilities which would emerge. He pointed out that it is vital to seize on opportunities to obtain international agreements in space as expeditiously as possible. His summary remark was: "It is never too early."

Habitat Organization and Government

Dannenberg emphasized that the early phases of setting up an organizational structure are the most difficult. It is necessary to carry out the early steps so there will be a base upon which to build. The guiding principle should be the value of the concept for all mankind, specifically in relation to today's problems of resources, population, and energy. Broad-minded management is essential, and strategies are needed which are not bound by immediate, simple-minded, cost-effective criteria. Early incorporation of world-wide participation and the tackling of problems on an international team basis could lead to increased international understanding and cooperation.

Many of the proposed activities can be simulated on Earth. One could examine, for example, ecological systems, power systems, and many other components of the future habitat. As an initial step, Dannenberg recommended the establishment of an education broadcasting service, broadcasting directly into homes (as is now possible with the ATS satellite) on a world-wide basis, and perhaps modeled on the INTELSAT experience. Good organization is of fundamental importance, and the United Nations might be the institution to implement such an endeavor. In the meantime, however, seed money should be devoted to further exploration of the concept.

Falk addressed some preliminary speculations on new options for self-government in space habitats. Because there now exists a certain mood of loss of hope and loss of confidence in the future on the part of many people, the space colony could offer one of the greatest hopes for the restoration of such confidence, and also for the restoration of the esteem of science and technology as instruments to solve human problems.

Some of the pathways followed in the formation of INTELSAT could perhaps be examined as approaches for a space habitat program in the future. For example, Rauschenbach noted that it was essential for each member country to see some advantage for itself in belonging to the organization; this is indeed a key point.

On the subject of international law, and in particular its applicability to space habitats, Finch noted that the Aerospace Law Committee of the International Law Section of the American Bar Association has established a new, permanent subcommittee on space colonization. United Nations Resolution No. 1721 states the principle that outer space, including celestial bodies, is free for exploration and use by all states, but is not subject to national appropriation.

In 1967 the United Nations Committee on the Peaceful Uses of Outer Space, working on this basis, promulgated the Outer Space Treaty, with nine articles expanding on the basic United Nations resolution. The principles are international law, scientific exploration, national responsibility, prohibiition of the military use of space, the visualization of astronauts as envoys of mankind, and the principle of mutual cooperation.

Many details have been worked out since that time. Further treaties have appeared, such as he Astronaut Rescue Treaty and the Liability for Damages Provision. The United States would be in full compliance with the 1967 United Nations treaty if it proceeded with a space habitat program, given the following three assumptions:

• Weapons systems would be kept out of space stations or habitats

• Solar energy would be used for power

• Stations would not, initially, be self-governing.

Finch believe that a space habitat would necessarily fall under the jurisdiction of the launching sponsor, whether the launching sponsor be an international or national organization. He also feels that there must be a degree of regulation within the habitat, and that various mechanisms could facilitate such regulation, for example, the development of a common language. At a later date, self-government might be achieved.

It is not possible to project feasible options for the future without making certain restrictive assumptions about the circumstances surrounding the establishment of space habitats — an immensely difficult task, in view of our inability to preduct the future realistically. Falk reiterated Dannenberg's view on the critical importance of early habitat experience on the options for self-government, and postulated certain restrictive but optimistic conditions on which a self-government model constructed at this time should be based:

• There is no global catastrophies

• Global unification has not occurred

• National diversity therefore remains

• Vastly improved mechanisms for coordination exist

• The United Nations or other international bodies will become more important

- There will be some form of global agency for space settlement

- Well supported goals will have arisen for space habitats

- There will be many more supranational actors on the scene

- Space habitats will have some autonomy but will still be subject to Earth control

- Habitats cannot wage war on Earth or on each other

- Any adverse developments on Earth cannot imperil the habitats.

Under such circumstances, Falk thought there would be four shared values as a framework for the development of a self-governing community: minimum violence, economic well-being for all, a guaranteed social and political justice structure, and a commitment to the maintenance of environmental quality. If the colony has a self-governing structure, it could act as a step in the evolution of human culture; that is, the systems evolved in the habitat could be tried out on Earth. In turn, such terrestrial systems could provide further experience for the evolution of the habitat in an iterative and symbiotic process.

Constitutional guidelines for self-government might fall into four categories: procedures for checks and balances, the protection of minimum human rights, the minimization of bureaucratic intrusion, and maximum participation by the citizens in the authoritarian system. Some experiments surely would fail, and government is far from being the only human factor to consider. An important aspect might be the need to have the habitat well-adapted to preliminary social and economic characteristics. These habitats offer an opportunity to achieve the philosopher's dream of creating a civil society from a state of nature; in fact, to create a just society. Falk urged experimentation in constitution-building based on normative and operational guidelines, the central issues being individual freedom, incentives, legitimacy, authority, maintenance of order, and the protection of the common interest.

Four possible options for a minimum state of self-government for small populations could be a canton-type of government, where the central government is weak but the peripheral governments are stronger; a larger concept of the just state; a

functional state dedicated to very specific purposes for that particular habitat; and combinations of the foregoing.

Cultural Aspects

Maruyama showed how different cultures looked at similar situations in different ways and emphasized the advantages of heterogeneous systems over homogenous systems. One basic principle of biological, social and even of some physical processes is an increase of heterogeneity and sympathization. This is because biological and social systems are based on mutual interaction, and mutual interaction can increase differentiation and heterogeneity. He went on to say that heterogeneity has survival value for at least three reasons: the possible symbiotic nature of heterogeneous populations; a potential for diverse utilization; and a higher probability of survival in the face of unforeseen catastrophe. This has been pointed out also by those biologists who have taken a systems approach to our ecosystem here on Earth. Heterogeneity also facilitates a higher speed of cultural evolution and therefore we should have heterogeneity among space communities, both between communities and within an individual community.

There are different logics by which we live, and these logics can be used in the design of communities. Maruyama gave some examples: there is the hierarchical, homogenistic, uniform pattern type of logic; there is the individualistic, isolationistic and "do-your-own-thing" type of logic; and then there is a third category, mutual interaction, which is a heterogeneous, interactive and symbiotic mode. There are two sorts of heterogeneous design: localization and interweaving. In localization, homogeneity is confined within one locality and heterogeneity is achieved by a mix of localities.

In order to optimize the matching between the individual and the culture, there should be space communities based on these different cultural principles. Maruyama proposed to set up four types of communities based on these principles. Community A would be homogenistic, with everything fairly standardized; for example, with identical apartments, residences divided into groups in such a way that each group is homogeneous, and with large public recreation areas. Community B would embody the individualistic principle: each building lot is like a castle; each living unit is large enough to include recreation areas; there are no public parks; there is minimum interaction between people: "you do your own thing". Community C is based on the heterogenistic principle: houses are all different; apartments are all different; and there are different types of family structure, life styles and individual philosophies. Care is taken to place symbiotic people next to each other; for example, old people who like babies are placed near families with babies. Community D is an interweaving of all three principles.

One of the disadvantages of migration between these communities, which occurs when people are too free to move from one community to another, must be guarded against. That is, those who like communities stay, and those who don't, leave; in the end this has an inbreeding effect, and the community tends to become too homogeneous and intolerant towards nonconformists. Certain types of heterogeneity are maximized where there is a large number of small communities, whereas other types are maximized when there is a small number of large communities. For example, heterogeneity of books and libraries is maximized by having a small number of large libraries rather than having a large number of small libraries.

As in all other areas of human factors, our ability to predict the future in this area is very poor, and we should therefore take a flexible approach; that is, we should be prepared to examine the results of the experiments, restructure the plan, and start all over again as necessary.

Architectural Environments

Glaeser's focus was on trying to define the architectural environment which would be required, starting with functional specifications, before beginning his design; i.e., how is the environment significant? What are the significant points of the environment which affect any architectural design? It is necessary to have a structure, an interior, an architectural solution, which has to be attractive after the motives of heroism have faded away and work becomes routine. This design must affect the furniture, the shelter, the utensils, the clothing – all aspects of life. The competing requirements are the needs of the population and the enormous constraints on the shell of the structure within which the people live.

Model 1, the smallest of the proposed habitats, is certainly the most constraining. It is small, it is isolated, it is an experimental environment, but its success is an absolute necessity. If it were to fail, the project would be set back enormously.

The motivation of the people who go to Model 1

has to be very strong. They will go with the full knowledge of the difficulties. They will undoubtedly be highly skilled, versatile, educated; they will demand variety. What is the range of perceptions that are available to them? There is the curvature of the cylinder in which they are going to live; the quality of the light coming in through the windows around the sides; if the atmospheric pressure is low, this may have an effect on hearing; an inevitable awareness that the day-night cycle is mechanically controlled.

When the environment is perceived as different from what one likes, stress results, and that stress can be reinforced by a feeling of total isolation. The ways in which stresses can be relieved can be either by internal adaptation or by trying to relieve them via external changes. There is cost associated with both: reduced performance resulting from adaptation to stress, or the cost of remedial construction if you must constantly be rebuilding things.

How do you supplement your environment in order to alleviate stress? Do you simply try to simulate the Earth, for example? Would that be a positive inducement to get people to go and to stay and to be happy? If you do wish to simulate the Earth, to what detail? If you want a spreading oak tree, must you have the complete oak tree or would a plastic oak tree be satisfactory, or a titanium oak tree, or maybe just a hologram of an oak tree to look at? But the constant awareness of the artificiality of it all might itself be stressful.

There are other approaches. People could be trained ahead of time to adapt; you could force their behavior to be predictable, constrain the people to fit the model. This approach might work, but one questions whether or not the resulting activities of the society would really lead in directions benefical to the program.

Another approach is to keep the design open-minded, to offer the populace the opportunity for change. In the initial period, the least variety is demanded. The motivations will, indeed, be those that were brought from Earth, but as things settle down to routine, there will be a need for change to accommodate various social systems which may differ between groups or which the group itself may wish to change. The presence or absence of various types of areas can invite or discourage certain kinds of activities, so the mechanics of the structure must accept change and the social structure itself must control the changes. It was suggested that something like modularization and standardization would be available to permit a changing ar-

247

chitectural environment. Just because the terms modularization and standardization are used, we do not mean that one has to envision monotony. There will be enormous variety.

It will be necessary to take a very close look at what happens in Model 1 and try to envision the possibilities for later versions. The objections of the design approach are to set up the requirements for alleviation of stress, to aim at the success of the first colony and to try to understand the functional requirements, and finally to formulate a program for a successful architectural design.

One question might be whether there is any Earth analog we can look at to judge the time rate of change of a small society. How rapidly do people want to turn everything upside down and start over again? There does not appear to be any good Earthly analogy. Even on Pitcairn Island, the Sun rises in the east and sets in the west and the waves wash on the shore, so it was not that unique or isolated. And although it will be possible – albeit expensive – to travel back and forth to Earth from L5, people will tend to stay there a while and the sensations of the "unknown" and the "isolation" are still important.

Protection from Hazards

Hannah discussed meteorites and cosmic rays. Meteorites do not present much of a problem; although a one-ton meteorite would be quite serious, the probability of such a strike is one every ten million years or less.

Smaller meteorites are more likely. A 100-gram meteorite would cause a pretty big hole: about two meters in diameter, resulting in a leak-down time for half an atmosphere of about eight hours. Such a hole would have to be fixed in a hurry. The most likely ones, which might strike once every few years, are the order of 0.3 gram, and would break one of the windows, causing a loss of 1% of the atmosphere per hour. These could be located and fixed automatically in a routine manner.

Cosmic rays are a more serious problem. The flux of cosmic rays, excluding solar flares, doesn't seem to be too bad, and is probably able to be protected against with minor shielding. The ionizing power, the damage a particle does to the body, is greatest for slow-moving particles, not fast particles. For example, iron nuclei, which are heavily charged, are extremely damaging. It is estimated that the astronauts on their way to the Moon and back lost somewhere between 10^{-7} and 10^{-4} of their non-reproducible nerve cells due to ionization from heavy nuclei cosmic ray particles. We therefore use as a design criterion that in thirty years the population of a colony must receive no worse a dose than the astronauts did on a lunar flight.

One way of accomplishing this is to use a shield made of leftover debris from lunar ore materials. A shield density of about 130 g/cm^2 would slow down high-energy relativistic cosmic rays just to the point where they are capable of doing their greatest damage. So this type of shielding doesn't solve the problem by slowing the cosmic rays down; it might, perhaps, make it even worse.

Another idea is to put large superconducting coils around the endcaps of the colony and create a dipole magnet – make a little Earth, whose magnetic field will deflect particles away from the structure. This might be accomplished with niobium superconductors, but there is still work to be done to make sure that the magnetic flux does not cause damage to the people who are living inside. One problem in maintaining the necessary 4K superconductor temperatures, which in itself Hannah believes to be relatively routine, is the necessary discharge of heat into space. It doesn't appear to be an enormous problem, but we certainly have to pay attention to it.

The magnetic field around the colony will generate a Van Allen belt, trapping electrons and eventually building up an ionosphere and a charged atmosphere. This charged atmosphere will itself become a shield against cosmic rays also, but the magnetic field is needed to set it up. It does not, by the way, bother communications. Entering spacecraft must be careful to neutralize their electric charge before docking, but that doesn't seems to be overwhelmingly difficult. In general, magnetic fields appear to be the best way to avoid cosmic ray damage, which does seem to be the most serious problem requiring attention.

DISCUSSION

Q. Normal gravity puts a strain on the cardiovascular system, but what is the effect on longevity of long-term exposure to partial gravity?

A. The effects on the cardiovascular system tend to be on the distribution of blood volume. In other words, gravity simply pulls the blood down into the lower parts of the body, and our body system is designed to counter that at all times.

Of course, we know it fails sometimes; for example, when we faint. One of the problems, if you become weightless for a long period of time, is that you lose that capability to withstand normal gravity.

Now, some reduced gravity might indeed turn out to be perfectly satisfactory. The critical question is whether you can function efficiently and normally when you suddenly transfer back to a normal 1-gravity environment. If you are out in space for a long period of time, it could well be that the change in the distribution of blood volume, which is adaptive to that weightless or partial-gravity situation, may be perfectly tolerable.

Q. *What is your opinion of the vulnerability of a space habitat to sabotage or blackmail from deranged individuals or perhaps disaffected groups or plain adventurers? When one considers 150 able-bodied people on a jumbo jet being taken hither and yon by men with a wooden gun, it would appear that this is a problem worth considering. This may impose severe constraints upon both the architecture and the possibility for social experimentation in the habitat. The architecture in particular might need to provide for compartmentalization.*

A. There are several choices. You can, of course, impose a very restrictive political or jurisdictional approach to prevent that type of thing, but it would require selection, monitoring, and other objectional features. But there is another approach, and that is to build into the system a very high degree of redundancy, so that no real activities by aberrant people would, in fact, totally devastate the community. But this does constitute a major problem.

Q. *Concerning the nitrogen replacement, have any studies or experiments been done on possible replacement of nitrogen by other inert gases and, if so, what possible candidates are beyond the experimental phase?*

A. There is one major candidate: helium. Helium is used on a worldwide basis by deep-sea divers to replace nitrogen for a variety of reasons, and no ill effects have ever been shown. In fact, helium is much better than nitrogen, in the sense that you can dive much deeper without becoming narcotized by the very large mass of gas that you absorb at great depth. So, helium is a good candidate, and I would also point out that helium is also lighter than nitrogen. Other gases

are very unlikely. The heavier inert gases tend to be narcotic as you go up the atomic scale. Helium appears to be the only good possibility at this time, but others could be examined.

Q. *Do we have enough information now on the effects of radiation on human genetics to be able to extrapolate over a period of many generations at any level that we might choose to shield this colony?*

A. We have good information for the effects of the sorts of radiation which are common here on Earth: gamma rays, X-rays, and proton radiation. But we know very little about the effects of high energy cosmic-ray nuclei outside the atmosphere. We would therefore need a decade or so of extensive experimentation with high-energy accelerators or other machines here on the Earth. The Bevalac, for example, which is a conversion of the famous Bevatron at Berkeley into a machine capable of accelerating not only the lightest nuclei – protons – but also heavier ones up to energies a hundred times as great as those that were available just four years ago, makes possible much more relevant direct experimentation of the effects of these heavy ions. And it's not just the genetic effects, but also the somatic effects that have to be explored and well understood.

Q. *What data exist on the effects of low gravity environments on male and female fertility?*

A. None

Q. *Even though plants can withstand quite a bit of radioactivity, it would seem that in a rapidly recycling ecology there might be a buildup of radioactivity by biological mechanisms which could be harmful to the people who eat these plants. Can you comment on that?*

A. It simply does not occur. Cosmic ray particles cause damage simply because they are moving very fast. The secondary radiation induced by cosmic ray particles on objects is very small. Meteorites found on Earth have been exposed to cosmic radiation for perhaps billions of years, and they exhibit undetectably low levels of residual radiation.

Q. *I have heard that fish can live in zero gravity by simply keeping them in a moist atmosphere. Is that true?*

A. The rationale for that argument is that if you

take a fish out of water on Earth, gravity collapses the gill surface and the fish dies, but in zero gravity, with no force to collapse the gill surface, the oxygen flow across the gill surface might be maintained in moist air, say 100% relative humidity. This would require far, far less water than ponds or lakes. However, the experiment has never been tried; it might be an interesting one for a marine biologist to propose for Spacelab.

4. Applications and Developments

Gerard K. O'Neill
Princeton University

In reviewing the key question of economic payoff, we should keep in mind the essential points of what we might call a permanent "beachhead" in free space: unlimited, continuous solar power and easy availability of lunar materials. Efficient manufacturing requires a local work force, fully self-sufficient for its necessities. The free-space environment permits the coexistence in close proximity, but without interference, of the three basic activities of modern humanity: living, agriculture and manufacturing.

A free space community would use solar power for all its energy needs. One of these is the growing of crops in enclosed farms where the day length, climate, and season can be controlled to any desired degree. Solar energy can be concentrated by low-mass mirrors for reliable, low-cost industrial process heating. It would also serve at L5 as a free, inexhaustible, pollutionless source of heat to drive turbogenerators supplying all electrical needs. Through each square meter of free space at L5 there flows unused, each year, ten times as much solar energy as falls on an equal area in even the most cloud-free portion of the American southwest. The economic benefits of an L5 industrial complex derive from the full-time availability of that solar energy, from the efficiencies of assembly in zero gravity, and from the presence of the Moon as a source of raw materials for products whose end-use would be in high orbit above the Earth.

It appears that the first application of a space manufacturing facility may be the construction of satellite solar power stations. Glaser described the basic idea, of which he has been, perhaps, the best-known champion over a period of years. It is a large solar array, either of solar cells or of concentrating mirrors, located in geosynchronous orbit about 38,000 km high, always over a fixed point of the surface of the Earth. There, solar energy would be available more than ninety-nine percent of the time. It would be converted to microwave power and transmitted from a phased-array antenna about a kilometer in diameter, driven by a large number of small amplifying tubes. At a fixed receiving antenna on the ground, about ninety percent of the beam power is contained within a width of about seven kilometers. For an installation able to deliver 5000 megawatts to the power grid, about one percent of the total electrical capacity of the United States at the present time, the average power density is low, less than half of that of direct sunlight. An overall transmission efficiency of fifty-six percent has so far been demonstrated in tests. The target figure is from sixty-three to seventy percent, which seems fairly close to realization.

The question of possible dangers to humans or animals from long-term exposure near the antenna site requires more study. As yet there is no internationally recognized tolerance standard for microwaves, but there certainly should be such a standard. Meeting it will be mainly a question of the diameter of the barrier fence. If you move it one kilometer further out, you reduce the intensity of the radiation by a very big factor.

Glaser emphasized the three basic numbers which control economic feasibility of an Earth-launched satellite power station: the mass of the powerplant, the cost of the plant before launch, and the lift cost. At present, solar cells cost about $15 per watt; they would have to be reduced to around thirty cents per watt. As for mass, no operational satellite has done much better than about 20 kilowatts per ton of solar array, and a reasonable expectation for the future might be around 35 kW per ton. To make the ground-launched satellite power station practical, one needs to achieve something in the range of 220 to 1,000 kW per ton: an improvement by a factor of from six to thirty. Lift costs to geosynchronous orbit have also to be reduced to the range of $80 to $220 per kg from the present figure, which is well over $1,000 per kg. Davis had showed the type of large, totally reusable vehicle system required to achieve that kind of figure.

Woodcock described an alternative satellite solar power station concept for which an extensive design study has been carried out. The microwave technique and performance assumed are identical to those of the solar cell version; the power generation, however, is by a closed Brayton-cycle turbogenerator, probably using helium as the working fluid. Basically, it consists of a system of concentrating mirrors which direct solar radiation to a helium heater, a conventional turbo-generator, and a waste-heat radiator. It is necessary to use a large number of turbogenerators of rather small size, about 300 MWe each, and a launch vehicle of rather large size; about 250 metric tons payload, in order to bring up a turbine as a complete unit.

Woodcock assumed a specific power of about 200 kW per ton and lift costs of only about $100 per kg to geosynchronous orbit. He pointed out the necessity of using discounted economics; that is, an increased requirement for earnings to take account of the fact that during the construction period, which might be five years for a typical powerplant, no earnings would be arriving and interest would have to be paid on the capital investment. He concluded that earnings would have to exceed 13% of the capital cost for interest charges of 8%. The installed cost of the plant might be around $1300 per kWe.

In my own view, the two alternatives given by Glaser and Woodcock compare as follows: the solar cell approach requires an enormous improvement — a factor of six to thirty — over current technology if it is to succeed economically. On the other hand, its technology lies in the area of solid state physics, which is a rapidly developing field. The turbogenerator approach has the appeal of current technology; the machines required can be designed in great detail on the basis of existing or almost existing engineering practice. By the same token, there does not seem to be room there for a great improvement over the numbers which Woodcock has already assumed. If I had the choice to make, I'd probably place my bets on the turbomachinery, but I am notoriously conservative, as everybody knows. Certainly it makes sense to continue development of solar cells on the off-chance that there is going to be a major breakthrough that will tip the economic scales.

Continuing with my own views, I believe that both studies of ground-launched systems suffer from the same basic objections:

- They can demonstrate economic feasibility only if a whole series of goals can be achieved, each within rather tight limits such as ten or twenty percent.

- Since those achievements could, at best, only be achieved by pushing the state of the art very hard, there doesn't seem to be a lot of room in them for any dramatic reductions in energy costs with further development.

- Both methods depend critically on the achievement of very low lift costs to geosynchronous orbit. This would require advanced vehicles with development costs which are probably in the several tens of billions of dollars, and we have some experience, as for example with the C5A, that sometimes such developments lead to disastrous cost overruns.

- Because in both approaches the entire mass of the power plant has to be carted up through the atmosphere, the question of environmental impact has to be studied carefully. Current estimates are that in the year 2000, this country alone will need at least 85,000 MWe per year of new generator capacity. Assuming Woodcock's figures, that would require the transport up through the atmosphere of about half a million tons per year of payload, an amount high enough to raise the possibility that a program which initially made sense economically might be blocked or made much more expensive by a strong environmentalist objection that might arise long after its inception. Boeing has already experienced one rather damaging experience of that kind with the cancellation of the supersonic transport.

Although I list these concerns, both studies are,

in my opinion, very worthwhile, especially for the spin-offs that may come from them. I think they may be among the most important studies now being carried out within the aerospace field, and even though I want to solve the problem in a different way, I would vote that these studies be supported very vigorously indeed.

Our work at Princeton on the same subject has suggested an alternative approach in which the satellite power station would be built at an L5 space manufacturing facility as one complete unit, out of lunar surface material transferred to L5 by a mass driver. The estimated cost of transporting the raw materials seems to be a few dollars per kg for the initial operation; around a dollar per kg when mass drivers can be manufactured at the space facility, and perhaps as low as a few cents per kg when mass drivers can eventually be manufactured on the Moon; that is one manufacturing operation which I feel can be justified for the lunar surface. The approach, therefore, has the advantage of growth potential; it's not sensitive to errors of even a factor of two or four in the lift cost estimates from the Moon. It is also insensitive to lift costs from the Earth, and the lift costs we assumed were around a factor of five to ten higher than those assumed by Glaser and Woodcock.

In our approach, the power station would be built in a large, zero-gravity construction sphere, with an atmosphere, just outside the space community. The workforce would be ordinary heavy-industry technicians rather than astronauts, and at the end of each shift, they would return in a few minutes to their families living in comfortable one-gravity surroundings within the habitat. There would be no limitations on turbomachinery size, so the unit size would be optimized for the economics. With what I believe are large safety factors for the initial learning situation, a cost estimate for a first satellite power station was shown in Table 2, reproduced from my paper in *Science*. I have assumed rather high figures for assembly costs, even though such operations are carried out under quite decent conditions within an eclosed environment. For comparison, I've used a more conservative figure of 100 kWe per ton rather than the 200 kWe per ton in Woodcock's study, and have assumed 63% microwave transmission efficiency rather than 70%. The factor of two in kilowatts per ton makes a big difference. Woodcock estimates perhaps a ten-year development program and the use of exotic materials like columbium to reach 200 kWe per ton, because that figure requires using high temperatures at the turbine inlet. In contrast, and in a private conversation with Woodock, he remarked

that if we could live with the 100 kWe per ton figure, which was what I have assumed in Table 2, it could be obtained with existing materials on a time scale of "next week."

In the Princeton approach, the completed and tested power station, which would have a mass of about 80,000 tons, would be relocated in geosynchronous orbit over a period of from one to four months by a mass-driver reaction motor which would be identical to the one assumed for the Moon. Reaction mass is available at the space habitat in the form of pulverized industrial slag; but to be on the safe side, I have assumed that it would be brought specially from the Moon. It is interesting to look at a couple of numbers; in reality, it may be that the most convenient reaction mass will be liquid oxygen. In the course of processing half a million tons of unselected lunar surface material at L5, one could obtain around 115,000 tons of metals, 100,000 tons of silicon, and about 200,000 tons of oxygen, so liquid oxygen may be cheaply available at L5 as a waste product.

The advantages of this approach seem to be as follows:

- It can achieve economic feasibility even if any or several of the input numbers are in error by a factor of two

- The construction process does not use Earth materials or energy

- It avoids the need for advanced lift vehicles and bypasses the resulting environmental questions

- Perhaps of special importance, it offers the potential of dramatic reductions in energy cost on Earth, because lunar lift costs by mass driver and L5 processing costs can be expected to follow a steeply falling curve with time.

The possibility of such reductions in energy cost may be important, because they will be necessary in the long term if such options as a hydrogen-economy substitute for fossil fuels is to be exploited. The catch, of course, is that one requires first the establishment of a space manufacturing facility to carry out the construction.

The costs of setting up such a facility seem to be of the same order of magnitude, but possibly somewhat greater than, the costs of developing the very advanced vehicle systems which would be required in the alternative Earth-lift approaches.

The differences in the two approaches are that the costs of energy from power stations made in space manufacturing facilities can come down to much lower values than for Earth-launched powerplants, and that in the Earth-launched approach, the next step after putting up the first one or two power stations would be the development of an even bigger launch vehicle system using more materials and energy from the Earth and causing even greater environmental impact. In contrast, the placing of the first space manufacturing facility permits the continued expansion of industry in space and the construction of any desired number of power stations, without using materials or energy from the Earth and with minimal need for transport vehicle operations from the Earth.

The economics of satellite power station construction at a space facility were brought out by Hopkins in a comment from the floor. He reported that even assuming the high figure of $130 billion for the cost of the space manufacturing facility, and with high interest rates and discounted economics, if one could achieve a rapid penetration of the space manufacturing facilities into the powerplant market, it would lead very quickly to investment payback and soon afterward to high and increasing profits of many tens of billions of dollars per year.

Salkeld discussed lift vehicles just beyond the near-term and rechecked the lift cost estimates made by Tischler and Davis and reviewed by Grey. He was in close agreement with the estimates made independently by these different people.

In order to match the fastest possible construction schedule for the space manufacturing facility, aimed at having the first habitat in place by 1988, Salkeld found that upgrading the shuttle by substitution of environmentally cleaner kerosene-liquid oxygen engines would be needed only around 1983, and a single-stage-to-orbit vehicle using the same engines in 1988. This was for cost minimization; if one was willing to pay more money, one could continue the older technologies later. I must confess to some satisfaction that the lift cost estimates by these three men, and generated independently by the NASA Marshall Space Flight Center at Huntsville, are all lower than were used in our cost estimates; e.g., see Ref. 4.

Much of Salkeld's discussion concerned the transport from Earth to low orbit. For the long-term development of space habitats, it's appropriate to consider the second step, from low orbit to L5. I've looked into this, mainly from the viewpoint of passenger transport, since in our approach there will never be any need for a large amount of freight transport from Earth to L5.

To minimize the costs, and also to minimize the environmental burden on the Earth, I've considered the use of a large ship, built at L5, powered by a mass-driver reaction engine, and refueled, if you want to use that phrase, with reaction mass presumably from the industrial slag at L5. The size of the vessel could be optimized for the economics, because one could build things of any size desired in zero gravity. The vessel, of course, would never have to enter the Earth's atmosphere. The earliest time-scale, even on the most ambitious, fastest possible time scale, would only be the late 1990's. The ship would use an advanced version of the mass-driver, with a specific impulse of about 750 seconds. Table 1, which I had cited earlier, indicates some of the possibilities for development of the mass driver. With a full load of reaction mass, the ship would spiral in slowly from L5 to low orbit. The powerplant could be solar turbogenerators, or there might be a mass advantage in providing the ship with a large microwave receiving antenna and having its power supplied from geosynchronous orbit through a microwave link.

The ship would take on its passenger load at low orbit from the kind of shuttle vehicles described by Salkeld, and it would then use its remaining reaction mass to spiral out to L5. The return trip, with passengers, would be much faster because most of the reaction mass would have been expended during the inbound trip. The total mass would be about 18,000 tons and the mass ratio 6.5. For present-day specific powers of 100 kW per ton, the outward trip time would be about three weeks. For a specific power of 290 kW per ton, about forty percent better than that assumed by Woodcock for a 1985 system, the power would be 311 MW, the thrust about four tons. The outward trip time, which is the thing that would matter most to the passengers, would be around eight and a half days, which is typical of transatlantic ship times. If the powerplant mass could be cut to around 0.7 ton per megawatt, as it might be for an antenna alone, the thrust could go up to about 22 tons and the trip time then would be so short that on the outward leg, one could use an approximation to a Hohmann orbit, with substantial savings in total reaction mass and mass ratio. A ship of that kind could probably carry a passenger load of around 2,000 to 6,000 people. Even on the fastest possible schedule of development of space manufacturing facilities, I don't see any need for a vehicle of that kind earlier than about twenty years from now. It is comforting that we already have a fair idea of how to build one.

McCreight discussed zero-gravity industry, particularly in low Earth orbit, for high-value products such as pharmaceuticals and semiconductors. I was rather struck by the fact that even in the year 2000, this total market was estimated to be low enough to require only about one shuttle flight per week. Clearly, then, it appears to me that no substantial industrialization of space will occur through that approach, although it is an extremely useful process to follow, obviously very worthwhile if high-value pharmeceuticals can be manufactured much more effectively by sending up materials from the Earth, processing them in low orbit, and bringing them back down again.

Von Puttkamer discussed project transitions from early study through to realization, emphasizing, to me at least, that in the absence of any single well-defined goal, future operations in space seem likely to become rather institutionalized, with progress only at a very slow pace, in micro-steps, and with rather limited paybacks. Von Puttkamer implied that NASA is capable of studying alternatives, but that any major thrust toward a new goal is really outside its charter, and can only come from outside NASA through a decision at the executive or Congressional levels.

Freitag, in his presentation, said "I have observed that the most common element that brings support to large United States space programs is the simple and objective characteristic: 'Why is it good for the USA?' " I think that makes excellent sense. And after identifying several "drivers," he stated "In the decades of the sixties, there was a great spirit of adventure attached to the space program. The elements of exploring the unknown, the pressing back of new frontiers – be they technological, physiological, or sociological – were well supported." We do not see that spirit of adventure in the space program as it exists at the present time. Freitag also noted that his program does not give great priority to such justifications as "search for knowledge," or "scientific exploration". I think it is pretty obvious that if a considerably larger scale space program is established for sound economic reasons, that some of us scientists can, in a sense, have some of our science "tag along" with an economically driven program.

Freitag's summarization of the major problems now visible included the development of a closed ecosystem in space, which because the Earth will be only three days travel time away, he did not believe would be necessary for quite a long time. I would like to point out, however, that at a cost in terms of square meters of growing space, we can very easily afford to have vegetables, chickens, pigs, turkeys, and so on.

Freitag also identified lunar material transport as a major problem. But here a modest effort will go a long way. It is difficult to convey the sense of excitement that goes with being in at the beginning of a technological development, not writing the twenty-fifth paper after twenty-four previous authors have already milked the subject for all that it is worth. In just a few hours, for example, several of my colleagues and I, working with good numbers, found that a laser-fringe counting method of measuring all six of the velocity errors of the lunar mass driver looked to be perfectly reasonable, to accuracies considerably better than those which were needed. What I want to try to convey is that we're at the point where, with a very small investment of thought and almost no money, it's possible to carry entire concepts to much greater definition than is possible in a mature technological area.

Freitag identified as further major problem areas large structures and engineering development, better understanding of specialized machines and methods, and habitat structural design. He noted that based on historical perceptions, we are now building up to a possible time of decision which might occur within the next one to two years.

Concluding Remarks

Much of the point of this Conference was to get initial insights into the possible economic benefits from building a space manufacturing facility, not to arrive at definitive numbers, but to look for directions and new options. In that regard, what we call the "bootstrap principle" is central to the whole concept. The establishment of the first productive habitat, constructing products from lunar materials with the aide of solar energy, makes it possible to build larger facilities with greater industrial capacity without drawing energy or critical materials from the Earth; it also makes possible building additional mass-drivers and so reducing still further the cost of obtaining materials.

The economics of the use of lunar material at L5 can be illustrated, I think, by two examples. One is in powerplant construction: If a powerplant weighs ten tons per megawatt, the energy cost of lifting those ten tons from the Moon to L5 is about 160 dollars at two cents per kilowatt hour. Even the initial mass-driver, which has to be built on the

Earth and lifted from here, should operate at a few dollars per kg or around $70,000 for ten tons. The value of the electricity produced by that ten tons of powerplant in one year is $175,000, if that powerplant is in the full sunshine of L5. So the payoff is only a few months.

A second example relates to the reusability of vehicles. Reusability is the key to reducing lift costs. The space shuttle is the first step toward a partially reusable system. A very advanced vehicle might be able to lift materials from the Earth to L5 or to geosynchronous orbit with a round trip of six days.

The buckets of a lunar mass-driver correspond, in a real sense, to reusable vehicles. The bucket mass is about five kilograms, the payload about nine kilograms, and the recirculation time for a single bucket is about two and a half minutes, which includes one minute for automated inspection, reloading, and rebalancing. In the course of the six days during which a large Earth-launched vehicle might make one round trip carrying less than its own mass, a mass-driver bucket would have made 3600 round trips and would have lifted 6500 times its own mass. That is why the costs of launching materials from the Moon are so insensitive to details of how complicated or expensive the mass-driver buckets are. If the buckets were to cost even a million dollars each (a fairly absurd example), their cost would still be only ten cents per kilogram of payload lifted, because in a year, running only 50% of the time, a single bucket could lift a thousand tons of payload. Because the buckets are ideally suited to mass production even on Earth, and the mass-driver is inherently a device of rather high thermodynamic efficiency, the long-term limit of cost toward which continued development would lead would be that of the power alone, and that is less than two cents per kg of mass lifted to L5.

The philosopher and scientist Ernst Schumacher has stated a principle of technology which is, I think, profound, though simple. It is that no technological option should be pursued unless its development, when projected through a long period of growth, does not encounter absurdities. I think it may be an unexpressed realization of that principle which killed the supersonic transport. I'm quite sure that it is an expression of that principle, expressed or not, which has so very much delayed and blocked the construction of nuclear power stations and which makes people so apprehensive about fast breeder reactors.

We must, therefore, take a good look at the space community concept from the viewpoint of what we might call the "Schumacher Principle." The long-term "limits to growth" in the space environment described in this Conference are really absurdly high: a total land area several times that of the Earth. And as Grey very properly pointed out, the Moon could remain almost untouched by growth of that kind, because later mining operations could be shifted to the asteroids.

As human beings, we like to think that we have an opportunity to improve the world in which we live, and, if possible, to improve the human condition. Realistically, we can only accomplish such improvements if our goals are shared by many other people – if they are, in fact, genuine goals, widely shared.

In developing space manufacturing facilities, we seek these returns:

- Tapping an inexhaustible, non-polluting energy source

- Stimulating the economy by developing non-military products for which there is a large market

- Reducing the likelihood of nuclear terrorism through taking the solar power alternative to a massive program of breeder reactor development

- Improving the environment, by reducing the pressures for strip-mining coal and for intensive exploitation of oil, and by reducing the waste heat released to the biosphere.

From a humanitarian viewpoint, I think there may be few more effective contributions we could make to the solution of the world food problem than to provide underdeveloped nations with an inexhaustible source of low-cost energy for making the chemicals needed in high-yield agriculture.

The interest which the space community concept has aroused during its first year of open discussion seems to stem in part from an additional return which is less tangible: the glimmering of hope that our near-term future may not be one of despair or resignation in an increasingly rigid, resource-limited society, but of freedom and new opportunites on a frontier which is just within our reach.

DISCUSSION

Q. *What would be the source of nitrogen at L5, for Earth-normal atmosphere and fertilizer?*

A. In the near-term, the Earth; the mass budget involved is not very big. In the longer term, perhaps the asteroids. But I don't share the point of view that says we have to go to an Orion-type nuclear power system in order to get materials from there. In fact, the velocity interval between the Earth and L5 is almost the same as the velocity interval between the asteroids and L5. A mass driver transporter looks to be perfectly capable of doing the job.

Q. *Is there no real source of nitrogen on the Moon?*

A. None that I've been convinced of. Criswell has suggested the possibility of sieving to reap the hydrogen harvest of the solar wind which has impacted the Moon during the last several billion years. One would get much smaller quantities of carbon and nitrogen from this process, however, and there is little convincing evidence that there is enough carbon and nitrogen on the Moon without processing an inordinate amount of the lunar surface to get it.

Q. *Are there other economical ways of getting energy down from orbit, such as manufacturing it, starting up super fly-wheels, and shipping them down?*

A. That's simply a question of one's degree of conservatism. The big barrier to strong industrial interchange between the Earth and possible space habitats has always been the question of mass transport back and forth. From this point of view, the transport of energy rather than mass really looks much more attractive than aything else that I have seen. If you can get a high-value commodity down to the surface of the Earth without having to go through the whole business of recycling mass back and forth between geosynchronous orbit and the surface, the process is bound to be more cost-effective. For a 5,000 MWe powerplant located in geosynchronous orbit, the value of the power produced on the surface of the Earth is around $1 billion a year.

Q. *The approaching decision point that Freitag referred to bears many strong similarities to the 1961 Apollo decision. We had a falling of national prestige and self-image at that time, and the Apollo program, together with the other aspects of what President Kennedy called "The New Frontier," helped us to regain a sense of ourselves. Today, there is a feeling that science is doing bad things, and the country needs to be involved in human-oriented pur-*

suits—pursuits that are good for us, that will help us, that will not hurt others, and that will not hurt the world. This then provides an opportunity for the program you have called the "High Frontier"—an opportunity for us to have a national goal that would have feedback of various kinds, not only in a scientific way, once we have a restoration of hope and faith in the directions in which we are going.

A. (None.)

Q. *We don't need a new commitment. I think we have already made the commitment to develop cheaper forms of pollution-free energy for this country. This commitment is now generating funding considerably in excess of 130 billion. It is only necessary to show that this project dominates the other alternatives, most of which also involve tremendous investment and new technology. All that's needed for the next year or two is a support level of a few hundred thousand to continue study work. If our economic analysis can show that this program does indeed dominate the other energy alternatives, isn't that in itself sufficient to get funding?*

A. That is my hope. It is to our advantage to try to bring these numbers as much into the open as possible. We should open up our notebooks. To the best of my knowledge, there is nothing so weak in any of the studies that have been done up to the present time that it has to be concealed. It is to our advantage to stimulate critical comment if it can produce an interchange in the literature in which these facts are brought out.

Q. *Could you elaborate on the forthcoming summer study?*

A. The summer study will involve about twenty faculty members from a variety of disciplines, fairly heavily engineering-oriented, working full time for 10 weeks. It will be at the NASA Ames Laboratory near Stanford University and is cosponsored by NASA-Ames and Stanford. We must be careful not to load too much in the way of expectations on that summer study. For the most part these twenty young people will come into it "cold". They have been selected from over a hundred applicants for their talent and good background, but they do not come as well prepared on this subject as many of the people at this conference. They are not aerospace professionals for the most part, and there are many classes of activity which are very important in our research which we can't ask them to take on, because they simply don't have the background.

Q. *When you reach the second generation of a colony, individuals who have never had Earth experience, wouldn't you then have something that's never before existed — a civilization without a past, except maybe a scientific one? It would seem that all of history and almost all of literature would be inconceivable to them because there would be no actual frame of reference for understanding.*

A. The analogy that immediately comes to my mind is that as transportation costs on the Earth have gone down, thousands of our nation of 200 million people atavistically return to examine their past every summer by jet aircraft. That will happen again. The round-trip travel cost from here to L5 for the second generation, which may be in the early years of the next century, without assuming any new nuclear or other technology, could be as low as $3,000. There are places on Earth that are almost that expensive to get to today.

Q. *What are the immediate steps that those of us who are enthusiastic about the idea might take? I would like to assist in the development of a broader political constituency, for example.*

A. That's a hard question to answer. There's a great deal of future shock associated with this concept, although we know, when we look at it deeply, the technology is really not that new in terms of capability. It seems terribly new to everyone simply because the option has not been widely explored. The first thing that would presumably happen is that political or even news leaders would turn to technical experts and ask them what they think. Now, my own experience with technical experts is that their initial reaction is to be "turned off." The initial reaction is one of shock and disbelief. Only after they have had time to go off and work the problem out for themselves, slowly and carefully, going through each step, have they concluded that maybe there is something in it after all.

The most important thing that we who have technical training can do is to write articles and get those articles published. It is not difficult to place competent articles on this question in respected journals because it has suddenly become topical. The important point is to get articles into the literature which are of very high quality and completely accurate.

Q. *In considering this matter of cost, we must realize that $100 or $130 billion is rather more than twice as much as we have spent on space activity in all the years to date. It is nearly as much as we have spent on the Viet Nam War. It is an incredibly large sum of money. I would guess that we will end up needing perhaps only a third or a fourth that much, perhaps even less. Consider the major elements of the system: the L5 construction site, at some $17 billion (but there are some incredibly simple-minded things we can do, like using the disposable shuttle tanks, which may cut that by several billions of dollars); perhaps an upgraded shuttle, at as little as $5 billion; and a lunar farside station and mass driver. That will be expensive, but is it going to cost almost as much as a war? Although I don't want to commit us to as low a figure as $20 or $30 billion, I do want us to realize that $100 or $130 billion, which is the kind of talk that scare many of our legislators, may be out of the ballpark.*

A. I agree. If someone were to come up to me today and give me $30 billion and *carte blanche* to run ads in the newspapers, hire good engineers, and get the job done, I think I would be willing to guarantee that it could be done, and certainly with a 13 to 15-year time scale and something like $40 to $60 billion. The difficulty is that in very large-scale programs there is always a great deal of inefficiency. One very good aspect so far, and one we want to preserve, is the highly positive interaction between the people who are enthusiastic about this work and NASA. Considering that NASA people had really not even heard of these concepts a year ago, it's amazing how far we have come.

I don't want to create an adversary situation by saying we can do the job at a third the price. When I talk to the NASA people in great detail, what I really find is that each time I go one layer deeper into the cost estimates, I find big concealed safety factors, many of which can be argued down point by point. What I think this means is that yes, maybe each one of these costs can be pushed down, but if they *do* get the job, something that nobody thought about might come up which will raise the price by some amount. My own estimate of that safety factor is about three.

Q. *The concept you propose is of a magnitude and creativity that many people have been looking for. This conference has demonstrated that it isn't just the "old pros" who are for it, but also the younger generation, and that is where the game will be played. The appeal that the L-5 concept has for the younger generation is one of the most important features of this concept.*

When we look at the energy supply for Earth, the concept of the satellite power station was primarily designed to present an option which offers a way to use solar energy on a large scale. Whether we use solar cells or turbines is not really important. I have always assumed that the necessary space transportation would be developed if it were needed. If the development of space transportation through L5 is the more cost-effective way, then obviously that's the way it will be done, because in the end, we can only develop those things which society will find beneficial. The ultimate limit, and perhaps the limit to any scheme that we may address is the rate of capital formation. Whatever we do we have to be able to afford it, and the steps we take towards it will only be those which will achieve that objective. Hopefully this conference will be a step towards the large-scale use of solar energy, which will have to come in order for our civilization as we know it to continue.

A. I agree, and consider this an excellent note on which to conclude this conference.

REFERENCES

1. Farquhar, R.W., "The Control and Use of Libration-Point Satellites." NASA TR-348, 1970.

2. Kolm, H.H., and Thornton, R.D., "Electromagnetic Flight." *Scientific American 229*, 4, 1973, pp. 17-25.

3. Baldwin, G.C., and Khoklov, R.V., "Prospects for a Gamma-Ray Laser. "*Physics Today 28*, 2, 1975, pp. 32-39.

4. O'Neill, G.K., "The Colonization of Space," *Physics Today 27*, 9, 1974, pp. 32-40+

5. Hyde, R., Wood, L., and Nuckolls, J., "Prospects for Rocket Propulsion with Laser-Induced Fusion Microexplosions," AIAA Paper 72-1063, American Institute of Aeronautics and Astronautics, 1972.

6. "Space Station Study," McDonnell Douglas Corporation, Final Report on Contract NAS8-25140, August 1970.

7. "Space Station Program Phase B Definition," North American Rockwell Corporation, Final Report on Contract NAS9-9953, July 1970.

8. Adams, John, and Billingham, John. "MOONLAB: A Design for a Semipermanent Lunar Base," Proceedings of the Seventh Annual Working Group on Extraterrestrial Resources, Denver, Colorado, June 17-18, 1969.

9. Sharpe, Mitchell R. "Living in Space," Doubleday Science Series, Doubleday, Inc., Garden City, New York, 1969.

10. Ehricke, K.A. "Planning Space Stations for Long Range Utilization of Space for Earthians," Presented at Short Course on Space Station Technology and Utilization, Brussels, Belgium, September 1971.

11. "Solar Electric Propulsion Stage Final Report," Lockheed Missiles & Space Company, Inc., Contract NAS8-30315, January 28, 1975.

12. Glaser, Peter E., et. al, "Feasibility Study of a Satellite Solar Power Station," NASA CR-2357, February 1974.

13. Heitchue, Regis, D., Jr., "Space Systems Technology," Reinhold Book Corporation, New York, 1968.

14. Koelle, H.H., Editor, "Handbook of Astronautical Engineering," McGraw-Hill Book Company, New York, First Edition, 1961.

15. Dipprey, D., and Runkle, D., "A Forecast of Space Technology: Volume IV. Management of Energy," from *Outlook for Space 1980-2000*, Jet Propulsion Laboratory, California Institute of Technology, Pasadena, Calif., Second Draft, Feb. 5, 1975, pp. 4-3 to 4-39.

16. Salkeld, R., "Single Stage Shuttles for Ground Launch and Air Launch," *Astronautics & Aeronautics*, Vol. 12, No. 3, March 1974, pp. 52-64.

17. Gomersall, E.W. and Horby, H., "A Single-Stage-to-Orbit Shuttle Concept," NASA Ames Research Center, Report MO-70-2, July 20, 1970.

18. Koelle, D.E., and Broderson, H., "Feasibility Study of a Single-Stage Reusable Booster System – BETA," Federal Ministry for Scientific Research Contract RFT 1017, Bonn, Germany, NASA Translation (TT) F-13, 427, August 1969.

19. Salkeld, R., "Shuttle: An Alternative to Solid-Rocket Boost," *Astronautics & Aeronautics*, Vol. 13, No. 5, May 1975, p. 2.

20. Salkeld, P., "Deep Space Shuttles: Chemical vs Nuclear; Direct Flight vs Near-Orbit Rendezvous," *Journal of Spacecraft and Rockets*, Vol. 7, No. 11, Nov. 1970, pp. 1369-1371.

21. "Military Space Operations 1975-1995," Report NDS 13, Aerojet-General Corp., Sacramento, Calif., November 1969.

22. Salkeld, R., "Economic Implications of Extracting Propellants from the Moon," *Journal of Spacecraft*, Vol. 3, No. 2, Feb. 1966, pp. 254-261.

23. Levinson, A.A., and S.R. Taylor, "Moon Rocks and Minerals," Pergamon Press, New York, 1971.

24. Mason, B., and W.G. Melson, "The Lunar Rocks," Wiley-Interscience, New York, 1970.

25. Geake, J.E., "The Physics of Lunar and Planetary Surfaces," *Contemporary Physics*, Vol. 15, 1974.

26. Von Zeerleder, A., "Technology of Light Metals," Elsevier Publishing Co., New York, 1949.

27. Toth, C., and A. Lippman, "The Quest for Aluminum," *Mechanical Engineering*, September 1973, pp. 24-28.

28. Fidler, J., "Aluminum at Half the Price – If Toth's Idea will Scale Up," *The Engineer*, 2/9, August 1973, pp. 38-40.

29. Apollo 17 Preliminary Examination Team, "Apollo 17 Lunar Samples: Chemical and Petrographic Description," *Science*, Vol. 182, 16 November 1973, p. 667.

30. Peters, F.A., and P.W. Johnson, "Revised and Updated Cost Estimates for Producing Alumina from Domestic Raw Materials," U.S. Bureau of Mines, Information Circular 8648, 1974.

31. Ampion, S.G., "Lime-Soda Sinter Process," U.S. Bureau of Mines RI 6933, April 1967.

32. Lainer, A.I., and E.I. Tagiev, "Sulfuric-Acid Treatment of Zaglik Alunites," *The Soviet Journal of Non-Ferrous Metals*, Vol. 11, No. 1, 1970, pp. 43-45.

33. Scott, T.R., "The Recovery of Alumina from Its Ores by a Sulfuric Acid Process," International Symposium on Extractive Metallurgy of Aluminum, Vol. 1, G. Gerard and P.T. Stroup, Editors, Interscience Publishers, New York, pp. 305-349.

34. Conversation with John E. Husted, Engineering Experiment Station, Georgia Institute of Technology, Atlanta. Subsequent to this conversation a reference was found to a 1966 Bureau of Mines Report (RI 6744) which presents the results of a study of acid leaching of anorthosite.

35. Elger, G.W., D.E. Kirby, S.C. Rhoads and W.A. Stickney, "Synthesis of Rutile from Domestic Ilmenites," U.S. Bureau of Mines RI 7985, 1974.

36. Shelton, R.A.J., "Chloride-Volatilization Processes in Extractive Metallurgy," *Metallurgical Review, Vol. 16,* 1971, pp. 88-89.

37. Sanders, A.P., "Extraterrestrial Consumables Production and Utilization," NASA TM X-58087, MSC-06816, May 1972.

38. Dalton, C., et al., "Conceptual Design of a Lunar Colony," NASA CR-129164, September 1972, N73-11236.

39. Rosenberg, S.D., G.A. Guter and F.E. Miller, "Manufacture of Oxygen from Lunar Materials," *Annals of New York Academy of Sciences*, Vol. 123, 15 July 1965, pp. 1106-1122.

40. Khalafalla, S.E., and L.A. Haas, "Carbothermal Reduction of Siliceous Minerals in a Vacuum," *High Temperature Science*, Vol. 2, No. 2, June 1970, pp. 95-109.

41. Dietz, E.D., "The Glassy State," *International Science and Technology*.

42. Britton, M.G., "Glass Derivatives, a New Direction for Research," Conference on Emerging Priorities in Ceramic Engineering and Science, *Materials Science Research,* Vol. 8, 1974, pp. 165-179.

43. Molineux, K.J., "Glass as a Material of Construction for Chemical Plant," *BCE & Process Technology*, Vol. 16, September 1971, pp. 796-799.

44. Kapecky, L., and J. Voldan, "The Cast Basalt Industry," *Annals of New York Academy of Science,* Vol. 123, 15 July 1965, pp. 1986-1105.

45. Vasilos, T., "High Performance Ceramics," Symposium on Emerging Priorities in Ceramic Engineering and Science, *Materials Science Research,* Vol. 8, 1974, pp. 217-234.

46. Kesterke, D.G., "Electrowinning of Oxygen from Silicate Rocks," Bureau of Mines Report of Investigations 7581, 1971.

47. "Materials and Man's Needs," Summary Report of the Committee on the Survey of Materials Science and Engineering, National Academy of Sciences, Washington, D.C., 1974.

48. Ehricke, Krafft A., "Lunar Industries and their Value for the Human Environment on Earth." *Acta Astronautica*, Vol. 1, pp. 585-622, Pergamon Press, 1974.

49. Nishioka, Kenji, et al., "Feasibility of Mining Lunar Resources for Earth Use, Circa 2000 AD; Vol. 1: Summary," August 1973, Ames Research Center, Calif., NASA TM-X-62, 267.

50. Pfann, W.G., "Zone Melting," 1st edition, John Wiley & Sons, 1958, p. 93.

51. Ulrich, D.R., Chung, A.M., Yan, C.S., and Mc-

Creight, L.R., "Economic Analysis of Crystal Growth in Space," Final Report on NASA Contract No. NAS 8-27942, General Electric Company Space Sciences Laboratory, July 1972.

52. Deeg, E.W., "Glass Preparation in Space," *Space Processing and Manufacturing*, NASA Pub. ME-69-1, 1969.

53. Space Processing and Manufacturing, Report No. MS-69-1, NASA Marshall Space Flight Center, October 21, 1968.

54. Wuenscher, H.F., "Manufacturing in Space," *Astronautics & Aeronautics*, 10, p. 42, September 1972.

55. Wechsler, A.E., "Spherical Forming and Composite Casting in Zero-G," *Space Processing and Manufacturing*, NASA Pub. ME-69-1, 1969.

56. Final Report on Space Processing Skylab Experiments: MS512 Facility accommodating experiments M551, M552, M553, M479; M518 facility accommodating experiments M556-566.

57. Frederickson, D.S. and Lees, R.S., "Familial Hyperlipoproteinemia, Chapter 23, The Metabolic Basis of Inherited Disease," McGraw-Hill Book Co., New York, 1966.

58. Peeters, H., "Electrophoretic Separation of Lipoproteins," proposal to NASA from Simon Stevin Institut, March 1972.

59. Blaton, V., et al., *Protides of the Biological Fluids, 13*, 315 (1965).

60. Lowy, P.H. and Borsook, H., "Preparation and Properties of Erythropoietin Concentrates from Rabbit Plasma and Human Urine." *Erythropoiesis, 33*, 1962, Grune and Stratton.

61. Goldwasser, E.W., White, F., and Taylor, K.B., "On the Purification of Sheep Plasma Erythropoietin." *Erythropoiesis, 43*, 1962, Grune and Stratton.

62. Goldwasser, E.W. and Kung, C. K-H, "Purification of Erythropoietin," *Proc. Nat. Acad. Sci., 68*, USA, 697, 1971.

63. Wickerhauser, M., VI Congress of the World Federation of Haemophilia, July 25-27, 1970.

64. Cohn, E.J., et al., *Journal of the American Chemical Society 68*, 459, 1946.

65. Johnson, A.J., et al., *Thrombosis et Diathesis Haemorrhagica, Suppl. 26,* 377, 1967.

66. Newman, J., Johnson, A.J., Karpatkin, M.H. and Paszkin, S., *British J. Haematol. 1*, 21, 1971.

67. Neurath, A.R. and Rubin, B.A., "Viral Structural Components as Immunogens of Prophylactic Value," *Monographs in Virology* Vol. 4, S. Karger, New York, 1971.

68. Sarkar, S., *Z. Naturforschg. 21B,* 1202, 1966.

69. Information abstracted from Wayne State University proposal "Electrophoretic Separation of Antibodies," March 28, 1972.

70. Hannig, K. and Wrba, H., *Z. Naturforschung, 19B,* 860, 1964.

71. *C&E News*, July 31, 1972, p. 12.

72. Hannig, K. and Zaller, K., "*Z. Physiol. Chem. 350*, 467, 1969.

73. Holzberg, E. and Zeiller, K., European Div. Intermat. Soc., *Haematol.,* Abst. 293, 1971.

74. Zeiller, K. and Hannig, K., *Z. Physiol. Chem. 352,* 1162, 1971.

75. Hannig, K., Max Planck Institut, Munich, Germany – private communication.

76. Ellis, N. K., Merle Jensen, John Larsen, and Norman F. Oebker, "Nutriculture Systems," Station Bulletin #44, Department of Horticulture, Agricultural Experiment Station, Purdue University, March, 1974, p. 4; also, personal communication, Merle Jensen.

77. Meyers, John Richard, "Feeding Livestock from the Hydroponic Garden," Master's thesis, Arizona State University, May, 1974.

78. Berman, Gerald A., and Kate H. Murashige, "Synthetic Carbohydrate," NASA Contract NGR-05-020-409, School of Engineering, Stanford University, 1972, p. 40.

79. Poleman, Thomas T., "World Food: A Perspective," *Science*, Vol. 188, No. 4188, May 9, 1975, p. 514.

80. "Small Grain Variety Test," Univ. of Arizona Agrifile No. 2M, Q-39-AF-108, Sept. 1972.

81. Meyers, John Richard, "Feeding Livestock from the Hydroponic Garden," Master's thesis, Arizona State University, May, 1974, p. 28.

82. *Science*, Vol. 188, No. 4188, May 9, 1975, p. 627.

83. Milthorpe, F.L., and J. Moorby, "An Introduction to Crop Physiology," Cambridge University Press, 1974, pp. 72-73.

84. Clark, Colin, "Man's Space Requirements," Institute of Economic Progress, Mannix College, Monash University, Clayton, Victoria, Australia, March 1968; unpublished paper.

85. *Science*, Vol. 188, No. 4188, May 9, 1975, p. 627.

86. Fontes, Miguel R., "Controlled Environment Horticulture in the Arabian Desert at Abu Dhabi," *HortScience*, Vol. 8, No. 1, Feb. 1973, pp. 13-16.

87. Evans, G. Clifford, "The Quantitative Analysis of Plant Growth," University of California Press, 1972, pp. 16-17.

88. Jensen, M.H., and Eisa, H.M. 'The Use of Plastics for Agriculture on the Desert Seacoast of Abu Dhabi," Environmental Research Lab, Tucson, Arizona, Reprint No. 42.

89. "Arizona Agricultural Statistics," 1974, pp. 30-39.

90. Taylormade livestock feed formulas No. 3201, 5701, and 5401.

91. Sprague, G.F., *Science*, Vol. 188, No. 4188, May 9, 1975, p. 555.

92. Olson, Kenneth S., "A Proposal to Investigate the Potential of Producing Rabbits and Rabbit Food in the Same Facility," the University of Arizona, 1975.

93. Dr. Kenneth Olson, personal communication.

94. "Raise Rabbits," Carnation-Albers feed brochure, Shawnee Mission, Kansas.

95. Myers, John Richard, "Feeding Livestock from the Hydroponic Garden," Tempe Arizona State University, May, 1975, p. 43.

96. Frederick, Howard, "A Little Bit about a Lot," in "Bleatings," Arizona Dairy Goat Association, September 1974.

97. Drake, G.L., C.D. King, W.A. Johnson and E.A. Zuraw, "The Enclosed Life Support System," Ames Research Center, NASA SP-134, April 14-15, 1960, p. 42.

98. Piatt, V.R., and E.A. Ramskill, "Progress Report – Chemical Research in Nuclear Submarine Atmosphere Purification," NRL Report 7037.

99. "Exodus," *The Holy Bible*, 3:17.

100. Glaser, P.E., "Power from the Sun: Its Future," *Science*, Vol. 162, November 1968, pp. 857-886.

101. Feasibility Study of a Satellite Solar Power Station," NAS 3-16804, Arthur D. Little Inc., NASA CR-2357, February 1974, NTIS N74-17784.

102. Glaser, P.E., U.S. Patent 3,781,647, December 25, 1973.

103. Woodcock, G.R., and Gregory, D.L., "Derivation of a Total Satellite Energy System," AIAA paper 75-640, AIAA/AAS Solar Energy for Earth Conference, Los Angeles, April 24, 1975.

104. Brown, W.C. and Maynard, D.E., "The Adaptation of Free Space Power Transmission Technology to the SSPS Concept," AIAA/AAS Solar Energy for Earth Conference, Los Angeles, April 24, 1975.

105. "Microwave Power Transmission System," NASA Lewis Research Center, Contract No. NAS 3-27835.

106. "Reception Conversion Subsystem (RXCV) for Microwave Power Transmission System," JPL Report No. 953968, Contract NAS 7-100.

107. Kline, R., and Nathan, C.A., "Overcoming Two Significant Hurdles to Space Power Generation: Transportation and Assembly," AIAA/AAS Solar Energy for Earth Conference, Los Angeles, April 24, 1975.

108. "Space Based Solar Power Conversion and Delivery Systems." NASA Marshall Space Flight Center, Contract NAS 8-31308.

109. Goltz, "Uber die physiologische Bedent: ung der Bogengange des ohrlabyrinths." *Arch. f. d. ges. Physiol.* 3:192, 1870.

110. Flourens, P., "Recherches experimentales sur les proprietes et les fonctions du systeme nerveux vertebres" (Experimental investigations concerning the properties and functions of the nervous system of vertebrate animals). Paris: J.B. Bailliere, 1842, 2nd Ed. Chapt. 27-31, pp. 438-501.

111. Darwin, E., "Zoonomia: On the Laws of Organic Life." London, 1794, 2 Vols. Sect. 20 "of vertigo," Vol. 1, p. 227.

112. Purkinje, J., "Beitrage zur naheren Kenntnis des Schwindels aers Heautognostichen." Datn. Med. Jb., Wien., 6:79-125, 1820.

113. Meniere, P., "Menaire sur les lesions de P'oreille. Paris interne donnant lieu in des symptomes de congestion cerebrale apoplectiforme." *Gaz. Med. de Paris* s. 3 16:597-601, 1861.

114. Mach, E., "Grundlinien der Lehre von den Bewegungsempfindunger," 1875, Leipzig, Wilhelm, Engelmann, p. 127.

115. Crum-Brown, A., "On the sense of rotation and the anatomy and physiology of the semicircular canals of the internal ear." *J. Anat.,* Lond., 8:327-331, 1874. (Also *Proc. Royal Soc. Edinb.*, 8:225-257, 1874).

116. Breuer, J., "Uber die Funktion der otolithenapparate." *Pflug. Arch. ges. Physiol.*, 48:195-306, 1891.

117. Ewald, J.R., "Physiologische Untersuchungen uber das Endorgan des Nervus Octavus," 1892, Bergmann, Wiesbaden.

118. Steinhausen, W., "Uber Sichtbarmachung und Funktionsprufung der Cupula terminalis in den Bogengangsampullen des Labyrinthes" (Opening to view of and testing the function of the cupula terminalis in the ampulae of the semicircular canals of the labyrinth). *Pflug. Arch. ges. Physiol.*, 217:747-755, 1927.

119. Dohlman, G., "Some practical and theoretical points in labyrinthology." *Proc. R. Soc. Med.*, 50:779-790, 1935.

120. Kreidl, A., "Weiter Beitrage zur Physiologie des Ohrlabyrinthes," *Sitzungsb ARad Wissench Math-naturs cl*, 102:149, 1893.

121. Versteegh, C., "Ergebnisse partieller Labyrinthex-stirpation bei kaninchen." *Acta Otolaryng.*, 11:393-408, 1927.

122. Tait, J., and McNally, W.J., "Some features of the action of the utricular maculae (and of the associated action of the semicircular canals) of the frog." *Phi. Trans. B.*, 224:241-286, 1934.

123. Barany, R., "Die Untersuchung de reflektorischen vestibularen un optischen Augenbewegungen und ihre Bedeutung fur die topische Diagnostik der Augen-muskellohmungen," *Munchner Med. Wochenschr.* 1907, Nr. 22 und 23.

124. James, W., "The sense of dizziness in deaf mutes." *Amer. J. Otol.*, 4:239-254, 1882.

125. Sjoberg, A., "Experimentelle Studien uber den Auslosungmechanismus der Seekrankheit" (Experimental studies on the releasing mechanism of seasickness). *Acta oto-larygn.*, Stockh., Suppl. 14, 1-136, 1931.

126. Anson, B.J., Harper, D.B., and Winch, T.G., "The vestibular and cochlear aqueducts: Developmental and adult anatomy of their contents and parietes." In:"Third Symposium on the Role of the Vestibular Organs in Space Exploration." NASA SP-152, pp. 125-146. Washington, D.C., U.S. Government Printing Office, 1968.

127. Igarashi, M., "Dimensional study of the vestibular end organ apparatus." In: "Second Symposium on the Role of the Vestibular Organs in Space Exploration," NASA SP-115, pp. 47-53, Washington, D.C., U.S. Government Printing Office, 1966.

128. Spoendlin, H., "Structurelle Eigenschaften der Vestibularen Rezeptoren" (Structural Characteristics of the Vestibular Receptors). *Schweiz. Arch. Neurol. Psychiatr.*, Vol. 96, No. 2, pp. 219-230, 1965.

129. Graybiel, A., Clark, B., and Zarriello, J.J., "Observations on human subjects living in a "slow rotation room" for periods of two days." *Arch. Neurol.*, 3:55-73, 1960.

130. Clark, B., and Graybiel, A., "Human performance during adaptation to stress in the Pensacola Slow Rotation Room." *Aerospace Med.*, 32:93-106, 1961.

131. Guedry, F.E., Jr., Kennedy, R.S., Harris, C.S., Graybiel, A., "Human Performance during Two Weeks in a Room Rotating at Three RPM." BuMed Project MR005. 13-6001 Subtask 1, Report No. 74 and NASA Order No. R-47, Pensacola, Florida, Naval School of Aviation Medicine, 1962.

132. Graybiel, A., and Knepton, J., "Direction-specific adaptation effects acquired in a slow rotation room." *Aerospace Med.*, 43:1179-1189, 1972.

133. Fregly, A.R., and Kennedy, R.S., "Comparative effects of prolonged rotation at 10 RPM on postural equilibrium in vestibular normal and vestibular defective human subjects," *Aerospace Med.* 36:1160-1167, 1965.

134. Graybiel, A., Thompson, A.B., Deane, F.R., Fregly, A.R., Colehour, J.K., and Ricks, E.L., "Transfer of habituation of motion sickness on change in body position between upright and horizontal in a rotating environment," *Aerospace Med.*, 39:950-962, 1968.

135. "The Proceedings of the Skylab Life Sciences Symposium," NASA TMX-58154, Vol. 1, p. 169.

136. Maruyama, M., "The Second Cybernetics: deviation-amplifying mutual causal processes," *American Scientist* Vol. 51, pp. 164-179; 250-256, 1963.

137. Ulam, S., "On Some Mathematical Problems Connected with Patterns of Growth Figures," *Proceedings of Symposium on Applied Mathematics*, Vol. 14, pp. 215-224, 1962.

138. Maruyama, M., "Generating Complex Patterns by means of Simple Rules of Interaction," *Methodos* Vol. 14, pp. 17-26, 1963.

139. Buckley, W., "Modern Systems Research for the Behavioral Scientist", Aldine, 1968.

140. Myrdal, G., "American Dilemma," Harper and Row, 1944.

141. Myrdal, G., "Economic Theory and Underdeveloped Regions," Duckworth, 1957.

142. Maruyama, M., "Paradigmatology and its Application to Cross-disciplinary, Cross-professional and Cross-cultural Communication," *Cybernetica* pp. 136-156; 237-281, 1974.

143. Camara, S., "The Concept of Heterogeneity and Change among the Mandenka." *Technological Forecasting and Social Change*, Vol. 7, 1975.

144. Maruyama, M., "Symbiotization of Cultural Heterogeneity: scientific, epistemological and esthetic bases." *Co-existence,* Vol. 11, pp. 42-56, 1974.

145. Wright, S., "Evolution in Mendelian Population," *Genetics* Vol. 16, pp. 97-159, 1931.

146. Reichenbach, H., "Direction of Time," University of California Press, 1956.

147. Maruyama, M., "Monopolarization, Family and Individuality," *Psychiatric Quarterly*, Vol. 40, pp. 133-149, 1960.

148. Tonnies, F., "Gemeinschaft und Gesellschaft," 1887.

149. Hsu, F.L.K., "The American and the Chinese."

150. Maruyama, M., "A Critique of Some Widely Held Assumptions on the Relationship between Culture and Mental Health," *Revue de Psychologie des Peuples,* Vol. 14, pp. 273-276, 1959.

151. Maruyama, M., "The Multilateral Mutual Simultaneous Causal Relationships among the Modes of

Communication; Sociometric Pattern and Intellectual Orientation in the Danish Culture," *Phylon* Vol. 22, pp. 41-58, 1961.

152. Kluckhohn, C., "The Philosophy of Navaho Indians." In "Ideological Differences and World Order," edited by F.S.C. Northrop, Yale University Press, 1949.

153. Maruyama, M., "The Navajo Philosophy: an esthetic ethic of mutuality." *Mental Hygiene* Vol. 51, pp. 242-249, 1967.

Appendix A

Proceedings of the Princeton Conference
on
The Colonization of Space
May 10, 1974

An informative historical background for the Princeton Conference on Space
Manufacturing Facilities (Space Colonization) held May 7-9, 1975.

Edited by

Jerry Grey, AIAA

December 1976

Appendix A

TABLE OF CONTENTS

A-I INTRODUCTION

Roger W. Miles
Princeton University

In 1969, Gerard K. O'Neill of the Physics Department of Princeton University began studying the possibility of large-scale human colonization of space, with the restriction that only near-term technology be employed. In 1972-73, lectures on this topic were given at various universities, and by early 1974 a number of technical problems had been worked out in principle. A meeting was convened at Princeton University on May 9-10, 1974, to discuss the colonization of space as a serious possibility. Supported by the Point Foundation of San Francisco, the meeting's goal was to begin to formulate information which up to that point had been circulated only by word-of-mouth and a modest distribution of internal reports. The unique feature of this technical meeting, in contrast to those convened to discuss well-recognized topics having a standard literature, a research tradition, and a group of research workers who are well acquainted with each other, is that the space colonization work described in this Appendix was, up to this point, primarily an individual effort of Dr. O'Neill's.

The first day of the meeting, May 9, 1976, was by invitation only. Those attending were: Joseph Allen of NASA/MSC, David Anderson of Columbia University, Eric Drexler of the Massachusetts Institute of Technology, Freeman Dyson of the Institute for Advanced Study, Gerald Feinberg of Columbia University, Eric Hannah of Princeton University, George Hazelrigg of Princeton University, Gerard K. O'Neill of Princeton University, Gerald Sharp of NASA, Theodore Taylor of International Research & Technology, and Robert Wilson of NASA.

Topics discussed at the May 9th meeting were presented in lectures at the open meeting on May 10, except for an informal discussion by Freeman Dyson of the number, volume, age and constituents of comets, giving evidence for the large total mass and wide elemental abundance of cometary materials. Subsequent chapters in this appendix present an overall summary and detailed discussions of the specific topics covered by the speakers.

A-II. SUMMARY

Roger W. Miles
Princeton University

The space colonization concept was introduced by G. K. O'Neill, in the form of one possible design for a full-sized community of from 0.2 to 20 million people occupying several hundred square miles of "land" area in a closed manufactured habitat located at the L5 Earth-Moon Lagrange libration point. An illustrative scenario, based on the assumption that Model 1 would be in place at L5 and self-supporting by the late 1980's, suggested that full-sized communities could replicate with a six year doubling time beginning about 2014. With these assumptions, the space colonies appeared able to remove nearly all industry from the Earth's biosphere, even with no reduction of the present 2% annual population growth rate. This scenario indicated a population peak of about 16 billion for the Earth around 2050, followed by a rapid decrease due to emigration to the space colonies.

Gerald Feinberg discussed social implications of space colonization, emphasizing historical analogues. The rapid colonization of the Americas by Europeans in the 16th and 17th centuries profoundly affected Europe itself by the introduction of new ideas, the option of emigration for individuals and groups of independent spirit, and the return of new plant species. In the case of the space colonies, the analog for the latter might be industrial products whose fabrication would be unique to the space environment.

Dr. Feinberg pointed out that colonies, even though originally controlled from the mother country, tended to become independent with time. The possibility that the space colonies, being self-sufficient, might tend to develop individual social systems and experiment with new methods of societal accomodation was explored. He recalled the formation of the German Rocket Society in the mid 1920's and its culmination in the Apollo lunar flights, and suggested a comparable relationship between the present meeting and the growth of space colonization technology by 2024.

George Hazelrigg described the characteristics of the Lagrange libration points. He reported on performance specifications and cost estimates for rocket systems more advanced than those used in earlier assumptions; e.g., the solid-core hydrogen-propellant nuclear rocket which could be used for transfer from low Earth orbit to L5. He also described the more speculative plasma-core nuclear rocket.

Joseph Allen characterized the age-old steps in the acceptance of a new technical possibility, from "It's crazy" through "maybe it will work but who needs it?" to "I always said it was a good idea". He discussed living and working in zero-gravity conditions and concluded that, based on definitive SKYLAB experience, there seems to be every reason to believe that workers in gravity-force environments can perform their construction tasks with the same skills (and clumsiness) that they exhibit at one gravity. He showed SKYLAB films of oscillations in large liquid "drops", the precession of a bearingless gyroscope under applied torques, and the motion of a long liquid-filled bottle initially set spinning about its long axis. With frictional damping of the liquid motion, combined conservation of angular momentum and energy led to rotation about a new shifting axis. (This problem, incidentally, is avoided in the space colonies' geometry by the physical linking of two parallel counter-rotating cylinders).

Robert Wilson described a system for freight transport from the Earth to L5, based on using, in an unmanned freight-hauler, the new high-performance engines now being developed for the space shuttle. Most of the orbiter, including all the payload bay, controls, and man-rated sections, would not be used; the engines and avionics would be re-used. Cost estimates ranged from $400 to $200 per pound. Dr. Wilson emphasized the large number of alternative approaches possible, each with a cost minimization to be studied. He also pointed out that with agreement and determination such a system could easily be developed by the early 1980's, because it falls completely within well-understood technology.

Eric Hannah described in more detail a system of the kind sketched by Dr. Wilson; he also showed staging optimization curves and outlined in numerical detail a launch sequence delivering payloads to L5 at a cost of $190 to $250 per pound.

Eric Drexler and David Anderson summarized data on the composition of the lunar surface. The Moon is an excellent source of aluminum, iron, titanium, silicon and oxygen, all usable in colony construction, but is poor carbon, hydrogen and nitrogen.

Eric Drexler reported that the asteroid belt is assumed to be logistically unreachable until approximately the time of Model 3, to be started about 1995 at the earliest in O'Neill's scenario. Once it is accessible, though, it should prove a rich source of carbon, nitrogen and hydrogen, in carbonaceous chondritic asteroids. This could permit Model 3 to be the first colony built with minimal aid from the Earth.

Dr. O'Neill concluded the meeting with a detailed description of space colony technology. He outlined the details of the suggested Transport Linear Accelerator, a linear electric motor device to launch lunar materials to be used for colony construction from the surface of the Moon to L5. It would have a total length of 13 km and develop an acceleration of about 29 g's. Magnetic fields would be held below 10,000 gauss. Energy storage capacitator banks would be spaced about 50 meters apart, supplying linear motor segments through local switchgear by way of control feeders which would also serve as guideway supports. For a system with capacity to transfer 500,000 tons of material in six years at a 25% duty cycle, the mass estimate was 1500 tons, 80% of which would be in the power-plant and power handling equipment. The total estimate for the lunar base was given as 3000 tons.

Model 1, for 10,000 people, was assigned a nominal total mass about equal to that of a present-day supertanker: 500,000 tons. Of this, 30,000 tons would be aluminum and glass made at L5 from lunar material; 420,000 tons would be lunar soil and rock as a matrix for agriculture and as unstressed construction material. 5400 tons of liquid hydrogen, to provide 50,000 tons of water, would have to brought from the Earth, as well as 1000 tons each of special hardware, generator plants, and initial structures. Machines and tools require 800 tons; 2000 people -- the work force -- another 200 tons; and dehydrated food, rich in carbon, nitrogen and hydrogen, another 600 tons.

The final construction cost estimate for Model 1 is 31 billion dollars. Apollo's cost, in the same 1972 dollars, was about 33 billion dollars. The largest single items are: transport from the Earth to L5, $10.7 billion; transport from the Earth to the Moon, $6.6 billion; and salaries for the workers on Earth, $7.2 billion. Ordinary equipment for L5 was capitalized at $180 per pound; machines and tools at $625 per pound, and equipment for the Moon at $400 per pound.

For industrial products made at L5 from lunar material and intended for the construction of Model 2, a value of $250 per pound for transport costs saved should be added. Model 1, therefore, would appear able to pay off its own cost in from one to three years.

A-III. THE COLONIZATION OF SPACE

Gerard K. O'Neill
Princeton University

This meeting has been convened by individuals interested in exploring the possibilities of space colonization: the construction of habitats in space which could be richly productive and delightful to live in. The time scale is not the distant future, but now, using the science and engineering of the 1970's. I believe that the technical imperatives of these new ideas are such as to encourage self-sufficiency, small-scale governmental units, and a high degree of independence.

The basic notion in accomplishing this goal, discussed at some length in a talk given in the Physics Department here about eighteen months ago, is to treat space as a culture medium which is rich in matter and energy ripe for exponential growth. To live, people need energy, land, water, air and gravity. Energy from the sun is free and easy to use in space, but solar energy is difficult to use conveniently and efficiently on Earth. Materials are present in vast quantities on the Moon and in the asteroid belt.

The goal today is a kind of existence proof, not to show the "only way" that things can be done, in a particular specification, but rather to give some idea of what can be done with the virtually unlimited resources of matter and energy that exist in space.

A preview of the logic we are following is as follows: Using the hardware which is already under development for the space shuttle program in the early 1980's, we propose to set up a mining and processing plant of modest size on the Moon. With the same kind of conventional propulsion system, over a period of six years we would send to the L5 Lagrange libration point, which forms with the Earth and Moon an equilateral triangle, about 10,000 tons of equipment and about 2,000 people.

Figure A-1 shows the location of the L5 Lagrange libration point, 60° behind the Moon in the orbit of the Moon around the Earth. There are several other libration points to be discussed in a subsequent presentation. Neglecting the gravitational influence of the sun, the L5 point is stable. An object located at L5 would stay there forever.

The next point in the sequence is to send to L5 about half a million tons of metallic ore, oxides and lunar soil over a period of about six years, shipped directly from the Moon by a new type of solar powered, automated materials-transfer system. At L5, using the constant and plentiful solar power which is available there (unlike the lunar surface, where the solar power supply gets turned off by the lunar night for two weeks out of every four), we would build a habitat.

The space colony that we would put at L5, Model 1, could then grow its own natural food and continuously support a population of about 10,000 people. It could become a site for a solar powered, pollution-free industry to construct nearly all the materials which are needed for Model 2, which could be ten times larger. With each step one could build a habitat ten times larger than the one before it. As time went on, the materials source would become the asteroid belt rather than the Moon.

Figure A-1. Location of the Lagrange Libration Point L5.

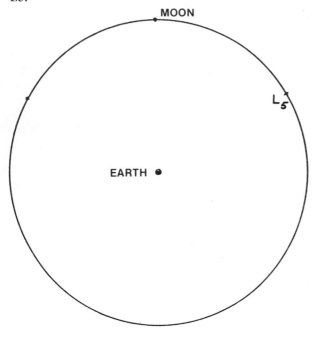

None of the technical tricks which are needed for this task is beyond 1970's technology. Today's detailed discussion is mainly about Model 1. It is, in our terms, a modest effort, although 10,000 people and half a million tons of mass sounds startling compared to what has been put into space so far. An attractive feature of this concept, I believe, is that it is possible to keep this project to the same general cost range as that of the Apollo project, which we have already done. Whether we could do it again at the present time and in the present climate of opinion is another question, but that we can discuss later.

If these ideas are followed, people could be living and working in space within the next fifteen to twenty years, if they want to. By the early years of the century, the successively larger space colonies could reach a size capable of supporting between two hundred thousand and perhaps ten million people. Thereafter, it is enough that each full-sized community replicate itself in a time short compared to the thirty-year doubling time of the human population. For a six year replication time, the development would then unfold in such a way that, perhaps as early as 2050, most of the manufacturing carried out by the human race would be conducted in space rather than on Earth; presumably people would follow their jobs and would live near the places where they would be working, since the living conditions in space could be much better than in even some of the more attractive places on Earth.

By the middle of the next century, or even earlier, the cost of manufacturing and distribution in space colonies should be lower than on Earth. Manufacturing costs have three major components: the mining and shipping of raw materials; the processing and fabrication of finished goods; and the distribution of goods to consumers. In the long run, it can be agreed, all three of these can be done quite efficiently in space.

First, in the asteroid belt and on the Moon, rich sources of minerals can be found without deep mining or drilling. Our experience on Earth is that shipping is cheapest by sea because ocean freight can be carried on very large ships at a small cost and energy, without the need for large crews. Shipment in space is the direct analogue of ocean freight, but even more advantageous in the long run. There is almost no limit to the size of vessels that can be built, and solar power provides a dependable free source of energy. There is no weight in space, and navigation there is easier than on Earth's oceans. Therefore, there is probably no need for a human crew at all; a computer of a simple, inexpensive sort is quite adequate to navigate a vessel from the asteroid belt to the region of the space colonies, which is fairly near the Earth.

Second, processing and fabrication should be inexpensive in the space colony because the labor force can be housed in comfort, in a clean environment, and only a few minutes travel time from the factory. Electric power ought to be cheap, because the source is free and the powerplants can be simple. They shouldn't require much maintenance; moreover, the power will never have to be transported more than about twenty miles. On Earth, much of the cost of electric power is in the distribution system. Process heating by solar power will be free, completely dependable and clean. In addition, whenever anyone needs them, vacuum processing and zero gravity fabrication are readily available.

Finally, shipping finished goods to consumers will be cheap, because all colonies will be accessible to each other by vehicles which don't have to have any engines or highly trained crews. Such vehicles, taking advantage of the vacuum environment and the absence of any strong gravitational field, can be launched by electric motor from one of the colonies and be picked up by another. These economic reasons lead me to believe that by a century from now, industrial manufacturing could virtually disappear from the Earth. By 2074 more than 90% of the human population could be living in space colonies. I say could, because all of these things are so far only technical possibilities. Whether we can do them politically, and whether there is a consensus of opinion that we should, is a separate issue. But people could be living in space, with a virtually unlimited clean source of energy for everyday use. They could have an abundance and a variety of food and material goods, a great deal of freedom to travel, and independence from large-scale governments.

The Earth could become a world-wide park, free of industry, and slowly recovering by natural means from the near death-blow that it received from the Industrial Revolution. A beautiful place to visit for a vacation!

There are a number of basic tricks which are essential to making this plan economically practical. These are, first, to reconfigure some of the available hardware which has been developed for the space shuttle program, so as to obtain minimum-cost transport for freight from the Earth to L5; second, to gain a factor of almost ten in the efficiency of producing water at L5 by transporting liquid hydrogen from the Earth and combining it at L5 with oxygen from the plentiful oxides of the lunar surface material; third, to use an automated electromagnetic transport system which takes advantage of the low gravity and vacuum environment of the Moon to transport inexpensively from the Moon at least 98% of the materials that

are needed for construction; and finally -- an important concept very different from what has been done in space so far -- the production of successively larger models of these communities in space rather than on Earth. In the not very long run, this avoids the whole business of expensive shipping from the surface of the Earth up into space.

There are those among us who say that it is ridiculous to have everything so Earth-like; we should immediately go to a zero-gravity environment and we will find that zero-gravity is much better than one normal Earth gravity. To that I can only reply: fine, if you want to do it that way. Colonies could be built along those lines. But for the initial discussion I am interested in possibilities which are very Earth-like, because if this concept is to compete for funds, whether governmental or private, I think it has to be shown to be of potential benefit to a great many people who themselves cannot imagine living in any but Earth-like environments.

Figure A-2 shows Model 1, a rotating cylinder in space about a kilometer long and 200 meters in diameter. The cylinder rotates once every twenty seconds, so that the people who live inside it would experience one Earth gravity. They could carry on normal Earth-like activities, and although the view from a land area of Model 1 would be different from that of the Earth in that the residents would not look up at clouds and a distant blue sky, the color quality of the sunlight received could be made to be Earthlike by tinting the glass. The distant view would clearly be that of a cylinder interior.

The cylinder would be subdivided into six segments. Three would be land areas used for intensive but conventional farming; three would be window areas. An important, although certainly not profound technological trick that would be employed (I say not profound because it could have been imagined three hundred years ago), is that the axis of the cylinder would always point in the direction of the sun. The natural sunlight would be brought in by means of three planar mirrors. They would be low in mass and would be connected to the cylinder by many low-mass cables.

Anyone looking up at one of these mirrors would see the disc of the sun, not rotating once every twenty seconds, but simply standing there, stationary in the sky. It would appear normal, of the same size and disc shape as is the sun when seen from Earth. The only difference (it is one which

Figure A-2 The "Model 1" Space Colony

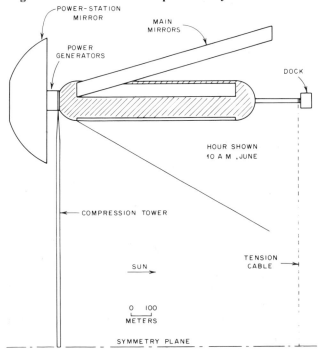

could not be resolved with the naked eye) is that the disc of the sun itself would rotate about its center, once every twenty seconds. The sun's disc is so nearly circular that the rotation would not be visible.

Now, any physics student will realize that there would be an enormous angular momentum with 500,000 tons of mass rotating once every twenty seconds. It would be a lovely gyroscope pointing always at a particular constellation of the big stars. In order to make the concept work, it is necessary to precess that gyroscope around, once per year, so that its axis would always point toward the sun. One simple solution is to connect the front end of the rotating cylinder by a bearing, through a cable, to another identical cylinder. For Model 1 the cable could be as little as a centimeter in diameter. At the back end of the cylinders, one would need a compression tower a little like two television towers back-to-back. It too could be of very low mass. It would provide a compression force so that the net force on the two-cylinder system would be zero, but there would be a gentle torque applied. The forces required to precess even this big gyroscope in such a long time as a year are really very small; it turns out, in fact, that for the Model 1 cylinder you need only about sixty pounds of force in the cable and on the compression tower at the other end.

The mirrors, in Figure A-2 are at a particular angle corresponding to a time of 10:00 A.M. in the month of June. The idea is that as the day goes on, the inhabitants could control the sun angle in the sky by pulling in or letting out the main mirrors. Therefore, even with something as primitive as Model 1, it is possible to have the conventional day-night cycle and to have the length of day as you wish it.

The electric power could be generated by conventional steam-electric generating plants, which are shown in Figure A-2 as being supplied with solar energy from a parabolic mirror at the back end of the cylinder. A substantial amount of the mass budget for this powerplant would have to go into infra-red radiators needed to radiate away the waste heat dictated by the second law of thermodynamics. This plant would work at a fairly high temperature, not requiring new technology, but at the limits of present day technology.

There could be a non-rotating dock at the other end, so spacecraft could dock onto the colony without having to match the 3 rpm rotation rate.

Figure A-3 Possible Arrangement For The End Cap Of A Model 1 Space Colony

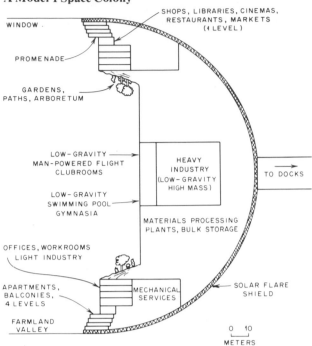

Figure A-3 is a view of the hemispherical end cap of a possible Model 1, illustrating what might be done with 200 meters of diameter. The sun would be off to the right. To make sure that the residents aren't damaged by the cosmic rays of solar flares, they would be shielded by a certain amount of lunar surface material on or in the end-cap shell.

For the 10,000 or so people who could be living in Model 1, there would be rather comfortable, spacious living quarters in a series of apartments. It would be like urban living in this country, with the difference that instead of looking into the windows of another apartment one would be looking out onto farmland. One could imagine having a promenade of shops, cinemas, restaurants, markets, and libraries, extending all the way around the cylinder. Of course, Model 1 would have a high-density population, so one could not have all the beautiful parks that one would like to have in the bigger communities. However, I am sure that the people living there would love to have trees and flowers, so I've shown a little garden in Figure A-3.

Even with Model 1, some new possibilities for sports and ways of living would become possible. One of the simplest and most appealing to some of us is human-powered flight. At the axis the force of gravity would be zero, and almost any muscle-powered flying machine would work, including ornithopters of the kind invented by Leonardo Da

Vinci. In Earth's normal one-gravity such machines are almost impossible, but up there it would be easy to fly them.

One could imagine that there would also be low-gravity swimming pools, which offer innumerable possibilities. For example, you could dive off a diving board and take ten seconds before hitting the water, and when you did hit the water, the splash would go up in beautiful slow motion. It would be delightful.

To conclude this discussion of Model 1, I'd like to emphasize again that the geometry shown for the colony, like all other details, is simply one possibility. Our intention at this point is to show at least one solution for each technical problem; the choice among solutions can wait until much later.

Figure A-4 shows the scale of the largest colony that could be built within the limits of the strengths of conventional materials. I call it "Model 4", and it could be as much as four miles in diameter. It would be large enough to be quite Earth-like -- not in the sense that you would be "fooled" and couldn't guess that you were in a space colony -- but in the sense that the atmosphere would be deep enough (four miles across) so that the cloud layers would be local to the particular valleys.

Figure A-5   Scale of End Cap in Model 4 Space Colony

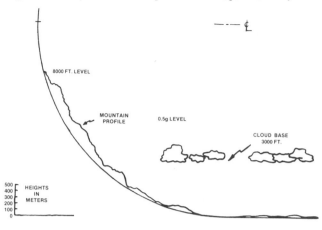

That effect is indicated in Figure A-5, which shows what the end-cap of one of these large space communities might look like. The distance from the axis to the cylinder wall would be about two miles. The typical cloud heights on a nice summer day would be as I have shown them here. One could quite naturally model mountains; the particular profile that I have shown was traced from an air view of the Grand Teton mountains. In a deliberately constructed habitat you wouldn't normally model something ugly, of course; you would be guided by the nicest parts of the Earth.

Figure A-4   Scale of 4-mile-diameter Model 4 Space Colony

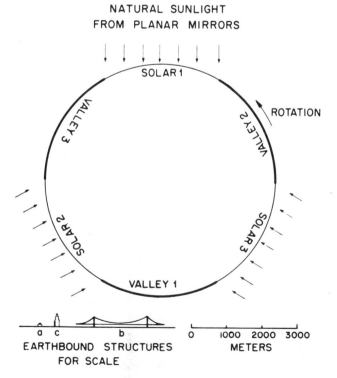

Figure A-6   Overall Diagram of Model 4 Space Colony, Showing Separate Agricultural Areas

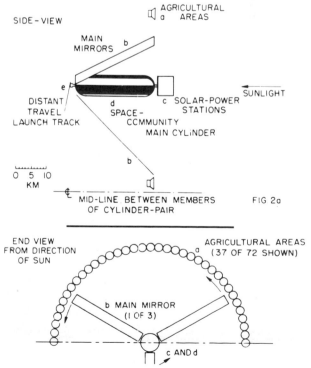

Consider, for example, starting out on a mountain hike in a space community. You would always know that it was going to be a nice day, unlike the Earth. You would start your hike climbing up the mountain, working as hard against gravity as you would on the Earth. However, the higher you go, and the more tired you get, the lower the gravity forces would become. By the time you arrived near the top, you would be bounding and skipping along.

Figure A-6 is an overall diagram of Model 4, which we see to be simply a version of Model 1. By the time space colonization goes that far, however, it may be preferable to separate completely the growing of food from environment for habitation. Perhaps the whole land area of Model 4, some 100 square miles, could be devoted to parks and forests and natural environments; places where people and animals would roam freely. Perhaps all of the food-growing could be banished to an area which need not be Earth-like at all. Figure 6 shows such an area in the form of agricultural cylinders on the outside perimeter. They would not rotate as a group, although individually they would rotate to develop any level of gravity which by then would have been found best for rapid plant growth.

There are several attractive possibilities in this concept. First of all, unlike Earth, food would only be transported a distance of twenty miles; therefore everything could be fresh. There would be no need for frozen food processing. Because the agriculture would be initiated without harmful pests that have evolved on the Earth, both food crops and the residents' gardens could grow without the need for pesticides and insecticides. There would be the additional possibility of arranging weather conditions and the seasonal cycle of each cylinder, phasing them individually for January, February, March, April and so on, so there could be, for example, fresh strawberries every month of the year.

As a matter of interest, the Model 4 space colony could enclose more than half of the island of Bermuda in one of its valleys. Or, if you prefer, the pleasant residential community of Los Altos Hills, near San Francisco, or perhaps Carmel Bay, from Pebble Beach down to Point Lobos. Eventually the population density need be no higher overall than that of Switzerland; we are not talking about people crammed in like sardines. The earliest colony would have a population density intermediate between that of San Francisco and those of attractive villages in Italy and Southern France.

Figure A-7 A Scenario for Future Population Growth on Earth and in Space Colonies

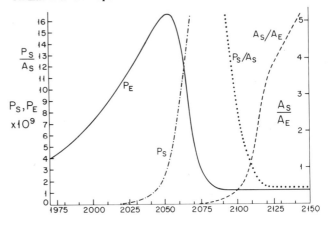

The subject of population density raises some interesting questions as to what impact space colonies could have on future world population growth. Figure A-7 shows just one of many possibilities for development. There are now four billion people on the surface of the Earth. If the population growth rate continues as it has in the recent past, at about two percent per year, there will be sixteen billion people by about the year 2050.

If we were to start space colonization soon, it would be possible, given the growth rate of new land area in the space colonies, to have the population in space begin at least to appear on the graph of Figure A-7 by about the year 2020. The land area in space could grow very quickly because of the possibility for replicating the colonies by using the virtually unlimited materials and energy available in space. Therefore one possibility, though certainly not the only one, is that the attractive living conditions of the colonies could attract people to emigrate from the Earth. The population of the Earth could then be stable, possibly even at a lower value than it is now. In Figure A-7 I have arbitrarily shown a population of 1.2 billion. That happens to correspond to the year 1910, which we all feel nostalgic about because almost none of us were there.

The population density (people per unit area) in space is shown in Figure A-7 to drop from a density limit corresponding to Model 1 to a low density typical of Model 4. In that final case only a couple of hundred thousand people would be spread out over several hundred square miles. That is, the population density in space could end up quite low. This particular scenario shows the area in space increasing above that of the total land area on Earth within a time which is roughly 150 years from now, then slowing as the density gets down to a low value, and finally nearly stabilizing with only a slow increase from then on.

It is certainly not my purpose in proposing this kind of possibility to say that it would be desirable for the human race to grow to twenty thousand times its present size, but I want to point out the incredible potential of what we are suggesting by saying that there is room enough for that. In contrast to our experience with expanding civilizations on Earth, in space colonization there would be no destruction of indigenous primitive populations; nothing corresponding to the Indian wars of 19th century America.

DISCUSSION:

Q. *How would you provide gravity?*

A. To answer that I'd like to contrast the ways of providing gravity. Gravity obtained from a planet is inefficient for space flight because you can't get normal gravity on a planet without also having a deep gravitational potential to go with it. Gravity is produced by a large amount of mass distributed throughout the planetary volume; we have something like 10^{12} tons per human being to hold us down on the surface of the Earth. That is fairly wasteful; besides, it means that when you try to get away from the planet and travel somewhere else, you have to fight a large gravitational potential.

It has been known for several hundred years that it is possible to produce an acceleration which would feel like normal gravity, by building a cylinder in free space and rotating it at a certain speed. If you were to stand on the inside of such a cylinder, the acceleration would be V^2/R, with (V) the tangential velocity of the cylinder and (R) its radius. If the rotational speed were correct to make V^2/R equal to one normal Earth gravity, anyone standing on the inside would feel as if he were on the surface of a planet with a gravity of one-G.

By providing an artificial gravity we avoid conflict with the several million years of evolution that have brought our bodies to this particular point. We need gravity in order to be healthy for a long period, and to have things related to gravity that we are used to, like an atmosphere, clouds, and trees that grow in a well-defined "up" direction rather than

sideways. The use of centrifugal acceleration rather than a planetary mass also makes use of the great advantage, for space flight, of not being deep in a gravitational potential well. If one goes to the axis of a rotating cylinder in space and goes outside at its end, one could get into an ordinary spacecraft and go a long distance, for example to another colony, without having to expend energy to climb out of a deep potential well. This is the reason why the cost of freight transport in space will be less than on the surface of the Earth.

Q. *You only have to start it rotating once?*

A. That is right. As soon as you put the cylinder in rotation it will sit there spinning forever; you don't have to provide more power to keep it going.

Q. *I understand that some considerable portion of the research and the costs of certain aspects of the space program have been taken over by free enterprise; for instance, portions of space communications development and portions of the research involved in space manufacturing. You seem to assume that most of the costs of the initial colonies will be borne by the government. In view of the facts that I just mentioned, do you really consider that necessary, or just inevitable?*

A. I hope the answer will turn out to be no, to both questions. The reason for comparing space colonization to the Apollo program is that Apollo constitutes a kind of existence proof. We know that we were able once before, as just a single nation, to carry out a task of that magnitude. The Apollo project, although spectacular and interesting was, I believe, far less rewarding in the long run for the human race than space colonization could be. As to how space colonization could be realized practically, there are several possibilities. As you may know, in the shuttle program, there is already considerable cooperation between this country and the European nations. These nations are producing the Spacelab. Also, as you point out, there has already been an involvement of private enterprise in space. Many of the communications satellites were developed by private enterprises. I think that in the long run that is a much more healthy way to go. Therefore I wouldn't like to try to specify or define how we could accomplish a space colonization program.

A-IV   SOME SOCIAL IMPLICATIONS OF SPACE COLONIZATION

Gerald Feinberg
Columbia University

Introduction. The setting up of self-supporting human colonies on other planets has been one of the staple themes of science fiction as well as detailed scientific analyses. Several of these discussions, especially those in the science fiction stories, have also suggested some of the societies that might emerge in such space colonies, as well as the impacts of the colonies upon life on Earth. However, the increased knowledge that we have gained from manned and unmanned space flights and from sophisticated Earth-based astronomy about the physical conditions on other planets of the solar system indicates clearly the utter inhospitability of these planets to human life. They now appear to be unsuitable for permanent colonies of the type envisioned by science fiction writers.

One might have thought that this would make the discussion of space colonization uninteresting, until such time as we develop either the capability to modify the conditions on other planets to make them more fit for human life, or the capability to travel to yet undiscovered extrasolar planets, or the capability to create, through biological engineering, alternate forms of humanity that could survive under present conditions on the solar-system planets. The technology needed to exploit these possibilities, although they are interesting, would seem to be so relatively far in the future that they are not of immediate concern.

A more interesting development, pointing to the need for further consideration of the social effects of space colonization, is the suggestion by G. K. O'Neill (see preceding section) that such colonies could be set up not on other planetary bodies, but instead in the inside of hollow, manmade planetoids that are in orbit either in the neighborhood of Earth and Moon, or around the Sun. O'Neill's analysis suggests that it is within our present technological capabilities to construct self-supporting colonies of this type, and in sufficient numbers that they could, by the middle of the 21st century, become the permanent home of large numbers of people.

If that is the case, then it becomes much more important to examine the implications of such a process of colonization, especially if, as suggested by O'Neill, it could begin within the next ten years or so. One reason such an examination is needed is that the construction of the first few colonies is likely to require much time and effort by Earth dwellers, most of whom will not be among the future colonists. It would be well to indicate both to those workers and to our elected representatives, who might have to vote for the money to build the colonies, what the consequences of such an effort might be.

More generally, if the colonization of space follows a growth curve at all resembling past human expansions into open territory, it is likely to continue over a very long period of time, to involve immense numbers of people, and eventually to have a major influence on the future history of our species and perhaps on the history of life in our part of the universe. It would therefore seem prudent to consider, even before beginning space colonization, what some of its specific effects might be on human life. In this I include both the lives of the colonists and the lives of those continuing to live on Earth. Through a consideration of such questions, we could hope to arrive at some conclusions about the desirability of the whole venture, and, if it does appear desirable, to get some insights that would be valuable in determining the precise ways in which space colonization is carried out. Indeed, such an analysis of long-term social consequences is desirable for almost any proposed major technological innovation, but has rarely been carried out in advance.

An accurate analysis of long-term social implications of innovation is not at all simple, and may not even be feasible. The complexity of social systems, and the difficulty that a human observer has in being sufficiently objective about the idiosyncrasies of his own time and place, make the task seem formidable, perhaps impossible. Nevertheless, since we have no better option than to use our best guesses about the future to guide our actions, and with the view that even a somewhat inaccurate analysis may have some value, I offer these speculations on some long term social implications of space colonization. Because they offer the best opportunity for accurate forecasting, I shall consider only those implications that involve large groups of people in a similar way, rather than those involving small numbers, or involving people in diverse ways.

I shall assume that the general physical description given by O'Neill will characterize the future space colonies with some accuracy. That is, I assume that these colonies are self-sustaining systems, containing from 10^4-10^7 people, living under local environmental conditions not very dissimilar from those on Earth. The precise technology by which this is accomplished is not very important for my purposes, and I shall follow O'Neill in assuming that the technology is not too different from that currently foreseeable. Truly radical developments in technology would tend to make my analysis less reliable. For example, a transportation method that would allow travel from Earth to the colonies in a few hours would make the accomplishment of independence of the colonies more difficult. Similarly, a lack of self-sufficiency of the colonies, in the sense that they remain dependent on Earth for essential elements of their existence, would be a qualitatively different situation which might render my analysis inapplicable.

Purposes of Space Colonization. An important part of the analysis of social implications of space colonization is to try to determine what human purpose it would serve and what purposes it might hinder. It would therefore be helpful to have a set of explicit statements of some human purposes. My book, *The Prometheus Project,* points out that no such list is readily available, even though a consensus on such purposes would be an invaluable guide for judging the merits of all technological innovations. In the absence of such an explicit list, I will try to indicate how space colonization fits in with a number of purposes that seem to be implicitly contained in much of the human activity that is generally considered desirable.

A general purpose that would be served by space colonization is that it would be another step in the process that our species has been following since prehistory, that of learning to live in a wider and wider set of conditions, in many cases differing from those under which we originally evolved. It is fashionable among some people nowadays to call for a return to a natural life. This call has sometimes been based on an appeal to the theory of evolution. It is argued that humans have evolved in a very different environment than the man-made one in which many of us now spend our time. It is said that, as a result, we do not function as well as we would in the original environment, for which our bodies and psyches are better adapted. This argument seems to me to be based on a logical misconception of the principle of natural selection. According to that principle, humans, as well as other organisms, have evolved. This does not imply that humans as they are now constituted could not function better in an alternative environment to that one. The fallacy involved in this view is that in natural selection the environment is kept fixed and the genotype varies, while in human activity we vary the environment, keeping the genotype fixed. There is no reason to expect the result reached in the first case to represent the optimum possible in the second case. In fact, it seems obvious that humans function better and more happily in an increasingly more man-made environment than they did in their original environment.

Furthermore, it is clear in any case that no return to the latter situation is possible for any large number of people, and such a return is not even desired by any large number. The capability of living independently of natural conditions has been instrumental in the "humanization" of mankind, i.e., has permitted the flourishing of those activities that most distinguish us from other species, such as art and science. It is hard to see how these activities could flourish if we had continued to live in, or returned to, anything like the "natural" environment in which we evolved.

Space colonization would take the process of living in new environments one step further, in that the colonists would become independent of the Earth altogether, except as a source of some original raw materials. By making possible such life independent of Earth, we would be expanding the scope of life in the universe in several important ways.

We would be creating for life a new ecological niche which did not exist previously. That is, we would be carrying the age-old progress of life through another step, into another environment, and in this case into an environment that would not be filled by ordinary evolution for eons to come, if ever. Most of us, even those devoted to life as such rather than to human life in particular, would consider this extension of the domain of life desirable.

Developments in the 20th century have made the future of life on Earth, especially human life, somewhat more uncertain than it previously was, by making possible such events as as all-out nuclear war or environmental disaster on a global scale. While I do not consider the probability of either of these as very high, it is not zero, and must be taken into account in any estimate of the future of life. At the least, such disasters might destroy our present civilization, which depends on a delicate web of inter-relating activities; at the worst, human life, or even all life on Earth, might be destroyed. The existence of self-sufficient space colonies, with substantial numbers of people and other forms of life living on them, would provide an important form of insurance against the effects of such disasters. They could act as a repository for the technical knowledge, materials, and trained people that might be destroyed on Earth in a breakdown of industrial civilization. In the case of a greater catastrophe involving the destruction of all life on Earth, they would insure that life and our species would nevertheless survive in our part of the universe. One may grant that this could probably be insured in other ways, say by colonies deep underground, but probably not in a way of life that would appeal to many people. Space colonies might even be proof against catastrophes caused by extraterrestrial influences, such as sudden increases in the intensity of solar radiation or sharp increases of ionizing radiation due to supernova explosions in nearby stars. As I treasure humanity, its achievements, and its future potential, I welcome

any feasible way of safeguarding us against destruction by blind nature or by unthinking people, and the dispersal of some of our population off the Earth appears to me an important step in that direction.

Another important purpose served by the creation of space colonies would be to allow a significant increase in the number of human beings in the universe, comparable to the increase allowed by the invention of agriculture. This statement contradicts the implicit message of the recent movement to limit population growth on Earth, and it is useful to explore the basis for that contradiction.

There is an obvious distinction to be made between limiting population growth out of need, because it is difficult or impossible to support the additional population, and limiting it out of desire or the conviction that there is no value to having more people. A case can be made for limiting growth because of need, at least on Earth. Although it is not completely clear that we have reached the limits of human population that could live well on Earth, we will soon do so if we continue increasing at our present rate. However, this argument is clearly irrelevant to limiting the population of space colonies, if the increased population can live well in these colonies. We therefore must face the question of the intrinsic desirability of having more people, assuming that space colonies afford us that option.

An important argument in favor of more people is that the individual human is the only bearer, so far as we know, of a unique quality: conscious mind. To the extent that we act to increase the number of thinking human beings, we increase the amount of the universe endowed with consciousness and purpose, a trend that seems wholly desirable. There may be other ways to increase the scope of consciousness in the universe, but they are not yet known to us. It therefore seems preferable to have a given amount of matter incorporated into conscious human brains (to the extent that this is possible) than to have the corresponding matter remain in rocks, atmospheric gases, or even in the bodies of other animals whose level of consciousness is lower or absent.

There is a related but more pragmatic argument in favor of more people. There are certain activities that only people have been able to perform well, such as creating art, making choices, etc. To the extent that we all benefit from these activities, we may expect that when there are more people to do them, we will all be better off. This depends on the use of technology to provide multiplier effects, such as millions of records of a single musical performance. Also, it appears that the number of extremely talented people does not increase as rapidly as the population, so that the increase in population has not resulted in a proportional acceleration of the rate of artistic and intellectual creation. However, there has certainly been some increase, both in the production and total consumption of the most admired products of our species, connected with the increase in population in the last century.

It is also worth mentioning that some activities are simply impossible without the coordinated efforts of large numbers of people who can work towards a common end. This is especially true for those projects whose aim is the accomplishment of some group goal rather than of many individual goals. They typically involve many steps that must be carried out independently, and only people thus far have been able to supply the elements of mind necessary for their accomplishment. This is true both for projects that have been accomplished in the past, such as Apollo, and for others proposed for the future, such as Dyson's multigenerational interstellar trips, which might require 10^9 man-years of effort to launch. To a certain extent, the things that are considered possible at any time are determined by the number of people available to work on them. A society with 10,000 people does not have as many options open to it as one with 10,000,000, even if the resources available to each member of the two societies are comparable. Conversely, the example of contemporary China suggests that human effort can, to some extent, be substituted for resources in carrying out large-scale enterprises.

Finally, it might be determined that space colonization could interact synergistically with another possible technological development of great importance: the extension of the human lifespan. If, as some gerontologists have suggested, it becomes possible sometime in the near future to slow down the aging process, this would have the effect of extending our functional lifespan significantly. If this happens, it is likely that the human population would increase by a substantial amount, perhaps by a factor of two to ten over a period of several hundred years. This would happen even if the eventual birthrate adjusts downward to match the new lower death rate, just because of the skewed age distribution in the population at the time of the change. It is questionable whether Earth can support such an increase in the human population. However, it seems more plausible that space colonies could do so, and therefore these might play a key role in furthering another age-old dream, that of extended life.

These arguments seem convincing evidence to me for the proposition that having more people living is, everything else equal, a desirable situation. This does not necessarily mean that space colonies should increase in population until their natural resource limitations are reached. There has developed in the industrialized countries, especially in the last generation, a desire on the part of many individuals to limit their childbearing and child-raising, regardless of the economic prospects for their offspring. If this represents a general long-term trend, it could happen that the space colonies would not expand much in population because of individual choices, even if the human race would be better off with a greater population. After all, the opposite is happening on Earth, where the population continues to increase, even though we would probably be better off if the increase stopped. However, I imagine that there are enough people who enjoy child-raising so that a source for population increase of the space colonies will exist, and that the population will grow.

I conclude that space colonization can serve a number of significant general purposes that seem to be implicitly accepted by people. I believe that the contribution of space colonization to these purposes provides a strong argument for setting about it. Other arguments in this direction emerge in the next section, when I consider what may result from the colonization of space.

Some Effects of Previous Colonizations. Whatever the purpose that we have in mind when we begin the colonization of space, there are no guarantees that the result will be to carry out these purposes. We can at best give some direction to the future course of any enterprise, but we can not determine it precisely. The analysis of the implication of space colonization should therefore consider what *might* happen, independently of what we set out to accomplish. There have been a number of successful efforts at colonization on Earth, and the effects of these have often been different than the colonies' founders expected or desired.

We might therefore expect to gain some insights into additional social effects of space colonization by examining the effects of several colonizations that have occurred on Earth. One of those is the colonization of the Western Hemisphere, first by migrants ffrom Asia in prehistoric times, then by Europeans and Africans in the 16th through 19th centuries. Another is the colonization of Australia by Europeans during the 18th to 20th century. Still another is the colonization of parts of the western Mediterranean coast by Greeks and Phoenicians between 1000 and 500 B.C. These colonizations occurred under varied technological circumstances, different amounts of feedback to the parent civilization, and differing degrees of expansion into indigenious populations that could help or resist the colonization. Nevertheless, enough similarities are present to suggest that some inferences drawn from those past colonizations may be valid extrapolations for future colonization of space.

One fairly general feature of past colonizations is that the population of the colonies increased with time until they became comparable to, and sometimes surpassed, that of the parent group. This was the case both for the Greek colonies in the western Mediterranean and the European colonies in America. The rate of increase of population has varied and has been responsive both to technological circumstances, such as ease of travel to the colonies and living conditions in the colony and in the parent country. Since one reason for colonization has been population pressure on arable land in the parent country, there is a tendency for the population of the colony to grow more rapidly than that of the parent. However, this is typically not accompanied by a depopulation of the parent country through emigration. Long-term growth of the colony is usually due mostly to births that occur there rather than from migration. For example, the population of the U.S. increased by about 70 million in the 19th century, but the total immigration here was only about 20 million and the population of Europe increased rather than decreased in spite of the emigration.

I would therefore guess that while the population of space colonies may increase rapidly once they begin to be constructed, and the total population living in them may eventually become comparable to or even surpass the population of Earth, it is unlikely that the population of Earth will decrease significantly through migration. One reason is that a certain type of psychological bent is required for people to be willing to leave their accustomed place and way of life for another, except under extreme circumstances. This particular psychology, while common enough, varies enough in its occurrence in the population that a large fraction will remain

behind in almost any voluntary migration. The ones that do migrate tend to be a selected set in many ways, and this tends to make the character of the colonial societies somewhat different from that of the parent country.

The stable or increasing population of the parent society has sometimes been a direct consequence of some type of support from the colony. Thus the introduction of corn, potatoes, and other crops developed by the Amerindians in the Western Hemisphere and brought to Europe after the European colonization made possible a significant population increase in a number of European countries, such as Ireland, and even in China. Such feedback from space colonies to Earth might well occur also. For example, it could be that some of the food to be consumed in the colonies could be produced there more easily by chemical synthesis or other non-agricultural methods than by the methods commonly used on Earth. If this turns out to be true, such techniques of food production might well be useful on Earth as well, and help to solve some of our nutritional problems. While this could also occur without space colonization, the colonies might be the needed spur to its development. More generally, the new environment and its different set of survival problems are almost certain to lead to the development of new technologies in the space colonies, as occurred in the Western Hemisphere, and these cannot but influence life on Earth eventually.

The existence of self-sufficient space colonies could play an important role even in the absence of physical feedback to the Earth. For most of human history, there have been places on Earth that were sparsely settled, without structured societies. Those areas have served as escape valves, in that people or groups dissatisfied with the particular society they inhabit could migrate to one of the unstructured areas and, hopefully, find or create conditions more to their liking there. This certainly played an important role in the colonization of North America by Europeans, and probably in some of the Greek colonizations as well. In addition, governments have sometimes used colonies as places to exile criminals or dissidents, as an alternative to harsher penalties. This was true in 17th century England, 19th century Russia, and also in 5th century B.C. Athens.

At present, these possibilities hardly exist on Earth, because almost all livable areas are parts of well-organized societies and migrants to any region are more or less forced to follow the rules of the society already there, which may be no more to their liking than those of the society they have left. With the advent of space colonies, this situation could change again. Groups that wish to migrate, such as the Pilgrims or the Mormons, could set up their own colonies, and having done so, would be able to run them according to their own ideas. Individuals would have a harder task, but it might be expected that enough variation would exist in the lifestyles of the different space colonies that an individual could search for a congenial one.

The effects of reopening a safety valve of migration would, I think, be beneficial. The emigration of people that strongly dislike the practices of a given society, or who prefer practices that the society will not accept, would certainly tend to decrease social tensions within the migrant group and the society they leave. Perhaps more important, such migration would allow a much greater amount of social experimentation than is possible in organized societies, in which almost all activities must meet with the acceptance or toleration of the whole society. Many of these social experiments would probably fail, but some might be successful enough that they would serve as models for the rest of humanity. Such indeed was what happened as a consequence of the colonization of North America, whose most important contribution to human life has been not the technologies that have been developed here, but rather the social and political innovations developed in the various colonies, and summarized in the U.S. Declaration of Independence and the Constitution.

The forms of social experimentation that might be tried in space colonies are, of course, not limited to fixed ideas brought from Earth, any more than the social experiments in colonial America were all thought up in advance in Europe. The different physical environment of the colonies might itself lead to novel social arrangements. Alternatively, the possibility of designing the environment of a particular colony according to the desire of the inhabitants, rather than having to accept what a particular region of Earth happens to have, could make possible social experiments that are not easily done on Earth. Indeed, it seems likely that the massive effort involved in building and populating colonies would tend to encourage social experimentation, as much of the psychological inertia involved in such experimentation would already be overcome in the process of colonization. Finally, the selection process implied in the fact that some choose to be colonists and others do not would probably by itself tend to favor social ex-

perimentation, in that the colonists would be more open to radical changes in lifestyle than those remaining behind.

I conclude from this that the advent of space colonies would, for several reasons, lead to widespread social experimentation, and would probably eventually produce ways of life having elements in them that are preferable to those now existing. These ways might be attained directly on Earth without the need of space colonies, but that seems less likely in view of the barriers to social experimentation in most Earthly societies. I do not maintain that all social experimentation is likely to be beneficial; the system of slavery introduced in many of the colonies of the Western Hemisphere is an obvious counterexample. But I do think well enough of our species to believe that in the long run we are more likely to maintain and generally adopt those practices that serve some general human need rather than those practices which do not.

In order for space colonies to serve as the kind of safety valve I have described, and to be suitable places for social experimentation, it is probably necessary that the colonies become politically independent of Earth, otherwise there would be a strong tendency for the Earth governments to control the way the colonies develop and to pressure the colonies to live according to the prevailing ways on Earth. I believe that a good case can be made for believing that if the space colonies are economically independent of Earth, they would sooner or later become politically independent as well. Two arguments lead me to this. First, colonies in the past have usually become independent of the parent group fairly rapidly, provided that the colonists were technologically equal to citizens of the home country, and that they were not a small minority among a hostile majority. Even when these conditions have not been satisfied there has usually been an eventual movement toward political independence. In some cases, as in the Greek colonies, the parent country has made no effort to keep the colony under control. In other cases, the parent has attempted to forestall independence, and was eventually unsuccessful. I would expect that both of these patterns will occur with space colonies, with the same ultimate outcome as on Earth. The second argument is that people living in isolation from another group, and living lives substantially different from those of the other group, have a natural tendency to resent control over their lives by those whom they come to consider increasingly alien. This effect may be somewhat mitigated by the good communications that will exist between Earth and the space colonies, but in the long run I would expect a strong distinction to arise among colonists between themselves and the Earth-dwellers, a distinction which will outweigh other distinctions, such as the parent country of a particular colony. When such a strong self-identification develops among the colonists, it will act as a psychological stimulus to independence from Earth, and perhaps towards what could be the next step, a nation composed of some or all of the former colonies.

Independence of the space colonies would have some negative features, in that it involves a further political fractionation of humanity at a time when many reasonable people see the need for more unity. However, such unity, while it becomes more and more essential on Earth because of growing interdependence, might not be so important between Earth and its technologically independent colonies. One may hope for an eventual political unification, not of Earth alone but of all human residents of the solar system. Such unification, however, may require unforeseen technological breakthroughs in addition to political evolution.

Another probable effect of space colonization, although perhaps not strictly speaking a social one, is that the further exploration of the solar system and extrasolar space is likely to be carried out by those living in colonies rather than by Earth dwellers. There are several reasons for this, both technological and psychological. The technological ones have to do with the fact that exploratory expeditions, manned or unmanned, launched from space colonies would not have to expend the energy equivalent of the ten kilometers per second needed to escape from Earth. Such expeditions could therefore have substantially greater payloads for most trips within the solar system. They might also be able to utilize such advanced techniques as propulsion by light from the sun (solar sails), which are not as practical for expeditions beginning on Earth.

Still more important are the psychological factors involved. The long-term expansion of space colonies probably would require the use of the asteroid belt for raw materials. This by itself will act as a spur to further space exploration by the colonists. Furthermore, the colonists will be used to living in artificial environments, and so would probably be more willing to accept conditions required for long space voyages to outer planets of the solar system, or even the multigeneration trips that interstellar voyages may require. Finally, since

the space colonists will originally be self-selected through their willingness to undertake a trip to a colony, and to live in conditions somewhat different from those on Earth, it is to be expected that they and their descendents will have more psychological disposition to undertake further voyages of exploration than those remaining on Earth. The past is somewhat ambiguous on this issue, in that the European countries that colonized the Western Hemisphere continued their explorations in other parts of the Earth, while the colonists largely confined their efforts to their own areas. However, this may have been a matter of convenience. In any case, the enthusiasm for extended space exploration appears to have diminished appreciably on Earth since the end of the Apollo program, and it is possible that if the space colonists wish to do such exploration, they will have the field to themselves.

Concluding Thoughts. The analysis thus far has largely stressed affirmative aspects of space colonization, and indeed I believe that these affirmative aspects substantially outweigh the negative ones. However, the spirit of objectivity requires the recording of certain possible negative social consequences of space colonization, so that the readers can weight their relative merits.

One possibility is than an extensive program of space colonization could lead to the impoverishment of the people remaining on Earth and their descendants. A large diversion of resources and human effort to the program of space colonization may result in a progressive lowering of the living standards on Earth. This depends, among other things, on how limited we will be in the next century by available resources and available people. Great differences in opinion exist on this matter among experts. However, it is obvious that the level of the space colonization program and the rate at which it expands are relatively adjustable, according to the amount of resources and effort available to it. Furthermore, if it is the case that most of the work of setting up later colonies could be carried out by residents of the earlier colonies and raw materials can be obtained elsewhere than Earth, there is no reason for the input from Earth to increase prohibitively as the space colonies expand.

Of course, even a small diversion of Earth's resources might be serious if we were in the situation of extreme poverty some have foreseen for the next century. I do not expect this to happen, but if it did, the space colonies already established would be left to continue the program on their own, as best they could. This could result in a situation similar to that of the Norse colonies in Iceland, Greenland and Vinland. The first of these survived being cut off from support by the home country, but the other two did not, because of bad climate and pressure from a hostile native population. Since the space colonies will be spared the latter, one may be more sanguine about their survival under similar circumstances.

Another unfavorable effect of space colonization on Earth could be a loss of the most gifted of Earth's population to the colonies, leading to a decline of culture on Earth. For reasons I have indicated above, I suspect that this would not occur systematically, because the people that would choose to emigrate would probably be a special subset of the population having a different array of talents, say, the leading scientists, artists, or other cultural leaders. This is indeed what happened during the European colonization of America, and there is no indication that culture in Europe declined as a result of emigration. In fact, if anything, creative activity in Europe flourished during and after the period of colonization. My guess is that at least for a long period, the space colonists would be too concerned with the actual building and expansion of the colonies to devote much effort to culture, and would leave that to Earth. But the alternative possibility does exist. In that connection, it is interesting that Greek science and philosophy had their origin in the Ionian colonies, such as Miletus, rather than the Greek mainland. It is unknown to me why this should have occurred, and whether something similar could happen in space colonies.

A final negative prospect of space colonization is that such an expansion may represent a diversion of human interest from other areas that ultimately could be more significant. One of these areas might be the effort to improve the biological and psychological functioning of humanity through application of scientific knowledge. Another would be the systematic exploration of consciousness in mankind and elsewhere. I would agree that the foreseeable consequences of these other efforts are probably more significant than the foreseeable consequences of space colonization. However, it is unclear to me whether there really need be an inhibitory effect between the different programs. It is likely that very different people would be involved in space colonization than are working toward the biological and psychological improvement of mankind, and the existence of one

would not divert people from the other. A more likely problem could be that the people of the Earth or of one of its nations may be unable to focus their attention on several innovations simultaneously, so that a concerted effort in one direction might preclude much activity in others, simply as a matter of group psychology.

This latter problem may be alleviated by the division of effort already alluded to. The early generation of space colonists would continue the major work of creating and populating later space colonies, while the exploration of new biological and psychological possibilities for mankind could remain the work of those remaining on Earth. Such a division seems quite natural on the basis of the probably superior biological research possibilities on Earth. Only if a continuous major input from Earth over many generations is required for space colonization would a direct choice be necessary between the colonization of space and the exploration of other avenues. However, there may be an ultimate decision required when some of these avenues have been explored. That type of decision will necessitate a much deeper understanding of what kind of species we wish to be in the long run, and requires more than the wisdom of any one of us to make rationally. Let us hope that we and our descendents will be able to bring that wisdom to bear when we must make the choice.

My own conviction is that the colonization of space is one of the roads that at least some of us should pursue. We are at present parasitic passengers on a minor planet. Through space colonization, we could create a new situation in which we inhabit environments designed by and for ourselves and in which the domain of life eventually becomes comparable to the extent of matter in the universe.

DISCUSSION

Q. *What's to stop these space colonies from the very beginning from falling under the influence of specific countries?*

A. There are two senses in which to interpret this question. One is that a given colony might be set up by a given country; that I think is hard to avoid. If some particular country wants to set up a colony and has the technical means of doing it, they will. However, drawing upon our past experience, that does not work for very long. That is, a given country might set up a colony, but after a certain period of time, which might vary from one generation to several generations, the colonists think of themselves not as people from the individual country that started them off, but as residents of whatever colony they are in. So that it doesn't matter too much where they start from; eventually they will be residents of New America or New Ghana or what have you.

The second sense of this question is that of literally physical control of the colony, by sending messages back and forth from Earth and so on. They would be fairly far away -- a few hundred thousand miles -- which tends to cut down on the amount of control that the home countries could have. I don't really know how susceptible the colonies would be to attack from Earth; that constitutes an interesting speculation. O'Neill's scenario is to try to make them as independent of Earth as possible, in the same sense that the European colonies in the Western Hemisphere were relatively independent of the European countries from which they came, Europe couldn't really exercise too much direct control, and after one or two hundred years, the colonies became politically independent.

Q. *You mentioned dissidents as being of possible social value for the Earth and for the dissidents themselves; I think this remark is strange. I think if we consider it a bit more deeply, we get a rather different picture than your brief remarks gave. It would, of course, be possible for some kind of governmental or philanthropic process to take the more vocal, the more talented, and either by their own choice or forcibly, in the Botany Bay style, send them off. But instead of having groups of individual dissidents, I think it much more likely in the near future that there will be groups of dissidents. There are large groups, extremely wealthy groups, who would be interested in finding a new world where the old order does not prevail. Have you considered these people as being interested in setting up colonies?*

A. I agree with you. Perhaps I gave you the wrong impression, but I really had in mind something very much like what you were saying; that is, groups of people with a common motivation, but one which is different from the rest of the population.

Q. *There's a strong flavor in the major dissident section of the population that is anti-technological. Wouldn't it therefore be incompatible for them to further their dissident motives by moving into such a highly technological and industrial enterprise?*

A. There is that flavor, although it's not uniform. There are dissident groups with and without this technological bias. It's possible that some groups would not be willing, and others would. I didn't mean to imply that all of the groups who don't like conditions on Earth now would be willing to go off into these colonies, but I think many of them would; that's perhaps the important point. I guess it was also true in the European colonization of the Western Hemisphere that not everybody who didn't like things in the home country was willing to go off to America; some of them stayed behind and fought it out there, but enough of them did go to foster the kind of phenomenon I mentioned.

Q. *Since human beings have had to evolve from cells and apes and so forth, and it has taken millions of years to get where we are now, wouldn't we have to allow a lot of time to evolve to where we could adapt to an artificial environment?*

A. One can answer that at several levels. On one level one can say that O'Neill's image is that the environment, although it would be artificial in the sense that it is not literally Earth, would have most of the aspects of Earth that are relevant to human life as we now have it. It would have air, water, soil, trees, and so on, so it wouldn't be that artificial. On another level, if we learn to change human biology, then we may very well be able to speed up the evolutionary process artificially; that is, adapt people by direct genetic manipulation to living in environments that would now seem impossible. I don't really know what possibilities there are.

Q. *The first part of your talk drew upon an anology between the space station and the Americanization of the New World. Is that really a valid anology? America was uncharted, an unknown place which was extremely vast and held unlimited promise. A space station, on the other hand, would be designed with very limited space, and the people on Earth would know exactly what its possibilities and capabilities are. So can you actually say that these space stations will be a new frontier, when they are so restrictive and also rely on the governments of the Earth for their inception?*

A. I do not believe the design of these stations or colonies would be that constrained. The kind of space colony that O'Neill has suggested is, first of all, relatively big, several miles across. Also, it seems to me there is no reason for them to be uniform. If one imagines that eventually there would be thousands of such colonies scattered through space, I don't see why a given group that wanted to set one up couldn't design it in their own interest. The technological requirements probably would allow a lot of variations in the kind of space colonies you can have. The first few projects might be very much constrained by design limitations, but I think eventually, space colonists would be in even a better position than the colonists that came to the New World, because they, although they may have had different expectations, were rather limited by conditions and there wasn't much they could do, once they arrived, to change the way things were. Because space colonists would eventually be able to design their colonies more or less as they see fit, their options may be much greater in the long run than were those of the immigrants to the New World.

Q. *Do you think that some governments would want to use the space colonies only for prisons and political dissidents?*

A. Yes, it's easy to envision that, following the anology with previous colonizations. I can't imagine that the only use of space colonies would be to send people to prisons, though. Besides, there is actually some kind of value to that kind of prison colony. At present, prison supposedly serves several functions; one is getting prisoners out of society so that society is protected from them, but another is so-called rehabilitation. The second function is not carried out very well in existing prisons; the first is done somewhat more successfully, and a prison colony would presumably carry it out even more successfully. You wouldn't have to worry about jail breaks very much. But what might happen is that the people on this colony, being separated from Earth, would be able to

pursue their own interests in the same way as the dissident groups I mentioned earlier, so they might evolve in a positive direction. I do believe, though, that Earth governmental control of colonies for very long is not in the cards. If the colonies can become self-supporting, which is part of the whole concept, long-term control from Earth is hopeless. I think that is a very good thing, and makes the entire idea worthwhile.

Q. *What is stopping a colony which wishes to expand? For instance, on Earth there are opposing claims by several countries over the vast mineral deposits in the oceans. What's to stop disputes between space colonies over claims on asteroids?*

A. That's a good question. I haven't thought at all about the technological feasibility of the colonies fighting with each other. Maybe that would happen. If there are a lot of materials which are there for you to take, then this kind of argument wouldn't be so reasonable. If there is as much in the next asteroid as there is in this one, there's not much point in fighting over it. You can just as well go to the next one and take that. Whether that's going to be true or not, I have no way of telling, so I can't really know whether that kind of fighting over raw materials is something that would take place or not. That's something we will have to leave to the future. Remember, though, that there's little possibility for partial destruction of one of O'Neill's colonies; a major puncture would, in all likelihood, be fatal to those inside, who depend upon the atmosphere. It means that fighting would be incredibly more costly and dangerous than it is on Earth, so people are much more likely to talk it out.

Q. *Would you personally advocate a shifting of priorities in the allocation of research funds to support the funding of this kind of research?*

A. I think that space colonization would not be competing as much with other scientific research as with other kinds of technological development--applied science, if you like. In this context, I would put it rather high on the list.

A-V. MORE DISTANT TECHNICAL POSSIBILITIES FOR SPACE TRANSPORTATION SYSTEMS

George Hazelrigg
Princeton University

Some time ago it was discovered that orbits around a central force field are conics (Figure A-8), i.e. the line of intersection of a cone and a plane is an orbit around a central force field. Kepler discovered that the orbits of the planets were ellipses around the Sun. In addition to ellipses, you can have circular orbits, hyperbolas, and rectilinear orbits.

A central force is an inverse square gravitational field; for that case Kepler discovered the three laws which are now given his name (Figure A-8):

1) The first law states that the orbits of the planets are ellipses. Ellipses and circles are periodic and repeat essentially forever.

2) The second law describes the rate at which an object moves around the central body.

3) The third law provides a measure of the orbital period of the object.

In real life, unfortunately, we do not deal with central-body gravitational fields (Figure A-9). In the case of the Earth, the Earth is revolving around the Sun, and in addition, the Moon is in that system. When we really take a step back and look at things, we see stars, other planets, other moons, asteroids, comets, and so on, all of which mess up this nice central-body force field and all of which cause perturbations in orbits.

On the other hand, most of the orbits of spacecraft are more or less elliptical (Figure A-10).

This is true because of the reference frame for these orbits. A spacecraft may have a nearly elliptical orbit around the Earth only because we now consider it relative to the Earth.

Kepler's law and Newtonian laws deal with an inertial space. The reference frame associated with Earth is not an inertial reference frame; it is accelerating because of the gravitational forces of the Sun, planets and other celestial bodies. However, we find that if we write the equations of motion around the center of the Earth, these other forces cancel out, because the reference frame itself is accelerating at a rate which exactly corresponds to the forces that are imposed by the other bodies. This is precisely true only at the center of the reference frame, so that we get more or less elliptical orbits if we put something in orbit around the Earth. The problem is that if we did put something in an ordinary, approximately elliptical orbit, it is not permanent, because of the forces of the Moon and the Sun; thus most near-Earth spacecraft orbits are fairly short-lived. That is, if we put them very high, the Moon and Sun perturbations become large, whereas if we put them very low, the atmospheric drag becomes large and causes them to decay fairly rapidly.

In the case of a space colony, we would like it to stay up for thousands of years. How do we accomplish that?

There is a phenomenon known as libration points (Figure A-11). If we look at the Earth-Moon system and draw ourselves a coordinate system which is centered on the Earth-Moon line, we find it is now a rotating coordinate system. In that coordinate system there are five points at which you can put an object and it will stay there; these are called libration points. They are numbered L1, L2, L3, L4 and L5. It turns out that L1, L2 and L3 are metastable; if you put something there it will stay there if you put it there precisely, but if something perturbs it a little bit from that position in certain directions, it will just wander away. However, in the case of L4 and L5, things do actually tend to stay there. They are called stable libration points. In the case of the Sun-Jupiter system, which also has these libration points, we have found the Trojan asteroids in the L4 and L5 points. If we place a space colony at the stable libration points of the Earth-Moon system we could expect that it would stay there indefinitely.

How do we travel in space? We travel in space by changing from one orbit to another orbit by means of a rocket engine. The rocket engine produces thrust. Thrust occurring for some period of time creates a velocity, and the velocity then changes the orbit that the spacecraft is in.

The "rocket equations" are as follows:

$$F = \dot{m}_p V_j$$

$$-\frac{m_f}{m_o} = \frac{m_o - m_p}{m_o} = e^{-\Delta V / V_j}$$

The first equation says that a rockets thrust F is equal to the product of the propellant flow-rate $\dot{m}_p$ out of the rocket and the velocity V_j with which the propellant comes out of the rocket. If you want to produce a given thrust for a given period of time, but use less propellant, you try to increase the velocity, called the effective jet velocity. Much of the work in rocketry strives toward obtaining higher jet velocities.

The second equation states that the mass of propellant m_p that is consumed in a given maneuver is a function of the velocity change ΔV which you are trying to acquire in that maneuver. Specifically, the ratio of the final total mass m_f of the vehicle to the initial mass m_o is equal to the exponential of that change in velocity divided by the jet velocity. Therefore, the jet velocity has a direct effect on how much propellant is required to do a maneuver.

To get to the L4 and L5 points requires essentially the escape velocity of the Moon, which is about 2.4 kilometers per second. To reach some of the other points requires different velocities. Now, we can come into the L2 point behind the Moon with

A-24

Figure A-8 Motion In A Central Field

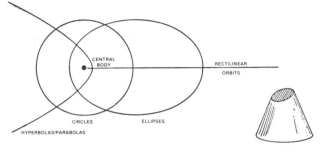

CENTRAL BODY

RECTILINEAR ORBITS

CIRCLES   ELLIPSES

HYPERBOLAS/PARABOLAS

KEPLER'S LAWS
1. THE ORBIT OF EACH PLANET IS AN ELLIPSE WITH THE SUN AT ONE FOCUS.
2. THE RATE OF DESCRIPTION OF AREA BY THE RADIUS VECTOR IS CONSTANT.
3. THE CUBE OF THE SEMIMAJOR AXIS IS PROPORTIONAL TO THE SQUARE OF THE ORBITAL PERIOD.

Figure A-9 The Real-Life Gravitational Field

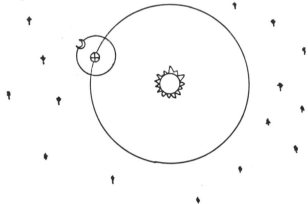

Figure A-10 Reference Frames

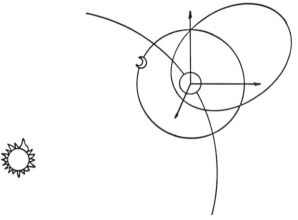

Figure A-11 The Earth-Moon System

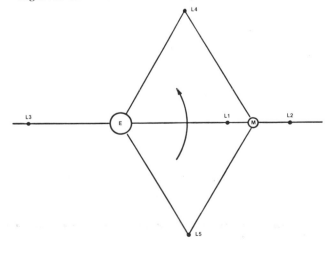

Figure A-12 Space Shuttle (As of May 1974)

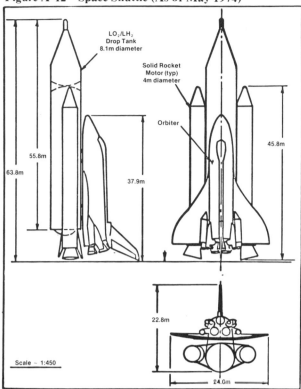

Figure A-14 High-Performance Chemical Rocket Engine (Pratt &Whitney RL-10)

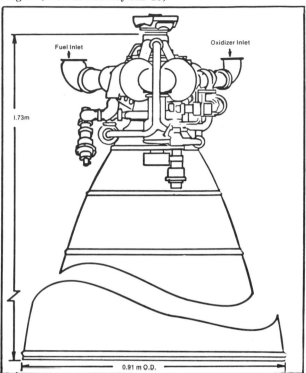

Figure A-13 Liquid Bipropellant Chemical Rocket Engines

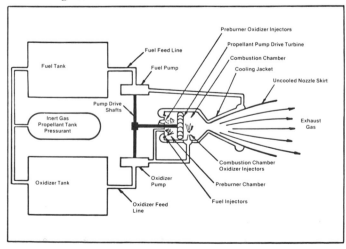

velocities somewhere around 100-200 meters per second; that is the velocity of the object which we have to stop. It turns out that you can get material to arrive at the L4 and L5 points at a much lower velocity; therefore the problem of stopping is not as great at these points.

How do we transport things? To date we have transported things through space using rockets such as a Saturn-5 or the upper stages of a Saturn-5. In the future we are going to have to start using reusable equipment. One such piece of equipment is

the space shuttle, an early version of which is shown in Figure A-12. The key thing about the space shuttle is that it doesn't take you where you want to go in space; it only takes you from the surface of the Earth to low Earth orbit, that is, between 200 and 800 kilometers above the surface of the Earth. It has a cargo bay which is about 18 meters long and 4.5 meters in diameter, and it can carry about 30,000 kilograms of cargo. One of the things which would be put in the cargo bay which would go to higher orbit is an upper-stage vehicle: an orbit-to-orbit shuttle or a space tug.

The space tug can be based on three types of advanced propulsion systems: chemical rockets, nuclear rockets or electric rockets. Figure A-13 is a diagram of a chemical rocket engine. A chemical rocket engine has a fuel tank (the high performance ones typically use liquid hydrogen) and an oxidizer tank, which would typically have liquid oxygen in it. These are pressurized by an inert gas such as nitrogen. The fuel flows out of the tanks through propellant pumps which are driven by a turbine in the engine. The hydrogen fuel is then used to cool the rocket engine prior to entering the combustion chamber. The hydrogen flows into the combustion chamber, some oxygen is brought in, and the mixture is partially burned, driving the turbine which in turn drives the pumps. The rest of the oxygen is injected into the region indicated by the

A-25

Figure A-15 One version of an Advanced Chemical Rocket Space Tug

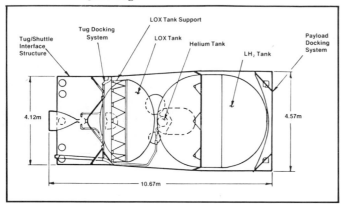

caption 'combustion chamber oxidizer burners', the combustion is completed, and the gases are expanded out through the nozzle to acquire the velocity which is required to produce thrust.

An advanced chemical engine would look something like the one shown in Figure A-14. It is a high chamber-pressure engine. It has a nozzle diameter of a little less than a meter, its throat is only ten centimeters or so in diameter, it is about one and three-quarters meters long, and the thrust is around 75,000 newtons.

Figure A-15 is a conceptual picture of one version of the advanced chemical rocket space tug. It has an empty mass of about 2,000 kilograms, carries about 25,000 kilograms of propellant, and develops a thrust of 80,000 newtons. The jet velocity, which is the critical performance parameter, is about 4.6 kilometers per second.

Figure A-16 Diagram of a Space Shuttle/Space Tug Operation

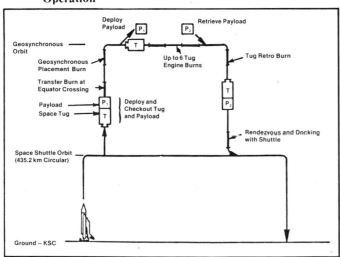

The mode in which this propulsion system works is shown in Figure A-16. The shuttle takes the vehicle and the payload up into low Earth orbit. The space tug and the payload are then taken out of the cargo bay of the shuttle, the tug propels the payload up to some orbit, which in this case is geosynchronous (it could be to the L4 or L5 point), and the payload is released. A new payload could then be picked up and brought back to the shuttle, and the shuttle can then return both the tug and the payload to the surface of the Earth. This sequence can then be repeated; the tug is reusable. If, however, we expend the tug and do not bring it back to the shuttle, it can take 8,500 kilograms of payload up to the L_5 point. In the reusable mode described here it can take up a payload of about 5,000 kilograms and come back empty or it could take up almost 2,000 kilograms and bring 2,000 kilograms back.

The cost of developing such a space tug is over $600 million (Figure A-17). It would be spread out as shown in the figure if we were trying to obtain the tug for use in the year 1983. In addition, the estimated cost of each tug would be about $19

Figure A-17 Cost and Schedule for Developing the Advanced Space Tug (see Fig. A-15)

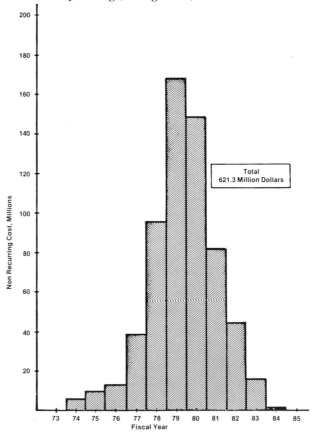

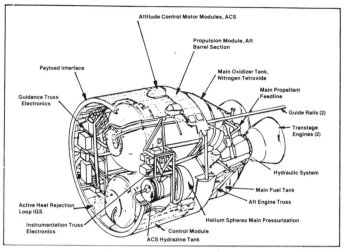

million. The tug can be used about 20 times; limiting factors are material problems. For example, there is a very high-technology nozzle in the rocket engine, and it is expected that there may be problems with the nozzle cracking. The tank can also develop cracks because of extremes in temperature during cycling. It is hoped that the number of times the tug will be able to be reused will increase as we gain experience with it.

In addition to buying the tug, the estimated cost for fuel and preparation for each flight is $122,000.

Facilities will also be required for maintaining personnel and keeping them in practice, which will require about $580,000 additional. These figures are based on about 13 flights per year. As the number of flights per year goes up, the cost figure will of course come down. This advanced version of the space tug will not appear in the early operational period of the space shuttle, but some kind of tug will appear.

Another version of the space tug is shown in Figure A-18, a diagram of the trans-stage from the Titan vehicle, which could be adapted to fit into the shuttle bay and would be compatible with the space shuttle.

The limitation of the chemical rocket is in the jet velocity which can be achieved, about 4.6 kilometers per second. This limitation results from the fact that the energy which is used to accelerate the products of combustion has to come from the chemical process of combustion itself. In the nuclear rocket, Figure A-19, an energy source which is external to the propellant is provided. We then have a choice of propellants, and hydrogen is chosen. We heat the hydrogen to whatever temperature we can, limited only by the technology of the materials which we are using. We can then obtain higher velocities than with the chemical rocket.

Figure A-19   Nuclear Rocket Engine Diagram

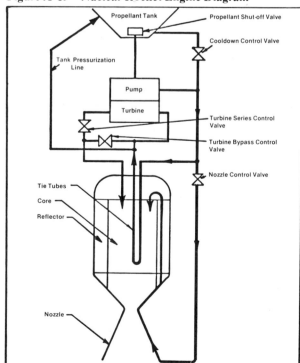

Figure A-20   Nuclear Rocket Engine Cross-Section

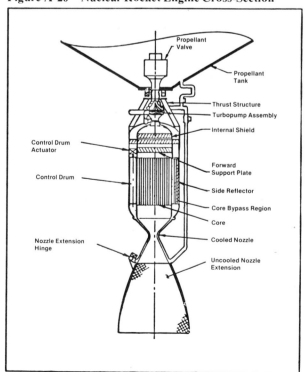

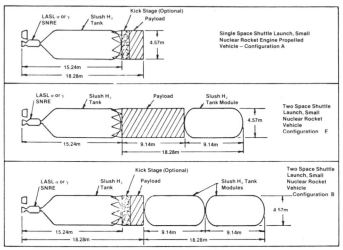

In the nuclear rocket, propellant flows out of the tank and cools the walls of the rocket engine. Some of it flows through the core, and is then used to power a turbine which drives the propellant pump. Propellant then goes through the core, is heated to its final temperature, and is exhausted out the nozzle.

A cross section of what an engine of this sort might look like is shown in Figure A-20. This particular engine was under development, but the program was cancelled in January 1973, although it has been brought sufficiently far along so that it could be developed further at any time.

The jet velocities obtainable with this engine are on the order of 9 kilometers per second, or just about twice that which can be obtained by a chemical rocket. This nuclear rocket would produce about 72,000 newtons of thrust, and operates at temperatures between 2,700 and 3,300 degrees Kelvin. The engine has a mass of about 2,600 kilograms and would be integrated into a vehicle that would look something like the one shown in Figure A-21. It would be compatible with the space shuttle.

Three versions of the vehicle are shown in Figure A-21. The upper one is capable of flying in one shuttle; the other two would be brought up with the front half and back half separate, in two shuttles. The upper one contains a propellant mass of about 12,800 kilograms of hydrogen and can deliver, on a one way trip to L5, about 15,000 kilograms. On a round trip, recovering the vehicle, it can deliver about 8,000 kilograms. The equal payload for a round trip, up and down, is 3,000 kilograms.

The nuclear rocket has an operational mode which is quite a bit more complicated than the chemical rocket space tug, primarily because once you have used the nuclear reactor, the engine is radioactive, and would be kept in space from that time on (Figure A-22). While it is in space, propellant is taken up to the vehicle and it is refueled in space. We can do that by disconnecting the tanks and bringing the tanks back to Earth, leaving the engine itself, which is the only part that is radioactive, in space. It would be cared for in space by a device which is called a command and control module.

The command and control module can stabilize the rocket so that it doesn't tumble and so that it can be acquired by the space shuttle manipulators or any other teleoperator device. There is a certain amount of propellant in the command and control module, which can move the engine around a little bit. It also has avionics which are necessary to perform all of these functions and to control the vehicle during the normal course of its flight. Shown in Figure A-22 is a fairly complicated series of maneuvers; we bring the propellant module out of the shuttle, attach it to the nuclear rocket, exchange command and control modules so that we can take the old one down to Earth and refurbish it, and finally prepare it for the next flight. Once it is ready for the next flight, it flies very similarly to the space tug; in fact, it looks like a space tug moving out to whatever position in orbit or in space that you want it to go, deploying payloads, retrieving payloads, etc.

The cost for developing the nuclear rocket is $784,000,000, shown in Figure A-23. It is spread over quite a few more years than the space tug because there are newer technologies here that are

Figure 22 Operational Plan for Nuclear Space Tug

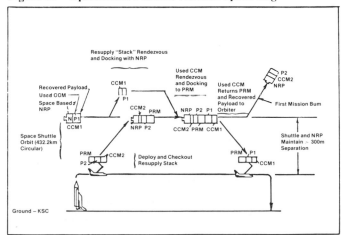

more complex than in the chemical rocket space tug. Once developed this rocket would sell for about $25,000,000: the propulsion module to which the engine is attached would cost about $10,000,000, the command and control module, which is just the avionics, would cost about $11,000,000, and the resupply modules and propellant modules would be about $2,000,000 apiece. There would also be about $129,000 in direct operating costs for each flight and about $470,000 for ground facilities and other activity-independent related items each time it is flown.

The basic limitation of this solid-core nuclear rocket is the melting temperature of the core. You cannot heat the core to more than about 3300 degrees Kelvin without melting it. Some years ago the idea of a liquid-core nuclear rocket was discussed. This idea was superseded by the concept of vaporizing the core and letting it go into the plasma state. This device is called the plasma core nuclear rocket, and looks, in one of its forms, like Figure A-24.

Figure A-24 shows, basically, a sphere with a pressure vessel shell around it. There is a moderator inside the shell, solid uranium fuel elements inside

Figure A-23 Cost and Schedule for Developing a Nuclear Space Tug

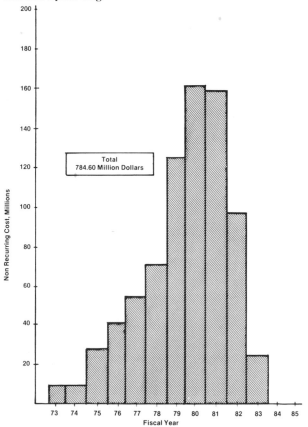

Figure A-24 Mini-Cavity Plasma Core Nuclear Rocket

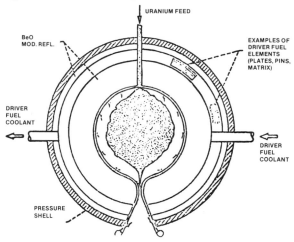

the moderator. With that alone, we can almost make this device go critical. We put gaseous uranium, such as uranium hexafluoride under great pressure, into the cavity inside of all this, driving the reactor critical, and, because we are now dealing with a plasma, we can allow the temperature to go up to whatever we want, e.g., the order of 50,000° to 100,000° Kelvin. We inject hydrogen around this; the hydrogen is heated by the plasma core and flows out through the nozzle to produce thrust. The concept requires that the uranium plasma be separated from the hydrogen and kept in the cavity while hydrogen is exhausted around it.

Another version of the plasma core nuclear rocket, called the 'light-bulb' version, is shown in

Figure A-25 "Light Bulb" Plasma-Core Nuclear Rocket Engine

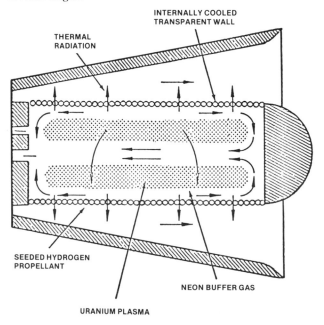

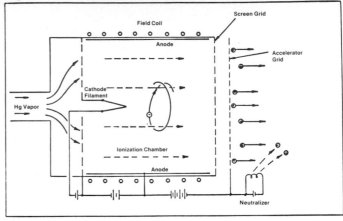

Figure A-25. Here the plasma is contained in a hydrogen-cooled quartz "light bulb". The propellant hydrogen around the light bulb is heated by radiative heat transfer through the walls of the light bulb.

At the present time we cannot estimate the performance of a plasma core nuclear rocket, as it is still in the conceptual stage. However, it is fairly clear that jet velocities between 20 and 30 kilometers per second are possible, a factor of two to three above the solid core nuclear rocket. The mission possibilities with this rocket are very interesting. Studies have been made of manned round trips to Mars of under 100 days using it. It will be able to move great amounts of mass and accelerate them to very high velocities.

In the quest for higher jet velocities, someone had the idea in the early nineteen hundreds of doing away with the problem of thermally heating the gas and then using the thermal energy to expand it, but rather to go directly to the atomic particles themselves and accelerate them with body forces. This is the concept of electric propulsion devices; e.g., see Figure A-26. The ion rocket is a reality: ion rockets have been built, they have been tested, they have been flown in space, and they have produced thrust in space.

In an ion rocket we use either mercury or cesium vapor. First, electrons are boiled off at a cathode. We then accelerate the electrons by an electric field. The electrons bump into the atoms of mercury (or cesium) and ionize them. The ionized mercury atoms are then accelerated through an electric field out through a screen grid and accelerator grids to very high velocities. They are then neutralized, because if they were not, the vehicle would become negatively charged, which means that the beam would go out a few kilometers, turn around, and come back, producing no net thrust at all. Thus the beam is neutralized with electrons, also keeping the spacecraft at zero net potential. Using the ion rocket, we can obtain jet velocities between 100 and 200 kilometers per second, which is very high, and the rocket equations tell us we can obtain very low propellant consumption for moving around in space. Because of operational problems, however, this device is not run at jet velocities that high; usually around 30 to 40 kilometers per second.

Figure A-27 is a slightly different view of this device. It is about the size of a sawed-off coffee can and not much heavier. The thrust it produces is measured in millinewtons. In space you do not need

Figure A-27   Diagram of Ion Rocket

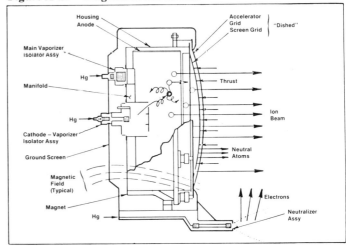

Figure A-28   Solar Power System for Spacecraft

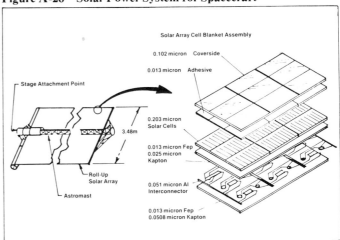

Figure A-29   Solar Electric Propulsion Stage

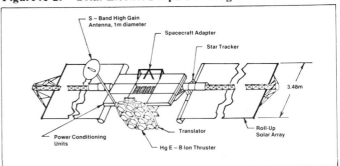

a lot of thrust, since you are already in orbit. If you apply properly a very small thrust over a very long period of time, it will move you around and effect the orbital changes that you want.

Ion rockets consume a lot of power. Two sizes are currently under development; one 8 centimeters in diameter and the other 30 centimeters in diameter. The 30-centimeter one consumes about 3½ to 4 kilowatts of electrical power, and 10 to 12 units might be put in one rocket.

How do you get electrical power in space? There are two basic ways. the first is to use a solar array as shown in Figure A-28. A solar cell is a device which converts electromagnetic energy (solar radiation) into electrical energy. It is advantageous to make solar arrays as light as possible; therefore, we arrange the cells on a film backing (Kapton film, similar to mylar). The film is then rolled up on a drum in what is called a solar array. General Electric is looking into the particular design of Figure A-28. they have constructed parts of it such as the astromast (extender). One panel like the one shown will produce about 10 kilowatts of electric power.

When solar power is combined with the electric rocket, we obtain what is called a solar electric propulsion stage. Figure A-29 is a conceptual view of what one might look like, with a bunch of ion thrusters on the back. The panels in the center are for power conditioning; because the power coming from the solar arrays is not the right voltage or current for the ion thrusters, the voltage must be 'stepped up' to what is necessary. This stage can push a spacecraft around in space; however, it takes quite a bit of time to get anywhere because the thrust is very low. This particular stage has a mass of about 900 kilograms and will carry about 500 kilograms of mercury propellant. It operates with a jet velocity of about 30 kilometers per second and a thrust of 920 millinewtons.

The operational mode for solar electrics is a bit complicated because of the Van Allen radiation belt (see Figure A-30). If you put a solar cell or solar array out in the Van Allen belt for any length of time, the high energy particles destroy it, so it is necessary to pass through the Van Allen belt quickly. This is done by using a chemical rocket space tug or some other space tug. Once the solar cell or solar array is above the Van Allen belt, it can take its time and push payloads around for very long periods of time. Shown in Fig. A-30 is a typical use of the solar electric stage to push spacecraft

Figure A-30 Operational Mode for Solar-Electric Propelled Spacecraft

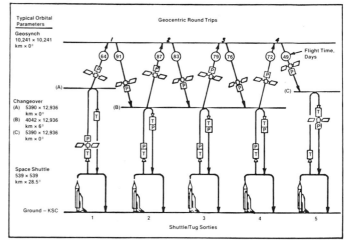

back and forth between higher Earth orbits and lower Earth orbits, which it can do over a long period of time. When it wears out, it is possible to bring it back to Earth with the space tug (after it has been folded up) via the shuttle and refurbish it for further use.

The cost of developing that stage is not nearly as high as the others, largely because solar arrays have

Figure A-31 Cost and Schedule for Solar Electric Propulsion Stage Development

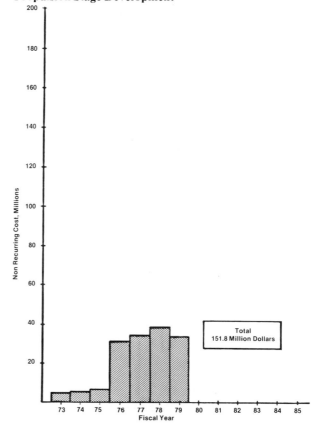

Figure A-32 Thermionic Nuclear Space Power Reactor Concept

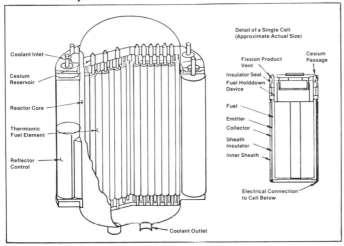

been under development for a long time. The total is projected to be about $151,000,000, as shown in Figure A-31. This stage could be ready to fly in the early 1980's, and it is hoped that it will fly its first interplanetary mission then. The cost to buy one would be about $19,000,000; the launch operations would be about $100,000 and the activity-independent costs for facilities would be about $300,000 based on about 13 flights per year. It could be refurbished at a cost of about $5,000,000.

Nuclear reactors are an alternative power source, as shown in Figure A-32. This particular concept is one of the most interesting power sources that I have seen come along in a long time. It is called the "flashlight reactor" or thermionic fuel element reactor. It is made up of a number of little things that look like D-cell flashlight batteries; they are about the same size and weigh about a quarter-kilogram each. They are fueled with uranium (U^{235}), either in the form of uranium oxide or uranium carbide-zirconium carbide mixed. The

uranium, when it is critical in the reactor, produces heat, and the heat causes the electrons to boil off the emitter. They are collected by the collector, producing about 250 watts for about seven or eight years. We put five to seven of these in a row, put them in a tube, and that becomes one of the tubes in the reactor. We then put 120 or so of these tubes in the reactor, to develop about 120 kilowatts for the next six or seven years. The interesting thing about it is that there are no moving parts, other than the control drums.

If we were to integrate that device into a stage for pushing things around in space, it might look something like Figure A-33. The reactor is at the end because it must be shielded; we don't want neutrons and other radiation contaminating the vehicle and the various parts of the payload. The ion thrusters are mounted so that they do not exhaust on the reactor; the payload is mounted on the opposite end. The cost for developing this stage is about $481,000,000, spread over a number of years as shown in Figure A-34. This reactor was under development by the General Atomic Company in La Jolla, California, but was cancelled

Figure A-33 Spacecraft Using Thermionic Nuclear Reactor Power

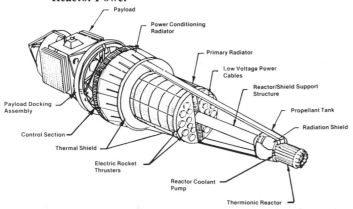

Figure A-34 Cost and Schedule for Development of a Thermionic Nuclear Reactor Powered Spacecraft Stage

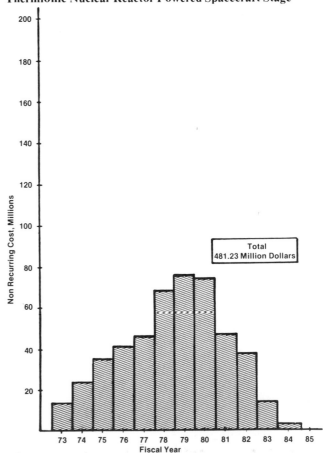

about a year and a half ago. They had actually built the fuel elements, tested them, and run them in excess of 10,000 hours in a reactor.

The stage shown in Figure A-33 would have a mass of about 3,600 kilograms and carry 2,000 kilograms of propellant. The jet velocities would be on the order of 30 to 50 kilometers per second. This particular one would have a thrust between 3 and 6 newtons, at a power of about 120 kilowatts. The first unit cost for a device like this would be about $27,750,000. It would cost about $100,000 per flight to use, plus $300,000 per flight for ground base activities.

DISCUSSION

Q. *Can you give a figure for the useful life of the electric propulsion unit before it would have to be replaced?*

A. The current design specification for thrusters is 10,000 hours. At that point, the thrusters will have to be removed and replaced. In the case of the nuclear electric propulsion stage, extra thrusters might be put on board, so there would not be a physical process of going near the reactor. Once the reactor has been started up, it becomes quite "hot", and would probably have to sit out in space for a year or so before you could get very close to it to replace the thrusters.

One interesting point about the nuclear reactor is that the six or seven year lifetime of these little flashlight cell elements is not due to fuel depletion, but to dimensional instability of the fuel elements, because as the uranium decomposes into lighter elements, the fuel tends to expand. This deforms the emitter surface and if the emitter surface comes into contact with the collector surfaces, the diode then shorts out. That is really what determines its lifetime. So as technology improves, we should be able to obtain even longer lifetimes out of those little flashlight cells.

Q. *How many "g's" of thrust do electric-propulsion stages develop?*

A. 10^{-5} roughly, or perhaps as much as 10^{-4}, depending on the design. The power goes up as the jet velocity goes up, which means that if you hold the power constant and let the jet velocity go up, the thrust goes down. That makes it take longer to get somewhere. That then drives you to try to obtain lower jet velocities, but the lower the jet velocity, the more propellant you use; that makes you want to use higher jet velocities. The final design is a compromise between these two problems.

Note, though, that the solar "g" is about a thousandth of one Earth "g" at one astronomical unit. Therefore, while these devices have very low thrust relative to Earth gravity, they are not "low thrust" if you are using them to push things around in heliocentric space. They do just about as good a job as any chemical rocket would out there. However, if you are trying to escape from Earth, a chemical rocket would do it in three to four minutes, but it would take as much as a year or so to escape from the Earth using an ion rocket. If you are pushing rocks around and you really don't care when the rocks get there, but you *are* interested in how cheaply you can get the rocks from point A to point B, then that is where these devices will really start to pay off.

Q. *Will you comment on the concept of solar sails?*

A. There has been some talk about solar sails, which use solar radiation pressure as their power source. However, there are a couple of problems with solar sails. First, when you sail a sailboat you need a keel, and I don't think that anyone has devised a very good keel for this device yet. The other thing is that the thrusts are very, very low and the trip times become very long.

A-VI LIVING AND WORKING
IN SPACE

Joseph Allen
NASA Johnson Space Center

The very idea of traveling into space is surely as old as the human race himself. Perhaps thoughts of a more comfortable existance away from the hardships of Earth were entertained by prehistoric man as he gazed at the Moon and the sky above his cave dwelling, wondered what sorts of places they were, and what it would be like to travel there. To be sure, the details of such journeys have changed drastically in the minds of those who have dreamed of them, just as the concepts of space have changed. To the ancients such a trip meant perhaps climbing high enough to reach out for the celestial ceiling and the fixed and wandering stars it accommodated, or perhaps it meant flying off, Icarus-style, from Mount Olympus up to that other world, the Moon. In the mid-1600's Johannes Kepler himself wrote a story of a man transported by magical means to the Moon. (Perhaps magic seemed at that time more plausible to Kepler than his own elegant calculations!) This has been followed by a steady stream of fanciful tales about space flights, and the heros of all these stories are there in the role of space traveler and space explorer.

In addition to the story tellers and writers, the forefathers of astronautics. Tsiolkovski, Oberth, and Goddard, always assumed that some of the first "payloads" would be the explorers setting off from planet Earth.

In April 1961 the stories of spacefarers changed from fiction to news articles when the USSR announced "The world's first space ship, Vostok, with a man onboard, has been launched on April 12 in the Soviet Union on a round-the-Earth orbit. The first navigator is Soviet citizen pilot Major Yuri Alekseyevich Gagarin". And so began the voyages of mankind away from planet Earth. It is astonishing to realize that, just a few years later, we are soberly discussing the possibilities of constructing extraterrestrial habitats!

Among the many scientific, technical, social and philosophical questions which must be addressed regarding the possible colonization of space is the rather practical question "can construction workers exist and work in zero-g for the time necessary to build the colony framework to the point just prior to spinning it into its artificial-g mode?"

One year ago, we could not have answered this question with any confidence. Indeed, fifteen years ago it was a matter of much speculation, and considerable doubt, whether people could survive, much less work productively, for any length of time in a weightless (zero-g) environment. We now have, however, the experience of the Mercury, Gemini and Apollo missions to look back on, and particularly we have the extremely valuable data of the recently completed Skylab flights from which to draw conclusions.

Flight crews of three men each worked aboard Skylab for periods of one, two and three months over the course of the period preceding this Conference. About one hundred different experiments were performed, most of which fell into one of three categories:

• Observations of the Sun with an array of solar telescopes

• Observations of the Earth with an array of remote sensing instruments

• Observations of physiological (and psychological) reponses of the crewman exposed to zero-g over the long duration.

We are particularly interested here in the results of the last category, which relates directly to the question of man's capability to live and to work for long intervals in space.

The medical experiments carried out on the Skylab crews included a monitoring of cardiovascular reponses to a variety of challenges, exercise tolerance, vestibular functioning, sleep quality and blood analysis, all as a function of the time aloft. A detailed review of all these medical experiments was held at the Johnson Space Center in August 1974. Proceedings of this symposium were published, as well as a number of individual papers in the appropriate journals. However, the general conclusion is that men and women can live and work effectively, and comfortably, in zero-g for at least six months and probably longer, and then return to the 1-g environment of planet Earth with no ill effects. This rather sweeping statement assumes only that a simple program of exercise (about one hour per day per person) is followed while in orbit to prevent cardiovascular deconditioning.

A few details of specific experiments follow. The cardiovascular response of each crewman was challenged during the space flight using a Lower Body Negative Pressure (LBNP) device. The tolerance (to lightheadedness and then fainting) of each crewman to this device decreases in zero-g, apparently due to a partial deconditioning in orbit of the muscle walls in the veins of the legs combined with a reduced total blood volume. Neither of these changes are sufficient to endanger the well-being of a crew member returning to 1-g. Further, the exercise tolerance (capability) is little changed in orbit from the 1-g capability of the crewman.

The vestibular function tests (response to motion-sickness-introducing head movements, carried out while strapped in a rotating chair) were particularly interesting. Crewmen became quickly immune to motion sensitivity while in flight, that is, in zero-g, but a day-to-day commute between a zero-g work-site and a finite-g living site would probably be unwise from an adaptation point of view.

Sleep quality in zero-g is essentially unchanged from the "baseline" established in 1-g. Changes in

blood cells and blood chemistry in zero-g are interesting, but I won't discuss them here. The major remaining question with regard to physiological changes resulting from months of exposure to zero-g has to do with calcium loss from the skeletal structure of the body. Calcium was lost by each crew-member during the Skylab flights. The total amount lost was not enough to be of serious concern during these flights, but it is not clear how much further loss could be tolerated if indeed calcium rejection continued during longer zero-g journeys.

Upon return to Earth, all nine Skylab crewmen were in good condition and were able to walk normally, albeit initially with a rather unsteady gait because of the deconditioned (totally turned off!) sense of balance. Within about one month from splashdown no residual physiological symptoms appeared to exist in any of the crewmen.

Thus, based on definitive Skylab experience, there seems to be every reason to believe that workers in zero-g can perform their construction tasks with the same skill (and clumsiness) that we exhibit in 1-g. The main difference is only that the degree of difficulty of a particular task in 1-g may increase, or decrease, when carried out in zero-g. Whether it increases or decreases depends less on the capabilities and training of those sent to accomplish the task than it does on the innovative planning and engineering of those designing the zero-g tasks and the hardware to perform them.

The absence of forces of acceleration in the site selected for the first space colonies of the planet Earth is just one of the unique features of this site. Proper utilization of this unique feature to our advantage will require much ingenuity on the part of those designing the construction of the first space colonies.

Allow me to turn from the question of working in the environment of space to the more difficult questions: Why undertake space flight at all? Why even consider a habitat away from planet Earth? The approach one takes in responding to such questions depends fundamentally on one's conviction about the destiny of humankind. Should we continue to sail outward on the new ocean of space as we have sailed in the past through the oceans and atmosphere of planet Earth? Or should we recognize that we are approaching a basic discontinuity in our evolution which demands that we turn our attention exclusively to the conservation and preservation of planet Earth? The answer to these basic questions depends in turn on one's estimation of the validity of the statements that space flight:

- Will aid in solving the difficult problems of environment and limit resources (Earth applications can be carried out from space stations, the precursors to space colonies).

- Will advance understanding about mankind's place in the world, the solar system, the universe.

- Will increase the understanding of other planets, which could prove vital in preserving planet Earth.

- Will provide the physiological information necessary to mount a long-duration manned mission to, for example, Mars.

- Guarantees scientific and technical strength of a nation.

- Will continue the American tradition of expanding across a frontier, stimulating the pioneering, adventuresome spirit of exploration on which this nation is based.

- If carried out in competition or in cooperation with other developed nations will help defuse the threat of war. In any case is a natural arena for international cooperation.

- Provides a satisfying challenge to the uncommon man, sparks the imagination, sidesteps a dully riskless society.

- Is an essential step toward preserving the course of evolution of mankind (extraterrestrial imperative).

- Could provide solutions to the major problems now facing the world (space colonization).

In addition to such considerations as these, it is vitally important to hold in one's mind the distant view of the subject, a view of such perspective that it encompasses an appreciation for the role of humankind.

Bronowski has spoken precisely to this in his essays on the "Ascent of Man". He argues compellingly that man is a singular creature. He has a set of gifts unique among animals so that, unlike them, he is not a figure in the landscape—he is a shaper of the landscape. In body and mind he is the explorer of nature. Among the multitude of animals around him, man is the only one who is not locked to his environment (space journeys are surely an ultimate proof of this!)—his gifts enable him to change it, and from age to age he has done so. This is a fact we know to be true, because whereas every animal leaves traces of what it was, man alone has left traces of what he created.

Every man, every civilization, has gone forward because of its engagement with what it has set itself to do. Ours is a scientific civilization; that means a civilization in which knowledge and its application are crucial. Our civilization is in the midst of adding to our knowledge, our understanding of the underlying order of the universe and its behavior. This activity we call science. Because of science we now have quite literally both the knowledge and the tools necessary to liberate ourselves from Earth, and, in the process, have a "a direct encounter with the universe," in the words of Norman Cousins.

Cousins goes on to emphasize precisely the point that, with space exploration, the individual human being has a direct access to the cosmos. For the first time in the history of mankind, the liberation of human beings from Earth gravity will enable the species to become less theoretical about, and detached from, the universe. We will begin for the first time to perceive the larger relationships, to have an increased sense of human uniqueness. The effect will be of lasting philosophical consequence. In Cousins' words, "What was most significant about the lunar voyage was not that men set foot on the Moon but that they set eye on the Earth. To be able to rise from the Earth; to be able, from a station in outer space, to see the relationship of the planet Earth to other planets; to be able to contemplate the billions of factors in precise and beautiful combination that make human existence possible; to be able to meditate on journeying through an infinity of galaxies; to be able to dwell upon an encounter of the human brain and spirit with the universe—all this enlarges the human horizon. It also offers proof that technology is subordinate to human imagination; we can do this not just because of technology but because of our imagination."

We travel into space for adventure, for curiosity, for knowledge, for perspective. Where one category stops and the next starts can be heatedly argued, but the precise boundary lines and differences need not concern us here. We travel into space for the same reasons that men and women and their tools have traveled the great and the small distances in the past – across new continents, into unknown reaches of the molecule; across new oceans, into the volumes of the atom; across the atmosphere of Earth, into the fundamental particles of the nucleus. We make and will continue to make these journeys in order to understand our universe, the fundamental laws that govern it and, the most important of all questions, the past, the present, and the future of mankind's role in the universe.

DISCUSSION

Q. Have there ever been any small mammals born under zero gravity conditions?

A. No, not to my knowledge. But the fish eggs that were carried aboard the spacecraft and taken into Skylab hatched. The tiny hatchlings which were produced were not confused at all, they always swam with their dorsal fins pointed toward some particular direction, whichever one they picked upon hatching; that was "up" to them, and they never turned over.

Q. I would like to know whether an alien gestation and birth process goes through all right under those conditions?

A. I think, to date, the life science experiments we have done in zero gravity are very unimaginative. It is quite possible that the most exciting answers will come out of that area as soon as the experiments are done. There is still an enormous mystery in the life science experiments which remain undone.

Q. Are there any chemical changes that take place in the body?

A. Yes, many. There are some definite changes that take place in the blood. They are all interesting, but none are dangerous.

Q. How long did it take the space crews to get back to normal?

A. It took the Apollo crews that had been to the Moon longer to come back to the level based on earlier base-lines than it did the Skylab crews, with the possible exception of the first Skylab crew, who were in space for twenty-eight days. The question is a little difficult to answer, as we were changing the exercise protocol that they followed based on what we thought we were learning. On the last Skylab flight we specified that they should exercise somewhat more per day and that some of the exercise should be in the legs. A key exercise was walking against a treadmill; the treadmill didn't move, it was just a piece of teflon and the astronauts were held in a harness, titled at an angle, so they would walk uphill on the teflon. They were· to take a walk every day. These astronauts returned to their pre-flight norms very quickly after they returned to the Earth.

Q. What do you mean by quickly?

A. That depends on which parameter you are tracking. It would take them longer to run a mile than before, but of course they had been away from training for a while. The Skylab crew were back to essentially normal in a week. It sometimes took the Apollo crews two weeks to approach that, and in some cases maybe a bit longer.

Q. Why didn't the crews black out, just trying to get out onto the aircraft carriers?

A. Well, it's a question of degree. Ultimately that's what might happen. Although the Skylab crew came out and got into a chair right away, the changes in their physiology were not so severe that they ran the risk of blacking out when suddenly confronted with one gravity.

A-VII.   SPACE COLONY TRANSPORTATION

Robert Wilson
NASA Headquarters, Washington, D.C.

One of the fundamental problems in establishing a space colony is transportation, and since humans are involved, it must be a two-way transportation system to be attractive.

The first important cycle of manned space transportation ended in July 1975 with the last flight of the Saturn V boosting system in support of the Apollo-Soyuz Test Program. This system was entirely expendable; only the unpowered command module containing the astronauts returned to Earth. Now, however, we are beginning the second cycle with the development of the reusable Space Transportation System.

The Space Transportation System is composed of three functionally different elements. The first element consists of an airplane-like orbiter, a large external liquid propellant tank and twin solid propellant boosters on each side of the tank. Together, this system is called the space shuttle. The second element is a tug, which is transported inside the orbiter to low Earth orbit with a payload attached to it. When the orbiter reaches circular orbit, the tug, with its attached payload, is removed from the orbiter bay and launched to higher-altitude orbits or possibly into deep space. The third element consists of a large cylindrical container, pressurized to normal atmospheric conditions, which is capable of operating in space as a manned laboratory, and is, therefore, called the Spacelab. This laboratory remains within the orbiter bay throughout its mission, and is capable of sustaining operations for a period of from 7 to 30 days before returning to Earth.

The first of these three functional elements of the space transportation system is shown in Figure A-35. The space shuttle is composed of three sub-elements: the orbiter, twin propellant boosters, and a large external hydrogen-oxygen tank between the solid boosters. The space shuttle is to be operational in 1980.

The orbiter, which is the large airplane-like device on top, has a cargo or payload bay which is about 18 meters long and about 4.5 meters in diameter. This bay has doors on the top which can be opened in orbit to expose the Spacelab, or anything in the interior, to the space environment. These doors also permit orbital deployment or retrieval of spacecraft. They are, of course, closed during the flight to orbit and the return to Earth.

The next sub-element is the external hydrogen-oxygen propellant tank located between the twin solid rocket boosters below the orbiter. It is made of aluminum, is about 47 meters long, and is entirely expendable. It is the source of all propellants which flow through the three rocket engines in the rear of the orbiter. This arrangement saves the expensive rocket engines, which are returned to Earth with the orbiter to be reused in future missions. As a result, the loss of the external tank on each flight represents only about 15 percent of the cost of a shuttle flight.

The twin solid rocket boosters on each side of the external tank provide together about 22 million newtons of thrust at launch. Together with the orbiter rocket engines, a total thrust of 29 million

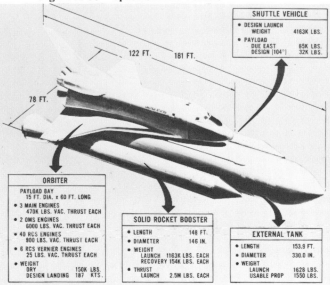

northeast to southeast from Kennedy and south from Vandenberg. These directions are controlled by the requirement that no launching shall be made over the continental United States. These constraints are imposed to prevent accidental impact of the parachuting solid rocket boosters into some congested land area. As a consequence, Kennedy launches produce orbits having low inclination, and only polar orbits are attained from Vandenberg. The external hydrogen-oxygen tanks, which are jettisoned when circular orbital altitude is reached, fall in the Indian Ocean for east-coast launches and in the Pacific Ocean, to the west of the southern tip of South America, for western launches.

newtons is attained. These boosters are jettisoned early, during the launching period, and are parachuted into the sea about 260 kilometers downrange. They are recovered by ship and refurbished for reuse.

The total mass of the shuttle system at launch is over 1,800,000 kilograms. This compares to about 2,700,000 kilograms for the Apollo system.

Figure A-36 shows a size comparison. The orbiter is the third object to the right. You can see that it is only a little more than half the size of a Boeing 747. Apollo was over 90 meters long; the orbiter, with its boosters, is only about 50 meters long.

Launch operations of the space transportation system will be from two sites: Kennedy Space Flight Center in the East and Vandenberg Air Force Base in the West. As shown in Figure A-37 we will launch

In Figure A-38 we show the sequence of what actually happens during flight. In the lower left hand corner of this figure, the shuttle stands vertically on a mobile platform, much like the Apollo used at Cape Kennedy. It rises vertically, with the two solid rocket engines and the three engines at the rear of the orbiter thrusting simultaneously. At about 40 km altitude, the solid rocket motors burn out and are jettisoned. They are recovered about 20 km away in the ocean.

The orbiter now continues flying, propelled by the three engines in its tail, and supplied by hydrogen and oxygen from the large central tank that is still attached. At about 160 km altitude, the propellants are fully consumed and the large tank is jettisoned. Since the orbit is still elliptical at this time, the tank falls into the sea. Soon after, two small 26,000-newton thrust engines in the orbiter commence thrusting. The elliptical orbit is thus converted into a circular orbit at 185 km.

Now the shuttle can begin its mission operations. Many things are possible: we can launch spacecraft

Figure A-36 Orbiter Comparison With Existing Aircraft

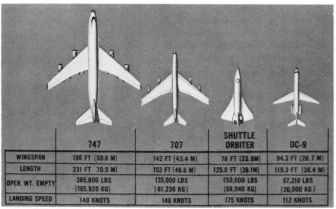

Figure A-37 Practical Launch Azimuth and Inclination Limits from Western Test Range (WTR) and Kennedy Space Center (KSC)

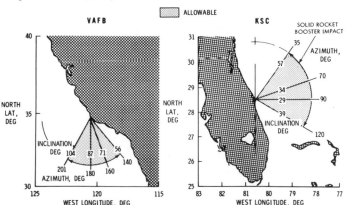

to higher orbit with a tug, or place them in an orbit near the shuttle; we can retrieve a spacecraft that we wish to return to Earth for repair; or we can begin operations with the Spacelab. After the performance of these functions, whatever they are, the orbiter can begin to de-orbit by reducing velocity with the small 26,000-newton engines.

The orbiter then goes into a downward elliptical flight, is slowed down by atmospheric drag, and begins its glide back to base. The orbiter is designed so that it can land on any 3,000-meter runway, but since it is approaching as a glider and has no turnaround capability, it would be a rather traumatic landing to schedule in the midst of a very busy traffic pattern. Nevertheless, the capability exists, and emergency landings could be made. Figure A-39 illustrates these operations more graphically.

Figure A-40 shows a tug returning a spacecraft from some high orbit to the space shuttle. Then the shuttle-attached manipulators, shown pointing forward from the bay, will reach up, attach themselves to the tug, and maneuver the combination into the bay. The doors will then close, and the shuttle will return to Earth with the tug and satellite for refurbishment and reuse.

Another important function and, we expect, a cost-effective one, is the servicing and repairing of satellites in orbit, accomplished without returning the entire system to the ground. Such an operation is pictured in Figure A-41. A large spacecraft has been brought down into the orbiter bay by the manipulator arms.

The spacecraft is attached to a docking ring and is in position to be serviced by mechanisms within the shuttle. This servicing, typically, might consist of the removal of faulty modules from the spacecraft and their replacement by new modules carried aboard the shuttle. The malfunctioning modules would be taken back to the ground and refurbished for reuse. This kind of service may be especially important for satellite systems which are required to operate over long periods of time; our studies show that program savings of as much as 50% are possible. An extension of this form of operation may be possible by attaching a modular exchange mechanism to a tug and sending it to geosynchronous orbit to service a satellite. This again may be a very important future form of operation.

Finally, the shuttle supports another new concept which is fundamental to the future of man in space:

Figure A-38   Diagram: Space Shuttle Mission Profile

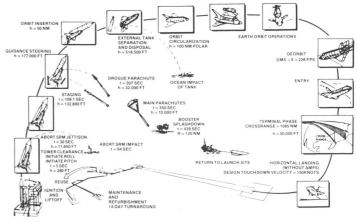

Figure 39   Illustration: Space Shuttle Mission Profile

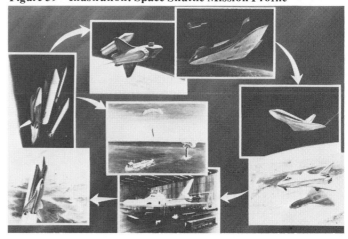

Figure 40   Delivery & Return of Propulsion Stage and Satellite for Refurbishment

Figure A-41   On-Orbit Maintenance of Payloads

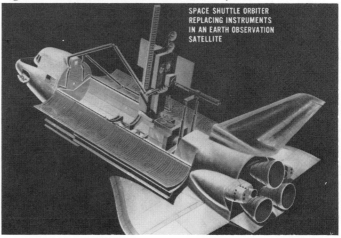

A-41

Figure A-42   Spacelab Concept

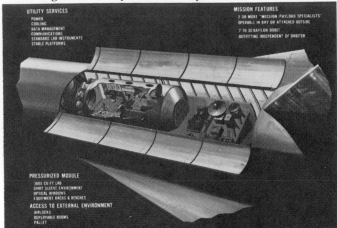

the Spacelab, shown in Figure A-42. We still have much to learn about the effects of the space environment on men and women; what they can do in this environment; what are the various kinds of supporting functions and mechanisms they need, not only to survive there, but to live in comfort. With the Spacelab, which is like a small space station, we hope that answers to these questions will be obtained. It is even possible to consider extrapolations of the Spacelab to a modular free flying space station in the not too distant future. This station could be serviced by the space shuttle and might represent a very primitive prototype of the space colony being considered here. Certainly the information we shall gain from the Spacelab and its derivatives will be of great value.

In order to penetrate space energy levels as high as the L5 libration point, very high energy transportation systems are required. In the second cycle of transportation development represented by the space transportation system, the element which produces this penetration is the tug.

We expect to have an initial reduced performance version of the tug, called the Interim Upper Stage (IUS), which is being developed by the Department

of Defense for combined use, by 1980. This early tug will be expendable. By 1983, a full-performance fully reusable tug is expected to be available. Data on this improved system are shown in Figure A-43. The tug is capable of placing 3600 kg into geosynchronous orbit and returning to the shuttle. Other payload-carrying combinations are also presented in the figure. If the tug is expended, then approximately twice this payload could be delivered to very high altitudes. Of course it has nowhere near the capability required to support space colonization, but the things we learn from this tug are generic to the development of that important part of the system that finally will do the job..

Figure A-44 shows estimated costs for six forms of transportation. These six systems represent estimates of improvements in transportation from 1970 to the year 2000. The upper curve is labeled "escape", but it also represents, essentially, the L5 energy requirements.

In 1970, the expendable Saturn V rocket represented the highest form of transportation technology in space. It was capable of carrying about 45,000 kg to escape velocity or to L5. At about $2 billion per vehicle, this results in a cost of about $4,400 dollars per kg ($2,000 per pound) of payload. The Saturn V could deliver payloads to a 160-kilometer orbit for roughly a third of that: about $1700 per kg ($770 per pound).

About 1980, or actually 1983, we expect to have the shuttle and the tug as the current representation of transportation technology. For this combination, it is possible to reduce the costs of launching payloads to escape velocity to about $3,000 per kg ($1400 per pound). Of course, this system is much too small to be useful for space colonization.

In 1985, things begin to get more interesting, at least as a possibility. This time period is represented by a concept called the Large Lift Vehicle, which uses the shuttle engines in the rear section of the orbiter but replaces the rest of the orbiter by a large set of propellant tanks and a payload. This combination is capable of projecting 13,600 kg (30,000 pounds) to escape velocity at a cost of about $1750 per kg ($800 per pound). If the engines (worth about $15,000,000) could be recovered, then the cost is reduced to about $880 per kg ($400 per pound). Now, the next system that may be available, say by 1990, could be a fully recoverable shuttle plus a tug. For this system, a new booster, capable of returning back to Earth, would have to be developed. This system would be capable of

Figure A-43   Space Tug

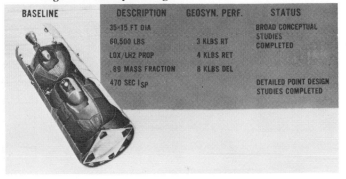

BASELINE	DESCRIPTION	GEOSYN. PERF.	STATUS
	35-15 FT DIA		BROAD CONCEPTUAL STUDIES COMPLETED
	60,500 LBS	3 KLBS RT	
	LOX/LH2 PROP	4 KLBS RET	
	.89 MASS FRACTION	8 KLBS DEL	
	470 SEC I_{SP}		DETAILED POINT DESIGN STUDIES COMPLETED

Figure A-44   Space Transportation Cost Estimates

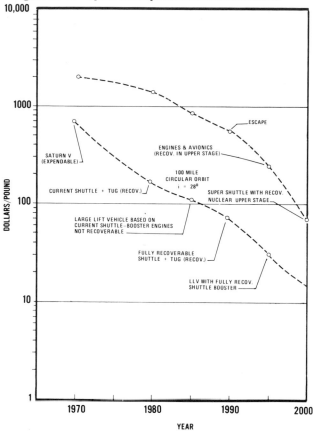

launching payloads to escape velocity at a cost of about $1200 per kg ($550 per pound).

If we apply this recoverable shuttle booster concept to the Large Lift Vehicle, we find that a significant reduction again occurs, and payloads could be launched to escape velocity at a cost of about $550 per kg ($250 per pound). In this case, the engine and avionics in the upper stage of the Large Lift Vehicle must be recoverable.

In the year 2000, it is possible to consider that a chemical-nuclear transportation system would be available. For this case, we would need a super shuttle, with a fully recoverable nuclear upper stage. This super shuttle would be much larger than the one we have at present; it would weigh about 9,000,000 kg. The nuclear second stage would, after its initial launching, always remain in space and go from low Earth orbit to L5 and back to low Earth orbit, over and over. The operation would consist of carrying a payload to low Earth orbit by means of the shuttle and then transferring the payload to the waiting nuclear stage. It would then deliver the payload to the L5 point and return for another load. The shuttle would also supply propellants to the nuclear stage.

This combination is capable of carrying payloads

to the L5 libration point for about $150 per kg ($70 per pound). A combination like this would be very difficult to beat by the year 2000. Additionally, at one thirtieth the unit cost of the Apollo system, it should go a long way toward solving the economics of space colonization.

DISCUSSION

Q. *When you speak of recoverability in terms of space tugs, what is the concept of the space tug not being recoverable?*

A. The space tug is recoverable when it needs propellants to return the system back to its origination point. This limits the payload mass it can carry to its destination. If, instead, the tug is non-recoverable, then all of the returned propellant could be converted into payload, or conversely, the return propellant could be expended going up and propel a given payload to a much higher velocity.

Q. *What, specifically, can a non-recoverable space tug not do?*

A. It cannot return things from synchronous orbit, for instance. Thus, we would not be able to do orbital servicing, where replaced modules could be brought back to Earth and put back into the system. In other words, it cannot bring anything back down.

Q. *Does non-recoverable mean that it can just go up to the L5 point?*

A. Yes. Then it would stay there. Basically, however, this would cost you more to deliver things to the L5 point, since the system would not be reusable and therefore less economical.

Q. *How much payload is the shuttle craft designed to return from low Earth orbit?*

A. From low Earth orbit, we can return 14,500 kg. If we have payloads on board greater than that, then something has to be jettisoned to bring the system back.

Q. *What are the economics involved in the recovery of the solid boosters? How much can you conceivably expect to drive the cost down to?*

A. I do not know the detailed numbers needed to respond to that question. It is, however, significant enough to produce economic benefits or we would not be recovering them.

A-VIII. MATERIALS AVAILABLE FROM THE SURFACE OF THE MOON

David Anderson
Columbia University

Since most of the materials needed for the early stages of space colonization will come from the Moon, we must know what is available. This paper provides a rough summary of the consensus of the reports to date on the lunar composition. A bibliography of these reports appears here as References A-1 through A-15.

Practically all of our information comes from the Apollo missions and the Luna 20 mission; before these missions, very little was known. Some interesting guesswork had been done (based, for example on albedos), but it provided only the roughest idea of the composition of the surface of the Moon. We were not even sure whether there had been volcanic activity. We have to rely, therefore, almost exclusively on the samples taken from about nine different places on the lunar surface.

It seems likely, though, that this is sufficient. The tremendous amount of splashing from meteor impacts should have resulted in an extremely uniform distribution of materials on the Moon's surface. If there were a large deposit of graphite somewhere, for instance, we would probably have found samples of it at one or more of the sites.

Table A-1 lists the abundances of the more important lunar elements, noting the chemical form in which the most common ones almost always occur. It can be seen that there is an ample supply of only a few elements.

Oxygen is the most abundant element and is usually found as an oxide. Silicon is probably the second most common element. Calcium and magnesium are the most abundant of the alkalis; aluminum and iron are the most abundant metals. But one of the biggest surprises resulting from the samples brought back from the first Apollo mission was the amount of titanium, in the form of titanium oxide, that was found: higher (percentagewise) than that found on the Earth. This high-strength stainless metal should find many new uses in space. The availability of inert gases (only helium is identified in Table A-1, but the others are present in smaller amounts) may prove convenient in providing pressurized, non-corrosive environments. Some of the other elements, such as the rare earths and the radioisotopes, are mainly of interest to geologists.

The shortage of some of the metals may cause problems; the scarcity of organic elements certainly will. The organic elements are vital in any venture to colonize. Hydrogen, nitrogen and even carbon will have to be supplied from elsewhere; i.e., from the Earth in the early colonies. This problem, the scarcity of some of the materials, is compounded by two factors: First, the rocks appear to be quite undifferentiated, so that there is little hope of finding ores – that is, anomalously high concentrations of a substance – and second, the rocks seem to be very fine-grained, which may make processing more difficult.

Tapping the Moon's resources will, by no means, be impossible, but it will be a real challenge.

Table A-1.   Important Elements in the Lunar Surface

Element	Chemical Form	Abundance
Alkaline Metals		
Sodium	Na_2O	.27-.53%
Potassium	K_2O	5% (.05-8%)
Lithium		9 – 23 ppm
Alkaline Earth Metals		
Calcium	CaO	6 – 13%
Magnesium	MgO	4 – 11%
Strontium		140 – 270 ppm
Barium		40 – 400 ppm
Metals		
Aluminum	Al_2O_3	3.7 – 14%
Iron	FeO	4 – 14%
Titanium	TiO	0.2 – 7.4%
Manganese	MnO_2	0.1 – .28%
Chromium	Cr_2O_3	0.12 – .28%
Zirconium		11 – 2200 ppm
Nickel		3 – 400 ppm
Copper		20 ppm
Zinc		25 ppm
Non-metals		
Silicon	SiO_2	15 – 40%
Sulfur		0.2 – 1.0%
Phosphorus		0.1%
Fluorine		150 ppm
Rare Earths		
Generally about 25 – 100 ppm (Europium is somewhat scarcer)		
Radioactive Elements		
Thorium		12 ppm
Uranium		5 ppm
Inert Gases		
Helium (in surface soils only: up to 0.19 cm³ /gm of soil)		
Organic Elements		
Oxygen	(various)	35 – 45%
Carbon		28-230 ppm
Nitrogen		30 – 160 ppm
Hydrogen		60 ppm

ppm = parts per million

A-IX. SYSTEMS FOR THE PRODUCTION OF ALUMINUM, GLASS AND OXYGEN FROM LUNAR MATERIALS

K. Eric Drexler
Massachusetts Institute of Technology

Structural aluminum, transparent glass, and oxygen for the Model 1 cylindrical space colonies can be produced by many processes. However, determining the costs and deciding between processes will be difficult. Assumed Model 1 requirements (Ref. A-16) are 80,000 tons of aluminum alloy (15,000 psi working stress), 10,000 tons of glass for solars and 26,000 tons of atmospheric oxygen. A plant scaled to supply this, operating 85% of the time over six years, must produce 0.5 kg/sec of aluminum alloy, 0.062 kg/sec of glass, and 0.16 kg/sec of oxygen. Aluminum production is the central concern in processing design, as over 70,000 tons of oxygen and a large amount of partially purified silica are byproducts of the aluminum production.

In designing a process we must decide whether to reduce the lunar rock first, and then separate the aluminum from the resulting metals, or to separate the aluminum oxide from the rock first and then reduce it to metal. The first choice sidesteps the problem of breaking down and separating the components of silicate rock, but creates other problems: in the electrolytic reduction process these include (1) the amount of energy consumed in reducing silicon and calcium, (2) electrode consumption, (3) electrolytic contamination, and (4) lack of known technology. In the other major process, carbon reduction in an arc furnace, they include (1) the amount of energy and carbon consumed in reducing silicon, (2) high temperatures, and (3) probable loss of carbon in the wastes.

One problem common to both aluminum reduction methods is the separation of aluminum from silicon, iron and other metals. Zone refining might be an answer, but it runs into problems with eutectics, such as an 18% silicon solution, and with intermetallic compounds such as $FeAl_3$, which it cannot by itself separate. Zone refining is generally effective in recovering an alloy which contains several percent of the required metal from an alloy containing parts per million of the metal, but the further separation which is necessary usually requires additional techniques. A purely thermal process, involving fluoride or chloride vapors, is effective with many aluminum alloys and is one which is used on Earth.

If a solar furnace can replace the arc furnace in the carbon reduction process, and if the carbon can be recovered effectively, then this process may merit close attention. Since this information is lacking, I will concentrate on the reduction of separated metal compounds.

Two major choices are available: (1) converting metal oxides to volatile fluorides followed by distillation, and (2) dissolving metal oxides in acid followed by selective precipitation.

In the first, the fluoride process, oxygen is displaced by fluorine, producing free oxygen together with metal fluorides that are separable by distillation. Free metal is recovered by potassium displacement, producing potassium fluoride, which is then electrolyzed to recover the potassium and fluorine. Among the problems are: (1) the corrosiveness of the fluorine and fluorides being circulated through the equipment, and (2) all the oxides are converted to stable fluorides which, in order to recover the fluorine, must be converted to the even more stable potassium fluoride and electrolyzed. This latter problem infinitely worsens the inefficiencies of the reduction-first processes.

In separation by acid leaching, an acid is desired that is (1) effective, (2) produces separable compounds in solution, and (3) requires a minimum of non-lunar material to make up losses. Studies have been made by the United States Bureau of Mines of comparable processes using nitric, hydrochloric, and sulfuric acids (Refs. A-18, A-19). Using the above criteria, the best choice appears to be sulfuric acid. The major problem with this process is uncertainty concerning the equipment mass necessary to separate the metal sulfides it produces and the recycling of the acid.

Aluminum oxide reduction processes in current use include Hall-Heroult electrolysis, the carbide process and the nitride process (Ref. A-17). The Hall process uses carbon electrodes in a molten fluoride bath to electrolyze dissolved alumina; the carbon from the electrodes is consumed. The carbide process reduces alumina with carbon in an arc furnace, producing an $Al-Al_4C_3$ alloy containing up to 80% uncombined aluminum, which is cooled slowly and the aluminum separated by leaching with molten chlorides. The carbide is recycled in the arc furnace. The nitride process uses both carbon and nitrogen to produce aluminum nitride from alumina in an arc furnace. The aluminum nitride is dissociated into aluminum vapor and nitrogen in a vacuum furnace.

Little information is available to help in deciding which, if any, of the above processes would be preferred in space. While the Hall process is usually most economical on Earth, it is hard to estimate the effect in space of cost factors such as mass and recycling. If electric power for the arc furnaces used in the carbide and nitride processes is a dominant cost and if it is possible to substitute solar power, then these processes could be very attractive. However, experimentation would be required to determine whether the idea of solar power would be workable.

I will now describe a possible process, based closely upon well known technologies, for producing the desired materials (Figure A-45). It is almost certainly not the process that will ultimately

be used, but it has been included as a demonstration of feasibility and as an illustration of some typical trade-offs in electrolysis cell design.

Acid leaching requires a SiO_2 to CaO ratio greater than three (Ref. A-20); within that constraint we wish to maximize the Al_2O_3 content. Meteorite impacts on the moon have thoroughly scattered samples of the lunar crust; therefore the samples from the Apollo missions probably reflect virtually every significant lunar surface material. Lunar sample 60015.54 (Ref. A-21) is representative of the material desired. Its composition is:

27.00%	Al_2O_3
45.0%	SiO_2
14.8%	CaO
7.0%	MgO
4.8%	FeO

A deposit of this composition will be taken as a hypothetical raw material. Some samples from the lunar surface contain in excess of 35% Al_2O_3, but have an overabundance of CaO.

Lunar materials preclude the use of aerospace alloys containing copper and zinc. Typical of the alloys that can be made is "Alcoa 56s" which contains 5.2% Mg, 0.1% Mn and 0.1% Cr. Its ultimate tensile strength is 62,000 psi at an elongation of 6% (Ref. A-22). At a recovery rate of 80%, raw materials containing 0.02% MnO and Cr_2O_3 and 1.3% MgO could supply the necessary alloying elements. These levels are common, but could be supplemented by processing some ordinary lunar basalt.

Materials preparation and leaching would be carried out in a process developed at the United States Bureau of Mines (Ref. A-20). The rock would first be melted in a solar furnace and then quenched to a glass; it would then be pulverized, rendering it susceptible to attack by hot sulfuric acid. The result would be a solution containing aluminum and other sulfates, as well as a residue of fairly pure silica. Some of the silica, with further acid leaching and the addition of other oxide byproducts, would be melted to make the required glass.

The sulfate solution would be separated into two parts by means of precipitation: the first, aluminum sulfate and alloying metal sulfates, and the second, waste products. The actual nature of the separating

Figure A-45   A Present Technology Process for Producing Aluminum, Glass, and Oxygen

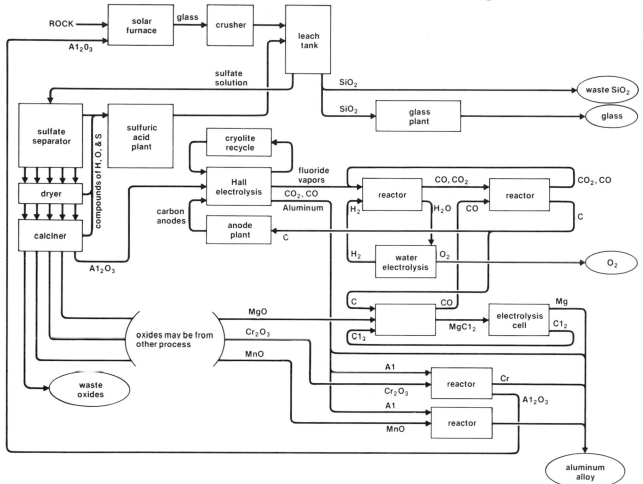

system will require experimental work, but will be similar to processes already tested. Typical operations include: precipitation through evaporation, variations in temperature and pressure, reactions and the addition of other solvents and solutes; ion exchange; and electrolysis. Once separated, the sulfates would be dried and calcined at high temperature. This would produce metal oxides and would recover hydrogen and sulfur compounds for recycling into acid.

The sulfuric acid plant would produce sulfuric acid from water and various sulfur compounds. It should consume most of its energy as heat and be fairly simple. Some sulfur can be recovered from the incoming rock to make up any losses.

The aluminum oxide would then be electrolyzed by the Hall process, consuming electricity and carbon, and producing aluminum and carbon dioxide. The carbon would be recovered as a powder in the Bosch process, releasing free oxygen, and must be formed into new anodes for the electrolysis cells.

Magnesium would be produced by a carbon-chlorine displacement reaction, yielding $MgCl_2$ and CO, followed by electrolysis. Manganese and chromium would be produced by reduction with aluminum metal. These metals would then be melted together, producing the desired alloy.

For a space process such as this, estimating equipment masses is both important and difficult: important because mass is a dominant factor in process selection and cost, difficult because chemical engineers seldom care about equipment masses and have published little information on present equipment masses and even less on how that mass might be reduced. For the major electrolysis stage in this process, a crude mass optimization and estimate can be made. Available information may permit similar estimates for competing processes.

The basic trade-off in electrolysis unit mass optimization is between electrolysis cell and power plant mass. A greater current density means a lower cell mass, but a greater power requirement per unit of aluminum (Ref. A-16):

$$\text{Power} = eI = (R/A)I^2$$

where e is the decomposition potential of alumina (1.7 volt), I is the total current, R is the resistance of one square meter of electrode area (including electrolysis bath, etc., assumed to be 2.52×10^{-4} ohm), and A is the total electrode area. Now,

$$I = d/f$$

where d is aluminum demand (0.5 kg/sec), and f is the Faraday efficiency (3.64×10^{-8} kg/amp-sec). The total system mass is then:

$$M_p[ed/f + (R/A)d^2/f^2] + M_s A$$

where M_p is the powerplant mass factor (10^{-5} tons/watts, from Ref. A-16), and M_s is the cell mass factor (0.5 tons/m^2, estimated). The optimum area is then given by:

$$A = (d/f) \; (RM_p/M_s)^{1/2}$$

and the optimum mass by:

$$M = (d/f) \; [2(M_p M_s R)^{1/2} + M_p e]$$

This yields the results:

Mass of power plant	=	722 tons
Mass of electrolysis cell	=	488 tons
Total Mass	=	1210 tons

If we assume 80% net recovery of aluminum from rock, we would have to process 4.4 kg/sec in leaching. Assuming a dwell time of 15 minutes (Ref. A-20), a generous mass estimate for tank and acid (minus oxygen) is 10 tons. The sulfate separator mass might be 300 tons, with comparable mass for the remainder of the processing equipment. Electrolysis of water in the Bosch process, at 0.11 kW-hr/mole, accounts for another 110 tons of powerplant mass. The estimate for the total system mass, based upon these assumptions, is approximately 2000 metric tons, including the powerplant.

The following conclusions may be drawn:

• The task of supplying structural aluminum, transparent glass, and oxygen to the Model 1 cylindrical space colonies can be accomplished essentially with known technology, but at a higher cost in equipment mass.

• Alternative methods of aluminum reduction, including non-electrolytic processes, may yield significantly lower equipment masses and should be explored.

• Structural materials with lower energy requirements, such as iron alloys and basalt-glass fiber, are probably worth attention during the period when production equipment is supplied from the Earth.

• In constructing the Model 1 cylinders, the strength-to-mass ratio of materials will almost certainly prove less important than the ratio of strength to required equipment mass.

A-X. SPACE COLONY SUPPLY FROM ASTEROIDAL MATERIALS

K. Eric Drexler
Massachusetts Institute of Technology

The probable composition of the asteroids, together with the opportunities presented for processing materials in space, indicate that the asteroids can provide sources for the high quality materials needed by a technological civilization living in space. They would be a source of native nickel-iron, which could provide most metals, and of Type I carbonaceous chondrite, which could supply most non-metals. Both types of material appear to be widely distributed in the asteroid belt. Meteorite analyses have provided detailed compositions of these materials (Refs. A-23, A-24).

Taking current United States consumption as a baseline, subject to modification by differing economic and technical considerations (i.e., Earth versus space), we can compare supply to demand for some of the more important elements and materials. Table A-2 shows the amounts of various materials recovered in processing 10 tons of both nickel-iron and carbonaceous chondrite materials. Ten tons of nickel-iron was chosen as a crude approximation of steel consumption in space, given the greater amounts of structure per capita, and because it yields many other metals in amounts comparable to present United States consumption. The figure of ten tons of carbonaceous chondrite material was chosen largely for convenience.

Figure A-46 illustrates a possible processing system. It is assumed that the distillation stage recovers 80% of the desired metals from the nickel-iron. The metal issuing from the initial stage would have superior mechanical properties to the steel produced on Earth (Ref. A-25).

Among the non-metals, only nitrogen and chlorine presently suggest any problem of supply. The concentration of nitrogen varies with the metamorphic grade of carbonaceous chondrite material. The most volatile-rich grade yet found among meteorites would yield enough nitrogen to provide 70 m^3 of atmosphere with a nitrogen partial pressure of 5 psi. There is reason to believe that some of the carbonaceous chondrite materials of the asteroid belt have a higher nitrogen content than found in meteorites. (Asteroids at a greater distance from the Sun have lower temperatures, and their consequently low mechanical strength would decrease their chances of surviving entry into the Earth's atmosphere.)

Chlorine has been found to compose 0.8% of the extractable salts which constitute 5% of carbonaceous chondrite material (Ref. A-28). This would result in a potential 4 kg of chlorine from 10 tons of material. Although the United States consumes some 60 kg per capita, much of it is used for water purification and in bleaching. With recycling, the available supply could probably cover the hard-core of uses in a space chemical industry.

It should be pointed out that every naturally occurring element is present in carbonaceous chondrite material, and that the non-volatile elements are present in abundance. Dry carbonaceous chondrite material also contains enough free carbon to reduce its iron oxide content (about 37%) to metal. If the remaining silicates came into contact with the molten iron for a time, a synthetic nickel-iron alloy would be produced (much of it was

Table A-2. Products from 10 Tons of Nickel-Iron and 10 Tons of Carbonaceous Chondrite

Material	Terrestrial Uses	U.S. Consumption*	Product	Comments
Carbon	Biomass, fibers, plastics, CO_2, wood	?	350 / 500	with no consumption as fuel, superabundant
Nitrogen	atmosphere, biomass, chemical	? / ?	about 30	see text
Water	biomass, domestic, chemical	?	500 / 2000	with recycling, probably superabundant
Oxygen	atmosphere, chemical		450 / 1800	from water; more available by reduction of CC iron oxide
Chlorine	water purification, bleaching, chemical	60	about 4	see text
Sulfur	sulfuric acid, other chemical	44	about 500	super-abundant
Glass	light trans-mission, structures		undefined	from CC residue with sulfuric acid process
Hydrocarbons	plastics, organic chemicals, fuel	(fuel)	about 150	30% recovery from CC organics by retort
Steel	structures, machinery	575	about 9500	would be the basic structural material
Aluminum	light structures, conductors	20		from other materials, see text
Magnesium	light structures	0.4	up to 125	from CC material magnesium salts
Nickel	alloy steels, plating	0.7	320 / 5000	much would be left in ordinary steel
Cobalt	magnetic alloys, superalloys	0.03	30 / 74	see text
Chromium	steel alloys, refractories	1.5	0.04 / 19	see text
Manganese	steel alloys	3.8	about 4	from CC material salts, see text
Molybdenum	steel alloys		0.018 / 0.2	see text
Tungsten	steel alloys, tungsten carbide	0.03	0.006 / 0.02	see text
Lead	batteries, cable sheathing, pipe, etc.	6.5	about 0.001	see text
Zinc	galvanizing, die casting alloys	8	0.024 / 0.032	see text
Tin	cans, solder	0.23	0.008 / 0.18	see text
Copper	wire, alloys	10	0.01 / 8	see text
Silver	photography, coin, jewelry brazing	0.02	0.00008 / 0.008	see text
Gold	precious metal, industrial	0.001	about 0.01	see text
Platinum Group Metals	catalysts, chemical equipment	0.0002	about 0.3	see text

*U.S. consumption compared to production (metals from 10 tons of Ni-Fe, non-metals from 10 tons of CC material unless otherwise noted). Production figures represent a range of expected yields from some meteoritic materials (Refs. A-26 through A-30).

*In kg/year per capita, from Ref. A-31.

Figure A-46 Processing of Nickel-Iron (Ni-Fe) and Carbonaceous Chondrite (CC) Material

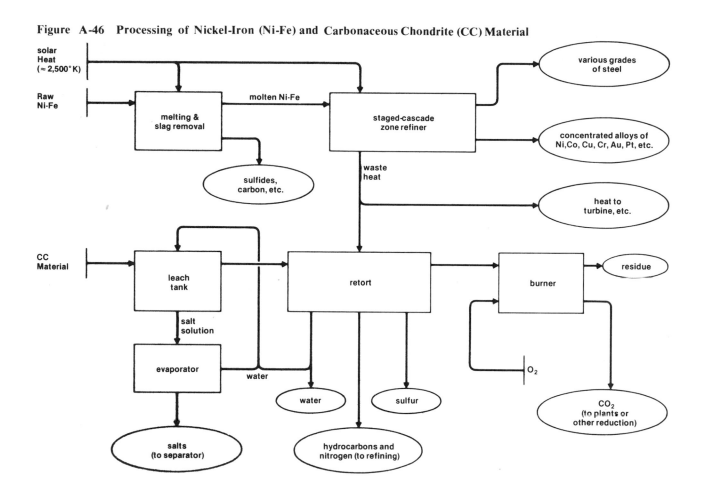

in many asteroids), opening the possibility of supporting a space colony on carbonaceous chondrite material alone. For the distant future, it should be noted that cometary nuclei probably resemble a mixture of various ices with carbonaceous chondrite material.

The evaluation of the supply metals in the asteroid belt is complicated by variations in the composition of the raw materials. There is considerable variation in the composition of meteoritic nickel-iron, which apparently reflects segregation during the solidification of core material in the asteroids. It will be necessary to determine the best raw materials or combinations of materials as a source of the metal required, because the same processes used in concentrating one group of desirable metals can deplete another group. This will require the examination of many nickel-iron analyses, with consideration of the segregation theory and the economics of metal demand.

The demand for metal is determined largely by its price in relation to other metals, which in turn is determined by the quality of the raw materials and the processing technology in use. Industry in space

will probably produce large amounts of structural steel (primarily nickel and iron) and smaller amounts of steel and other metals for machinery and tools (containing relatively high concentrations of the less common metals). Industry on Earth, lacking effective separation methods, seldom recovers alloying metals from scrap; industry in space, with some distillation unit refining, should find scrap to be an enriched raw material. Extensive recycling will be encouraged in space because of economic advantages.

All metals from nickel to manganese in Table A-2 have value in steel alloys, but nickel and cobalt cost ten times as much as chromium and manganese on Earth. In space, chromium usage should be lowered and manganese usage should fall drastically with competition from the low-cost nickel and cobalt which will be available from materials from the asteroid belt.

Molybdenum use is less elastic, but may face some erosion. Tungsten, because of its strength and heat resistance, may be hard to replace in many applications. It is not in abundant supply in the asteroids and its consumption may have to be augmented by the recycling of worn industrial tools, and, possibly by limited replacement with some of the platinum group metals.

Aluminum and magnesium are not found in nickel-iron, but as oxides in other materials. Silicate meteoritic materials have been found with up to 27.2% Al_2O_3 (Ref. A-26), placing them within the range of materials considered as substitutes for bauxite on Earth. While sea salts provide the major source on Earth of magnesium, salts containing some 25% magnesium have been found in carbonaceous chondrite material (Ref. A-28).

On Earth, lead and tin are largely replaceable metals, used because of local convenience and low cost. Lead for solder seems to be the most severe shortage caused by the limited supply from the asteroids. Tin's major uses on Earth are for cans and solder; while cans should play a small part in a space agricultural system, tin solder may be in short supply.

The major use of copper is for electrical wire, where it is subject to displacement by aluminum in many applications. The expected supply from the asteroids should suffice. 25% of the silver produced on Earth is used in photography. It is rarely found in nickel-iron; therefore silver-salt-based imaging may have to be limited, and careful recycling of materials may be necessary. Gold, on the other hand, is comparatively abundant in the asteroids. On Earth, 30% of the gold produced is used for industrial purposes.

The platinum group metals (ruthenium, rhodium, palladium, rhenium, osmium, iridium and platinum) have interesting and useful properties. They are used in some hard, wear-resistant alloys and as catalysts; osmium has a melting point exceeded among metals only by tungsten. On Earth their cost is extremely high; however, their properties suggest many unexplored uses. Their production should be comparable to the production of tin on Earth.

Other unusual metals would be produced in quantity; i.e., germanium, in amounts of 0.0l to 4 kg, and gallium, which has a melting point of 30°C and has been used in solders, in amounts of 0.0l to 0.8 kg.

Among the factors in any material's cost are mining and transportation. These have special bearing on the ease of establishing the first colony. Carbonaceous chondrite material should be found at the surface of any asteroid in which it occurs. Because of its friable texture, it could probably be mined by shovel in open pits. The nickel-iron of the original belt asteroids is believed to have formed in their cores; it may be found in the cores of some more recently formed asteroids or on the surface where it has been exposed by impacts and fragmentation. The nickel-iron content of the asteroid, ranging from 10 to 90% in the rock containing it, should have a strong influence on the method chosen for reducing it to manageable pieces (3 to 10 meters in size).

The first choice for mining and transportation would be an asteroid with both nickel-iron and carbonacous chondrite material exposed on its surface, formed either through fragmentation of a layered asteroid or accretion of two bodies of different makeup. These are unfortunately rare, although a search would be worthwhile. Another possibility would be to find a layered asteroid with a nickel-iron core, a silicate mantle and a carbonaceous chondrite material surface. Under low gravity, it would be easy to mine the core after sinking a wide shaft through up to several hundred meters of rock. It is not known if asteroids with differentiated cores contain low temperature carbonaceous chondrite material. A third possibility, and the most certain, would be to locate two asteroids of the desired compositions that are close in velocity space. The belt contains thousands of objects a few kilometers in diameter, each representing over 200 years' supply for a million people.

Carbonaceous chondrite material is processed by leaching with water to dissolve out salts (acid might or might not be desirable), then heating at about 200°C to drive out both the original and added water; further heating at about 500°C pyrolyzes organic compounds and releases them as oil, then burning releases the remaining carbon as carbon dioxide. This process is heat intensive in an environment where cheap heat is available from the Sun. The cost of processing should be comparable to that of processing oil shale on Earth, which yields a product cheap enough to burn.

The cost of recovering chlorine and manganese from the salts will probably be higher than on Earth, where they are quite inexpensive. The cost of glass-grade silica, processed from the carbonaceous chondrite residue, will be higher than that of good quality sand on Earth, but again, sand is quite inexpensive.

Nickel-iron will be processed by first melting it

under acceleration to draw off an insoluble slag (containing sulfides, silicates and possibly lumps of carbon), then passing the metal to a low pressure distillation unit. The distillation unit, operating at about 2000°C and 5 torr pressure of iron vapor, draws its heat through a tungsten sheet from a black-body cavity solar furnace.

While a more detailed design is in progress, the preliminary numbers are promising: allowing for generous margins of inefficiency, the processing of 10 tons per capita per year, with better than 80% recovery of virtually all metals but nickel and cobalt, requires about 100 m^2 of mirror area at 2.3 AU from the Sun, or about 20 m^2 at Earth's distance.

A small processing station on the carbonaceous chondrite asteroid could ship the needed materials to the main colony at low cost, possibly with reusable liquid hydrogen-oxygen rockets. The cost of obtaining raw materials from the asteroids should not be an overwhelming factor in space colonization. Fortunately, the raw materials and processes examined in this paper seem capable of supplying virtually all needed materials, and the cost of transportation and processing seems quite reasonable.

A-XI.   COSTS OF TRANSPORTING MATERIALS FROM EARTH TO L5

Eric Hannah
Princeton University

The question of the practicability of a Model 1 space colony is directly tied to the question of how a large quantity of material goods, produced on Earth, can be economically transported to the vicinity of L5. If the operation is economically possible, then the feasibility of Model 1 is, to a large extent settled. If it is not economically possible, then Model 1's feasibility is definitely refuted.

Let us consider the mass budget that we face. Table A-3 shows the assumed breakdown of mass into the various categories needed. In total, about 10,000 tons of material must be shipped from Earth over the duration of Model 1's construction. The cost argument is thus as follows: The cost of shipping mass to the Moon for the Apollo program has been roughly \$900/kg (\$2000/lb). Even at a reduced cost of \$450/kg (\$1000/lb) to L5, the total cost of transporting 10,000 tons is \$22 billion, as compared to our postulated cost limit of \$32 billion for the entire project – essentially the cost of the Apollo program. Such a large cost could result in serious program cost overruns; thus \$450/kg is probably too much.

The basic physical constraint to lifting mass from the Earth is gravity. The gravitational force F between two masses M and m separated by a distance r is given by

$$F = -\frac{GMm}{r^2}$$

where G is the gravitational constraint.

Integrating this to infinity defines the potential energy needed to overcome the gravitational "binding energy":

$$U = -\int_r^\infty F(r)\,dr = -\frac{GMm}{r}$$

Thus, to lift a mass m from a distance r from the Earth's center to infinity requires sufficient initial velocity v to provide a kinetic energy T to overcome this potential, where

$$T = \tfrac{1}{2}mv^2$$

The total system energy $E = U + T \geq 0$ when $v \geq 0$ at infinity ($r \to \infty$). The initial velocity needed to accomplish this, called the escape velocity, is then

$$v_{\text{escape}} = \sqrt{\frac{2GM}{r}}$$

so that for Earth,

$$v_{\text{escape}} = 11.2\ km/s\ (6.95\ mi/sec).$$

In other words, any mass, given 11.2 km/second velocity from the Earth's surface, will escape to an infinite distance, if we neglect air resistance.

The mechanism which performs this velocity boost is a rocket, which, by burning the fuel it carries up with it on its flight, produces a thrust or force to overcome the gravitational force. Rocket dynamics analysis starts with Newton's Law of

Table A-3. Mass required for the First Model Space Community

Mass (Tons)	Description	Purpose
1,000	Water	50% Relative Humidity in Air
4,400	Water	Soil Water Content & Community System
1,000	Machines & Tools	Construction
2,800	Special Structural Fabrications	Construction
200	2,000 People & Equipment	Construction Work Force
600	Dehyd. Food	6 yrs. supply at 0.5 lbs./man-day
10,000	Total Mass Required *From Earth* over 4.6 years.	
110,000	Aluminum or Glass Fiber	Exostructure
350,000	Soil, Rock, Glass	Land, Windows, Buildings
460,000	Total Mass Required *From Moon* over 4.6 years.	

Motion, expressing the thrust force F in terms of momentum p:

$$F = \frac{dp}{dt}$$

The change in momentum dp is the mass dm expelled multiplied by the rocket propellant jet velocity v_0

Thus

$$\frac{dp}{dt} = F = v_0 \frac{dm}{dt}$$

This force changes the rocket (mass m) momentum by increasing its velocity v; hence, in the absence of other forces such as gravity, aerodynamic drag, etc.,

$$\frac{dp}{dt} = m \frac{dv}{dt}$$

so that

$$m \frac{dv}{dt} = v_0 \frac{dm}{dt}$$

Integrating,

$$log_e \frac{mi}{m_f} = \frac{\Delta v}{v_0}$$

where m_i = initial rocket mass
m_f = final rocket mass
Δv = total velocity change of the rocket.

The change in the mass of the rocket is essentially fuel loss. This final equation is the well-known rocket equation.

Taking $m_i = m_f + m_p$, where m_p = mass of propellant,

$$log_e (1 + m_p/m_f) = \Delta v/v_0.$$

This is plotted in Figure A-47, which shows that Δv's up to the jet velocity v_0 are cheap to obtain in terms of propellant mass, but a Δv twice the jet velocity v_0 is very costly in terms of propellant. The solution to this problem of diminishing returns is to go roughly to the jet velocity v_0 in velocity change and then get a new rocket. In engineering terms, this is called staging; we throw away all the useless mass such as tanks, which once served a useful purpose by holding propellant, and then, with a new streamlined rocket, achieve another velocity increase equal to the jet velocity v_0, at which point we stage again. This continues until we achieve the overall net velocity change Δv we need to achieve our end – such as escaping the Earth's gravity well.

We propose, for illustration purposes, the following scheme for large-scale freight transport from Earth to L5. Culbertson and Wilson (NASA) have suggested that the cheapest practical system to solve this problem is to use a truncated shuttle configuration. Instead of mounting the orbiter as in Figure A-48, we would replace all the man-rated portions with freight storage areas, keeping only the orbiter's three engines and some steering hardware. This approach uses already proven equipment, produced essentially on a mass production scale, thereby minimizing costs. The external tank is also modified by segmenting it into three separable parts, to enable us to stage the flight.

To show how the final cost of shipping is calculated, I have outlined a "paper launch" (Table A-4) which reveals the kinds of numbers we are dealing with.

Figure A-47 Plot of the Simple Rocket Equation

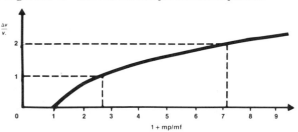

Figure A-48 Space Shuttle Flight System

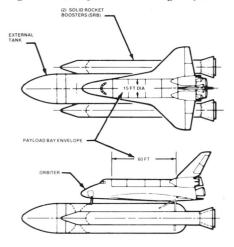

The shuttle starts its flight at a gross mass of 4,027 kilopounds and its engines produce an exhaust velocity of 2.85 miles/second, which is extremely good for a chemical rocket; it is a third again as much as conventional rockets. In the test launch, it is assumed that all the tanks have a dry mass (empty of propellant) equal to 8% of their gross mass (i.e. full of propellant). From the shuttle numbers, we find at first staging, which occurs at 126 seconds and about 143,000 feet (we have lost our solid-propellant rocket), that we have burned 367 kilopounds of propellants in the external tanks, plus the solid rocket propellants, to gain a velocity change of 0.86 miles/second. As we have dropped the solid-propellant rockets and the first third of the

external tank, we have a post-staging mass of 1,303 kilopounds.

It is assumed that there are two more burn stages. It is necessary to optimize where the second staging will take place; If you make it too early, you throw away too much hardware, whereas if you make it too late, you carry too much hardware up. It turns

Table A-4. "Paper Launch" of Modified Shuttle Payload

$$v_0 = 4.6\,km/sec = 2.85\,mps$$

$$W_{Lift} = 4.027 \times 10^6\,lb = 4,027\,kilopounds\,(kp)$$

Assume tank dry mass $=8\%$ of gross mass.

(1) 1st Staging: Lose Solid Rockets $+\frac{1}{3}$ E.T.

$$t_{staging} = 126s., h = 142,800\,ft.$$
$$\Delta W_p = 367kp, \Delta W_{Tank} = 31kp$$
$$W_{1\,stage} = 1303\,kp$$
$$v_1\,stage = 4715\,ft/sec = 0.89\,mps$$

(2) 2nd Staging

Require Δv_t (from 1st stage $v = 0.89\,mps$) of $6.95\,mps - 0.89 - 0.25\,mps$

Thus: $\Delta v_t = 5.81\,mps$ to escape Earth.

Optimal staging:

$$\Delta v_2 + \Delta v_3 = 2\Delta v_2 = \Delta v_t$$
$$W_2 = (1303kp)^{-5.81/(2)\,(2.85)} = 470kp$$
$$W_2 + = W_2 - (W_1 - W_2)\,(.08) = 403\,kp$$
$$V_2 = 0.89 + 2.9\,mps = 3.79\,mps$$

(3) 3rd Staging (no tank drop)

$$W_3 = W_2 + e^{-2.90/2.85} = 145\,kp$$
$$W_{Tank} = (W_2 + - W_3)\,(.08) = 20\,kp$$
$$3\ Engines + controls = 20kp$$

Thus: $W_{Pay} = 145 - 40 = 105kp \sim 50$ Tons.

out that the optimum staging is in equal velocity increments, as established by Malina and Summerfield in the early 1940's. In other words, that 8% factor could be 10, 12 or 15%; no matter how it changes, staging is optimal when the stage Δv's are equal.

To escape the Earth, given our existing velocity of 0.89 miles/second, we need a further velocity change of 5.81 miles/second. It should be noted that I included a velocity component of 0.25 miles/second gained from the Earth's rotational speed by launching due East from Kennedy Space Center. Optimal staging in two more steps requires that the velocity change in each stage be equal to one-half the total velocity shift we desire. The rocket equation gives us the remaining mass at second staging (after burning fuel) of 470 kilopounds. After subtracting 8% of the amount of fuel, we have 403 kilopounds remaining, and a net velocity of 3.79 miles/second.

At third staging (after the third burn) we have a final mass of 145 kilopounds, which includes the now empty tank mass. The tank mass is 20 kilopounds, the mass of the third-stage engines and controls is 20 kilopounds, so we have a final payload mass of 105 kilopounds, roughly 50 metric tons. At this rate we would need 200 flights to transport the entire 10,000 tons to L5.

The cost of the full shuttle is about $100 million: $60 million for the man-rated part which we are not using; $30 million for the engines, which we assume will be recovered; and $10 million in non-recoverable hardware, i.e., the external tank. If we assume a shuttle launch cost per flight of $10.5 million and a loss of $10 million per flight from the external tank, then each flight will cost about $20 million, excluding the initial non-recurring cost of the recoverable engines. This gives us a cost of $190/pound for shipping to L5, using this system.

To cross check the assumption that the hardware lost really is about $10 million, we take the amount of lost mass (the external tank), roughly 100 kilopounds, and assume a manufacturing cost of approximately $60/pound, the cost of commercial aircraft construction, for a total of $6 million. This checks rather well with the assumed value of $10 million.

We therefore conclude that even without esoteric transport systems, we can raise the required mass to L5 from Earth for the bargain-basement price of $200/pound.

A-XII. SUMMARIZATION OF CONFERENCE: THE COLONIZATION OF SPACE

Gerard K. O'Neill
Princeton University

The purpose of this summary is to bring together the input numbers which will allow a first estimate of overall costs. However, Freeman Dyson has suggested that the approach described here is much too conservative and too large in scale. He would like to see us establish a first space colony for a tenth of the cost of Apollo and scale it down in size accordingly. Although it will take much more detailed work before we know how cost does scale with size (certainly not in direct proportion), it *is* important to emphasize that there is no special magic in the base-case example of 10,000 people. There must be, of course, a minimum number of people for an efficient operation: a work force large enough to produce material in quantity and to include an adequate range of skills and specialties. I do not know what that minimum is, but I feel reasonably confident that 10,000 people would be enough to be an effective work force. I don't know how far below that population we could go without losing the basic concept, but I certainly would agree with Dyson that there is no special magic to the number of 10,000.

The base-case specifications for a colony at the L5 libration point include a total mass of about half a million tons and a population of about 10,000 people. The colony would be able to support itself continuously without support from the Earth after it once became established. Though rather small, it would be big enough to build more colonies, either of the same size or perhaps ten times larger. Cost reductions would occur as the work force increased to include a more complete range of skills and as the need for components from the Earth decreased correspondingly.

For economy, it is essential that only one or two percent of the material for Model 1 be brought from the surface of the Earth. I propose that the necessary raw materials be transported from the Moon to L5, making use of the two great advantages of the lunar environment: the excellent vacuum and the very low escape velocity, 2400 meters per second (1.5 miles per second), less than a quarter the escape velocity from the surface of the Earth. To bring a kilogram to L5 from the Moon takes less than 5% of the energy required to take a kilogram from the Earth.

Two methods have been proposed, both of which appear to be workable. Both are based on using electric power from a conventional turbogenerator powerplant employing solar energy. In both cases I assume that the system would run only during the lunar day, the night being used for scheduled maintenance, crew rest, and possibly materials processing. To be properly conservative, I assume an additional factor of two due to unscheduled breakdowns. Each system is thus assumed to be running only one week in four.

Figure A-49 shows the first device: something I call the Rotary Pellet Launcher. It would be like a big airplane propeller, and would act like a sling shot. Its symmetrical tapered arms would be logarithmically shaped, to maintain the stress constant at every point within the material. The best material for the launcher arms has been extensively used in the aerospace industry: a boron filament matrix. Working at about 80% of the stress/density limit, which has already been achieved in high technology military aircraft, one could run this

Figure A-49   Rotary Launcher

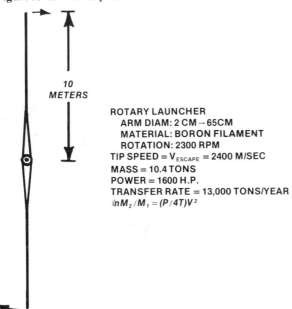

10 METERS

ROTARY LAUNCHER
ARM DIAM: 2 CM → 65CM
MATERIAL: BORON FILAMENT
ROTATION: 2300 RPM
TIP SPEED = V_{ESCAPE} = 2400 M/SEC
MASS = 10.4 TONS
POWER = 1600 H.P.
TRANSFER RATE = 13,000 TONS/YEAR
$ln M_2 / M_1 = (P/4T)V^2$

Figure A-50   Transport Linear Accelerator

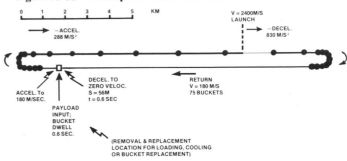

device fast enough so that the tip would rotate as fast as the escape velocity from the surface of the Moon. Through the arm would be fed small pellets of about five grams each, released at a precise time calculated by a computer. They would leave the Moon at escape velocity, but by the time they came up to the L5 potential hill, they would be moving relatively slowly.

The device would be run by an electric motor of about 1500 kW. Its basic mass would be about ten tons, and the through-put would be very large indeed: over 3,000 tons per year, including the conservative load-factor estimate of ¼. To transfer 500,000 tons in six years we would need about twenty-six such devices, or a total power of about 32 megawatts. Also, the pellets would have to be steered precisely to a very high accuracy, probably by using a magnetic or electrostatic deflection plate system which would follow the launch point and would correct the pellet transverse velocity so as to correct the pellet dispersion, permitting easy collection at L5.

The advantages of the Rotary Pellet Launcher (RPL) would be compactness, a low overall mass, and redundancy in case of breakdown. If one of these devices were to break down, only 4% of the system would be out of service. The disadvantages would be the need for pelletizing and the small pellet size, which would make collection more difficult. Fortunately, on the Moon it would be cheap to form ideal spheres by heating material to the melting point (with solar energy) and using a drop tower. It would take a long time on the Moon

for things to drop, so they would have plenty of time to achieve a good spherical shape.

The second method, called the Transport Linear Accelerator (TLA), would use the technologies of magnetic levitation and the linear synchronous motor, which have been developed for urban transportation systems during the past five years by groups at MIT, Brookhaven and Stanford as well as in Germany and Japan. At high speed the lift/drag ratio (L/D) of a magnetically levitated vehicle becomes very good, typically over a hundred to one when the levitating field is produced by a superconducting coil and from twenty to fifty to one for fields which are produced by samarium-cobalt permanent magnets.

The TLA would consist of a recirculating system of small passive vehicles which I call buckets; each would have no moving parts but would contain superconducting coils. The buckets would accelerate a payload, perhaps nine kilograms, to escape speed along a magnetic levitation linear synchronous track. Modest acceleration would then release the payload, and the bucket would be decelerated down to a speed of perhaps 180 meters per second, slow by comparison with escape speed, but a reasonable speed for turns of a magnetic levitation track. The bucket would return, pick up another payload and start again. Figures A-50 and A-51 show diagrams of this sequence.

Figure A-50 is the Transport Linear Accelerator. It would be an acceleration-deceleration track, of total length about thirteen kilometers, with a launch rate of one payload per second. The total inventory of buckets would be about two hundred. Including a factor of three to allow an inventory of spares, there would be three tons of buckets, so even if they were to cost as much as $10,000 a pound, their total cost would be small compared to the cost of the rest of the system.

Figure A-51 is the end view of the Transport

Figure A-51 End View of Transport Linear Accelerator

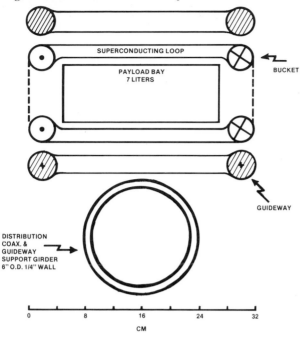

Linear Accelerator. It shows one version of the magnetic levitation guideway, which would be ordinary non-superconducting aluminum, and indicates the cross bars which would be part of the coils of the linear synchronous motor. The vehicle, the bucket, is shown inside. It would have superconducting loops top and bottom and a payload bay of about seven liters, so that it could carry as much as nine kilograms of a material having as low a specific gravity as 2.

Minimum system cost is achieved if the linear synchronous motor is driven by capacitor banks not continuously distributed along the whole length, but located at discrete points, discharging their energy into a particular set of cross-bar exciting coils by way of a distribution coaxial line. The distribution line would be simply a six-inch diameter, quarter-inch wall aluminum pipe. Because such a pipe would be extremely rigid, it is used also for the supporting structure.

The system parameters are detailed in Table A-5. The acceleration chosen is 29 gravities, which is negligible for non-biological materials. In fact, complicated things like radio transmitters have been successfully launched from a cannon with accelerations of 50,000 gravities, and they work nicely in orbit after that experience. 29 gravities is only about twice as much as human beings routinely take in centrifuge tests.

The average accelerating force would be about 900 pounds. The maximum magnetic fields in the system are held to 10,000 gauss, because superconductors are affected adversely by very high fields.

The bucket dry mass would be 5 kilograms, the payload 9 kilograms, the repetition rate one per second, and the transport rate 750 tons per day. To equal that 750 tons per day would require a minimum of 70 complete shuttle launches from the surface of the Earth. The number of buckets on the acceleration line at any one time is eight; the sector length would be fifty meters. The ohmic losses in the feeders would be about 15 megawatts and the overall power required about 55 megawatts. About 60% of that 55 megawatts would actually go into the kinetic energy for the acceleration of payloads, making it a fantastically efficient system compared to a rocket.

Table A-6 shows the TLA mass breakdown. The generator station, on the basis of known technology, will be 550 tons; the capacitor stations would be another 280 tons, the coax and girders 225 tons, switch-gear another 135 tons. To be conservative the actual device, which would include things like the LSM guideway, connectors, fittings and so on, is estimated to be only 20% of the final mass; an 80% allowance is left for items that are not considered when the system is first conceived.

The advantages of the TLA are that it requires no high-strength materials, it accepts raw, uncompacted payloads, and offers convenient payload size, which would even allow attachment of a locator transmitter into each one of the payloads. The transmitters would not have to be cheap

Table A-5   Characteristics Of Transport Linear Accelerator

Acceleration	288 m/sec^2
Av. accel. Force	900 lbs.
Max. Field	10,000 gauss
Bucket Dry Mass	5 kg
Payload	9kg
Rep. Rate	1/second
Transport Rate	750 tons/day
Buckets On Accel.	8
Sector Length (Accel.)	50 m
Inductance/Meter	0.6dHy.
Peak Stored Energy/m.	10.4 kJ
Max. Frequency (LSM)	2500 Hz
Instant. Length Driven	2 m
Bucket Coil Current	75,000 amp-turns
LSM Peak Current	136,000 amp
Acceleration Power	40MW
Ohmic Losses (Feeders)	15MW

Table A-6   Transport Linear Accelerator Mass (Tons)

Generator Station (55MW)	550
Capacitor Stations (270 Sectors)	280
Coax. &Girders (13.5 km)	226
Switchgear (675 Stations)	135
LSM Guideway	100
Connectors & Insulators	100
Footings	100
	1490

Table A-7   Model 1 Mass Breakdown (Kilotons)

Aluminum (Container, Structures)	20
Glass (Solars)	10
Water	50
Generator Plant (100 MW)	1
Initial Structures	1
Special Fabricated Hardware	1
Machines & Tools	0.8
Soil, Rocks, Construc. Materials	420

because they would be recovered at L5 and shipped back in carload lots every now and then. The TLA would also be relatively easy to maintain. Its disadvantage would be that of a less convenient geometry, extending over a distance of ten or thirteen kilometers.

Both the RPL and the TLA would be straight-forward problems in engineering development and cost minimization, within the limits of present technology, as compared, for example, to such things as, say, hydrogen fusion power. I am much in favor of the present efforts on Earth to achieve hydrogen fusion power, but fusion is an example of a really new technology with a lot of unanswered questions. In contrast, either of these two methods for getting material from the Moon could be built and tested on Earth and made to work within a three to four year period, given a moderate amount of money and a good staff of physicists and engineers. The TLA also offers opportunities for direct carry-over of mathematical techniques that we have developed over the last twenty years for high-energy particle accelerators and storage rings. The six degrees of freedom of the bucket have their analogues in the phase, radius, etc., of circulating space charge; the mathematical machinery of the separatrix and the resonance lines will surely be reused if the TLA gets built.

Model 1's mass breakdown is shown in Table-A7. About 98% of the total mass could be provided by the RPL and the TLA from lunar surface material. Model 1 would be too small to carry out a wide variety of manufacturing processes, but it does have solar power 100% of the time. The ideal product for Model 1 would not be labor intensive, because it will be necessary to economize on the size of the working force, but would be large in terms of total tonnage. Model 1 could produce aluminum, glass, and oxygen from lunar regolith, for example. The making of glass panels of uniform size would be a good mass production operation.

A major item in the total mass budget is 50,000

tons of water. That appears to be a luxurious amount of water to take to Model 1, but only about 11% of the mass of water is in the hydrogen; the other 89% is oxygen, and we know that the Moon is made almost entirely of oxides. It does not make sense to take liquid water from the surface of the Earth and haul it up at great cost by rocket to L5, when all that is necessary is to lift liquid hydrogen and combine it at L5 with oxygen brought by the TLA from the surface of the Moon at low cost. From just over 5,000 tons of hydrogen we could obtain 50,000 tons of water. Even the first spartan space colony model could be lush with vegetation.

Most of the smaller things would have to be brought from the surface of the Earth: the generator plant, initial structures, hardware and machines. Large quantities of lunar soil, rock and construction materials will be required, but these can be of low strength as long as they are not asked to sustain big loads. For example, lunar surface oxides could be heated in a slow speed centrifuge and allowed to melt to form cylindrical shapes.

Table A-8 lists items which must be brought up from the surface of the Earth. Model 1 would be too small to make a wide variety of manufactured parts; that would be impossible with a group of only 10,000 people. It probably would make sense to carry this specialized hardware from the Earth; 1000 tons are budgeted for such hardware, including things like window seals between the glass and the aluminum. At the beginning, of course, there would be no Model 1 to live in, so there would have to be an initial structure which might be rather

Table A-8   Model 1: Mass Required from Earth (Tons)

Liquid Hydrogen	5400
Spec. Fab. Hardware	1000
Initial Structures	1000
Generator Plant	1000
Machines & Tools	800
2000 People & Equip.	200
Dehyd. Food	600
	10,000

Table A-9   Costs of Miniaturized and Aerospace Equipment

Item	Quantity	Example	Cost/Pound
Apollo Command Modules	10	$ 10^8/7000 lbs.	$ 14,000
Ion Drive Units	10-20	$ 0.25×10^6/45 lbs.	5,600
HP45 Calculators	100,000	$ 325/9 oz.	580
Military Aircraft	200	$ 14×10^6/2.8×10^4 lbs.	500
Wristwatches	10,000	$ 50/2 oz.	400
Small Computers (8K)	2,000	$ 1.1×10^4/80 lbs.	140
Aircraft Electronics	5,000	$ 450/3.7 lbs.	120
Commercial Aircraft	500	$ 8×10^6/1.3×10^5 lbs.	62
Sailplanes	50-100	$ 12,000/400 lbs.	30

like a big space station. Another 1000 tons are budgeted for that.

If aluminum were made by the Hall process, about eighty megawatts would be needed to make eighty thousand tons of aluminum in a 4-year period, so I have allowed one hundred megawatts. Model 1's generator would be about one tenth the size of a typical large Earth-based generator station; I have budgeted about 1000 tons for it. The machines and tools — low-mass computers and a lot of very specialized machines to help people work efficiently — account for another 800 tons.

There would be 2,000 people and their equipment needed for the construction work force, and about 200 tons of dehydrated food. Carbon and nitrogen are not found on the surface of the Moon, so until we are in a position to obtain materials from the asteroid belt, where nitrogen and carbon are thought to be plentiful, we would have to count on bringing them up from the surface of the Earth. Perhaps 500 tons would be needed.

Table A-9 provides a feeling for the costs of high technology components. At the top are the Apollo Command modules: only about ten of them were built; they cost 100 million dollars each; and their cost per pound was fantastically high.

Ion rockets of the kind discussed by Hazelrigg are high because they are complex and light; they cost about $250,000 apiece, but weigh only about 45 pounds. A good example listed in Table A-9 is the Hewlett-Packard HP-45 calculator. At the moment these calculators cost $325 and they weight nine ounces. That works out to $580 per pound. So, whenever I talk of numbers in the range of $200 to $500 a pound, you can compare these costs with those of HP 45 calculators.

Military aircraft are usually made in short production runs; they always represent the absolute limit of the state of the art, because the real issue is whether one aircraft is going to shoot down another aircraft before it gets shot down first. Therefore they are very expensive: around $500 per pound.

Wristwatches are around $400 per pound. Small computers made in quantity, like the PDP-11 or the HP 2100, which are very powerful but which are physically small enough to put into a relay rack, have a cost per pound of only about $140, probably because they are made in lots of at least a couple of thousand.

Aircraft electronics run about $120 per pound. Commercial aircraft, even averaging over the expensive avionics and engines, are only around $62

Table A-10   Model 1: Estimated Costs, 1972 Dollars

Item	Unit Cost	Total ($ Billions)
Launch Vehicles	$0.3	0.9
Transport E→L5	$425/lb.	8.5
People E→L5	$1000/lb.	2.2
Transport E→M	$1000/lb.	6.6
Equip for Moon	$400/lb.	2.4
Equip. for L5	$180/lb.	1.2
Machines, Tools(L5)	$625/lb.	1.1
Salaries (L5)	$50,000/man-yr.	0.6
Salaries (E)	$30,000/man-yr.	7.2
		30.7

(Per year, $5.1 billion)

per pound. Sailplanes are about $30 per pound, not very different from Wilson's figure for the cost of the big propellant tank for the space shuttle.

Using Table A-9 as a guide, it is now possible to sum up the cost for Model 1 (Table A-10). The unit cost of the shuttle launch vehicles, at $300 million each, is $0.9 billion. The cost of the Apollo project, normalized to 1972 dollars as has been done here, is about $33 billion. This figure will constitute our yardstick.

For transport from Earth to L5, numbers vary from Hannah's $190 per pound through Wilson's $500 per pound. With development, Wilson's numbers drop to $250 per pound, and ultimately to $100 per pound, or with a nuclear upper stage, $60 per pound. I have selected a much larger number, $425 per pound: it constitutes more than a quarter of the total cost of the entire operation. The cost of bringing people from the Earth to L5 is taken to be even higher – $1,000 per pound – because life support systems would have to be provided, and the density is smaller. That includes not just the construction work force, but all the ten thousand inhabitants of Model 1. Each person is allowed 70 pounds of personal possessions.

The cost of transport from the Earth to the Moon is taken at $1,000 per pound. For the complete lunar installation mass of 3,000 tons, including a station and the Transport Linear Accelerator, that comes to $6.6 billion. Equipment for the Moon, at $400 per pound (worth its weight in HP 45's) totals $2.4 billion.

Most of the equipment for L5 is taken as equivalent in cost to computers: about $180 per pound, or $1.2 billion total. The specialized machines and tools cost $600 per pound.

The salaries of the L5 crew would be a relatively small sum, but there is a large force of Earth-based engineers, designers, artists, architects, biologists, geologists, and every other specialty needed to establish the initial colony. Their salary costs would total a quarter of the cost of the project.

The grand total is about $31 billion, about $5 billion per year, which is comparable to NASA's peak budget in the late 1960's. That is two or three percent of what our government spends each year.

The ten thousand people of Model 1, living and working in space and totally self-supporting, would be enormously more productive than any com-

parable investment in space so far. The U.S. and the USSR have probably spent $100 to $200 billion in space so far. One can estimate the payback time from Model 1 by assuming an output of five thousand pounds of industrial products per worker per year. Those would be the components of Model 2: the whole idea of space colonization is to nucleate and grow. Model 1 must build Model 2 more cheaply than Model 2 could otherwise be built. Every pound is worth, at L5, an additional $250 to $425. Every pound produced in finished industrial products at L5 is worth that additional $250 per pound to $425 per pound because it would not have to be brought up from the Earth; it would be made out of lunar material. The resulting industrial output of Model 1, with one worker per average family of three, would be over $4 billion a year. Model 1 could thus produce an output equal to its entire construction cost in less than eight years.

DISCUSSION

Q. *Why do your assume the cost of equipment to be closer to aircraft than to Apollo command modules?*

A. It's partly a question of quantity production. There were less than ten of the Apollo command modules.

Q. *But there will be only one orbital station. Won't a great deal of that be as specialized as the command modules were?*

A. No. You may be thinking in the wrong scale. The hardware that I am talking about would be extremely repetitive. The Apollo command module was only three and a half tons altogether, and it was crammed with one-of-a-kind avionics. Most of the hardware of Model 1 would be standardized, replicated parts such as window seals, which would be brought up to make a seal between a standard shaped window and a standard opening in an aluminum panel. Even $60 per pound would probably be too high for the average hardware that I am talking about, but to put it in at $180 per pound is, I think, quite safe.

Q. *What should we do now?*

A. First of all it is necessary to discuss the topic widely, and to bring in a wide variety of people with various interests, desires and specialties. We have to publish the proceedings of the meeting. We must spread the word of the existence of this possibility and to bring people with skills that we need into making estimates and adding their suggestions. We need chemists, we need architects, we need everybody. There is no sort of skill or specialty that can't be used in this concept; it's world building. So the most important thing is to spread the word and bring it to the attention of other people. If you have better ideas, I would love to hear them.

Q. *Have you been able to test the ear of a national politician? You can't stay within the scientific community. It's going to take government.*

A. I have taken the fairly idealistic view up to now that the government would be the last people I would talk to rather than the first. Of course we can't realistically think of this sort of operation unless it is tied, at least initially, to a national or an international government program. Eventually, though, it's going to be possible to homestead the asteroid belt. It will be possible, not just for communities, but for an individual to take off in a relatively cheap vehicle with his family and start mining the asteroid belt and building a homestead on his own, but that may be a hundred or two hundred years away.

Q. *Have you given any though to approaching business people and having them invest? A colony cannot exist for its own sake, on its own terms; it will have to return on investment, and I'm a little perplexed as to how you expect to do it.*

A. First of all, business rarely looks beyond the next five years. In the real limit, Model 4 and its replications, there would be a regime in which the actual production costs in space would be lower than they are on Earth; but that's a hundred years away. Business is not going to invest in something which is a hundred years off.

Thus we need completely different economic justification for Model 4 and its successors, as compared with Model 1. If you nucleate with Model 1, Model 2 is going to have ten times as many people and only cost the same amount. Model 3 is going to have a hundred times as many people and probably cost less, because it would be possible to stop using the Earth at that point. By the time you go about that far, it's

simply replication. At present, though, the time scale seems to me too long for large scale support from business. Small scale support may be possible

Q. *You've mentioned production costs, but transportation costs would also be a fairly large factor.*

A. Yes. But you can make a good argument that the transportation costs should be lower in space than they are on the surface of the Earth, eventually. The cheapest kind of transportation would be between colonies. Travel to the Earth would be relatively cheap because the atmosphere could be used for reentry, but if you go farther into the future, perhaps as little as one hundred years from now, most of the consumers are not going to be on the Earth. It *is* possible that you could sell to the Earth at lower prices than things could be built here one hundred years from now, but that's a separate issue.

Q. *It occurs to me that modern aircraft carriers weigh eighty thousand tons, and cost $3 to $5 billion. You propose something six times as large for $30 billion. Do you really think that you can build a station, in orbit, for only six times the cost of an aircraft carrier?*

A. Yes, for two reasons. First of all, an aircraft carrier is stuffed full of ultimate-limit technology, designed to shoot down aircraft from other countries. We're not building that kind of militaristic hardware in a space colony. Second, of Model 1's five hundred thousand tons a rather small fraction is hardware. The actual materials that go into Model 1 are roughly twenty to one hundred thousand tons of aluminum and glass, about four hundred thousand tons of just plain soil brought up from the surface of the Moon, and about fifty thousand tons of water. The actual hardware, the material that you might quite properly compare in some sense to an aircraft carrier, would be more like twenty to one hundred thousand tons: less than the mass of one aircraft carrier. I am suggesting that with no military hardware, you could build something in space for six times the cost of that carrier. I don't think that is an unreasonable comparison.

Q. *You described the colony as being completely independent and self sufficient. Do you have in mind people living the kind of life that's possible for them in our present industrial civilization on Earth, in the sense that the full range of consumer goods that people buy would be available to them?*

A. Very much so. I wouldn't expect that with Model 1, of course; Model 1 would be a very restricted environment. But by the time the population in space grows to the population of a big industrialized nation like Japan, with fifty, one hundred or two hundred million people, there would be sufficient capability to manufacture the entire range of goods that we use.

Q. *How do you plan to manufacture all the amenities of civilization in an entirely new technology? The economy in space colonies will utilize entirely different technology than is currently used for manufacture.*

A. Not necessarily. You'd make television sets exactly the same way that you do on Earth.

Q. *Then you plan to operate all the mining and material processing industry with the same technology. That doesn't make sense. If you're going to mine the asteroid belt, the existing capital equipment and engineering knowledge of the mining industry is not applicable; it would have to be created from scratch more or less on the level of current space technology.*

A. Perhaps, but we have plenty of time. That kind of business is twenty to forty years off. You can develop a lot of technology in that time. You're absolutely right that the raw materials technology would be different. In particular, steelmaking would be very different in space. But there would be new possibilities open: many operations would benefit from zero-G. It doesn't make sense to fight gravity when dealing with large masses of materials.

Q. *The cost of developing the technology for living in space as opposed to building the colony has not been factored into the calculations. From the social point of view, there's a question of comparing the overall costs and benefits of living in space, and having to make additional investments to do so, with improving the environment on Earth. You have demonstrated that you can create this colony, but you have not defined the relative economies of living out there.*

A. Even in Model 1, and certainly in the big models, ordinary living would be similar to what we are exposed to here. People would be living in normal gravity and in a normal atmosphere; they would have space to move around in; they would be growing their food by conventional agriculture. In the Model 4 community, at a low density, it would not even have to be very efficient agriculture. The transport of the finished agricultural produce to the living area would be over a rather short distance, only about twenty miles. That is quite favorable as compared to what it is here on Earth.

Q. *But only 25% of consumer expenditure is what most people pay for agricultural products. That's not what people are working to produce and consume.*

A. Well, let's list the major places where money goes. In our present society, first of all, we spend a lot of money on transportation. In particular, we spend a great deal of money on automobiles, because it's difficult to travel reasonable distances on the surface of the Earth without a car. In a space colony, the distance within a colony would never be more than about twenty miles. The weather would be predictable, and in general good, so that small electric powered vehicles or bicycles would be completely adequate for getting around in the ordinary way. There would be no need to go seventy miles an hour.

Between communities, there would be a new transportation option which does not exist on Earth. The vacuum environment, the absence of any weather, and the existence of zero-G imply a vehicle which is as big as you like, but which would not have to have on-board engines or crew. It would be nothing more than a life support capsule like the fuselage of an ordinary commercial airplane, but which could be accelerated by using the enormous mass of the community as the reaction mass. Only a launch track and an electric motor would be needed. You would accelerate the vehicle outward on a computer-directed track by means of the colony's centrifugal force, to be picked up with an arresting cable at another colony. This technology is not profound, but it is inherently cheap because there is no fuel cost. The vehicle would utilize solar energy in the form of electrical power for a minute or so during acceleration. After that, no power would be needed. So that that particular element of living cost ought to be less in the space colony than it is on Earth.

Another element is food. Shelter on the surface of the Earth is partly a question of population density. With indefinite amounts of growth into new land, as we would have in the colonies, there's no reason why any particular amount of land should be enormously expensive. You could always go and build a new colony. If you go item by item down the list of living expenses, it's hard to find one that would be more expensive in a space colony, and it's easy to find a number that would be cheaper.

Q. *What do you expect the birth rate, that is, the rate of natural increase in the population to be?*

A. One can only use historical analogy. The arguments that Prof. Feinberg made were persuasive, because they were not theory, but rather an appeal to what's happened in the past in analogous situations on the Earth. The evidence from what's going on in the United States and in other highly developed industrial nations is that when the standard of affluence gets high enough the birthrate tends to go down. Elements of the population which have very high birthrates tend to be the deprived sections of the population. At least by historical analogy, then, possibly the best way to control

population for the human race is to give people the very high standard of affluence that they would have in the space colonies. Then they might limit themselves by individual choice.

Q. *The people who would colonize space at the outset would be almost entirely young adults, so they would be likely to double in a period of five years or so. Thus if you wanted a population of ten thousand people in a colony at the end of a ten year period, you couldn't put more than perhaps four or five thousand in the colony. Also, the children could change the economic features of the population; that is, there would be a high dependency—a large population of people who consume, but produce very little.*

A. I'm not sure that that would be true. The children don't produce here on Earth, but that's partly because so many of us are superfluous. A lot of what we do in our jobs is not productive because there is not very much room to produce new things. The child labor laws were set up a hundred years ago in a period when labor was drudgery, but in a space colony, especially one of the early ones, it's likely there would be no child labor laws. It would be normal for a child to go to a fairly concentrated school up to perhaps one o'clock in the afternoon, and then to work. Probably all children would have jobs. They would work for perhaps half a day, and they would probably enjoy life more. Their productivity would be low, but so is their consumption until they get to be teenagers.

REFERENCES

A-1 Adler, Isidore, et al., "Lunar Composition from Apollo Orbital Measurements" *Naturwissenschaften* (Germany) LX No.5. pp. 231-42, May, 1973.

A-2 Adler, Isidore. "Geochemical Exploration of the Moon and Planets", Springer Verlag, Berlin, New York, (1970).

A-3 Cooper, Henry, S. "Moon Rocks", Dial Press, New York, 1970.

A-4 Fiedler, Gilbert. "Geology and Physics of the Moon, a Study of Some Functional Problems", Elsevier, Amsterdam, New York, 1971.

A-5 Green, Jack (ed), "Geological Problems in Lunar and Planetary Research." Tarzana, California; American Astronautical Society, 1971.

A-6 Helmke, Philip, et al., "Major and Trace Elements in Materials from Apollo 17 Deep Drill Core". *EOS Trans. Am. Geophys. Union*. LIV. No. 6, p. 595, June 1973.

A-7 Levinson, Alfreda, and Taylor, Ross, "Moon Rocks and Minerals; Scientific Results of the Study of the Apollo 11 Lunar Samples with Preliminary Data on Apollo 12 Samples," Pergamon Press, New York, 1971.

A-8 Mason, Brian H., and Melson, William G., "The Lunar Rocks." Wiley Interscience, New York, 1970.

A-9 Rhodes, J.M., "Major and Trace Element Chemistry of Apollo 17 Samples." *EOS Trans. Am. Geophys. Union*. LIV No. 6, pp. 609-610, June 1973.

A-10 Taylor, Stuart Ross, "Geochemistry of the Lunar Highlands," *Moon* (Netherlands), VII, No. 1-2, pp. 181-95, March-April, 1973.

A-11 Turkevich, Anthony L., "Comparison of the Analytic Results from Surveyor, Apollo and Luna Missions," *Moon* (Netherlands), Vol. V, No. 3-4, pp. 411-21, November-December 1972.

A-12 Wilshire, H.G., et al., "Apollo 16 Rocks: Petrology and Classification." *Journal of Geophysical Research*, LXXVIII, No. 14, pp. 2379-92, 10 May 1973.

A-13 Zussman, J., "The Minerology, Petrology, and Geochemistry of Lunar Samples – A Review." *Moon* (Netherlands), Vol. V, No. 3-4, pp. 422-35, November-December, 1972.

A-14 Lunar Sample Preliminary Examination Team, "Preliminary Examination of Lunar Samples from Apollo 14," *Science*, Vol. 173, No. 3998, pp. 681-93, 20 August 1971.

A-15 Brett, P.R., et al., "Apollo 14 Preliminary Examination Team: A Report on Apollo 14 Samples," paper presented at the 52nd Annual Meeting, American Geophysical Union, Washington, D.C., April 1971

A-16 O'Neill, G.K., private communication.

A-17 Vachet, P., "Aluminum and Aluminum Alloys," *Kirk-Othmer Encyclopedia of Chemical Technology*, Second edition, Vol. I, p. 941, Interscience Publishers, 1963.

A-18 Peters, F.A., Johnson, P.W., and Kirby, R.C., "Methods for Producing Alumina from Clay: an Evaluation of Five Hydrochloric Acid Processes," Bureau of Mines Report of Investigation 6133, 1961.

A-19 Peters, F.A., Johnson, P.W., and Kirby, R.C., "Methods for Producing Alumina from Clay: an Evaluation of Three Sulfuric Acid Processes." Bureau of Mines Report of Investigation 6229, 1963.

A-20 Iverson, H.G., and Leitch, H., "Extraction of Aluminum from Silicate Rocks and Minerals Containing Aluminum," U.S. patent 3,507,629, 1970.

A-21 Laul, J.C., and Schmitt, R.A., "Chemical Composition of Apollo 15, 16, 17 Samples," Proceedings of the Fourth Lunar Science Conference, Vol. 2, p. 1349, Pergamon Press, 1973

A-22 Brady, G.S., "Materials Handbook," p. 42, McGraw-Hill Book Company, 1971.

A-23 McCord, T.B. and Gaffey, M.J., "Asteroids: Surface Composition from Reflection Spectroscopy," *Science*, 186, Vol. 4161, p. 352, 1974.

A-24 Chapman, C.R., "The Nature of Asteroids," *Scientific American*, Vol. 232, No. 1, pp. 24-33, January 1975.

A-25 Knox, R., Jr., "The Yield Strength of Meteoritic Iron," *Meteoritics*, No. 5, p. 63, 1970

A-26 Mason, Brian H., "Meteorites," John Wiley and Sons, New York, 1962.

A-27 Gibson, E.K., Moore, C.B., and Lewis, C.F., "Total Nitrogen and Carbon Abundances in Carbonaceous Chondrites." *Geochimica et Cosmochimica Acta*, 35:599, June, 1971.

A-28 Fanale, F.P., Johnson, T.V. and Matson, D.L., "Io: A Surface Evaporite Deposit?," *Science*, 186:922, 1974.

A-29 Hayes, J.M., "Organic Constituents of Meteorites – A Review," *Geochimica et Cosmochimica Acta*, 31:1395, September 1967.

A-30 Smales, A.A., Mapper, D., and Fouche, K.F., "The Distribution of Some Trace Elements in Iron Meteorites as Determined by Neutron Activation." *Geochimica et Cosmochimica Acta*, 31:673, 1967.

A-31 "Minerals Yearbook, Vol. I, 1972." Bureau of Mines, USGPO, Washington, D.C., 1974.